## HIGH SCHOOL BIOLOGY: BSCS GREEN VERSION
RAND McNALLY & COMPANY, Chicago

BIOLOGICAL SCIENCE: AN INQUIRY INTO LIFE (BSCS Yellow Version),
Harcourt, Brace & World, Inc., New York

BIOLOGICAL SCIENCE: MOLECULES TO MAN (BSCS Blue Version),
Houghton Mifflin Company, Boston

> QUARTERLY TESTS AND FINAL EXAMINATIONS (for each
> version), available from the version publishers
> PROCESSES OF SCIENCE TEST (for all versions),
> The Psychological Corporation, New York

BIOLOGICAL SCIENCE: PATTERNS AND PROCESSES (BSCS Special
Materials), Holt, Rinehart & Winston, Inc., New York

> UNIT TESTS AND FINAL EXAMINATION FOR BIOLOGICAL
> SCIENCE: PATTERNS AND PROCESSES, The Psychological
> Corporation, New York

BIOLOGICAL SCIENCE: INTERACTION OF EXPERIMENTS AND IDEAS (BSCS
Second Course), Prentice-Hall, Inc., Englewood Cliffs, N.J.

> QUARTERLY TESTS AND FINAL EXAMINATION FOR BIOLOGICAL
> SCIENCE: INTERACTION OF EXPERIMENTS AND IDEAS,
> Prentice-Hall, Inc., Englewood Cliffs, N.J.

BSCS LABORATORY BLOCKS (13 titles), D. C. Heath & Company, Boston

> TESTS AND TEACHER'S RESOURCE BOOK (for LABORATORY
> BLOCKS), D. C. Heath & Company, Boston

RESEARCH PROBLEMS IN BIOLOGY: INVESTIGATIONS FOR STUDENTS
(Series 1–4), Doubleday & Company, Inc., Garden City, N.Y.

INNOVATIONS IN EQUIPMENT AND TECHNIQUES FOR THE BIOLOGY
TEACHING LABORATORY, D. C. Heath & Company, Boston

BSCS SINGLE TOPIC FILMS (40 titles), Rand McNally & Company,
Chicago; Harcourt, Brace & World, Inc., New York; Houghton
Mifflin Company, Boston

BSCS INQUIRY SLIDE SERIES, Harcourt, Brace & World, Inc.,
New York

BIOLOGY TEACHERS' HANDBOOK, John Wiley & Sons, Inc., New York

BSCS PATTERNS OF LIFE SERIES (16 titles), Rand McNally & Company,
Chicago

POPULATION GENETICS: A SELF-INSTRUCTIONAL PROGRAM,
Silver Burdett Company, Morristown, N.J.

BSCS BULLETIN SERIES (Nos. 1–3), BSCS, Boulder, Colo.

THE CHANGING CLASSROOM: THE ROLE OF THE BIOLOGICAL
SCIENCES CURRICULUM STUDY (BSCS BULLETIN No. 4),
by Arnold B. Grobman, Doubleday & Company, Inc., Garden
City, N.Y.

BSCS SPECIAL PUBLICATIONS (Nos. 1–7), BSCS, Boulder, Colo.

BSCS NEWSLETTER, BSCS, Boulder, Colo.

BSCS INTERNATIONAL NEWS NOTES, BSCS, Boulder, Colo.

BSCS PAMPHLET SERIES (24 titles), BSCS, Boulder, Colo.

STORY OF THE BSCS (information film), BSCS, Boulder, Colo.

BIOLOGICAL SCIENCES CURRICULUM STUDY • *University of Colorado, Boulder*
P. O. Box 930
Boulder, Colorado

*Revision Team:*
HAVEN KOLB, Hereford High School, Parkton, Maryland, *Supervisor*
NORRIS A. ANDERSON, Burlingame High School, Burlingame, California
RICHARD G. BEIDLEMAN, Colorado College, Colorado Springs, Colorado
DONALD S. FARNER, University of Washington, Seattle, Washington
VICTOR LARSEN, Adelphi University, Garden City, New York
WILLIAM V. MAYER, Biological Sciences Curriculum Study, Boulder, Colorado
ELRA M. PALMER, Baltimore City Public Schools, Baltimore, Maryland
ELIZABETH PERROTT, University of Stirling, Stirling, Scotland
PAUL G. PEARSON, Rutgers, The State University, New Brunswick, New Jersey

*Editors:* WILLIAM B. MILLER and CAROL LETH
Rand McNally & Company, Chicago, Illinois

**BSCS** GREEN VERSION

# HIGH
# SCHOOL
# BIOLOGY

SECOND EDITION

RAND McNALLY & COMPANY
Chicago

Printed in the United States of America

*Cover:* Ruth Kirk, *The Olympic Rain Forest,* University of Washington Press, Seattle. Photo by Johsel Namkung.

*Title page:* Photo by Grant Heilman.

## SECOND EDITION    FIRST EDITION

| SECOND EDITION | FIRST EDITION | |
|---|---|---|
| *First printing,*<br>*March, 1968* | *First printing,*<br>*August, 1963* | Prepared by the BSCS<br>with support from the<br>National Science Foundation |
| *Second printing,*<br>*August, 1968* | *Second printing,*<br>*January, 1964* | |
| *Third printing,*<br>*September, 1968* | *Third printing,*<br>*May, 1964* |  |
| *Fourth printing,*<br>*January, 1969* | *Fourth printing,*<br>*January, 1965* | |
| *Fifth printing,*<br>*December, 1969* | *Fifth printing,*<br>*June, 1965* | |
| *Sixth printing,*<br>*June, 1970* | *Sixth printing,*<br>*June, 1966* | Printed and published by<br>Rand McNally & Company |
| | *Seventh printing,*<br>*May, 1967* |  |
| | *Eighth printing,*<br>*September, 1968* | |

The copyright owner will grant permission to domestic persons of the United States and Canada for use of this work without charge in the English language in the United States and Canada after January 1, 1974. For conditions of use, permission to use, and other permissions, including foreign publication, adaptation, and translation, apply to the Director, BSCS, University of Colorado, Boulder, Colorado 80302, U.S.A.

## THE WRITERS

More than one hundred high school and university teachers participated in writing the experimental forms of this book in 1960 and 1961. Their names are listed in the first commercial edition (1963). That edition was produced by a team consisting of:

HAROLD DURST, Southeast High School, Wichita, Kansas

HAVEN KOLB, Overlea High School, Baltimore County, Maryland (*Supervisor*)

VICTOR LARSEN, Adelphi University, Garden City, New York

WILLIAM MILLER, Rand McNally & Company, Chicago

ELRA M. PALMER, Baltimore City Public Schools, Baltimore, Maryland

JONATHAN WESTFALL, University of Georgia, Athens, Georgia

The members of the revision team for the 1968 edition are listed on the title page.


## THE BSCS STAFF (Current)

ADDISON E. LEE, *Chairman*, BSCS Steering Committee

WILLIAM V. MAYER, Director

MANERT H. KENNEDY, Associate Director

GEORGE M. CLARK, Assistant Director

KEITH L. BUMSTED, Business Manager

PATRICK E. BALCH, Staff Consultant

THOMAS J. CLEAVER, Staff Consultant

JAMES T. ROBINSON, Staff Consultant

HAROLD A. RUPERT, JR., Staff Consultant

RICHARD R. TOLMAN, Staff Consultant

## ILLUSTRATIONS STAFF

## RAND MCNALLY

# REVIEWERS

**A.** A number of biological societies appointed reviewers whose comments have been helpful in preparing the revision:

**American Association of Physical Anthropologists:** Dr. Robert Ascher, Cornell University, Ithaca, New York; Dr. William Laughlin, University of Wisconsin, Madison, Wisconsin; Dr. Lawrence Oschinsky (deceased), University of Toronto, Toronto, Canada

**American Physiological Society and Society of General Physiologists:** Dr. Robert D. Allen, Princeton University, Princeton, New Jersey; Dr. Leon Goldstein, Harvard Medical School, Boston, Massachusetts; Dr. Eugene M. Renkin, Duke University Medical Center, Durham, North Carolina; Dr. R. R. Ronkin, University of Delaware, Newark, Delaware; Dr. William G. Van der Kloot, New York University School of Medicine, New York, New York

**American Phytopathological Society:** Dr. E. H. Barnes, Michigan State University, East Lansing, Michigan; Dr. Carl Boothroyd, Cornell University, Ithaca, New York; Dr. R. J. Campana, University of Maine, Orono, Maine; Dr. J. L. Dale, University of Arkansas, Fayetteville, Arkansas; Dr. Ralph J. Green, Jr., Purdue University, Lafayette, Indiana

**American Society of Agronomy:** Dr. Frank Himes, Ohio State University, Columbus, Ohio; Dr. Darrell A. Miller, North Carolina State University, Raleigh, North Carolina

**American Society of Animal Science:** Dr. Duane Acker, Kansas State University, Manhattan, Kansas; Dr. A. W. Burger, University of Illinois, Urbana, Illinois

**American Society for Horticultural Science:** Dr. W. A. Sistrunk, University of Arkansas, Fayetteville, Arkansas

**American Society for Microbiology:** Dr. David E. Contois, University of Hawaii, Honolulu, Hawaii; Dr. Gordon Roberstad, South Dakota State University, Brookings, South Dakota; Dr. Kenneth Temple, Montana State College, Bozeman, Montana

**American Society of Range Management:** Dr. Wayne McCully, Texas A & M University, College Station, Texas

**Botanical Society of America:** Dr. Adolph Hecht, Washington State University, Pullman, Washington; Dr. John Mooring, University of Santa Clara, Santa Clara, California; Dr. Irwin Spear, University of Texas, Austin, Texas

**Central Association of Science and Mathematics Teachers:** Mr. Louis E. Shrode, Oak Park – River Forest High School, Oak Park, Illinois

**Chemical Education Materials Study:** Mr. Robert L. French, Westminster High School, Westminster, California; Dr. Richard Merrill, Albany, California

**Entomological Society of America:** Dr. Robert V. Travis, Mainesburg, Pennsylvania; Dr. Howard Owens, Prince George's County, Maryland

**Mycological Society of America:** Dr. Robert W. Lichtwardt, University of Kansas, Lawrence, Kansas; Dr. Arthur L. Weldon, Tulane University, New Orleans, Louisiana

**National Catholic Educational Association:** Sister Julia Marie Van Denack, O.S.F., Holy Family College, Manitowoc, Wisconsin

**National Science Supervisors Association:** Mr. Richard Kay, Idaho State Department of Education, Boise, Idaho; Mr. John Leake, Jefferson City, Missouri; Mr. LaVar Sorensen, Supervisor of Science, Salt Lake City Public Schools, Utah

**Society of American Foresters:** Mr. Stanley Jepsen, Chevy Chase, Maryland; Dr. Orie L. Loucks, Department of Botany, University of Wisconsin, Madison, Wisconsin; Dr. Harrison H. Payne, State University College of Forestry, Syracuse, New York

**B.** The following individuals reviewed all or part of the 1963 edition:

DR. DAVID AUSUBEL, University of Illinois, Urbana, Illinois

DR. ROBERT M. W. TRAVERS, Western Michigan University, Kalamazoo, Michigan

**C.** The following individuals provided consultant service on aspects of the 1968 revision:

DR. HARRY BRENOWITZ, Adelphi University, Garden City, New York

MISS NINETTE CAMENS, Adelphi University, Garden City, New York

DR. DELAPHINE WYCKOFF, Wellesley College, Wellesley, Massachusetts

**D.** In 1965 and 1966 the following high school teachers attended feedback meetings, where their interaction in criticism of the 1963 edition provided the background for revision:

FOSTER AARON, Burr & Burton Seminary, Manchester, Vermont

VERYL ALLEN, Salida High School, Salida, Colorado

VIRGINIA F. ALLEN, P. K. Yonge School, Gainesville, Florida

GARY G. ALLENSTEIN, Badger High School, Lake Geneva, Wisconsin

JAY ANDERSON, Powell County High School, Deer Lodge, Montana

DONALD B. ASH, Pleasant Grove High School, Pleasant Grove, Utah

LAWRENCE E. BACH, Ithaca High School, Ithaca, New York

JAY M. BERNHISEL, Fort Bragg High School, Fort Bragg, California

PAUL A. BRICKER, Coronado High School, Scottsdale, Arizona

DOROTHY L. BROCK, West Fulton High School, Atlanta, Georgia

GEORGE R. CARMICHAEL, JR., Medill Bair High School, Fairless Hills, Pennsylvania

MARTIN CHRISTIE, Lee High School, Springfield, Virginia

KERMIT DAUM, Derby Senior High School, Derby, Kansas

GEORGE DAWSON, Waggener High School, Louisville, Kentucky

HARRY DAWSON, McMinnville High School, McMinnville, Oregon

ROBERT DeBISHOP, Southington High School, Southington, Connecticut

R. EHLI, Billings Central High School, Billings, Montana

CAROL JOY ERICSON, Middleburg Heights, Ohio

LLOYD G. FARINASH, JR., Parkersburg High School, Parkersburg, West Virginia

DONALD R. GARREN, Sullivan High School, Sullivan, Illinois

BARBARA K. HOPPER, Cleveland High School, Reseda, California

R. DeWITT IVEY, Sandia High School, Albuquerque, New Mexico

VICTOR LaCOURSE, Mount Edgecumbe High School, Mount Edgecumbe, Alaska

ROBERT LYONS, Wheatridge High School, Wheatridge, Colorado

EDNA L. MEADOWS, Stephen Decatur High School, Decatur, Illinois

HENRY E. MELTON, Crisp County High School, Cordele, Georgia

MERLIN MILLPACK, Ogden Senior High School, Ogden, Utah

TY MINTON, Putney School, Putney, Vermont

HILDA B. NEWMAN, Tyner High School, Tyner, Tennessee

ART PAPENFUSS, Golden Senior High School, Golden, Colorado

ELIZABETH PENTON, Holmes County High School, Bonifay, Florida

JERRY PETERSON, Franklin Senior High School, Livonia, Michigan

VERA B. REMSBURG, Herndon High School, Herndon, Virginia

RICHARD W. SCHUETT, North High School, Omaha, Nebraska

KENNETH L. SHIRLEY, Ben Lomond High, Ogden, Utah

ANNAJEAN SLATER, Valley Forge High School, Parma Heights, Ohio

GLEN E. SOULIER, Hillcrest High School, Midvale, Utah

JIMMIE STOTHART, Coushatta High School, Coushatta, Louisiana

ROSEMARY B. STROTHER, Clarke County Jr. High School, Athens, Georgia

GERALD TAGUE, East High School, Wichita, Kansas

SISTER M. TOMAIS, O.P., St. Mary's High School, Cheyenne, Wyoming

EDWARD D. TRINER, Carl Sandburg High School, Orland Park, Illinois

WILLARD L. UNSTADTER, JR., Glen Rock High School, Glen Rock, New Jersey

EDGAR WARREN, South High School, Denver, Colorado

DOROTHY WENDT, Waipahu High School, Honolulu, Hawaii

PRESTON WHITE, Brattleboro Union High School, Brattleboro, Vermont

# A FOREWORD

We live in an age of science, and it is essential that students of today, who will occupy positions of leadership in the twenty-first century, have the background of a modern and forward-looking program in science. As biology may be the first, last, and only science to which the majority of students are exposed in their formal education, it must be accurate and modern in biological content and must instill a comprehension of both science and the scientific enterprise.

For years many of our better teachers have been expressing dissatisfaction with the tools with which they have had to work. They wanted to teach modern biology in an imaginative, investigative, and inquiry-oriented fashion, but the texts available to them fostered the rote memorization of lists of names, facts, and dates. This decade has witnessed a spectacular improvement in biological education, and the Biological Sciences Curriculum Study has played an important role in that improvement. The Biological Sciences Curriculum Study was organized to improve biological education at all levels of instruction.

The initial goal of the BSCS was the production of classroom materials for average students in a first course in biology at the secondary school level. The materials were structured around a series of major themes: science as investigation and inquiry; the history of biological concepts; complementarity of structure and function; diversity of type and unity of pattern; change of organisms through time as evolution; genetic continuity; the complementarity of the organism and its environment; regulation and homeostasis; and the biological basis of behavior. These themes were presented through the use of a variety of organisms best illustrating the concept in question. Thus, use of microorganisms, plants, and animals conveys the pervasiveness of these themes in all living things. At the same time, cognizance needs be taken of a balanced consideration of all levels of organization of life—from the molecule through cells, tissues, organs, individuals, populations, species, communities, and the world biome. It is the interweaving of the themes with organisms and levels of organization that gives biology a structure as a science. Recognition of this structure makes possible a series of patterns that tremendously increase the effectiveness of instruction in biology. Each program includes materials selected for their applicability in the latter half of the twentieth century and their ability to illuminate the principles and concepts that underlie biological science. The BSCS program presents a balanced approach to the science of biology without presenting excessive details. Content has been carefully selected by learned biologists and educators as that most contributory to understanding the basics of biological science.

The first experimental editions of three versions of BSCS books were completed in 1960 and were tested in approximately 100 schools throughout the country. From this experience, the three experimental versions were revised in 1961 and subjected to trials in 500 schools during the 1961–62 school year and in 950 schools the following year. After three years of extensive trial and revision, the three experimental versions were reorganized to become the commercially published editions that appeared in 1963.

The present book is a complete revision of one of the 1963 versions and is based upon feedback of the last five years together with the most recent scientific information available. The BSCS deeply appreciates the singularly important contributions to the improvement of biological education made by 1,000 teachers and 150,000 students who used the experimental editions and reported their experiences to us. Over two million pupils have studied from the first editions of these books; to them and their teachers the BSCS is indebted for many constructive suggestions that have been incorporated in the present volumes.

A unique BSCS contribution to the development of teaching materials for high school biology has been a fruitful cooperation between college biologists on the frontiers of research and high school teachers on the frontiers of teaching. This cooperation has continued over a period of years. The procedure of producing text materials, with the active involvement of cooperative teams of writers and extensive classroom testing, has obvious advantages over the work of either a single author or small groups of authors. It could not have been accomplished without the support provided the BSCS by the National Science Foundation.

In addition to the three versions of a first high school biology program (including text materials, integrated laboratory exercises, quarterly tests, a comprehensive examination, and teacher's guides), the BSCS has produced a wide variety of course materials that offer the teacher maximal flexibility in programming—and the student, optimal use of his talents.

The BSCS is a continuing curriculum study concerned with the improvement of biological education. It welcomes observations from interested persons, and such comments may be sent to the Director, at the University of Colorado.

ARNOLD B. GROBMAN
*Chairman*, Steering Committee
Biological Sciences Curriculum Study
Rutgers, The State University
New Brunswick, New Jersey 08903

WILLIAM V. MAYER, *Director*
Biological Sciences Curriculum Study
Post Office Box 930
Boulder, Colorado 80302

# PREFACE

FOR EDUCATORS

Few things have been more characteristic of the period since the publication of the first commercial edition of this book than the rapid recognition of the overriding importance of the biological problems facing modern man—and of their ecological roots. Problems pertaining to population control, biological energy requirements, and waste disposal crowd the news media, demand discussion in legislatures, and deserve the best thought of all citizens. Events have fully vindicated the belief of Dr. Marston Bates, Professor of Zoology at the University of Michigan and original architect of this course: that an ecological viewpoint is a logical and necessary emphasis in a high school biology course for our times.

But the rationale of the ecological approach to the study of biology in high schools is fully explained in the *Teacher's Guide* to the *Green Version*. The *Guide* should be consulted by educators. The textbook has not been written for them, but for students.

## FOR THE STUDENT

There are two major aims in studying any natural science.

One aim is to become acquainted with scientific facts and with the general ideas that are built upon them. These are ideas that have greatly altered our views of man's place in nature and that have tremendously enlarged human abilities to use the forces and resources of nature. These are the ideas that make our lives today so different from those of our ancestors.

The second aim in studying a natural science is even more important: to understand what science *is*—to recognize its spirit and to appreciate its methods. Upon this understanding depends our ability to participate intelligently in the life of our scientific age.

If most citizens in a democracy think of science as a kind of magic, our scientific civilization will certainly not endure. For science is not magic. Science is a complex process by which we can arrive at reliable knowledge of our surroundings. It is compounded of curiosity, observation, and thought. It has no *necessary* connection with efforts to improve the circumstances of human life, although it brings about such results more frequently than does any other human enterprise. It is a social undertaking, depending on accurate and free communication. It is a progressive activity, each generation building on the accumulated knowledge of the past.

Science, then, is a human activity, without any element of magic about it. If science is to flourish, the whole community must understand to some degree its aims, its methods, and its consequences. Thus all of us—not only those of us who are scientists or who wish to become scientists—must understand what science is.

It might be possible, by using textbooks only, to achieve the first aim of studying science—that is, to become informed. But to pursue the second aim—the more important aim—requires experience in scientific work. Such experience cannot be gained by reading; it cannot be gained by listening—even listening to the most accomplished scientists; it can be gained only by doing the kind of things scientists do in the laboratory.

The laboratory, in its broadest sense, is the place where the work of the scientist is carried on. It may be either outdoors or indoors, but it is always a place where the scientist is asking questions of nature. It is a place where accurate observation is of first importance, where precise measurement aids observation, where controlled conditions make it possible to conduct experiments from which clear conclusions can be drawn by logical thinking. Only with laboratory experience is it possible to see what science really is.

Your success in gaining this experience will depend upon more than mere "laboratory work." The laboratory is the heart of the scientific enterprise, but no scientist locks himself alone in the laboratory. He needs libraries, so that he can view his own work in relation to the whole of science; he needs conversation with fellow scientists, so that he can obtain the stimulation of many viewpoints; he needs skill in writing, so that he can report his work for checking and verification. Locked in the laboratory, you might become skilled in handling laboratory apparatus, but you could never gain the experience of science.

The book that lies before you, then, is but a fragment of a biology course. It contains part of what you will need for a biology course. In addition, a biology course requires materials and equipment. And it requires living things. But most important, it requires *you*. Without your eyes, your ears—all of your senses—your hands, your brain, there can be no biology course for you.

Parkton, Maryland      HAVEN KOLB
21120          *Supervisor*, BSCS Green Version
October 1, 1967

# CONTENTS

## ABOUT MARGINAL NOTES AND QUESTIONS

Even a well-read person finds the English language—like most other languages—full of surprises. And biology—like all the sciences—has its share of unfamiliar words, meanings, and usages.

The margins of this book contain notes to assist you in reading and understanding the text, and questions to encourage your further inquiry in certain areas. The notes do *not* contain basic information. Use them only as you need them for pronunciations, definitions, derivations, and reference to helpful materials in the text or elsewhere—or when your curiosity is aroused.

## A KEY TO PRONUNCIATION

All pronunciations given in this text are developed from the system used in *The American College Dictionary*, edited by C. L. Barnhart (New York: Random House, Inc., 1961), which follows:

| | | | | |
|---|---|---|---|---|
| ă | act, bat | p | page, stop |
| ā | able, cape | r | read, cry |
| â | air, dare | s | see, miss |
| ä | art, calm | sh | shoe, push |
| | | t | ten, bit |
| b | back, rub | th | thin, path |
| ch | chief, beach | th | that, other |
| d | do, bed | | |
| | | ŭ | up, love |
| ĕ | ebb, set | ū | use, cute |
| ē | equal, bee | û | urge, burn |
| f | fit, puff | | |
| g | give, beg | v | voice, live |
| h | hit, hear | w | west, away |
| | | y | yes, young |
| ĭ | if, big | z | zeal, lazy, those |
| ī | ice, bite | zh | vision, measure |
| j | just, edge | ə | occurs only in un- |
| k | kept, make | | accented syllables |
| l | low, all | | and indicates the |
| m | my, him | | sound of |
| n | now, on | | a *in* alone |
| ng | sing, England | | e *in* system |
| | | | i *in* easily |
| ŏ | box, hot | | o *in* gallop |
| ō | over, no | | u *in* circus |
| ô | order, ball | | |
| oi | oil, joy | | |
| o͝o | book, put | | |
| o͞o | ooze, rule | | |
| ou | out, loud | | |

*Foreign Sounds*

à   as in French *ami* [a vowel intermediate in quality between the ă of *cat* and ä of *calm*, but closer to the former]

KH   as in German *ach*; Scottish *loch* [a consonant made by bringing the tongue into the position for *k*, as in *key*, *coo*, while pronouncing a strong *h*]

N   [a symbol used to indicate nasalized vowels, as in *bon*. There are four such vowels in French, found in *un bon vin blanc* (œN bôN văN bläN)]

œ   as in French *feu*; German *schön* [a vowel made with the lips rounded in position for ō, as in *over*, while trying to say ā, as in *able*]

Y   as in French *tu*; German *über* [a vowel made with the lips rounded in position for o͞o, as in *ooze*, while trying to say ē, as in *easy*]

The symbol (′), as in moth·er (mŭth′ər), is used to mark primary stress; the syllable preceding it is pronounced with greater prominence than the other syllables in the word. The symbol (′), as in grand·moth·er (grănd′mŭth′ər), is used to mark secondary stress; a syllable marked for secondary stress is pronounced with less prominence than the one marked (′) but with more prominence than one bearing no stress mark at all.

# Section One

# THE WORLD
# OF LIFE:
# THE BIOSPHERE

How shall we start to study biology—the science of life?

We might begin grandly with the universe, work down to the solar system, to the planet Earth, to a pond somewhere, and then look at the teeming life that finds a home there. We might start by looking into some living thing to find the smallest parts visible under our microscopes, study the ways in which these parts are put together to make up individuals, and then discuss the many kinds of relations among different individuals. Or we might start with chemistry—with electrons, atoms, and molecules—because all living things are composed of atoms, and we find chemical processes wherever we find living things. We might even take a historical approach, searching for clues to the beginning of life and then examining the evidence in the fossil record to trace the development of living things to the present day. There are many ways to start a biology course.

You might think that some of these approaches to the study of biology would take you first to books and others, first to the laboratory. But biologists use libraries and laboratories together. It seems reasonable to suppose that high school biology students would also find this a good practice. We need an approach that will permit an immediate examination of some living things and one that will make use of the knowledge of living things each student already has.

So let us begin with the familiar living things around us. We might begin with ourselves—but there is some danger of becoming self-centered. Why not begin with a rabbit hiding under a raspberry bush?

# The Web
# of Life

Figure 1 · 1

## RABBITS AND RASPBERRIES

Rabbits. They turn up in nursery tales and comic strips, in candy shops and cabbage patches. They are a part of our folklore and our literature because they are common animals. In most parts of our country, even in parts of our cities, they are abundant. So all of us know something about rabbits. And we all know about raspberries—at least about the jam or about the bushes along the roadside, which tear skirts and trousers and make a fine place for rabbits to hide.

A rabbit and a raspberry bush: One moves around; the other is rooted in one place. One is an animal; the other, a plant. All of us can tell an animal from a plant, a rabbit from a raspberry bush!

This seems plain enough. But when we try to work out clear and precise definitions, we get into trouble. Everyone who has looked into the matter agrees that sponges are animals. Yet they are as fixed in position as any plant. Then there are things called slime molds, which are sometimes classed as plants but do a great deal of creeping about. And among microscopic creatures there are many that move about actively, as most animals do, but use the energy of sunlight for building up foods, as do most plants. Presently we find that we no longer know the difference between *all* plants and *all* animals.

Perhaps the world of living things is more complicated than it appears at first. But our rabbit certainly *is* an animal, and our raspberry bush a plant. So we can postpone worrying about the precise meaning of "animal" and "plant."

## PRODUCERS AND CONSUMERS

Let us try another way of looking at the matter. The rabbit is hiding under the raspberry bush. This is important, for most animals must have some place to hide, some kind of shelter. Even more important, the rabbit must have food. Rabbits usually do not eat raspberry bushes, though they would not scorn the young shoots in time of need. But rabbits and raspberry bushes do not live alone. Around the raspberry patch are many other kinds of green plants that rabbits like.

We can call such green plants the *producers* of the living world, since they build up foods by using the energy of sunlight, and the rest of the living world depends on this production. Rabbits, which cannot make food in this way, are *consumers*—that is, "eaters." Because they feed directly on the green plants, they are called *first-order* consumers. Foxes, cats, wolves, hawks, all sorts of things, eat rabbits. Besides these larger animals there are fleas in a rabbit's fur, worms in its intestine, and mosquitoes seeking out its pink ears. These are *second-order* consumers. But the foxes, also,

precise [prĭ sīs′]: exact, distinctly stated

sponges: See Figure 4 · 40.

slime-molds: See Figure 6 · 22.

microscopic [Greek: *mikros*, small, + *skopein*, to look]

Figure 1 · 2

Lion, giraffe, and acacia tree in East Africa. Describe the relationships among these organisms.

may have fleas, which are then *third-order* consumers. Even higher orders of consumers may be found, each order a step farther from the food producers.

Thus, the producers are the basis of a complicated network of consumers.

### BALANCE

The rabbits live off the green plants, and many other things (including men) live off the rabbits. At first sight this seems rather hard on the rabbits. But rabbits breed fast. We get a pair of rabbits, and presently the place is overrun with them. If rabbits multiplied without check, they would soon become numerous enough to eat up all the available plants, and therefore they would die of starvation. But foxes and other rabbit-eaters keep the rabbit populations in check. Rabbit reproduction is fitted to the hazards of rabbit life, and the same applies to reproduction in foxes, elephants, or any other kind of *organism* (living thing). This is one aspect of the balance of nature.

organism [ôr'gə nĭz'əm; Greek: organon, tool]

Balance? As you look about you, you can see that the living world is constantly changing. You see changes with the seasons: there are swarms of houseflies in summer and very few in winter. You see changes over the years: the rabbits in a particular field are much more numerous in some years than in others. And you know that changes have occurred over still longer periods of time: the dinosaurs and flying reptiles of the dim past have given way to the mammals and birds of the present. How, then, can we talk about balance?

dinosaurs [dī'nə sôrz'; Greek: deino-, terrible, + sauros, lizard]

The same thing often looks different, depending on how closely you view it. If you look at one of your fellow students, he or she seems "balanced"; that is, muscles, brain, digestion, breathing, all work together smoothly. Yet there are changes during the day—with work, rest, eating, and sleeping. Consider breathing. Sitting in the classroom, you are probably breathing 14 to 17 times per minute. When you are working out in the gym, your breathing rate increases; when you are sleeping, it decreases. There are more impressive changes over longer periods of time: from birth through childhood and adolescence to maturity, old age, and death. The healthy individual is in balance, but with time there is change.

In a similar way the whole living world tends toward balance at any given time. Yet it is subject to many changes, both short-term and long-term. Viewed in one way, the different parts fit together beautifully; viewed in another way, they are continually changing their relationships to each other. Like the balance of a seesaw, the balance of nature is a teetering sort of balance—a condition called a *steady state* by scientists.

## THE SCIENTIST'S VIEWPOINT

The apparently simple rabbit and raspberry have quickly led us into the complicated world of living things. We might look at this living world as artists, interested in the beauty of its forms; as philosophers, trying to find meanings in it; as engineers, attempting to shape it to our purposes. Artist, philosopher, engineer, scientist—all are necessary to a full appreciation of our world surroundings. But we are now studying *biology;* biology is a science, so we take the scientific point of view.

We have been making some very definite statements about living things. Have you accepted these statements as true? Does printing these statements make them true? Of

Nathan W. Cohen

Figure 1 · 3
Which activities of a scientist are illustrated in these photographs?

See Investigation 1.1, page 7.

hypothesis [hī pŏth′ə sĭs; plural, hypotheses, hī pŏth′ə sēs]

See Investigation 1.2, page 8.

Galileo Galilei [găl′ə lē′ō găl′ə lā′ī]: 1564–1642. Italian scientist

verified [Latin: verus, true, + facere, to make]

course not! We have merely been reporting what most biologists believe. Why do biologists believe these things?

In his own special field of work, each scientist bases his beliefs on his own careful observations, checked and confirmed by the observations of others. Skill in observing is, then, a basic requirement in science.

We could spend a lifetime observing in a helter-skelter manner without learning very much about our world. But mere observation is not science. The observations of the scientist are usually guided by the statement of a problem. Of course, we seldom become aware of problems unless we have observed at least a little. So the relation between problem and observation is something like the relation between the chicken and the egg: Which comes first?

One of the most frequent results of observation is to raise specific questions in the mind of the scientist. We do not know how this occurs, nor do we know why certain questions stir the curiosity of some persons and not others. But with curiosity aroused, the scientist applies his imagination to the task of designing a specific statement that can be tested. Such a statement is a *hypothesis*. It is the starting point for an *experiment*. An experiment attempts to determine the truth or falsity of a hypothesis. Again the scientist needs imagination to dream up an experiment that fits the problem. In more formal language, a scientist needs imagination to design an experiment that will produce *data* from which a decision concerning the hypothesis can be made. Even in an experiment observation remains a basic activity of the scientist, because these data are observations.

Often observations must be made indirectly by means of instruments. Some of the instruments used by scientists are quite simple and have been used for a long time. Others are quite complex and have been developed only recently. In biological science one of the most frequently used aids to observation is the microscope. Even beginning students in biology must learn to use the microscope effectively.

Finally, the modern scientist needs to state his observations in numerical form. To do this he must *measure*. Only thus are exact descriptions and meaningful comparisons possible. Indeed, modern science is often dated from the time of Galileo, who first realized the importance of measurement and the mathematical handling of numerical data for clear understanding of our world and universe.

But all this work of the individual scientist is still not science. Observations that other scientists cannot make, experiments that they cannot repeat—these have no standing in science. Only when his observations and experiments are *verified* (confirmed) should the scientist begin to have confidence in his information. This verification can be obtained only when others know about his work; so he must be able to report accurately what he has done and what he has observed.

Observing, experimenting, measuring, reporting — these are some of the activities that stand behind the statements we have been making in this chapter. And there are still other activities. But we cannot really understand the viewpoint of the scientist merely by reading. We can understand this viewpoint only by *doing* the things scientists do.

## INVESTIGATION 1.1

### OBSERVING LIVING THINGS

### PURPOSE

The basic purpose of this exercise is to give you an opportunity to observe some living things (or their dead remains) accurately — scientifically. To direct your observations, use the problem of separating organisms into two groups, plants and animals (page 3).

### MATERIALS AND EQUIPMENT

Labeled specimens of a number of
    organisms
Hand lenses
Microscopes

### PROCEDURE

Arranged around the classroom you will find many living (or recently living) organisms. Each is labeled with a number and a name. Take a position at one of the specimens, as assigned by the teacher. You will be allowed a definite length of time to examine the specimen. When a signal is given by the teacher, move to the specimen with the next highest number. Repeat at each signal until you reach the highest number; then go to number 1 and continue until you return to your starting point.

In your data book prepare a chart to aid in recording your observations, as follows:

| NAME OF ORGANISM a | COLOR b | SIZE c | ROOTS d | FLOWERS e | SEEDS f | EYES g | LEGS h | SHELL i | OTHER CHARACTERISTICS j |
|---|---|---|---|---|---|---|---|---|---|
|  |  |  |  |  |  |  |  |  |  |
|  |  |  |  |  |  |  |  |  |  |

In columns *d* to *i,* you need make a check only if the characteristic is present; leave the column blank if the characteristic is absent. In column *j,* you might record "scaly," "hairy," "lives in water," or any other characteristic you observe. The chart should help you to record your observations quickly.

### STUDYING THE DATA

Your recorded observations constitute the data on which you will base an answer to your problem. First you must study these data to see just what they tell about the problem.

Begin by placing the letter *P* in front of the name of an organism if you think it is a plant, the letter *A* if you think it is an animal, and *U* if you are undecided. Now look over the characteristics of all the organisms you have decided to call plants. Do the same with the ones you have called animals.

Decide which characteristics seem to belong to plants rather than to animals. On a sheet of notebook paper, list these under the heading "Plant Characteristics." Decide which characteristics seem to belong to animals rather than to plants. List these under the heading "Animal Characteristics."

As you think about these characteristics, you may find a need to change your first classification of some organisms. If so, do not hesitate to change the identifying letters in the first column of your chart. But the observations—the data —*should not be changed* unless you go back and observe the specimens again.

• Are there still any organisms that seem to fit in neither the plant nor the animal group (those marked *U*)? If so, can you name any characteristics that they all seem to share? (1) • On the basis of your data, do you think it would be safe to answer the statement "All organisms are either plants or animals" with a definite Yes or No? Why or why not? (2)

## INVESTIGATION 1.2

### THE GERMINATION OF SEEDS: AN EXPERIMENT

#### PURPOSE

Forming a hypothesis and designing an experiment that will result in data from which a conclusion can be drawn are difficult tasks. Among other things, they require a great deal of experience. If you are interested in a scientific career, this kind of experience is worth getting as soon as possible. During this course, the teacher will point out opportunities to do these things. At present, however, we are concerned with the way in which a biological experiment is carried out. Therefore, the hypotheses have already been formed and the designing has already been done.

The experiment tests two hypotheses:

1. If seeds are soaked before planting, the germination of the seeds will be altered.

2. If different kinds of seeds are germinated, the time required for germination varies.

#### BACKGROUND INFORMATION

A mature seed consists of a small plant and a store of food surrounded by a protective coat. When you plant a seed, the young plant that has been inactive within it begins to grow. As a result of this growth, part of the young plant breaks through the seed coat. This is called *sprouting.* Sprouting is one phase in the general process of renewed growth called *germination.*

Figure 1 · 4

Steps in setting up Investigation 1.2.

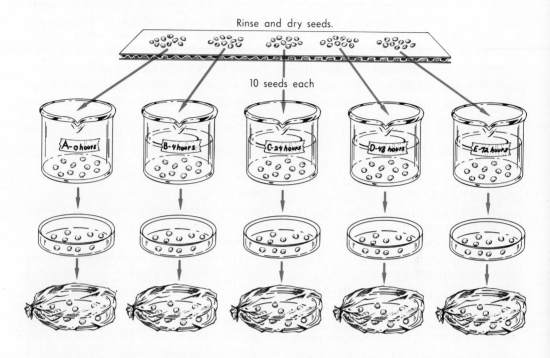

Rinse and dry seeds.

10 seeds each

A - 0 hours    B - 4 hours    C - 24 hours    D - 48 hours    E - 72 hours

## MATERIALS AND EQUIPMENT
### (for each team)

Seeds, all of one kind, 50

Beaker or jar, large enough to hold all seeds, 1

Fungicide, 300 milliliters (abbreviated ml)

Beakers or jars, each large enough to soak 10 seeds, 5

Glass-marking crayon, 1

Waste jar for fungicide (1 per class)

Paper towels, 2

Petri dishes, 5

Filter paper or paper toweling, cut to fit the petri dishes, 20 pieces

Scissors, 1

Clear plastic bags, each large enough to contain a petri dish, 5

Rubber bands, string, or scotch tape, to seal plastic bags

Graph paper, several sheets per student

## PROCEDURE

Select one kind of seed you would like to study. (Check with the teacher, who may want you to work with a particular kind of seed.) Place 50 seeds in a beaker or jar and add fungicide solution until there appears to be two or three times as much solution as seeds. Avoid getting the fungicide on your skin. Allow the seeds to remain in the fungicide for the period of time recommended by the teacher.

While the seeds are being treated with fungicide, mark 5 beakers or jars (Figure 1 · 4) with a glass-marking crayon, as follows: $A - 0$ hours, $B - 4$ hours, $C - 24$ hours, $D - 48$ hours, $E - 72$ hours. On each beaker add your team symbol.

Pour off the fungicide solution into a container provided by your teacher. Rinse the seeds with water and spread them out to dry on paper towels. After the seeds have dried, place 10 in each jar. It is important that all the seeds, no matter how long they are soaked, should be set up for germination at the same time. Devise a schedule for the soaking so that all seeds will have soaked their allotted times when you are ready to "plant" them. At the times indicated on your schedule, add water to the soaking jars until there appears to be about three times as much water as seeds.

On the day scheduled for "planting," obtain 5 clean petri dishes and 20 pieces of filter paper. Cut each piece to fit snugly, without wrinkling, into the bottom half of a petri dish. Remove the top of each dish; place 4 pieces of filter paper in the bottom half. Wet the paper thoroughly. Drain off excess water; replace the top of each dish. Mark the dishes with the same labels used for the jars.

Pour any water from the soaking jars. "Plant" each group of seeds in the matching petri dish (A in *A*, B in *B*, etc.). Put each petri dish into a clear plastic bag. Seal the bag with a rubber band or scotch tape. Store in a place where temperature and light will vary little.

Observe the seeds each day for seven days, and record the number of seedlings (young plants) you see in each container. Record the data in a form like that below.

## STUDYING THE DATA

Draw 5 bar graphs, one for each petri dish. Place the number of germinated seeds on the vertical axis and the number of days on the horizontal axis. (See Figure 1·5.) On each graph show the *total number* of seeds that have germinated *up to and including* the time of each daily count. Thus, for all days after Day 0, you should add the data of all previous days.

Figure 1 · 5

Example of a bar graph: germination of zinnia seeds.

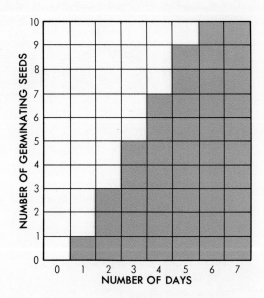

To test the second hypothesis (page 8), it is, of course, necessary to compare the results of teams using different kinds of seeds. This can best be done with numbers rather than with graphs. Using the data from the seeds that were soaked 0 hours (Group A), calculate the percent that germinated by the third, the fifth, and the seventh days. In a table drawn on the chalkboard, enter these figures opposite the name of your kind of seed.

| Kind of Seed _____ | | | | |
|---|---|---|---|---|
| | **HOURS SOAKED** | | | |
| | 0 | 4 | 24 | 48 | 72 |
| Day 0 | | | | |
| Day 1 | | | | |
| | | | | |
| Day 7 | | | | |

## CONCLUSIONS

From the data on the graphs, you may be able to draw a conclusion about the first hypothesis. However, no matter how carefully an experiment is designed, there is no guarantee that the data obtained will permit you to come to a clear conclusion. • Using the data from this experiment, can you give a definite Yes or No answer to the first hypothesis? Or are the data not clear in meaning—is the answer to the hypothesis left in doubt? Briefly state the reason for your answer. (1)

• Now, using the data obtained from all the teams in your class, draw a conclusion for the second hypothesis in the same way you did for the first. (2)

## DISCUSSION

Most experiments require at least two setups. These are alike in all respects except one. The one condition in which the setups differ is called the *variable*. A setup in which the condition is not varied, or is varied least, is the *control* setup. All the other setups (one or more) are *experimentals*.

• What was the variable for testing the first hypothesis? (3) • Which group of seeds serves as the control for the first experiment? (4) • Can you suggest more suitable soaking times for particular kinds of seeds? (5) • What was the variable for the second hypothesis? (6) • Was any one kind of seed a control for the second experiment? Why? (7)

## INVESTIGATION 1.3

### USE OF THE MICROSCOPE: INTRODUCTION

#### PURPOSE

This exercise is to acquaint you with the monocular microscope, its use and care.

#### BACKGROUND

There are many different kinds of microscopes. A magnifying glass is the simplest kind. But usually the word "microscope" refers to an instrument made up of a series of glass lenses in a tube—a *compound* microscope.

One type of compound microscope used in the biology laboratory is the *monocular microscope*. In working with this kind of microscope you use only one eye, so you see an image having length and width but little apparent depth. Most objects examined under the monocular microscope must be so small or thin that light can pass through them. You are able to distinguish form and structure in such objects because some of their parts absorb more light than others. Things seen in this way under the microscope are said to be observed by *transmitted light*.

#### MATERIALS AND EQUIPMENT
(for each student or pair of students)

Monocular microscope

Glass slides

Cover slips

Lens paper

Paper towels

Strips of newspaper

Scissors

Forceps

Medicine dropper

Finger bowl or beaker

Transparent plastic millimeter rule

Pieces cut from magazine photograph

Figure 1 · 6

A monocular microscope.

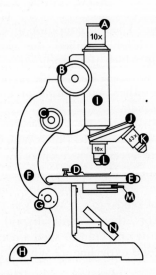

A ocular
B coarse adjustment
C fine adjustment
D stage clip
E stage
F arm
G inclination joint
H base
I body tube
J revolving nosepiece
K high-power objective
L low-power objective
M substage diaphragm
N mirror

## PROCEDURE

**A. Setting up the microscope.** Remove the microscope from its case or space in the storage cabinet. Grasp the curved *arm* of the instrument with one hand and place the other hand under the *base*. Always use two hands when carrying the microscope. Set it down gently on the laboratory table, with the arm toward you and the square *stage* away from you. The base should be a safe distance from the edge of your table.

**B. Identification of the parts of the microscope.** The teacher will help you identify each part of the instrument (Figure 1·6) and explain its use. Make certain that you are familiar with each part before proceeding further with this exercise.

**C. Preliminary adjustments.** Using the *coarse-adjustment* knobs, raise the *body tube* so that the *objectives* do not hit the stage when the *revolving nosepiece* is rotated. Turn the nosepiece so that the *low-power* (shorter) objective is in line with the *ocular,* at the upper end of the body tube. You will hear a click when the objective moves into position. Now turn the substage *diaphragm* to the largest possible opening. Adjust the *mirror* so that it reflects light upward through the opening in the stage. Never let direct sunlight strike the mirror. Why? Look into the ocular, and make final adjustment of the mirror so that the circular *field of view* is evenly illuminated. Adjust the diaphragm to eliminate any glare.

If the lenses of the ocular or the objective appear to be cloudy or dusty, wipe them gently with a piece of lens paper, using a circular motion and light pressure. *Never* use any other kind of paper or cloth. When a piece of lens paper has been used once, discard it. If this procedure does not clean the lenses, consult the teacher.

**D. Preparation of materials for examination.** Material to be studied under a microscope is usually placed on a piece of glass called a *microscope slide.* In most cases the material is covered with a small, thin piece of glass called a *cover slip.* Both slide and cover slip should be as clean as possible before use. Always handle them by the edges. Avoid touching their flat surfaces with your fingers.

To clean a slide, hold it by the edges, between index finger and thumb, and dip into water. Then wipe dry, using a soft piece of clean cloth or paper towel.

Cover slips are much more fragile than slides. To clean a cover slip, hold it by the edges, using the index finger and thumb of one hand, and dip into water. A piece of thin, soft cloth or lens paper should then be folded and held between the finger and thumb of the other hand.

Figure 1 · 7
Cleaning a cover slip.

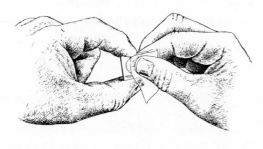

Figure 1 · 8
Making a wet mount.

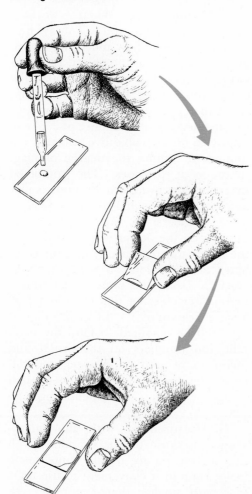

Next, insert the wet cover slip in the fold and apply pressure to *both* surfaces *at the same time* by bringing thumb and finger together (Figure 1 · 7). A gentle, circular, wiping motion is most effective.

Now prepare a *wet mount* for microscopic observation. Using scissors, cut out a piece of newspaper that includes at least one letter *e*. The piece should be not more than 3 millimeters (abbreviated mm) square. If possible, find a section that has printing on only one side of the paper. Place the piece of newspaper in the center of a slide, printed side up. Using a medicine dropper, put a single drop of water on the piece of newspaper. Some of the water will soak into the newspaper, but some should still remain surrounding it. If necessary, add another drop of water. The cover slip should then be placed over the newspaper. If this is done properly, the remaining water will spread out in a thin, even layer between cover slip and slide, with the newspaper sandwiched between them. It requires some skill to place the cover slip on the slide in such a way that no air bubbles are included in the mount. The best method is to hold the cover slip at an angle of about 45° to the slide; then bring the cover slip down to the slide until the lower edge touches the drop of water. Continue to lower the slip *slowly* until it is parallel to the surface of the slide (Figure 1 · 8). Remaining bubbles may be removed by *gently* tapping the cover slip with the tip of a forceps. A few bubbles should not interfere with your observation.

**E. Focusing the microscope.** Using the coarse-adjustment knobs, raise the body tube until there is a space of approximately 2 centimeters (abbreviated cm) between the low-power objective and the surface of the stage. Now place the slide on the stage of the microscope. Position the slide so that a letter *e* on the newspaper is located in the center of the stage opening and faces you as it would on a newspaper page. Use the *stage clips* to hold the slide in position. Looking at the microscope from the side, and again using the coarse-adjustment knobs, slowly lower the body tube until the lower end of the objective is approximately 1 mm above the upper surface of the cover slip. *Never* allow the objective to touch the cover slip. Some, but not all, microscopes are provided with mechanical stops that prevent this.

Now look through the ocular and slowly raise the body tube until the print on the newspaper becomes visible. If you still see no image after you have raised the objective more than 1 cm, you have missed the position for correct focus. Refocus—look at the microscope from the side, lower the objective to its original position, and try again. *Never* lower the tube with the coarse-adjustment while you are looking into the ocular. When you see an image of the printed material, rotate the *fine-adjustment* knobs to obtain the best possible focus. Further adjustment of the diaphragm will often improve the clearness of the image.

Compare the position of the *image* of the letter *e* in the ocular with the position of the printed *e* (the *object*) on the slide. • Is the image in the same position as the object seen with the unaided eye? If not, describe its position. (1) • While looking into the ocular, slowly move the slide from right to left. Which way does the image move? (2) • Move the slide away from you. Which way does the image move? (3)

Now rotate the revolving nosepiece so that the *high-power* (longer) objective is in line with the ocular. In doing this, make sure that the lower end of the objective does not touch the cover slip. If this happens, you will have to repeat the entire sequence of operations, beginning with focusing of the low-power objective.

When the high-power objective is in correct focus, its lower end will be much closer to the cover slip than was the low-power objective. The distance between the objective and the cover slip is called the *working distance.* Usually less than one full turn (in either direction) will bring the high-power objective into focus.

• Is the field of view larger or smaller? (4) • Does the switch from low power to high power change the position of the image? (5) • Is the illumination brighter or less bright than it is with low power? (6)

Remove the wet mount from the microscope and save it for later use.

**F. Magnification.** When working with the microscope, you will always find it useful to know how much the instrument is magnifying the object. If an object is magnified 50 diameters (50X), the image you see is 50 times longer and wider than if the object were viewed with the unaided eye at a distance of 25.4 cm. Engraved on each objective or ocular is a number indicating the degree of magnification it provides. The combined magnification produced by both ocular and objective is equal to the *product* of these numbers. If, for example, the number on the ocular is 5X and that on the low-power objective is 12X, the combined magnification is 5 × 12, or 60 diameters. Using the same ocular and a high-power objective that magnifies 45X, a magnification of 5 × 45, or 225 diameters, will be obtained. • Find the magnification numbers on the ocular and objectives of your microscope, and calculate the magnifications obtained when using low power. (7) • When using high power. (8)

**G. Measurement with the microscope.** Because objects examined with the microscope are usually quite small, biologists find it convenient to use units of length smaller than centimeters or millimeters for microscopic measurement. One such unit, commonly used, is the *micron* (1/1000 mm), for which the Greek letter $\mu$ (called "mu") is the symbol.

You can estimate the size of a microscopic object by comparing it with the size of the circular field of view. The size of the field may be determined as follows: Place a plastic millimeter rule on the stage. Following the directions already given for focusing, obtain a well-defined image of the divisions on the rule with the low-power objective. Carefully move the rule until its marked edge passes through the exact center of the field of view. Now count the number of divisions that can be seen within the field of view. The marks on the rule will appear quite wide; 1 mm is the distance from the *center* of one mark to the *center* of the next. • What is the diameter of the low-power field of your microscope in millimeters? (9) • In microns? (10)

To measure the diameter of the high-power field, use the following procedure: First divide the magnification number of the high-power objective by the magnification number of the low-power objective. Then divide the diameter of the low-power field of view by this quotient. This is the diameter of the high-power field of view. For example, if the magnification of your low-power objective is 12X and of your high-power objective 48X, the quotient is 4. If the diameter of the low-power field of view is $1600\mu$, the diameter of the high-power field of view is $1600 \div 4$, or $400\mu$. • Using this method of calculation, what is the diameter of your high-power field in microns? (11)

Remove the plastic rule and replace it with the wet mount of the letter *e*. Using low power, compare the height of the letter with the diameter of the field of view. • Estimate as accurately as possible the actual height of the letter in millimeters. (12) • In microns. (13)

**H. Resolving power.** Remove the slide from the stage and carefully lift off the cover slip. Discard the piece of newspaper. Dry the slide and the cover slip. Now prepare another wet mount, using a small piece of paper cut from a magazine photograph and following the procedure for preparing slides outlined in *D*, pages 12–13. • Examine this mount under low power. How does the magnified image of the picture compare with the photograph as seen with the unaided eye? (14) You have just seen an example of the *resolving power* of a microscope, the ability to clearly separate details. For most people, two objects that are less than 0.1 mm apart cannot be seen as separate by the unaided eye. The microscope permits us to detect space between objects that are much closer together than this.

You can observe the limited resolving power of your unaided eyes by studying the headlights of a distant automobile as it approaches you at night. At first you see only a single point of light. As the car comes nearer, you begin to see the lights as two separate points; at this distance your eyes have "resolved" the lights.

Thus a microscope actually does two things: it provides magnifying power, and it provides resolving power.

**I. Care of the microscope.** The microscope, like all other instruments in the laboratory, must be given proper care. It should always be carried in an upright position, with one hand firmly grasping the arm and the other hand supporting it under the base. If it is necessary to tilt the instrument, use the *inclination joint*, and always return the microscope to its untilted position when your work is completed.

At the end of the laboratory period, turn the revolving nosepiece until the low-power objective is in place. Adjust the position of the body tube so that the lower end of the objective is approximately 1 cm above the stage. Turn the stage clips so that they do not extend beyond the side of the stage. Make sure all slides are removed from the stage. Return the microscope to its storage space. Clean and dry all slides and cover slips used.

## FOR FURTHER INVESTIGATION

If a *stereoscopic microscope* is available in your laboratory, you may explore its use. This instrument is most often used to view whole objects by *reflected* rather than by transmitted light.

## INVESTIGATION 1.4

## USE OF THE MICROSCOPE: BIOLOGICAL MATERIAL

### PURPOSE

In this exercise you will learn how to prepare biological materials for microscopic examination.

### MATERIALS AND EQUIPMENT
(for each student or pair of students)

Beaker or finger bowl, for cleaning
    slides and cover slips
Glass slide
Small piece of white potato
Medicine dropper
Cover slip
Monocular microscope
Iodine – potassium-iodide ($I_2KI$)
    solution in bottle with dropper
Paper towel
Yeast culture
Mixed culture of microorganisms
Lens paper

### PROCEDURE

For setting up the microscope, cleaning slides and cover slips, and preparing wet mounts, follow the general procedures given in Investigation 1.3 (pages 12–16). Additional instructions will be included below when necessary.

**A. Mounting, staining, and observing starch grains.** Place a *small* piece of white potato in the center of a clean slide. Place the slide on the laboratory table and press the potato with your fingers until a small amount of juice is forced out onto the surface of the slide. Distribute this juice evenly over the center of the slide by moving the piece of potato in a circular pattern. Discard the piece of potato. Immediately add a drop of water and a clean cover slip to the slide, avoiding, if possible, the inclusion of air bubbles in the mount.

Using the focusing procedure you learned in the previous exercise, examine this preparation under low power. You can observe the starch grains more readily if you decrease the size of the opening in the substage diaphragm. This will increase contrast between the starch grains and the water surrounding them. Move the slide on the stage until you have located a field in which well-separated grains are clearly visible. Center a group of these grains in the field and switch to high power. • Describe the shape of an individual starch grain. (1) • Can you see any internal structure in these grains? If you can, describe what you observe.(2)

When you have completed your observations, turn again to low power. Now stain the starch grains, using the following procedure: Place a small drop of the iodine – potassium-iodide ($I_2KI$) solution on the slide, at one side of the cover slip. Tear off a small piece of paper towel and place the torn edge in contact with the water at the opposite edge of the cover slip. Water will be absorbed by the paper towel. As water is removed at one edge

Figure 1 · 9

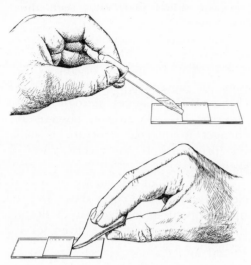

**B. Examining yeast cultures.** The *culture* of yeast that you are about to examine was prepared a day or so ago by placing a few grains of dried yeast in a solution of molasses and water. Yeast organisms multiply so rapidly that millions of them will be available for study.

Place a small drop of the culture on a clean slide, add a cover slip, and examine first under low power, then under high power. • Describe the shape of the yeast organisms. (7)

Study the arrangement of small groups of these organisms. • From your observations, can you come to any conclusions about how new yeast organisms are formed? (8) • What structures (if any) can you see in the organisms? Sketch any internal structures you observe. (9)

Using $I_2KI$ solution, stain the yeast in the same way you stained the starch grains. • Compare the effects of the $I_2KI$ solution on the yeast organisms with its effects on starch grains. (10) • Can you see any structures that were not visible in the unstained yeast organisms? If so, describe them. (11) • Using the method previously described, estimate the size in microns of an average yeast organism. (12)

**C. Examining a mixed culture of microorganisms.** Using a medicine dropper, remove a small amount of liquid from the upper part of the mixed culture of *microorganisms* (microscopic living things). Place one drop at the center of a clean glass slide and add a cover slip. Focus with low power and adjust the substage diaphragm to obtain good contrast. Move the slide around on the stage so that all areas under the cover slip are examined. A variety of organisms should be visible. Study these, with particular attention to variations in size, shape, movement (twisting, wiggling, crawling, etc.), and internal structure.

As water evaporates at its edge, the cover slip will be drawn closer to the sur-

of the mount, $I_2KI$ solution will be drawn under the cover slip at the opposite edge. Continue until the $I_2KI$ solution is drawn about halfway across the space under the cover slip. $I_2KI$ solution will then continue to spread slowly throughout the mount. By examining various regions of the mount, you can observe the effects of different amounts of $I_2KI$ solution on the starch grains. Examine under low power, then under high power. • What changes do you observe in the starch grains exposed to relatively large amounts of $I_2KI$ solution? (3) • What differences do you see between these grains and others exposed to smaller amounts of $I_2KI$? (4) • Can you observe internal structure in the stained grains? If so, describe what you see. (5) • Using the method given in Investigation 1.3, estimate the size in microns of the larger starch grains. (6)

When you have completed your observations, remove the slide from the stage, lift off the cover slip, and dip both slide and cover slip into the container of water. Dry them, and carefully wipe off any liquid that may have run off the slide onto the microscopic stage, using a piece of paper towel.

face of the slide. As this occurs, the movements of larger organisms will be more and more restricted. Locate one of the organisms that have either slowed down or stopped. Turn to high power and attempt to examine it under higher magnification. To follow moving organisms and keep them in the field, it is usually necessary to use *both* hands —one on the slide and the other on the fine adjustment.  • As organisms move about, they not only change position in the field but they also move in and out of focus. Why? (13)  If you do not continually readjust the focus, you will see only a part of the detail to be observed. • When seen under high power, do the organisms appear to move more rapidly or more slowly than when seen under low power? (14)

Now stain the mount, repeating the procedures used with the starch grains and yeast. • Do moving organisms continue to move when exposed to $I_2KI$? (15)  • What changes in color do you observe? (16)  • Can you observe any changes in internal structure as staining proceeds? If so, record these in sketches. (17)

At the end of the laboratory period, clean the slides and cover slips. Place the microscope in its storage place, following the procedures that were given for Investigation 1.3.

## THE FOUNDATIONS OF LIFE

Now let us replace rabbit and raspberry bush with another image: a cow chewing its cud in a meadow. Flies hover around the cow's ears; grasshoppers nibble the pasture grasses; birds pick off the grasshoppers; beetles bury the cow's dung. The image spreads like the ripples from a stone thrown into a pond. You can begin with *any* single living thing and, to a greater or lesser extent, develop beautiful strings of relationships. Biology begins at any place and leads in many directions, like a highway network on a map, like a spider's web.

Where shall we take hold of this web of life?

Whether we look at the individual or at the living world as a whole, we find that both the balance and the changes involve the flow of *energy* and of *matter*. The details of the flow will develop throughout the rest of our biology course. In this chapter we wish only to look at the broad outline.

energy [Greek: *en*, + *ergon*, work]

matter [Latin: *materia*, material, stuff]

### ENERGY

In every phase of life sketched in these preceding paragraphs, was there not some activity? The cow was chewing; the flies were flying; even the grass was actively growing; and the flowers in the meadow were opening in the sunshine.

Now activity always requires energy. Whenever anything *happens,* energy is involved. Physicists a long time ago developed an important principle called the Conservation of Energy: "Energy can neither be created nor destroyed." Although physicists have since found that matter and energy are interchangeable under certain conditions, life is not possible under these conditions. Therefore, whenever you see some biological activity, you can ask, "Where does the energy come from?"

**Source of energy.**   Where does *your* energy come from? No doubt you have heard that human energy comes from food. You have been urged to eat in order to grow and in order to play or to work—in other words, to be active.

It may require some imagination to look at a potato and see energy in it—or even at a hamburger and see in it the winning touchdown of the big game. For present purposes we need only point out that energy is not involved in activity *only;* it may be present when there is merely the *possibility* of activity. An automobile runs. There is activity—energy. The gasoline sits in the tank. The gasoline is not active, but the activity of the car is derived from it. Therefore we say that the gasoline contains energy. The energy in the gasoline is called *chemical* energy. Such energy is found in the bonds that hold together the atoms within the molecules of a substance. The potato and the hamburger also contain chemical energy in the bonds of their molecules; you can use this energy in your life activities.

Where does the chemical energy in the substances that consumers eat come from? Remember: we are operating under the physicists' principle that energy cannot be created under conditions in which life exists. So the question "Where from?" is inescapable. By this question we are led from one part of the web to another.

Suppose we consider the hamburger. It is made of meat that was once part of a cow. But where did the cow get the energy? It, too, must consume substances that already contain chemical energy—substances from other organisms. Nothing in its animal body allows for any other form of energy-capture. We animals—men, cows, lions—are all consumers. But the cow differs from the lion in one important way: the cow does not consume another animal; it consumes grass or grain. Like the rabbit, it is a first-order consumer, while lions are second-order consumers—as we are when we eat hamburgers.

The grass plant and the potato plant do not consume any other organism; they do not "eat." Then where does the green plant's energy come from? You know—from light. It is a little difficult to show that light can directly produce activity, but someone from the physics class may be able to demonstrate this. At any rate, light is a form of

*Note how new information causes scientists to modify their older ideas.*

*But what are we when we eat potatoes?*

Figure 1 · 10

Radiations from the sun form a continuous series, from those of very short wavelengths to those of very long wavelengths. Bands within the series have been given names. The band that we can detect with our eyes —light— is roughly the band used by producers in photosynthesis.

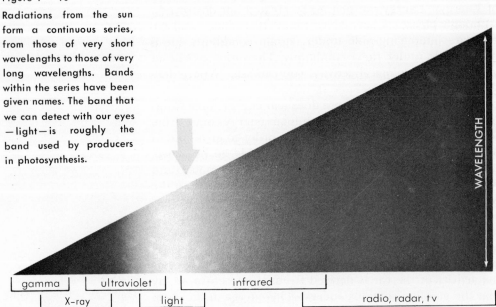

| gamma | ultraviolet | infrared |
| X-ray | light | radio, radar, tv |

WAVELENGTH

energy, and it supplies the energy for most plants. And the source of this light energy is the sun.

Are you going to ask, "What is the source of the sun's light?" We hope so. But for the purposes of this book, we stop here, since the question carries us too far from biology.

**Capturing light energy.** The energy we receive from the sun is not all visible light. Figure 1 · 10 shows the full range (in terms of wavelength) of the energy that comes from the sun. The portion of this *radiant* energy that human eyes can detect is what we call visible light. It happens that this is roughly the same portion of the sun's radiation that green plants capture.

Light is a form of energy, but no animal can use light directly for its activities. Only green plants and a few green microorganisms can change light energy of the sun to chemical energy—a process called *photosynthesis*. The stored chemical energy can then be used by the producers themselves or by other organisms.

Later we shall look at some of the details of photosynthesis. Now it is necessary to point out only that this process makes use of two materials: water and carbon dioxide. Together they form complex molecules, into which the captured light energy is bound. After the first step—converting light energy to chemical energy—is finished, the

Are there any limits to scientific inquiry?

radiant [Latin: *radiare*, to send out rays]

Plants can use light from any source, but under natural conditions they use sunlight.

photosynthesis [fō′tə sin′thə sis; Greek: *photos*, a light, + *syn*, together, + *thesis*, putting in order, arranging]

chemical energy can be shifted around among many sorts of chemical substances. All kinds of organisms can accomplish many of these shifts. But *only the producers* can accomplish the first step.

The emphasis on green comes about because photosynthesis requires the presence of a green substance, *chlorophyll*. Not all plants contain chlorophyll (toadstools, for example, have none), so not all plants are producers. Some living things that you might not want to call plants do contain chlorophyll and thus are producers. Furthermore, a very few microorganisms obtain their energy in a way that does not directly involve light energy. So great is the diversity among living things that it is quite difficult to make general statements in biology.

**Energy pathways.** Energy is brought into the system of living things through the producers. All other organisms are consumers of one kind or another. The grass plant, as it grows, puts energy into its own substance; the cow eats the grass; you eat the cow (or part of it). The energy is passed along—some of it. But the grass plant carries on its own activities of growth, so some of the energy that is captured from sunlight is used up before reaching the cow, even if the cow eats the whole plant. Likewise, the cow has its own activities which use energy—from ambling about the pasture to flicking flies with its tail. In fact, you get from the cow only a little of the original light energy.

Now you must enlarge your idea of "consumer." We have used the term as equal to "eater." But many consumers are organisms that do not "eat" in the sense that you and other familiar animals are said to eat. A toadstool that decays a dead tree has no mouth; yet it is using the energy stored in the chemicals of the wood. Thus it is a first-order consumer, just as is a cow that eats grass. But it does not take in the substance of the wood in the same way that the cow takes in the grass. More important, it attacks the wood after the tree has died; it does not kill the tree itself, though some of its relatives may have done so. It and other consumers that decay the substance of dead organisms are called *saprovores*. The toadstool is a first-order consumer, but what is a saprovore that decays a dead rabbit?

So far we have been showing that energy passes from one organism to another. Now where does the energy finally go? Figure 1·12 indicates that energy is constantly being lost from the living system. Eventually all the energy captured by producers is returned to the nonliving world. But it is not returned in the same form (light) in which it entered—with very unimportant exceptions, such as the light from fireflies. Chiefly, energy leaves the living system

chlorophyll [klōr′ə fĭl; Greek: *chloros*, green, + *phyllon*, leaf]

diversity [di vûr′sə tĭ; Latin: *dis-*, apart, + *vertere*, to turn]

Figure 1 · 11

Toadstool obtaining food from a dead tree.

Sawyer's, Inc.

saprovore [săp′rō vōr′; Greek: *sapros*, rotted, + Latin: *vorare*, to eat]

in the form of heat. Since heat cannot be used in photosynthesis, it follows that energy runs a one-way course through the web of life.

## MATTER

Living things get their energy from the sun. But they get their matter (substance) from the earth. Organisms are made from the same substances that make up the rest of the world. Let us take a look at these substances.

Probably you have already learned something about chemical elements and compounds. Elements are usually found combined in compounds. In your classroom there may be a chart of these elements arranged in a manner found useful to chemists. These chemical elements are basic materials of which both nonliving and living things (whether rabbits, grass, or men) are constructed.

A majority of the elements listed by chemists play little part in the composition of living things. And further, the proportions of the elements in living things are different from their proportions in the nonliving world. In other

Figure 1 · 12

Every living organism carries on activities that result in the release of energy. Therefore, each consumer level obtains a smaller percentage of the energy that was trapped by the producer. This forms an *energy pyramid.*

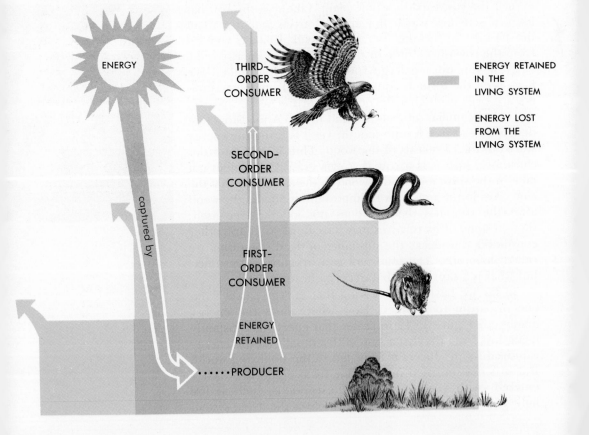

ENERGY

THIRD-ORDER CONSUMER

SECOND-ORDER CONSUMER

FIRST-ORDER CONSUMER

ENERGY RETAINED

PRODUCER

captured by

ENERGY RETAINED IN THE LIVING SYSTEM

ENERGY LOST FROM THE LIVING SYSTEM

words, organisms take in only certain substances from the nonliving world, and not the most abundant ones, either.

We have already traced the flow of energy from the nonliving world through various parts of the living world. Now we shall follow the flow of matter by referring to some of the basic chemical elements found in living things. Unlike energy, these elements circulate; that is, they move from nonliving materials into living things, back to nonliving, again into living, and so on, over and over. Such a circulation is known as a *cycle*. How a cycle operates can best be understood by looking briefly at some examples.

cycle [sĭ'kəl; Greek: *kyklos*, a circle]

**The carbon cycle.**   Like the rim of a wheel, a cycle has no beginning or end. It is, however, convenient to begin the description of the carbon cycle with the carbon dioxide ($CO_2$) that is in the air or dissolved in water (Figure 1 · 14). By the process of photosynthesis, carbon dioxide is built into a vast number of compounds that can be combined in various ways to make up the substance of organisms. These *organic* compounds are passed from the producers to the consumers. Whenever the producers or the consumers remove energy from organic compounds, carbon dioxide may be released again, either into the air or into the water, depending upon where the organism lives. However, as long as any usable energy remains, organic compounds also remain.

Both producers and consumers may discard their carbon-bearing wastes. And both may die, their bodies remaining as an accumulation of carbon compounds. The

organic [ôr găn' ĭk]

Figure 1 · 13

Some elements that occur (most of them only in compounds) in the living substance of organisms. Very small amounts of more than twenty others have been found. Compare the percentages in organisms with the percentages in the earth's crust.

| ELEMENT | SYMBOL | APPROXIMATE % (BY WEIGHT) OF A MAN | APPROXIMATE % (BY WEIGHT) OF EARTH'S CRUST | APPROXIMATE % (BY WEIGHT) OF A CORN PLANT |
|---------|--------|------------------------------------|--------------------------------------------|-------------------------------------------|
| Oxygen | O | 65. | 49. | 75. |
| Carbon | C | 18. | 0.09 | 13. |
| Hydrogen | H | 10. | 0.88 | 10. |
| Nitrogen | N | 3.3 | 0.03 | 0.45 |
| Calcium | Ca | 1.5 | 3.4 | 0.07 |
| Phosphorus | P | 1. | 0.12 | 0.06 |
| Potassium | K | 0.35 | 2.4 | 0.28 |
| Sulfur | S | 0.25 | 0.05 | 0.05 |
| Sodium | Na | 0.24 | 2.6 | trace |
| Chlorine | Cl | 0.19 | 0.19 | 0.04 |
| Magnesium | Mg | 0.05 | 1.9 | 0.06 |
| Iron | Fe | 0.005 | 4.7 | 0.03 |
| Manganese | Mn | 0.0003 | 0.08 | 0.01 |
| Silicon | Si | trace | 25. | 0.36 |

Figure 1 · 14
The carbon cycle. Use the
text to explain the diagram.

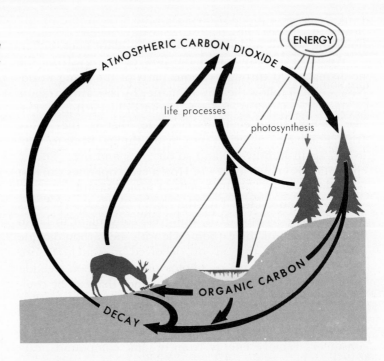

saprovores complete the process of releasing the carbon (in
the form of carbon dioxide) from such wastes and dead
bodies. Most of these final consumers—the saprovores—are
microorganisms, though some, such as the toadstool we
met earlier, are quite visible to the naked eye.

Sometimes the decay process carried on by the saprovores is extremely slow. Over millions of years large masses
of carbon compounds may accumulate in the earth as peat,
coal, and petroleum. Some organisms also sidetrack carbon
into shells that are deposited as rock. However, the main
pathway in the carbon cycle is from the earth's air (the
atmosphere) or waters into living things and then back
again.

atmosphere [ăt′məs fir′; Greek:
atmos, vapor, + sphaira,
sphere]

**The water cycle.** Life—at least, as we know it on
Earth—cannot exist without water ($H_2O$). Usually water
leaves the atmosphere and falls as rain or snow. It may fall
directly into the oceans; or it may fall onto the land, where
it begins a downhill journey through streams, lakes, underground channels, and rivers, eventually reaching the ocean.
In all these cases, some of it may go back into the atmosphere by evaporating. Thus there is a broad cycle of water
movement, from the atmosphere to the lands and seas and
then back to the atmosphere, as shown in Figure 1 · 15.

Land organisms may pick up water at various points in
this cycle. Most commonly, land animals get their water by

drinking, and land plants, by absorbing it from the soil. In *all* organisms some water becomes chemically incorporated into living substances, later to reappear when the substances are broken down. Furthermore, *all* organisms contain some water, in which most of the living processes take place. Thus water is always involved both in the structure and in the activities of living things.

On land both plants and animals lose water to the atmosphere: in plants, largely from the leaves; in animals, through breathing or evaporation from the skin. Still more water is released when animals discharge wastes. Eventually all water taken in by organisms returns to the atmosphere.

**The calcium cycle.**  The first four elements (oxygen, carbon, hydrogen, and nitrogen) listed in Figure 1·13 follow cycles that involve transfer of matter through the atmosphere. The remaining elements pass from organism to organism through water, soil, or rock. They all follow somewhat similar pathways; we use calcium as an example (Figure 1·16).

Calcium compounds are quite common in the rocks of the earth. Several of these compounds are rather soluble, so they are also found in water. Organisms usually pick up these dissolved calcium compounds with water they take in.

Land plants obtain calcium compounds from the soil. The calcium in the plants may be passed to a first-order

Here is one of the few times we can use the word "all" in a general biological statement.

calcium [kăl′sĭ əm]
The nitrogen cycle is considered in detail on pages 243–245.

soluble [sŏl′yə bəl; Latin: *solvere*, to loosen]

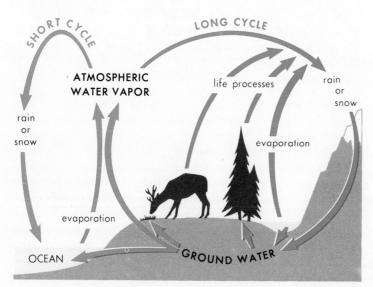

Figure 1 · 15
The water cycle. How would the absence of living things change this cycle?

Figure 1 · 16
The calcium cycle. Which of the other elements in living things follow a similar cycle?

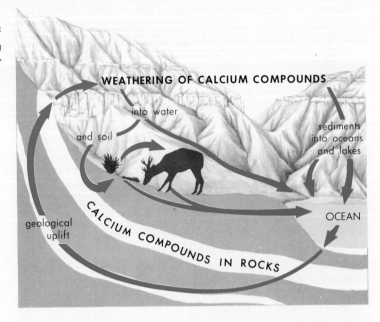

WEATHERING OF CALCIUM COMPOUNDS

into water

and soil

sediments
into oceans
and lakes

geological
uplift

CALCIUM COMPOUNDS IN ROCKS

OCEAN

consumer and then to a second-order consumer. Or at any stage the calcium may be returned to the soil or water by the saprovores.

Many kinds of organisms use such calcium compounds in building skeletons—often in the form of shells—that saprovores do not decay. When these organisms die, their skeletons accumulate on the bottoms of oceans, lakes, and ponds. During the course of millions of years, these remains may become tightly packed by the processes that shape the earth's surface. Thus they become rocks. Later these rocks may be thrust upward to form hills and mountains. Then the calcium compounds, again dissolved from the rocks in the never-ending cycle of water, move with the streams and rivers toward the ocean. Always the flow is back to the sea.

These rocks are chiefly limestones and marble.

## INVESTIGATION 1.5

### INTERRELATIONSHIPS OF PRODUCERS AND CONSUMERS

#### PURPOSE

During this laboratory work you will obtain data that will enlarge your understanding of the relationships between producers and consumers—especially their place in the carbon cycle. The hypothesis for this experiment is: A source of light energy is required for a producer-consumer system to remain in steady state.

## BACKGROUND INFORMATION

An *indicator* is a substance that shows the presence of a chemical substance by changing color. Bromthymol blue is an indicator that changes to a green or yellow color in the presence of an acid. Carbon dioxide ($CO_2$) forms an acid when dissolved in water. Therefore, in this experiment, bromthymol blue can be used to indicate, indirectly, the presence of $CO_2$.

## MATERIALS AND EQUIPMENT

Screw-cap culture tubes, 20×150 mm, 8

Glass-marking crayon, 1

Test-tube racks, 2

Small water snails, 4

Elodea (*Anacharis*), 4 pieces

Bromthymol blue solution

Container of melted paraffin

Pond water

Light source

A box or chamber, to keep some cultures in the dark

## PROCEDURE

Prepare two sets of four culture tubes each and label them *A1, A2, A3, A4,* and *B1, B2, B3, B4.*

Pour pond or aquarium water into each tube until the water surface is approximately 20 mm from the top. Add 3 to 5 drops of bromthymol blue solution to each tube. To each Tube 1 add a small snail; to each Tube 2 add a small snail and a leafy stem of elodea; and to each Tube 3 add elodea only. Do not add anything except the bromthymol blue to the tubes labeled *4* (Figure 1 · 17).

Place a cap on each tube and tighten. Dip the capped end of each tube in melted paraffin. After allowing the paraffin to cool and harden, test the seal by turning the tubes upside down for about five minutes. There should be no leakage.

Figure 1 · 17

Completed setup of Investigation 1.5.

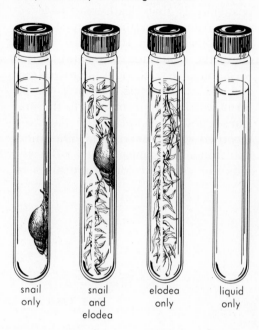

snail only

snail and elodea

elodea only

liquid only

If all tubes are watertight, place one set (*A1–A4*) in strong artificial light. Place the second set (*B1–B4*) in the dark chamber. Make observations on both culture series after the lighted series has had 24 hours of light. Record any changes in the color of the indicator (bromthymol blue) and in the condition of the plants and snails. Then place the *A* series in the dark and the *B* series in the light and repeat observations after the *B* series has been in light for 24 hours. Then return the *A* series to light and *B* to dark and observe after several days.

In your data book prepare a form for recording your observations.

## DISCUSSION

• In which tube did the organisms die first? (1) Since these organisms usually survive well in an aquarium or pond, we might suspect that being cut off from air might have had something to do with their death. • What substance in air may have been needed? (2) Another possibility is that death may have resulted from the accumulation of a poisonous material in the water. • What does the indicator show? (3) Recall what you have read about photosynthesis and the carbon cycle. • Using this information and your answers to the previous questions, explain the data you recorded while observing the other tubes that contain organisms. (4) • Did the indicator change color in the tubes labeled 4? If so, how might you explain this (keeping in mind the source of the water)? (5) • In the design of this experiment what would you call Tubes A4 and B4? (6) • What results might you have expected if all tubes had been kept in total darkness? (7)

## CONCLUSION

• Draw a conclusion concerning the hypothesis. (8) • Try to devise a new hypothesis about the carbon cycle. (9)

## THE WEB OF LIFE

You have seen how energy and matter are the foundations upon which the world of living things rests. They come together when photosynthetic organisms store energy in chemical form. After this the pathways along which energy and matter flow are complex.

complex [Latin: *cum*, with, together, + *plectere*, to twist]

## FOOD

For knowledge to be verifiable, scientists need to be as exact as possible in their communication with each other. One result of this need has been the coining of new words to fit new discoveries. Technical terms—such as "saprovore" —tend to make scientific reading difficult for the learner.

Even greater difficulty comes from the use of a familiar word in a particular scientific sense. Such a word is *food*. There are many definitions of this word in the dictionary. But in this course, we will always use it to mean *materials containing energy that organisms can use.*

What are the "plant foods" you buy to help your petunias or African violets?

Photosynthetic organisms do not need to take in foods from the environment; they produce them by using the energy of sunlight. But they cannot produce foods out of nothing; they must have raw materials. In our language, there is no word for all such raw materials, but we can refer to them in general as *inorganic* substances: water and calcium compounds are examples. For a consumer, foods are not only the direct source of all energy; they are also the source of most of the matter needed to build up the con-

Compare "inorganic" with "organism" (page 4) and "organic" (page 23).

sumer's body, though a few inorganic substances are needed, too.

Foods, then, are involved in both the flow of energy and the flow of materials through the living world. Therefore they are of particular importance in the biologist's efforts to untangle the web of life, to understand the world of living things.

### FOOD WEBS

If we look at a part of a single energy pathway, we can diagram what is known as a *food chain*. For example, if we study the plants that are eaten by the rabbit that, in turn, is eaten by the wildcat, we would diagram this food chain as:

Plants $\longrightarrow$ Rabbit $\longrightarrow$ Wildcat

However, a food relationship is seldom, if ever, this simple. Figure 1·18 shows a more complex but still highly simplified energy pathway that we could call a food *web*.

Figure 1 · 18

How many energy pathways can you trace?

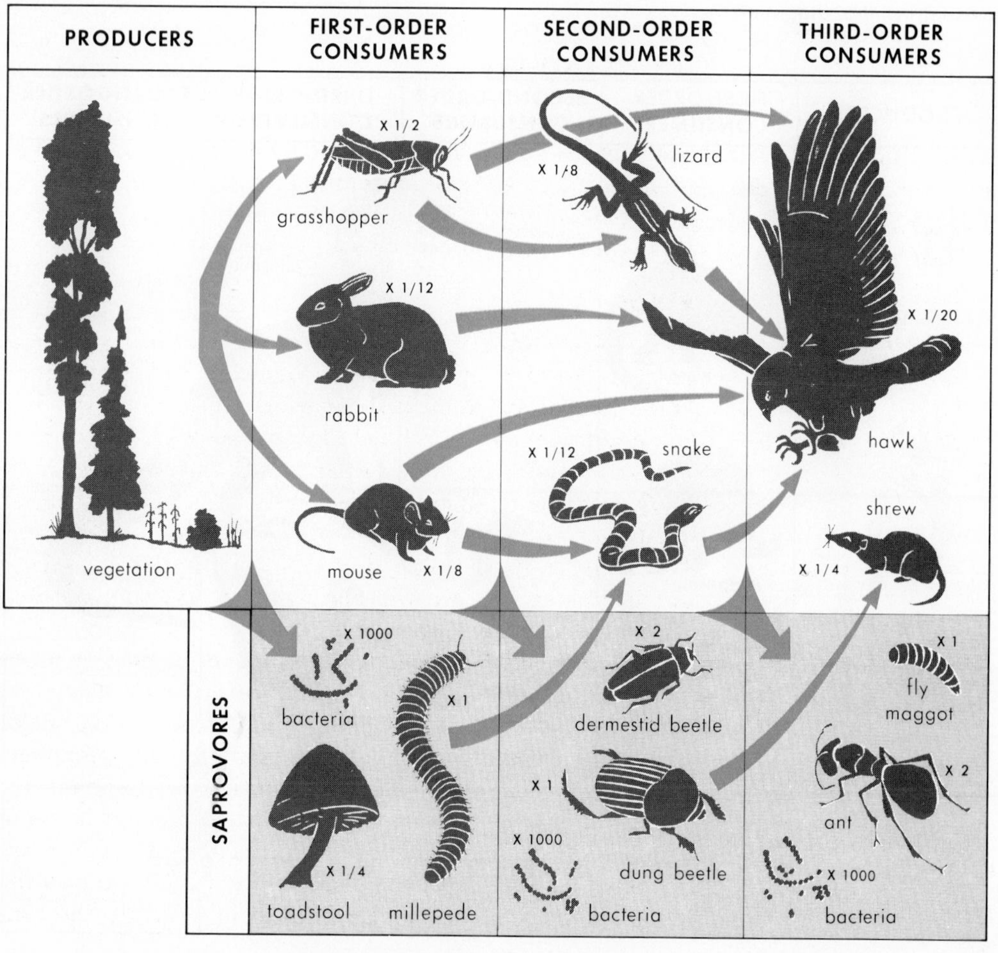

| PRODUCERS | FIRST-ORDER CONSUMERS | SECOND-ORDER CONSUMERS | THIRD-ORDER CONSUMERS |
|---|---|---|---|

vegetation

grasshopper X 1/2
rabbit X 1/12
mouse X 1/8

lizard X 1/8
snake X 1/12

hawk X 1/20
shrew X 1/4

SAPROVORES

bacteria X 1000
millepede X 1
toadstool X 1/4

dermestid beetle X 2
dung beetle X 1
bacteria X 1000

fly maggot X 1
ant X 2
bacteria X 1000

Even simple food webs include several kinds of producers, and these are eaten by several kinds of first-order consumers. Not every kind of plant is eaten to the same extent by every *herbivore*. Mice probably eat more of the fruits and seeds; grasshoppers, probably more of the juicy leaves; and rabbits, probably more of the coarser stems of weedy and small woody plants. Any one herbivore prefers certain plants to others, but each may shift from one plant to another in hard times. Similarly, there is considerable variation in the kinds of food eaten by the second-order consumers. These will choose the kind of food that is most easily captured, most preferred as to taste, and the best size for efficient eating. Notice, also, that the saprovores—the consumers that decay dead organisms—are involved in all parts of the food web.

Food webs have a history as long as the record of living things on earth. The evidence we have for organisms of the past—the fossils—includes records of both producers and

herbivore [hûr′bə vôr′; Latin: *herba*, grass, green crops, + *vorare*, to devour]

fossils [Latin: *fossilis*, dug up]: traces of organisms preserved in the earth (see page 340)

**Figure 1 · 19**

An ancient food web. What kind of evidence was used to construct this diagram?

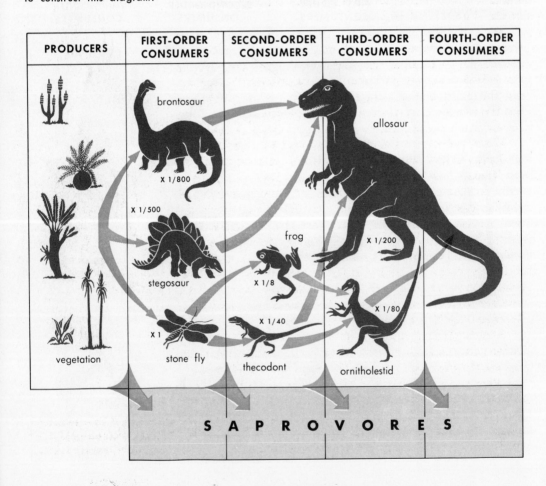

| PRODUCERS | FIRST-ORDER CONSUMERS | SECOND-ORDER CONSUMERS | THIRD-ORDER CONSUMERS | FOURTH-ORDER CONSUMERS |
|---|---|---|---|---|

brontosaur

allosaur

X 1/800

X 1/500

frog

stegosaur

X 1/200

X 1/8

X 1/40

X 1/80

X 1

vegetation

stone fly

thecodont

ornitholestid

S A P R O V O R E S

consumers. Early organisms were very different from most we know today, but apparently they played the same parts that modern organisms play in the interchange of energy and matter. Figure 1·19 gives an impression of what might have been going on about 180,000,000 years ago, when dinosaurs were the biggest animals around. Again we find that the balance of nature is a teetering balance, that the steady state is not static and fixed, but changing, dynamic. Most of the actors in this scene have disappeared; others have evolved and taken over their roles. But the *processes* have been continuous. The mechanisms that control this steady state allow for many kinds of adjustment to changing conditions. The process of adjustment, of control, that results in a steady state is known as *homeostasis*.

## THE BIOSPHERE

The rabbit and the raspberry bush have led you out into a wide world—the world of living things. So far you have only glanced at this world. As you continue this course, you will find it convenient to have a single word for the world of life. The word is *biosphere*.

We can think of the biosphere as consisting of all living things and the water, air, soil, and other matter that surround them—a rather thin layer on the surface of Earth. But in this book we shall emphasize a different viewpoint: not the biosphere as a *thing* existing in a particular place, but the biosphere as a *system* of relationships between living things and between matter and energy that surround them.

We ourselves are a part of this system. In a special sense we have various kinds of relationships with our parents, our friends, and other human beings. But in a general sense we have relationships with all things—living and nonliving—that affect us in any way. The relationship between a corn plant and us is very direct: it is the producer-consumer relationship. The relationship between us and smut (an organism that damages corn plants) is less direct; but clearly, damage to corn plants will affect our food supply. Even less direct is our relationship to those weather conditions that favor the growth of smut that damages corn that reduces our food supply!

A great deal of research may be required to show very indirect relationships. But in using the term "biosphere" we express the idea that relationships exist between all parts of the system whether they are known at present or not. Such an idea, which is based on a great deal of observation but goes beyond our present verified knowledge, is called a *concept*. A concept is one of several kinds of ideas from which any body of scientific knowledge is built up.

dynamic [dī năm′ĭk; Greek: *dynamis*, power]: here, active, moving

homeostasis [hō′mĭ ō stā′sĭs; Greek: *homoios*, like, same, + *stasis*, condition]

biosphere [Greek: *bios*, life, + *sphaira*, sphere]

smut: See Figure 3 · 10.

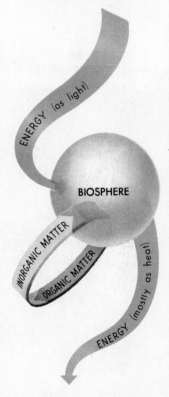

Figure 1 · 20

How does the flow of energy through the biosphere differ from the flow of matter?

## MAN AND THE BIOSPHERE

All existing evidence indicates that the organism we call man has been a strand in the web of life not much more than a million years. Yet the evidence from fossils indicates that there has been a biosphere for at least three thousand times a million years. If the evidence is correct, man is a relative newcomer to the biosphere.

Through most of his time in the biosphere, man apparently affected the web of life very much as any other organism did. But gradually he learned to use sources of energy from outside his own body. Today he has in his control enormous amounts of energy with which he changes the surface of the earth. In changing the earth he also tears apart many sections of the web of life. With each increase of his energy supply, he has had opportunity to increase his knowledge. More knowledge has led to the discovery of still more energy sources. And all this has brought about conditions favorable to increasing his own numbers. Today no other large organism is so numerous. And man's numbers are still increasing.

Figure 1 · 21

Standing room only? How many can the earth's resources of energy and matter support?

H. Armstrong Roberts

The unique position of man in the biosphere presents problems that are of tremendous importance to the future of all life forms. They are problems that face every student who reads this book. They are problems that will not be completely solved tomorrow or next year or perhaps even in your lifetime. But mankind will have to face them — there is no escape.

unique [ū nēk'; Latin: *unus*, one]: without a like or equal

These problems go far beyond the field of biology. But because they all concern man and the other living things on earth, the science that deals with living things — biology — should contribute to your understanding of them. Some of these problems are listed below. Keep them in mind as you study biology during the coming year. At the end of the year we shall return to them and consider in more detail how an understanding of biology may help man solve them.

A. Problems resulting from man's control of energy sources outside his body:
1. Can the effects of our interference with one part of the web of life be balanced by interference with another part — thus making possible the gradual achievement of a new steady state in the biosphere?
2. If not, then to what extent can we change the surface of the earth without so greatly disturbing homeostatic mechanisms that the steady state of the biosphere is destroyed?
3. To what extent can we change the surface of the earth without producing conditions in which we will no longer find life enjoyable or even worth living?
4. Have man's energy supply and his knowledge become so great that he is now completely independent of the rest of the biosphere and thus free to destroy anything and everything without fear for himself?
B. Problems resulting from man's increasing numbers:
1. In what ways might the increase in human numbers on earth eventually be stopped?
2. Can man control his own numbers? If so, should he?
3. How would eliminating the world food shortage affect the problem of human numbers?
4. As men become more and more crowded together, how can we avoid the stresses that seem to result?
C. Mixed problems resulting from both A and B:
1. How can we avoid accumulating vast quantities of wastes — both industrial and biological — which could ruin our planet as a place for living things?
2. How can our knowledge of the pyramid of energy help reduce the starvation that is present even now?

Archimedes, a scientist of ancient Greece, said that with proper use of levers he could move the world *if someone would give him a platform to stand on.* To do *any* job, it is necessary to have a starting point. In this chapter we have attempted to give you a "platform" for understanding the science of biology by developing the concepts of energy flow, cycles of matter, the web of life, the biosphere. These concepts have been built up by scientists through patient observation, the formulation of hypotheses, and the testing of hypotheses by experiment. Today scientists use these same procedures to gain new knowledge of our universe and of the living things in it. The work of future scientists may uncover facts that will force the change or even the abandonment of these concepts. But the concepts *seem trustworthy today.* This is the most that any scientist can demand of a concept. And it is the best that biologists can offer you as a platform from which to begin your work.

## GUIDE QUESTIONS

Use the following questions to test your understanding of the text.

1. How do consumer organisms differ from producer organisms?
2. How can the idea of balance be explained in a way that takes into account the constant changes in nature?
3. What is the basic activity in scientific work? Why is it so important?
4. Describe the essential features of any experiment.
5. Why must scientists be able to report their work accurately?
6. What is the source of energy for the living world?
7. Why may plants and animals be called "transformers of energy"?
8. Explain briefly the meaning of an energy pyramid.
9. Why are saprovores described as special kinds of consumers?
10. What is the source of the substances that make up the body of any organism?
11. How is the flow of matter through the living world basically different from the flow of energy?
12. In the biological sense what is a *food?*
13. What is the difference between a food chain and a food web?
14. What does the biologist mean when he speaks of the *biosphere?*

## PROBLEMS

The following problems require thinking or research. Some involve applications of your understanding of the text and the laboratory exercises. Others require further study.

1. How can we relate the energy we get from coal and oil to the activities of producer organisms? How are saprovores involved in the formation of coal and oil?

2. What might happen to the balance of nature in a pond if one of the species present suddenly increased greatly in number? Is it likely that the increase

would be permanent? Will your discussion be affected at all by the kind of organism involved? For example, first suppose it is a green alga (producer); then suppose it is a fish (consumer).

3. It is sometimes said that the sun is the source of all energy on the earth. Can you think of any exceptions to this statement?

4. We have started this biology book without defining "life." Try to define it for yourself.

5. Some people believe that potatoes grow better if the seed pieces are planted with the eyes up. How could you test this idea?

6. If all life on earth ceased, what changes in our atmosphere might you reasonably expect?

7. Would it be possible to apply scientific principles in determining which of two paintings is more beautiful?

8. In making a prolonged journey into outer space, man must take along a part of his biosphere. Try to design an efficient "package" of the biosphere for such a journey.

9. Using the approach of the scientist, can you think of any way to prove that something (for example, an appearance of ghosts) can *not* happen?

10. Collect magazine and newspaper articles that throw light upon the human problems mentioned in the section "Man and the Biosphere" (pages 32–33). Explain how each of the articles applies and to which specific problems it is the most applicable.

## SUGGESTED READINGS

BATES, M. *The Forest and the Sea.* New York: Random House, Inc., 1960. Pp. 9–13. (Puts the viewpoint of Chapter 1 into a somewhat different light.)

NACE, R. L. "Water of the World," *Natural History*, January, 1964. Pp. 10–19. (Details on the water cycle.)

ODUM, E. P. *Ecology.* New York: Holt, Rinehart & Winston, Inc., 1963. Pp. 37–64. (A good treatment of the material in Chapter 1. Fairly advanced reading.)

SIMPSON, G. G., and W. S. Beck. *Life: An Introduction to Biology.* 2nd ed. New York: Harcourt, Brace & World, Inc., 1965. Pp. 3–12. (Closely parallels Chapter 1 but will deepen your understanding. Fairly advanced reading.)

*In the same book:* pp. 13–18. (Goes far beyond Chapter 1 in discussing the biologist's viewpoint and methods. Advanced.)

STEHLI, G. J. *The Microscope and How to Use It.* New York: Sterling Publishing Co., Inc., 1961. (A brief but interesting introductory guide.)

STORER, J. H. *The Web of Life [A First Book of Ecology].* New York: The Devin-Adair Co., 1953. Pp. 13–18. (A somewhat poetic interpretation of the interrelationships of living things. Rather easy reading.)

# Individuals and Populations

### INDIVIDUALS

We have moved from rabbits and raspberries to energy, photosynthesis, and cycles of matter—to the whole system of living things on the surface of this planet. The system we can see only in our minds; it is a concept. But we have learned that concepts are built up from innumerable separate observations. And what do we observe in the biosphere? Primarily, we observe *individual* organisms—individual men, individual trees, individual insects, and so on. These we can count, measure, use in experiments; in short, from individuals we can, perhaps, come to understand the living world as a whole.

In general, life processes occur in separate "packages." Each of us is such a package; each of us carries on the processes of life within his own body, separate and distinct from the life processes in the bodies of his neighbors. We are individuals. So, too, are the cows in a herd of cattle, the bees in a hive, the trees in an orchard. Usually we can easily distinguish individuals from one another.

Sometimes, though, individual organisms are so closely packed together that several appear to be one unless closely examined. From a distance, a flock of ducks on the water may appear to be a single mass. Of course, we have only to startle the flock into flight to see that it is composed of individuals. It is more difficult to untangle the individual grass plants in a lawn.

We can find more puzzling examples than these. Figure 2 · 1 shows a sea animal called coral. Is this an individual? Looking at the coral, we see a mass of stony material containing holes. Projecting from each hole is a small organism with waving tentacles. Each organism seems to be inde-

individual [Latin: *individuus*, indivisible]

tentacles [tĕn′tə kəlz; Latin: *tentare*, to touch, feel]

X 2

Figure 2 · 1

Coral. Is this six individuals or one?

X 1/10

Figure 2 · 2

Iris. What seems to be two plants is shown to be one when the soil is removed.

geranium [jĭ rā′nĭ əm]:  See Figure 8 · 3.

originate [ə rĭj′ ə nāt′; Latin: origo, beginning, source]

pendent of the others—an individual. But if we examine the coral more closely, we find that all the tentacle-waving organisms are connected. Now, is each an individual, or is the whole mass an individual? Likewise, if we dig up a clump of iris (Figure 2 · 2), we find that the pieces are held together by underground parts. Yet if the connecting parts are cut, each piece gets along well by itself. What, then, among corals and irises, is an individual?

There is still another difficulty with the word "individual." We can break off a piece of geranium, put it in soil, and see the piece grow and become a new individual. Or we can watch a chick hatch from an egg that was laid by a hen. In each case the new individual is clearly a piece of the old. Apparently, new individuals always originate as pieces from existing individuals. All life comes from life; the living world is continuous in time. Yet, at any given moment it is also discontinuous—cut up into separate "packages," or individuals.

We may have difficulty deciding just what we mean by "individuals" in corals and irises or at just what moment the egg becomes an individual separate from the hen. But in the great majority of cases, we have little difficulty distinguishing individuals; we need not worry, then, about an exact definition. We have seen that science is based on

observation. It is not a matter of memorizing neat definitions. If we can fit all our observations into a definition,
good. If we cannot, then we must face the facts and get
along with imperfect definitions.

## POPULATIONS

A biologist is never interested in a single individual for
its own sake; because he is concerned with verifiable observations, he must in the long run deal with *groups* of
individuals. As soon as he starts dealing with groups of
individuals that are similar in one or more ways, he is
dealing with *populations.*

### BIOLOGICAL MEANING OF "POPULATION"

The word "population" comes from the Latin and
originally meant "peopling"—the number of people inhabiting a place. It still has this meaning. When we say
that the population of Pennsylvania is about eleven and
one-half million, we are talking about the number of human
beings in that state, not the number of squirrels or rabbits.
Long ago, however, biologists found the word useful in
studies of other organisms.

When we discuss a biological population, we need to
identify the *kind* of individuals we are talking about and to

space: Here we refer to our
biosphere—not outer space.

define their limits in *time* and *space.* Thus we can refer to
the population of pigeons during August, 1967, in New
York City, the population of apple trees this spring in a
particular orchard. Kind of individual, time, and place are
always involved, though sometimes one or more of these
may be implied. Usually we are also concerned with *quantity:* the number of deer in 1967 in Michigan; the number
of wolves during the first century A.D. in Italy.

censuses [sĕn′səs əz;   Latin:
censere, to enroll, tax]

The study of human populations has been going on
for a long time. The ancient Romans took censuses regularly, as did the ancient Chinese, primarily for tax purposes. The beginning of population study in modern
science can be dated from 1798, when Thomas Robert
Malthus published a little book titled *An Essay on the Principle
of Population As It Affects the Future Improvement of Mankind.* Malthus was an economist interested in human prob-

economist [ĭ kŏn′ə mĭst; Greek:
oikos, house, + nemein, to
manage]: a scientist who
studies the management of
resources, manufactures, and
commerce

lems though he brought much biological information into
later editions of his book. Basically, he presented evidence
to show that all kinds of organisms, including man, tend
to multiply up to the limit of their possible food supply
and that the results are misery, sickness, and starvation

pessimistic [Latin: pessimus,
worst]

for many individuals. Malthus' pessimistic conclusion

started arguments and investigations that are still continuing today.

Our present understanding of biological populations owes much to the students of human populations. But many population problems can best be investigated by experimenting—and of course we cannot experiment directly with people. In broadening their studies to include many kinds of organisms, biologists have used experimental methods that have greatly increased our understanding and at the same time have uncovered new problems—many of which apply to human populations.

### CHARACTERISTICS OF POPULATIONS

**Density.**   One of the first things we notice about a population is the number of individuals in relation to the space they occupy at a given time. Consider the student population of your classroom today. Suppose we count a total of 35 students: We can say there are 35 students *per* room. Or we can say there are 35 *per* 150 square meters (abbreviated 150 m²)—this depends upon the size of your room. Or we can say 35 *per* 450 cubic meters (abbreviated 450 m³)—again dependent upon room size. In each case we are talking about the *density* of the population.

Which space unit we choose depends upon our purpose. When we express density as "35 students per room," we are being rather indefinite, since rooms may vary greatly in size. But for some purposes, it is not necessary to be any more definite than this. If the school principal knows that all the biology classrooms in his building are the same size, he is able to assign students to classes.

Often, however, we must be more precise. The biology teacher who is interested in setting up a laboratory activity may want to know the number of students per square meter (m²). And the architect who designed the building had to allow for sufficient ventilation, so he needed to know the number of students per cubic meter (m³). To find the exact information needed by the teacher and the architect, we must measure the space involved, count the number of individuals in the population within the space, and divide the number of individuals (N) by the number of units of space (S). This is the population density: $D = \dfrac{N}{S}$.

For the teacher, we would calculate $D = \dfrac{35 \ (\text{students})}{150 \ \text{m}^2} = 0.23$, or a density of 0.23 students per m². For the architect: $D = \dfrac{35 \ (\text{students})}{450 \ \text{m}^3} = 0.08$, or a density of 0.08 students per m³.

Brown Brothers

Figure 2 · 3

Thomas    Robert    Malthus [măl'thəs]:    1766–1834. British economist.

**Figure 2 · 4**
Plan of an orchard. Each dot represents one tree. What is the density of trees in the orchard?

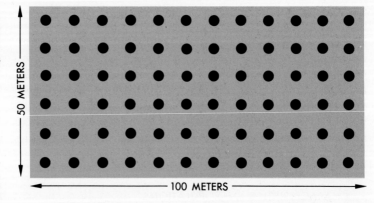

In working with land organisms, the biologist usually uses two-dimensional units of space, such as square meters; but if he is considering the fish population in a pond, he may use three-dimensional units of space, such as cubic meters.

Density is a measurement. Like all measurements, it is of no interest in itself. To say there are 240 persons per square kilometer (abbreviated $km^2$) in Massachusetts means little. But to add that there is only one person per $km^2$ in Wyoming may raise the question: Why the difference? This is a question on which we may gather information; it is the basis for a population problem. Or suppose we find that there were 1225 living white pines per hectare in a certain reforestation area in the year 1945, and 950 per hectare in 1955. Again, this raises a question. Differences in density, whether of time or place or any other factor, provide a basis for the investigation of problems.

A square kilometer equals about 0.39 square miles.

A hectare, 10,000 $m^2$, equals about 2.5 acres.

**Density changes.** Whenever the amount of one thing varies in relation to units of another thing (for example,

**Figure 2 · 5**
Under natural conditions organisms are seldom distributed evenly. Calculate the density of dusty clover in the field as a whole and then only in the northwest quarter. Compare.

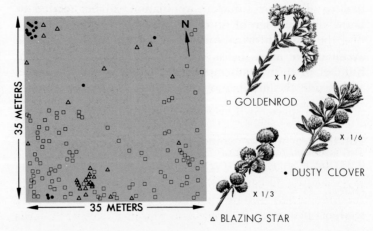

density varying with time), we can express the change as a *rate*. Let us use the data on the white pines to see how a rate is calculated. The first density was measured in 1945, the second in 1955. The difference in time, ΔT (read "delta T"), is 1955 − 1945 = 10 years. In 1955 the density was 950 trees per hectare, and in 1945 it was 1225 trees per hectare. So the difference in density, ΔD (read "delta D"), is 950 − 1225 = −275. (We must write the densities in the same order as the dates). Now we divide the difference in density by the difference in time: $\dfrac{-275 \text{ trees per hectare}}{10 \text{ years}} =$ −27.5 trees per hectare per year. The negative number tells us that the change was a *decline* in the population density; a positive number would indicate an *increase*.

This arithmetic can be summarized in the formula $R = \dfrac{\Delta D}{\Delta T}$; that is, the rate at which the density of a population changes is equal to the change in density divided by the change in time. Suppose that in 1965 in the same reforestation project the density was 770 living trees per hectare. Using the formula, we have: $R = \dfrac{770 - 950}{1965 - 1955} =$ $\dfrac{-180}{10} = -18$ trees per hectare per year.

Figure 2·6 shows the data for the white-pine forest in graph form. Our numbers show that the population decrease was less rapid in the decade 1955–1965 than it was in the decade 1945–1955. By the reduced slope of the second part of the line, the graph shows the same thing. In a graph of this kind, the closer a line comes to the horizontal, the smaller the rate; the closer a line comes to the vertical, the greater the rate.

**Kinds of density changes.** What happened to those 455 pines that were lost from each hectare during the twenty-year period? Since pines do not wander away, they must have died, by one means or another. We can thus speak of the decline in the pine population per unit of time as the *death rate*, or, as biologists would say, the *mortality*. Note that a death rate is a characteristic of a population, never of an individual; an individual dies only once, so it cannot have a death rate.

In the last paragraph, we assumed that there were no additions to the pine population during the twenty years. But this assumption may not fit the facts. Perhaps no new trees were planted, but the trees already there could have produced seeds that might have germinated and added to the population. As death tends to *decrease* a population, reproduction tends to *increase* it. Mammals are born, birds

rate [Latin: *ratus*, fixed by calculation]

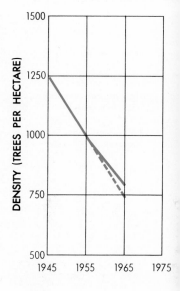

Figure 2 · 6

Graph of density change in a white-pine population. The dotted line continues the 1945–1955 rate.

The slope may be horizontal but it can never actually be vertical. Why not?

mortality [Latin: *mortis*, of death]

assumption: See Investigation 2.1.

natality [Latin: *natus*, born]

motile [mōt′əl]

immigration [Latin: *in-*, in, + *migrare*, to move from one place to another]

emigration [Latin: *e-*, out, + *migrare*]

are hatched, seeds of plants germinate — we have no single term for the reproductive process. But it is customary to use as a general term the word that is correctly applied to mammals — "birth." So the rate at which reproductive addition occurs is the *birth rate*, or *natality*. Again, note that this is a characteristic of a population, not of an individual.

Trees do not move about — though their seeds do. When we consider a population of *motile* organisms — which can move about by their own power — we must take into account two other ways in which its size may be changed. The population may be increased by individuals coming from other places *(immigration)*, or it may be decreased by individuals going to other places *(emigration)*.

**Interaction of rates.** Suppose we are studying the population of rabbits on a farm. During any considerable period of time — say, five years — some rabbits will be born and some will die. Further, unless the farm is extremely well fenced, rabbits will wander in and out. All four causes of change in the density of the rabbit population can be calculated as rates. Two of these (natality and immigration) *increase* the population; two of them (mortality and emigration) *decrease* the population. Will the density of the rabbit population on the farm be greater or less at the end of five years? Clearly, this depends upon the interaction of the two sets of opposing rates. We can answer the question only when we have numerical values for all four rates.

Consider again the student population of your classroom. We can assume that there is neither mortality nor natality. Suppose that the density is 35 students ("per room" is understood). Suppose the students come in (immigrate) at the rate of 5 every minute and leave (emigrate) at the rate of 5 every minute. What is the density at the end of any one-minute period? Mathematically, we can express this as $35 + 5 - 5 = 35$. Thus, the density is the same at the end of a minute as it was at the beginning. The individuals in the room may not be the same individuals that were there before, but no change in *density* has occurred. Now suppose that 5 enter and 10 leave every minute. What is the density at the end of a minute? We have $35 + 5 - 10 = 30$. The density has declined.

What would be the density at the end of *three* minutes?

The principle we have just used also applies to natality and mortality. Like immigration and emigration, these factors work in opposite directions.

**Summary.** Thus the population density of any kind of organism in any given space at any given time is the result of the numerical relations among mortality, natality, immigration rate, and emigration rate. We may call these four rates the *determiners* of population density. In any study of population change, the biologist must consider these four rates. In any experimental study of populations, these determiners must be considered as variables.

The size of a population has little meaning except in terms of space. If we are referring to changes in the size of a population within a given space, then we are referring to a density change, even if we have neither measured the space nor expressed the density numerically. Therefore, the phrase "population density" is often abbreviated to "population," and except for emphasis, we shall follow this practice in the future.

## INVESTIGATION 2.1

### POPULATION GROWTH: A MODEL

#### INTRODUCTION

Just as we need tools such as the microscope to help us extend our powers of observation, so we need mental "tools" to help us extend our thinking. One such mental tool is called a *model*. The model we are discussing here is not an object; it is a mental image. This kind of model simplifies a complex real situation so that we can more easily understand it. Because the model is a simplification, it differs in some respects from the real situation. The simplifications we make are called *assumptions*. To simplify, we assume certain things that may be only approximately true. We must keep these assumptions in mind whenever we use the model to try to understand a real situation.

Should the model give results similar to those given in the real situation, we can have confidence that the real situation "works" in the same way the model does. Of course, the two will never match exactly, but the degree of matching will determine the extent of our confidence in the model.

#### PURPOSE

In this work you will use a model to investigate the way in which a population might grow.

#### MATERIALS

Ordinary (arithmetic) graph
    paper, 1 sheet per student
Semilogarithmic graph paper, 1
    sheet per student

#### PROCEDURE

**Setting up the model.** Let us begin with a real organism—the house sparrow. Now imagine an island, and on that island, in the spring of 1967, an imaginary population of 10 house sparrows—5 male-female pairs.

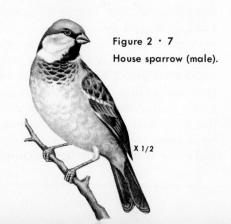

Figure 2 · 7
House sparrow (male).

X 1/2

Assumption 1: Each breeding season (spring), each pair of sparrows produces 10 offspring, always 5 males and 5 females.

Assumption 2: Each year all the breeding (parent) birds die before the next spring.

Assumption 3: Each year all offspring live through the next breeding season. (In most real situations some parents would live and some offspring would die. But taken together, Assumptions 2 and 3 tend to balance each other, thus reducing the difference between our model and a real situation.)

Assumption 4: During the study no other sparrows arrive on the island, and none leave.

**Growth of the population.** Now we want to see how this hypothetical population will grow. To do this, we must calculate the size of the population at the beginning of each breeding season. According to Assumption 1, in 1967 we have 5 pairs, each producing 10 offspring, a total of 50 offspring. According to Assumption 2, the 10 breeding birds of 1967 die before the next spring. According to Assumption 3, all of the 50 offspring live to the spring of 1968. Thus, at the start of the 1968 breeding season, there will be 50 house sparrows on the island. According to Assumption 1, these will be 25 males and 25 females—25 pairs, each of which will produce 10 offspring. Continue with this kind of reasoning to calculate what the island's sparrow population will be at the beginning of the breeding season in 1969, 1970, and 1971.

You now have a series of numbers; you can get a clearer idea of the way the population grows by plotting the numbers on a line graph. Construct the graph so that the years are shown along the horizontal axis and the number of birds along the vertical axis. You should make the vertical scale large enough to show the small 1967 population. Plot as many generations as you can.

No doubt you had difficulty plotting all the data on ordinary graph paper. This difficulty can be overcome with another tool—semilogarithmic (usually called "semi-log") graph paper. It is not necessary to fully understand the mathematics of logarithms to use this tool. The teacher will explain what you need to know to plot the data.

Construct your semi-log graph with the same data you used before.  • What advantage(s) does the semi-log graph have over the ordinary graph for plotting data on population growth? (1)

## STUDYING THE DATA

Put the two graphs in front of you. • How does the slope of the line connecting the plotted points change as you read from left to right (from year to year) across the ordinary graph? (2) • What does this mean in terms of rate of population growth? (3) • What kind of line shows the same thing on the semi-log graph? (4)  • If you were to continue to use the same set of assumptions to calculate populations for an indefinite number of years and plot them on a graph, what would happen to the slope of the line on the ordinary graph? (5)  • On the semi-log graph? (6)

Now you need to relate your results to the purpose of the investigation. • In one or two sentences describe the growth of a hypothetical population that is limited by the assumptions stated in the model. (7) • Do you think any real population might grow in this way? Why or why not? (8)

## FOR FURTHER INVESTIGATION

You can examine the effects that changes in assumptions have on the growth of the model population. This will give you a better understanding of factors involved in population changes.

1. Change Assumption 2 as follows: Each year two-fifths of the breeding birds (equally males and females) live to breed again a second year and then die. All other assumptions remain unchanged. Calculate the population size of each generation. Compare these results with the results from the original assumptions by drawing a graph on the grid used for the original data.

2. Change Assumption 3 as follows: Each year two-fifths of the offspring (equally males and females) die before the next breeding season. All other assumptions remain unchanged. As before, calculate the populations and draw a comparative graph.

3. Change Assumption 4 as follows: Each year 50 new house sparrows (equally males and females) arrive on the island from elsewhere. None leave. All other assumptions remain unchanged. Calculate the populations and draw a comparative graph.

4. Devise other problems for yourself by changing the assumptions in other ways.

## POPULATIONS AND ENVIRONMENT

We have been reasoning about the ways in which populations *might* vary. But we have said nothing about factors that increase or decrease the numerical value of the four determiners of population density.

If we can find out what factors influence mortality, natality, emigration rate, and immigration rate and to what extent the influences operate, we may be able to make some predictions about population growth and decline. Making predictions is an important part of scientific work. Predictions can be the basis for the development of hypotheses that lead to further discovery.

predictions    [pri dĭk′shənz; Latin: *prae-*, before, + *dicere*, to tell]

### SOME EXPERIMENTS

Let us first look at some experimental studies. Several biologists at the University of Wisconsin, working with John T. Emlen, cooperated in studying populations of house mice. In one experiment they established a small population in the basement of an old building. They provided the mice with 250 grams (abbreviated g) of food during each day of the experiment. At first, this amount of food was not completely consumed each day. But the mice reproduced quite rapidly, and the population grew. Eventually the mice were eating all the daily food supply. Soon after, the biologists began to capture some of the mice on the upper floors of the building, where mice had not previously been found. Mice continued to be born, and there was no evidence of a change in death rate. Evidently a shortage of food had become the limiting factor within the experimental space.

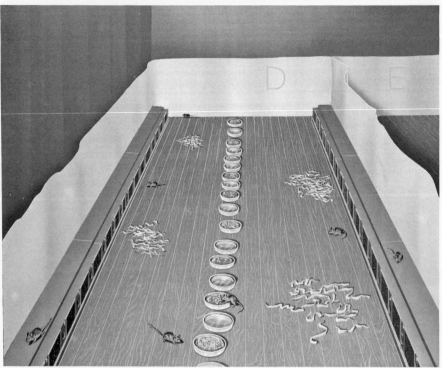

Charles Southwick

**Figure 2 · 8**

Part of one of the pens used in the Wisconsin experiment on crowding. Walls are of sheet metal; nest boxes line them.

famine [făm′in; Latin: fames, hunger]

cannibalism: A cannibal is an organism that eats others of its own kind.

Emigration was the determiner by which the population density in the basement area became *stabilized*, that is, held more or less at the level that the food supply could support.

Earlier, the same investigators had performed a similar experiment, but with one important difference: the mice were confined in pens. In this case, when a food shortage developed, emigration was impossible. Remembering Malthus (page 38), we might expect that there would have been famine and starvation—an increased mortality. Instead, when the daily supply of food became insufficient, fewer young were born—a decreased natality. Thus we see that a single factor (food shortage) may operate through different determiners (emigration or natality) to produce the same effect—a steady state in the population.

Now let us turn to a different factor. In a third experiment the mice were again confined in pens, but *more than enough* food was always provided. As the population density increased, there was a decline in *space per mouse*, or we might say the population became "crowded." This experiment was performed in different places, with different results.

At the University of Wisconsin, when the population became crowded, chasing, fighting, and cannibalism increased greatly. Females ceased taking proper care of their nests and young. Though mice continued to be born, more and more died from neglect. Eventually the mortality of the newborn reached 100 percent. Thus, further increase of the population was prevented by increased mortality in one part of the population—the young.

An experiment with a similar aim (to test the effect of space shortage when food is abundant) was conducted at about the same time in England. There the investigators found little of the chasing, fighting, and neglect of nests that had been so conspicuous at Wisconsin. And there was no mortality among the young. Instead, after the population had increased to the crowded point, reproduction completely ceased; that is, natality declined to zero.

abundant [Latin: *abundare*, to overflow]

conspicuous [kən spĭk'yŏo əs; Latin: *conspicuus*, open to view]

In both these experiments the population was stabilized. But at Wisconsin this came about through high mortality; in England it came about through low natality.

Now when apparently similar experiments produce different results, the scientist is especially stimulated. Could one or both groups of biologists be mistaken about their results? Here we see the self-corrective nature of science, which springs from the fact that science deals with verifiable observation. Close examination of the published descriptions of these experiments showed that the experiments were not really identical—there were differences in the construction of the pens and nesting boxes.

stimulated [stĭm'yə lāt'əd; Latin: *stimulus*, a spur]

Biologists at Rutgers University, in New Jersey, then undertook tests of the two experimental designs, using in both tests mice with the same ancestry to eliminate possible hereditary differences in behavior. The results of these experiments showed that with both the "Wisconsin" and the "English" designs the determiners of density were a *combination* of increased mortality of the newborn and a decrease of natality. At present, therefore, we must conclude that in a confined and crowded population the density is controlled through changes in natality or mortality or through some combination of these.

When we examine this group of experiments carefully, we see that all the factors influencing the determiners of population density came from *outside* the animals. In other words, the factors were in the animals' environment. Therefore, we need to examine further the relation of environment to population density.

environment [ĕn vī'rən mənt]

## EFFECTS OF ENVIRONMENT ON POPULATION

Everything outside an organism is its environment. It is convenient to divide the environment into biotic and abiotic parts. The *biotic* environment is everything in an organism's

biotic [bī ŏt'ĭk; Greek: *bios*, life]

surroundings that is alive or was recently alive. Thus all other organisms — human as well as nonhuman — are a part of *your* biotic environment — your father and mother, your classmates, your dog, the fleas on your dog, the trees along the street, the palms and camels in Arabia. Obviously, some of these are more important to you than others. Since your food is of plant or animal origin, it may also be considered a part of your biotic environment, even though you seldom eat things while they are still alive. The *abiotic* environment is made up of everything in an organism's surroundings that is not alive. This includes such things as soils, weather, and solar radiation.

abiotic [ā′bī ŏt′ĭk; Greek: a-, not, + bios]

solar [sō′lər; Latin: sol, the sun]

**Nutrients.**   In the mouse experiments food was one of the important variables. To any consumer food is always important. Producers make their own food, but to do so they must have both radiant energy and various kinds of matter — mostly inorganic substances. All substances that an organism obtains from its environment — whether foods or inorganic substances — are termed *nutrients.*

nutrient [nū′trĭ ənt; Latin: nu-trire, to suckle, nurse]

What makes a nutrient important as a factor affecting population determiners is not its quantity, but its availability. When the amount of food remained constant in the mouse experiments, its availability also remained constant as long as mice were free to emigrate. But when the mice were confined and the amount of food remained constant, the availability of food per mouse decreased as the population density increased. When any nutrient is abundant in relation to the number of individuals, it is not a factor in stabilizing population density; when the nutrient becomes scarce, competition for it among individuals increases its importance.

For producers the availability of nutrients depends upon the chemical nature of the soils or waters in which they grow. For example, when magnesium is abundant in soil, a plant may not be able to take in sufficient calcium — even though calcium is also abundant — because of chemical interference between these two elements.

**A place to live.**   Every individual organism has a "home"; that is, it requires living space. The amount of space required may be very small — so small that one individual may touch others. Or it may be very large: pumas (mountain lions) usually remain several kilometers from each other.

X 1/50

**Figure 2 · 9**
**Puma, also called cougar.**

We might suspect that the amount of space an organism requires could be related to the availability of nutrients. This certainly is true to some extent. But one of the mouse experiments indicates that there is (at least for mice) more to the matter. Even when food was provided in abundance,

a time came when the *space per mouse* became too small for
the normal activities of the mice to continue. Energy that
normally would have gone into reproduction and care of
the young went instead into fighting, chasing, hiding — activities that tended to maintain space between mice.

For most other organisms we do not have such good
evidence of a need for living space, for a home. But it
seems probable that at least for every motile organism,
home space is required. Often, too, it can be shown
that particular kinds of space are needed for a home.
Two tracts of woodland may have equal areas and equally
good food supplies, but very different populations of
raccoons. The difference in density can be traced to
difference in the number of hollow trees, which are homes
for raccoons.

X 1/8

Figure 2 · 10
Raccoon.

**Other organisms.**   In the mouse experiments we did
not consider a biotic factor that is often very important
— the effects of *other kinds* of organisms. Under natural conditions many consumers — snakes, foxes, hawks, etc. — catch
and eat mice. And many microscopic organisms that live
inside mice may weaken the mice so much that they die.
Populations of producers as well as those of consumers may
be similarly influenced by other kinds of organisms. We will
not carry this topic any further at present, for the influence
of one kind of organism on another kind is the subject of
Chapter 3.

**Weather.**   The mouse experiments fail to illustrate
another group of environmental factors — the abiotic factors we group together as weather. These are rainfall,
snowfall, and the like (*precipitation*); temperature; *humidity*
(the amount of water vapor in the air); evaporation; wind.
Each may be measured separately, but they all affect each
other.

precipitation [prĭ sĭp′e tā′shən;
Latin: *praeceps,* falling head-
long]

humidity [hū mĭd′ə tĭ; Latin:
*umere,* to be moist]

In the northern part of the United States, most mosquitoes disappear with the first heavy frost; the population
of adult mosquitoes drops close to zero. At about the same
time the robin population usually drops also, though not as
suddenly or to such a low level. Both these population
changes are related to one weather factor — temperature.
This factor affects the mosquito population through mortality but it affects the robin population through emigration, though with the same result.

Another example: In the deserts of southern Arizona,
after one of the infrequent rains, blankets of small, bright
flowering plants may appear on the formerly bare and
baked desert soil. In a few days the density of visible flowering plants springs from zero to a very high number.
Again the population change is clearly related to a single

weather factor—in this case, rainfall; and this factor operates through natality—through the germination of seeds.

Figure 2 · 11

**Interaction of factors.**    When changes in the density of a population are thoroughly investigated, we usually find that the changes involve the interaction of many factors. Consider the tomato plants in a southern New Jersey field in July. In some years the density of living plants may be nearly as high as when the plants were set out in April. In

Two ponderosa-pine forests. What environmental factors might influence the difference in population density?

U.S. Forest Service

Richard Beidleman

other years it may be much less, almost at zero. Three weather factors are involved: temperature, rainfall, and humidity (which is itself a consequence of the other two factors and is influenced by still other factors, such as wind). If temperature, rainfall, and humidity are high, tomato plants usually grow very well. But there is a certain fungus that also thrives in such weather. It may vigorously attack the tomato plants, with results that can be disastrous for the tomato-grower.

Some of the environmental factors that influence population densities are difficult to place in any of the groups we have been discussing. Usually they do not act independently but influence population indirectly through interaction with other factors. For example, radiation from the sun is the driving force behind all weather factors. But for producers solar radiation is an environmental factor that controls the food supply, since it supplies the energy for photosynthesis. And how much solar energy a particular producer receives depends upon a number of things: the time of day, the length of the day (which, in turn, depends upon the season), the amount of shade cast by other organisms growing nearby, and the latitude, or north-south location, of the producer.

Consider a raspberry plant in the United States. It receives more solar radiation at noon than at eight o'clock

Figure 2 · 12
The scene is in Colorado, looking toward the east. The north-facing slopes are thickly covered with Douglas firs, the south-facing slopes thinly covered with small bushes. Try to explain these effects of land slope on plant populations.

fungus [fŭng′gəs; plural, fungi, fŭn′jī]: A similar fungus is shown in Figure 7 · 2.

in the morning; it receives more in June than in December; it receives more if it grows among grass plants than if it grows under pines in a forest. If the plant is growing in northern Minnesota, the daily and seasonal variations in solar radiation cause the total annual energy received to be less than if the plant is growing in Tennessee.

Characteristics of the land are also important—particularly to plants. For example, some kinds of soil hold more water than others. Therefore, the composition of the soil influences the amount of water that can be used by a plant. Moreover, the kind of soil determines how much support a plant gets from its root system. Soils also influence consumers directly, especially those that spend their lives burrowing and feeding in it.

terrestrial [tə rĕs′trĭ əl; Latin: *terra*, the earth, land]

aquatic [ə kwăt′ĭk; Latin: *aqua*, water]

Thus far we have been thinking mostly about organisms that live on land—*terrestrial* organisms. Organisms that live in water—*aquatic* organisms—obviously have a different kind of environment. In water there are conditions that correspond to the atmospheric conditions we call weather, but they do not vary as much. Aquatic producers get their nutrients from the water; for these organisms water corresponds not only to atmosphere but also to soil. The characteristics of the bottom—whether sandy, gravelly, muddy, rocky, etc.—can also be important. For example, oysters build up large populations on rocky bottoms, which offer a firm attachment; but they cannot fasten firmly on sand and mud, which are constantly shifted by water currents. The factors that influence populations in water environments are different from those on land, but the general principle—that environmental factors influence the four determiners of population density—applies to both land and water environments.

X 1/2

Figure 2 · 13
Oysters thickly attached to a rock.

See Figure 2 · 11.

**Density itself as a factor.** If lightning strikes a pine tree in the woodlands of northern Arizona, the tree may be set afire and killed. But its neighbors are not likely to be damaged, because the trees are far apart (a low population density). If, however, a pine tree is struck by lightning in northern Idaho, a whole forest may be completely destroyed, because the trees grow very close together there (a high population density).

A hard freeze in Vermont may not kill all the adult mosquitoes; mortality depends on how many, in relation to the total population, find shelter. If most find shelter, mortality will be low; as the percentage of the population finding shelter decreases, the mortality increases. Thus the degree to which a certain factor affects the density of a population may be influenced by the density of the population itself.

**INVESTIGATION 2.2**

## STUDY OF A YEAST POPULATION

### PURPOSE

In Investigation 2.1 the data on the number of house sparrows were derived from the assumptions built into the model. We turn now from a model population to a real population.

This investigation is an experiment, so it requires forming a hypothesis. • After reading the procedure below and considering your experience with Investigation 2.1, state your hypothesis as precisely as you can.(1)

### BACKGROUND INFORMATION

Yeast organisms are used here not only because they reproduce at a rate that will allow you to complete the investigation in about ten days but also because they are conveniently small —several million can be kept in a test tube. Dry yeast grains are composed of

**Figure 2 · 14**

Yeast organisms in a microscope field. Magnification is greater than that obtained with the usual high-power objective.

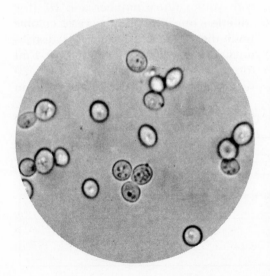

many inactive plants. These tiny plants become active and reproduce in a suitable *medium* (plural, media), a mixture of materials that will support their growth. A population of organisms in a medium is called a *culture*.

### MATERIALS AND EQUIPMENT

*For Procedure A*
*(amounts per team of 10 students)*
   Glass-marking crayon, 1
   Test tubes containing 10 ml of medium,
     1 per student
   Test-tube rack, 1
   Dry active yeast, 1 package
   Fine-pointed forceps, 1
   Square of aluminum foil, 1
*For Procedure B*
   Incubated culture tubes, 1 per student
   1-ml pipettes or medicine droppers,
     1 per student
   Microscope slides, 2 per student
   Cover slips, 2 per student
   Microscopes, 1 per pair of students
   Test tubes containing 9 ml of water,
     about 15 per team
   Test tubes containing 10 ml of
     medium, 1 per team
   Graph paper (arithmetic), 1 sheet
     per student

### PROCEDURE

**A. Growing the population.** Using a glass-marking crayon, mark each tube of medium with a team symbol. Then number the tubes from *1* to *10*. Assign one of these numbers to each of the team members.

From a package of dry, active yeast, choose 25 to 30 grains of yeast—all as close as possible to the same size. Put two grains of yeast in Tube 10 (that is, *inoculate* the medium). Be sure the grains are in the medium. Mix by holding the tube firmly between the fingers and thumb of one hand and striking the bottom of the tube forcefully with the fingers of the other hand. Place the tube in a warm, dark place; in other words, *incubate* it. Put the remaining grains of yeast in an aluminum-foil packet and label with the team symbol. Store the foil packet and the uninoculated tubes as directed by the teacher.

On each succeeding day take out the tube of medium with the next lower number (Tube 9, 8, 7, etc.). Using the yeast grains from the storage packet, inoculate (with 2 grains), mix, and incubate the tube. Make daily observations of any change in the yeast cultures. Record these observations in your data book.

**B. Counting the population.** When the last culture in the series (Tube 1) has been incubated for twenty-four hours, a count of yeast organisms in all 10 tubes is to be made. All counts must be taken at the same time. The members of each team will work in pairs—students 1 and 2 together, 3 and 4 together, etc. Each student will make a count from his own tube and a count from the tube of his partner. Thus there will be two counts for each of the 10 tubes. You will need to prepare in your data book a form like the one below.

Shake your own test tube until the yeast organisms are evenly distributed. Using a pipette, immediately place 0.1 ml of the culture on a clean slide (or using a medicine dropper, place 2 drops on the slide). Place a clean cover slip over the culture on the slide. Do not

press down on the cover slip. Position the slide on your microscope stage, and focus under low power; then switch to high power. Do not tilt the stage!

Count the number of individual organisms in 5 different high-power fields, as indicated in Figure 2·15. (Caution: Yeast organisms are difficult to see if the light is too bright.) Yeast organisms often stick together. Each individual organism in any clump is to be counted separately. Buds also count as individuals. Record the 5 counts in the form in your data book (line A).

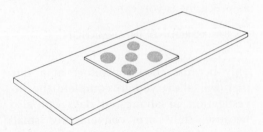

**Figure 2 · 15**

Approximate positions of fields for counts.

If the fields are too crowded for easy counting, you must make a *dilution* of the culture. To do this, obtain a test tube containing 9 ml of water; label this tube with your culture number and *D1* (for "dilution one"). Shake the yeast culture until the organisms are evenly distributed. Using a clean pipette, transfer 1 ml (or if you use a medicine dropper, 20 drops) of the culture into the dilution

| Team _____ | | | | | Culture No. _____ | | Dilution Factor _____ | |
|---|---|---|---|---|---|---|---|---|
| **MEMBER OF PAIR** | **FIELDS** | | | | | **TOTAL** | **AVERAGE** | **AVERAGE X DILUTION FACTOR** |
| | 1 | 2 | 3 | 4 | 5 | | | |
| A | | | | | | | | |
| B | | | | | | | | |
| | | | | | | | Pair Average _____ | |

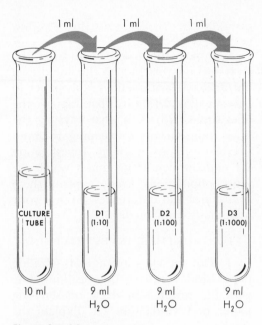

1 ml    1 ml    1 ml

CULTURE TUBE    D1 (1:10)    D2 (1:100)    D3 (1:1000)

10 ml    9 ml H₂O    9 ml H₂O    9 ml H₂O

Figure 2 · 16

A dilution series.

tube. Rinse the pipette (or medicine dropper) several times by running clean water in and out of it. Mix the contents of the dilution tube *thoroughly*. Now transfer 0.1 ml (with a pipette) or 2 drops (with a medicine dropper) from the dilution tube to a slide, and proceed to count the cells as directed above. If the field is still too crowded for easy counting, transfer 1 ml of the contents of Tube D1 to another test tube containing 9 ml of water. Mark this dilution *D2*. It may even be necessary to use a third dilution (see Figure 2 · 16). In Tube D1 the culture is diluted 10 times; in Tube D2, 100 times; in Tube D3, 1000 times. If you make dilutions during counting, record the proper number (10 or 100 or 1000) after "Dilution Factor" on the data form. If you make no dilutions, the dilution factor is 1.

Now your partner will make 5 counts of a sample taken from your culture, using the same procedure you used.

Record his counts in the form in your data book (line B).

As soon as you have finished recording the data, total the 5 counts in each line (adding across the line!). Then divide by 5 to get the average for the line. If your average (line A) and your partner's average (line B) differ by more than 10 organisms, prepare new slides and repeat the counts.

Repeat this entire procedure using samples from your partner's tube. He will enter his counts of his culture on line A of his record form and your counts of his culture on line B of his record.

One more job remains for each team: to make a count from a tube that has been incubated 0 days. This should be done by the pair that finishes first (or as assigned by the teacher). Put 2 grains of dry yeast into a test tube containing 10 ml of medium. Allow the tube to stand for 5 minutes, shaking occasionally. Proceed to count as directed above. One student of the pair that obtains these data will need to prepare an extra form in his data book.

## STUDYING THE DATA

You have already computed the figures for the "Total" and "Average" columns in your data form. Now you need to compute the last column by multiplying the average by the dilution factor. For example, if you made your count from Tube D2, the dilution factor is 100. If your average count was 15, then the number to be recorded in the last column is 1500. The "Pair Average" is obtained by averaging the two numbers in the last column. Record the "Pair Average" on the master form on the chalkboard. Here all the counts from all the teams will be brought together.

You have not counted the whole population in any of the tubes. You have obtained an estimate of the populations by a method called *sampling*. To increase the accuracy of your estimate, you have taken certain precautions. First, you shook the tubes in an attempt to distribute the organisms evenly through them. Second, you counted the organisms in 5 different fields of view. By averaging these, you tended to "smooth out" chance differences in the fields you counted. Third, two people made counts from the same tube, and you averaged their counts. Fourth, you averaged the differences between the figures obtained by all the teams, which further tended to smooth out chance differences between the tubes. What you finally have for the population at each period of incubation is a density expressed as *average number of organisms per high-power field of view*.

Using ordinary graph paper, list the age of the cultures, in days, on the horizontal axis; list the density of the populations on the vertical axis. Plot the data from each team separately, using a different color for each team. Then use black to plot the averaged data of all teams. • On the basis of the discussion in the preceding paragraph, explain the similarities and differences among the graph lines. (2)

### CONCLUSIONS

Compare the line drawn from the class average (black) with the line drawn on ordinary (arithmetic) graph paper in Investigation 2.1. • In what ways are the lines similar? (3) • In what ways are the lines different? (4) • Keeping in mind the assumptions made in Investigation 2.1 and the conditions under which the yeast populations lived, explain these similarities and differences. (5) • Is your hypothesis confirmed? (6)

### FOR FURTHER INVESTIGATION

1. Plot the class average on semi-log paper and compare the resulting line with the graph you drew on semi-log paper in Investigation 2.1. Explain the similarities and differences.

2. How does temperature affect the growth of a yeast population? Repeat the whole procedure, but this time incubate the cultures at a constant temperature 15°C above or below the average temperature at which the tubes were incubated before.

### KINDS OF POPULATION CHANGES

A single measurement of population density has little meaning. We need at least two such measurements; we need a comparison. The measurements may concern different places at the same time: a comparison between the human population density of Pennsylvania and that of Oklahoma in 1960, for example. Or the comparison may involve different times, as in Investigation 2.2. The latter kind of comparison leads to questions about how populations grow or decline.

### GROWTH OF CLOSED POPULATIONS

Suppose we start with a small population of bacteria in a test tube of medium, or a few beetles in a box of cornmeal.

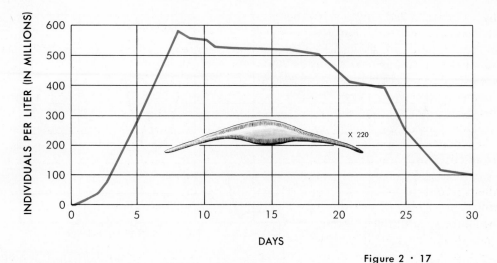

DAYS

Figure 2 · 17

Graph of changes in a laboratory population of a species of diatom, a type of microscopic photosynthetic organism.

Or we could begin with a few microscopic photosynthetic organisms in a beaker, beside a constant light source. What can we predict about the growth of such a *closed* population?

The hypothetical population in Investigation 2.1 represents one such closed system, so you might base a prediction on it. But since Investigation 2.1 you have learned that with real populations there are many environmental factors that the model left out of consideration. The results from Investigation 2.2 should provide a safer basis for prediction. Figure 2 · 17 supplies more evidence.

Such closed population systems are found chiefly in laboratory experiments. In general, natural populations are *open* systems, in which organisms are free to enter or leave and in which there is a continual change in complex environmental factors.

### POPULATION FLUCTUATIONS

Figure 2 · 18 is a graph based on data collected by David E. Davis of Pennsylvania State University during a study of the population of brown rats in a city block in Baltimore, Maryland. In 1942 the city health department conducted a poisoning campaign that apparently wiped out the rat population in the block. Of course it is difficult to count individuals in natural populations — even the United States census is not perfect — so there may have been one or two rats remaining or a few rats may have immigrated. In either case, a "new" rat population started early in 1945, much as you started "new" yeast populations during Investigation 2.2. You should, then, compare the part of Figure 2 · 18 that is based on data from early 1945 to late 1946 with your graphs from Investigations 2.1 and 2.2 and with Figure 2 · 17.

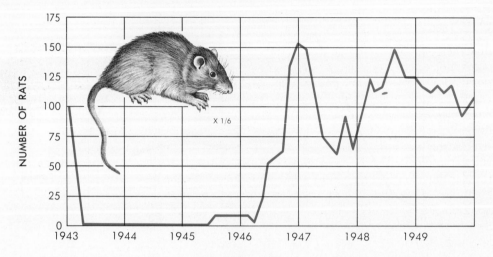

Figure 2 · 18

Graph of changes in the brown-rat population of a city block, Baltimore.

fluctuations [flŭk'chŏŏ ā'shənz; Latin: fluctuare, to wave]

Figure 2 · 19

Graph of changes in the snowshoe-hare population, Canada (based on skins traded at Hudson's Bay Company posts).

The new point we wish to make, however, concerns the later years of the study. As happens in closed laboratory populations, after a peak density was reached (late 1946), a decline in the population occurred (1947). Under natural conditions, however, there is usually a turning point; the population increases again—as it did in this example (late 1947). But again a limit set by the factors of the environment is reached, and again a decline occurs. Natural populations characteristically show such population *fluctuations*, ups and downs, when the population counts are plotted on a graph. We can recognize this as an example of steady state, the "teetering balance" that we discussed in Chapter 1 (pages 4–5).

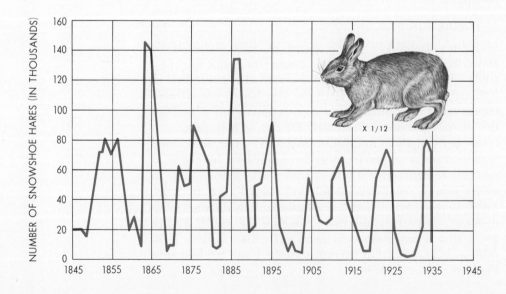

Sometimes population fluctuations are so regular that they are fairly predictable. Data gathered in Canada show that there are highs in the population of snowshoe hares, occurring about ten years apart (Figure 2 · 19). Similar population peaks occur in lemmings every three or four years. A number of other organisms have been shown to have such *population cycles*. Most of these are animals that live in the northern parts of Europe, Asia, and North America. Although cycles may seem to occur very regularly when plotted on a graph, some biologists think that this regularity is misleading. They point out that chance combinations of known environmental factors can produce apparently regular population peaks. Therefore, they say, the study of cycles is no different from the study of irregular fluctuations.

In the past the population of man has undoubtedly fluctuated like populations of other organisms. After Roman times there were few attempts to count people until fairly recently. But historical records make it clear that during the Middle Ages the population of western Europe declined sharply as a result of such plagues as the black death and then rose again. Within the last few centuries, however, such fluctuations in human population densities have tended to disappear in many parts of the world. In some regions, in fact, we have something that begins to look rather like your graph of a hypothetical population in Investigation 2.1.

If you have understood the discussion so far, you see that some large biological problems arise from that last statement. You will have to face these problems throughout your life—and not just in a biology classroom. But you will be able to do so more intelligently after you have gone farther in this course—after you have more thoroughly explored the biosphere, of which man is such an important part—after you have looked *into* organisms and seen something of how they are put together and how they react to their environments. So for the present we shall keep these human problems in the background and continue with our discussion of populations in general.

## POPULATION STEADY STATE

We can now make three generalizations. One: when a small number of organisms are introduced into a favorable environment (a "new" population), there is at first a characteristic pattern of growth. Two: after the initial growth period a population in a closed system develops differently from a population in an open system. Three: populations in open systems fluctuate.

X 1/3

Figure 2 · 20
Lemming.

plagues [plāgz; Greek: *plege,* blow, misfortune]: diseases of high mortality

See Problem 3, page, 70.

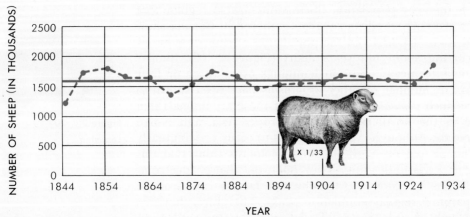

YEAR

**Figure 2 · 21**

Graph of changes in the domestic-sheep population, Tasmania (*dotted line*). The solid line shows an average around which fluctuations occurred. Try to explain how man was involved in this homeostasis.

analogy  [ə năl′ə jĭ;  Greek: *ana*, on, + *logos*, reason]: a comparison

thermostat      [thûr′mə stăt′; Greek: *therme*, heat, + *statikos*, causing to stand]

regulator [Latin: *regere*, to guide, rule]

effector [Latin: *ex*, out, + *facere*, to make]

We need to explore the third generalization somewhat further. Population fluctuations usually occur around some average density that is approximately constant. There is a *tendency* toward some definite level, but somehow the population keeps "overshooting" and "undershooting" this level. We have called the control of such a steady state "homeostasis." But what are some specific homeostatic processes?

**An analogy.**   The temperature in most classrooms is in a steady state—if the heat is controlled by a thermostat. When the heat supply is cut off, the room cools. At some preset temperature this cooling acts as a *stimulus* which causes the thermostat (the *regulator*), to "order" an input of heat. But before the furnace (*effector*) can deliver the heat, cooling has continued and the room temperature has dropped below the preset temperature. After the heat arrives, the rising temperature again reaches the preset point and this causes the regulator to shut off the heat. But before the heating system can be shut off, the temperature has passed the preset point. There is an average room temperature, but the actual temperature reaches periodic highs ("overshoots") and lows ("undershoots"). Homeostasis, then, involves a stimulus, a regulator, and an effector.

In population homeostasis we have a much more complex situation. The stimulus can be a shortage of nutrients, a shortage of space—any of the environmental factors we have discussed or any combination of them. The regulator lies in the ability of the individual member of the population to sense environmental changes: for example, there is some "preset" level of starvation to which the organism reacts. The effector is the set of population determiners: natality, mortality, emigration, and immigration; acting together they increase or decrease the population density.

Is this a good analogy? Like most analogies it is useful if not carried too far. One most important difference between the two situations involves the regulator. A thermostat operates on a simple "off-on" basis — it either turns on the heat or it doesn't. But we have seen that the amount of influence from an environmental factor usually depends on the density of the population: the greater the density of mice, the more severe the effect of space shortage. To improve the analogy the thermostat would have to continuously change the strength of its "order" for more or less heat. This emphasizes the major point: population control is vastly more complex than heat control.

**An example.**    Suppose we have a deer population that is increasing. After a time the kinds of plants that deer eat become scarce as more and more deer consume them. A few deer may begin to look elsewhere for food — they may emigrate (if they can). Those that remain will not be as well nourished as they were before and will be more easily caught by the second-order consumers that eat deer. As the population continues to rise, more and more deer will emigrate and more and more deer will be killed. But emigration and mortality tend to reduce populations. Eventually the deer population will begin to decline. This results in fewer plants being eaten. As the plants continue to grow, more food is available for the remaining deer. Deer may stop emigrating; in fact, attracted by the food supply within the area, deer may immigrate from elsewhere. With more food the deer will be better nourished and will not be killed so easily by second-order consumers. Some second-order consumers may even stop trying to catch deer and turn their attention to other sources of food. Thus immigration and a reduction in mortality tend to start the deer population increasing again. And this is where we started.

**A theory.**    What we have described in this example can be stated in a general form. Briefly, the theory states that changes in environmental factors tend to prevent populations either from becoming very large, on the one hand, or from disappearing, on the other. There may be natural populations to which this general theory of population control does not apply. If so, the theory must be changed. But it is useful, at least for the present, for guiding investigations into the mechanisms of population changes.

theory [thē' ərǐ; Greek: *theorein*, to look at]: A general statement of apparent relationships among observations, verified to some degree. See further, Chapter 17.

But *sometimes* populations decline to zero; they become extinct.

## INVESTIGATION 2.3

### POPULATION CHANGES IN OPEN SYSTEMS

#### PURPOSE

You will now investigate several kinds of population changes through the use of data collected from natural populations. Then you will compare these populations with the hypothetical population and the laboratory population that you have previously studied.

#### MATERIALS

Graph paper (arithmetic), 2 sheets per student

Red pencils, 1 per student

#### PROCEDURE

Gathering data on natural populations is difficult and time-consuming. For our present purpose it is not necessary that you gather the data yourself. Instead you will use data that biologists have collected during other studies.

| DATE | NUMBER PER 100 TRAPS PER NIGHT |
|------|---------------------------------|
| September 24, 1949 | 25 |
| October 9 | 45 |
| October 30 | 38 |
| December 4 | 30 |
| January 7, 1950 | 20 |
| February 26 | 14 |
| March 12 | 13 |
| April 16 | 8 |
| May 8 | 7 |
| June 16 | 11 |
| July 16 | 4 |
| August 16 | 13 |

**Figure 2 · 22**

Data on density of cotton mice, Florida.

**Florida cotton mouse.** The data in Figure 2·22 come from a study of cotton mice made by Paul G. Pearson near Gulf Hammock, Florida. Here the density is given as the number of mice caught per 100 traps per night. As is often the case in studying natural populations, the actual number of animals present in the area studied is not known. Thus, even in this real situation we have to make an assumption: that the actual density of the mice was always in proportion to the number caught.

Plot the data on a sheet of graph paper, using a vertical scale that will place the highest point for the population near the top of the graph. Compare the graph of the cotton-mouse population with the ordinary graphs made in Investigations 2.1 and 2.2.   • What part of this mouse graph is similar to the other graphs? (1)   • How does the mouse graph differ from your graph of the hypothetical house-sparrow population? (2)   • How can you explain the difference? (3)   • How does the mouse graph differ from your graph of the yeast population? (4)   • How can you explain the difference? (5)   • Which (if any) of the three populations was an *open*

X 1/11

**Figure 2 · 23**

Heath hen (*left*) and ring-neck pheasant (*right*).

population? (6)  • In which season of the year do you think natality was highest? (7)  • When do you think mortality and emigration were greatest? (8)

**Ring-neck pheasants.** A few ring-neck pheasants (native to Eurasia) were introduced on Protection Island, off the coast of Washington, in 1937. Counts of the population were made each spring and fall for the next five years. Figure 2·24 presents the data (derived from those published by A. S. Einarsen).

Plot the data on a sheet of graph paper and connect the plotted points with lead pencil.  • How can you explain the regular fluctuations shown on your graph? (9)

Now, using a red pencil, connect all the points representing spring counts, skipping the fall counts.  • What does this line tell you about the population? (10)  • If spring counts had been made after 1942, what do you think they

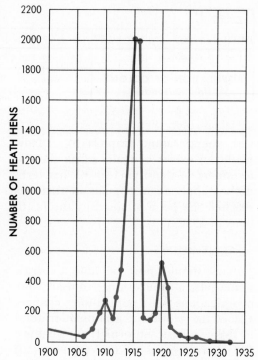

**Figure 2 · 25**

Graph of numbers of heath hens, Martha's Vineyard, Massachusetts.

| YEAR | SEASON | POPULATION SIZE |
|------|--------|-----------------|
| 1937 | Spring | 8 |
|      | Fall   | 40 |
| 1938 | Spring | 30 |
|      | Fall   | 100 |
| 1939 | Spring | 90 |
|      | Fall   | 425 |
| 1940 | Spring | 300 |
|      | Fall   | 825 |
| 1941 | Spring | 600 |
|      | Fall   | 1520 |
| 1942 | Spring | 1325 |
|      | Fall   | 1900 |

**Figure 2 · 24**

Numbers of ring-neck pheasants, Washington.

might have shown? Remember that this is a natural population. (11)

**Heath hens.** Heath hens were once common birds along the Atlantic coast from New England to Virginia. By 1880 they had disappeared from all locations except Martha's Vineyard, an island off Cape Cod. Figure 2·25 shows the result of a careful study of this population by A. O. Gross. In accounting for the various changes in the heath-hen population, biologists point out several factors: hunting pressure by man, then extreme efforts at preservation, killing by second-order consumers, disease, effects of forest fires and an excessive number of males.

• What do you think happened in 1907? (12)  • How does the heath-hen graph between 1907 and 1916 compare

| DAYS | | | | | | | | | | | | | | | | | |
|---|---|---|---|---|---|---|---|---|---|---|---|---|---|---|---|---|---|
| 0 | 7 | 14 | 21 | 28 | 35 | 42 | 49 | 56 | 63 | 70 | 77 | 84 | 91 | 98 | 105 | 112 | 119 |
| 1 | 1.5 | 2.5 | 4 | 8 | 16 | 22 | 32 | 40.5 | 50.3 | 55 | 62.5 | 72 | 72.5 | 71 | 82 | 78 | 81 |
| **POPULATION OF COLONY** (in thousands) | | | | | | | | | | | | | | | | | |

Figure 2 · 26

Data on numbers of Italian bees in an experimental colony.

with the pheasant graph? (13) • How might an excess of males affect the determiners of density? (14) • What term do we apply to a population that has reached the point attained by the heath hens in 1932? (15)

## CONCLUSIONS

You should now be able to draw some general conclusions from all your investigations of population change. • Does the growth of a population tend to follow a basic pattern? If so, what are the characteristics of this pattern? (16) • What is the chief difference between the graph for the hypothetical population (Investigation 2.1) and the graphs for the real populations (Investigations 2.2 and 2.3)? (17) • How do you account for the difference? (18) • Which of the graphs best illustrates a population in steady state? (19)

## FOR FURTHER INVESTIGATION

Figure 2 · 26 presents data collected by F. S. Bodenheimer on a population of Italian bees. Plot the data on arithmetic graph paper. Does this graph resemble the graph for the house-sparrow, the yeast, or the field-mouse population most closely? On the bee graph what is beginning to happen toward the end of the graph line? If you know something about bees, you should be able to tell what probably happened soon after the collection of data was discontinued. Which of the population determiners mentioned in the text is involved in the prediction you make?

## SPECIES POPULATIONS

Yeast, rat, tomato, heath hen — we have been discussing populations of many different *kinds* of organisms. The word "kinds" is used in many ways. We would probably agree that boys and girls are different kinds of people, that cauliflowers and cabbages are different kinds of vegetables, perhaps even that caterpillars and moths are different kinds of animals. But in none of these examples are we using the word in the same way that it was used in the first sentence of this paragraph. What, then, do we mean by "kinds of organisms"?

trivial [triv'i əl]: of little worth or importance

At first glance this seems a trivial sort of problem, but it has far-reaching consequences in all lines of biological research. Since science is concerned with testable, verifiable knowledge, the materials used in any scientific investigation must be identifiable—otherwise there is no way to insure a verifying retest.

The problem of identification is also important to those who are not biologists. Would you rather have a baseball bat made of hickory or one of pine? If an insect buzzes into your room, will you react differently to a fly than you will to a bee? Suppose you wish to plant a shade tree. To order "a shade tree" would be as indefinite—and unsatisfactory—as to order "a meal" in a restaurant. The nurseryman from whom the tree is ordered will need to know whether you want, say, a silver maple, red oak, eucalyptus, or china-berry. This is not only a matter of which kind you prefer. Also, depending on the environment in the region of your home, one kind may flourish and another may quickly die. The intelligent citizen, then, as well as the professional biologist, needs to distinguish between kinds of organisms.

eucalyptus [ū'kə lĭp' təs]

### APPEARANCES ARE DECEIVING

The names of trees mentioned in the previous paragraph are names of *groups* of organisms—of populations—not of individuals. We have pointed out that a population is a group of similar individuals. The key word here is "similar"—similar in what ways? And as "heads" on a coin implies "tails," so similarities within one group imply differences between groups.

A donkey differs from a horse: the donkey is smaller, has larger ears and shorter mane and tail, and brays rather than neighs. Both you and the professional biologist agree that donkeys and horses are different kinds of animals —but the biologist would say different *species*. All donkeys differ from all horses in many ways; and all donkeys are similar to each other in many ways, as are all horses. Yet organisms may look very different from each other and still be recognized by both you and the professional biologist as the same species. A Great Dane, a greyhound, a bulldog, a Pekingese—each is very different from the others; but we recognize that all are dogs. Why do we not recognize these different varieties as separate species?

For a long time biologists have argued among themselves: How similar must organisms be before they can be considered members of the same species? Or the same question worded in reverse: How different must organisms be before they can be considered members of different species?

X 1/90

**Figure 2 · 27**
**Donkey (left) and horse (right).**

species [spē'shĭz; Latin: *specere*, to look at; hence, a shape or appearance]

Pekingese [pē'kĭng ēz']

### MEANING OF "SPECIES"

If we consider *all* dogs—not just those that appear in kennel shows or are sold with expensive pedigrees—we can

pedigrees: records of ancestry

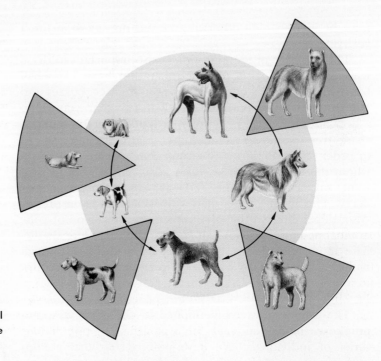

**Figure 2 · 28**
Varieties of dogs. Mongrel offspring are intermediate between "pure" breeds.

mongrels [mŭng′grəlz]: animals of mixed or unknown parentage

fertile [fûr′təl; Latin: ferre, to bear, produce]

easily see that there are many intermediate mongrels between such different "pure" breeds as Great Danes, greyhounds, etc. This is so because the different breeds of dogs can interbreed—mate with each other and produce vigorous intermediate offspring. These offspring can also mate and produce offspring that may be even more different among themselves than their mongrel parents were. Even if the most extremely different varieties of a species cannot do this, as would be true of the Great Dane and Pekingese dogs, they form a part of one related series because they can mate with intermediate breeds.

On the other hand, individuals belonging to two different species, even if they look alike to us, do not successfully produce vigorous, fertile offspring. If they did so, the characteristics of the two species (whether visible or not) would soon disappear, being bridged by an offspring population that would share the characteristics of the two original populations. Therefore, two species populations remain distinct from each other only so long as they fail to interbreed enough to produce a population of intermediate individuals.

The distinctness of species is maintained in several ways. In many cases no offspring are formed at all. Clearly, an elephant and a crab cannot mate and produce offspring.

X 1/10

Figure 2 · 29
Mallard (*left*) and pintail
(*right*). Females of these two
species are much more alike
than these males.

In other cases offspring are formed but die when young. If
the eggs of a bullfrog are fertilized by a common leopard
frog, the eggs develop for a short time but then die. Thus
no intermediate population ever results. In still other cases
the offspring are vigorous, but completely or partly *sterile*,
that is, unable to reproduce. The mule, which results when
the horse and the donkey are crossed, is almost always
sterile.

sterile [stĕr′ĭl; Latin: *sterilis,*
barren]

Species remain distinct in yet another way. Sometimes
individuals of two different species are able to form vigorous and fertile offspring in captivity but seldom do so in
nature. In these cases distinctness of the species is maintained not by lack of ability to interbreed, but by other
means. For example, the two species of duck known as
mallards and pintails are so different that every duck-
hunter can tell them apart. Though they are found in the
same places in many parts of North America, birds intermediate between them are rare in nature. Yet when they
are put together in the same pen, they will mate with each
other and produce fertile offspring. Apparently they do
not cross in nature because of differences in their mating
and nesting habits. The Alaska brown bear and the polar
bear provide a somewhat different example. In the Washington Zoo these species have successfully mated and produced vigorous, fertile offspring. No such cross has ever
been discovered in nature, however. The reason? The
Alaska brown bear lives in forests eating berries, small
animals, and fish that it catches from streams. The polar
bear lives on snowfields and ice floes, catching seals for its
food. Thus brown bears and polar bears rarely, if ever, see
each other — except in zoos.

In summary, then, we can say that a species is a population of individuals that are more or less alike and that are
able to interbreed and produce fertile offspring under
natural conditions.

X 1/75

Figure 2 · 30
Polar bear (*above*) and
Alaska brown bear (*below*).

adult male

immature male

X 1/2

indigo buntings

Acadian flycatcher

least flycatcher

X 1/2

**Figure 2 · 31**
Likeness in appearance is
not always a reliable guide
to grouping individuals in
a species. *Above:* These
dissimilar birds are both
indigo buntings. *Below:*
These dissimilar birds are
both red-winged black-
birds. *Right:* These very
similar birds belong to
different species; the populations they represent do
not interbreed.

male

female

X 1/2

red-winged
blackbirds

## DIFFICULTIES

This concept of species is far from perfect. First, it cannot be used for organisms in which only one individual is involved in reproduction. For example, many small organisms reproduce by simply dividing into two parts; in such cases the word "interbreed" is meaningless. Second, although the definition can be verified, it cannot really be tested in experiments, since it is dependent upon the behavior of the organisms "under natural conditions." And third, for practical use in identifying organisms, the definition is cumbersome. To use it, we need detailed information about breeding under natural conditions, and we have such data for only a small percentage of known species.

Thus, deciding whether a particular population is a species or not remains to some degree a matter of the opinions of biologists who are experts in the study of the organisms involved. But whenever the biological definition of species can be applied, it is valuable. We shall need to use it in thinking through many of the ideas ahead of us.

When we begin to observe the living world, we soon find that it is made up of individual living things. These individuals furnish the facts for the study of biology. We can take them apart and see how they are constructed, or we can group them and observe how they interact with each other. In this chapter we have taken the latter approach. We have seen that any defined group of individuals can be regarded as a population. Usually we include in our definition of a population the kind of organism, the space occupied, and the time at which our observations are made. By "kind of organism" we usually mean a species—a population of more or less similar individuals that can interbreed under natural conditions.

We may count the number of individuals in the population. If we express this quantity in relation to the space occupied, we have the population density. Within any space the rate of change in population density is determined by mortality, natality, immigration rate, and emigration rate. These determiners are influenced by a great variety of environmental factors. Many aspects of population changes can be studied by models and laboratory experiments. Most natural populations, however, are open systems in a steady state where fluctuations occur around an average population level. Biologists at present use a general theory of homeostasis as a guide to investigating the complex mechanisms of population control.

## GUIDE QUESTIONS

1. Why is it difficult to say exactly what we mean by an individual?
2. To define a group of individuals as a population, what things must we say about it?
3. Describe, in words, what this formula states in symbols: $D = \dfrac{N}{S}$.
4. How can we calculate the rate at which a population is increasing or decreasing?
5. Why are the terms "natality" and "mortality" — as defined in this text — not applicable to individuals?
6. Distinguish between immigration and emigration.
7. How do the experiments on mouse populations show the characteristics of scientific investigation?
8. What is meant by the biotic environment of an individual?
9. What are the major groups of environmental factors that influence population determiners?
10. How can the density of a population affect the extent to which an environmental factor may change that density?
11. Describe the characteristic form of a line graph that represents the growth of a "new" population living in a favorable environment.
12. Describe the characteristic form of a line graph that represents the changes in a well-established population under natural conditions.
13. How do biologists explain population fluctuations?
14. Why is the "species problem" important to both biologists and nonbiologists?
15. What are some of the factors that prevent a species population from losing its identity by interbreeding with another species population?
16. Why is the "biological definition" of a species inadequate?

## PROBLEMS

1. A biologist studied a population of box turtles in an Ohio woodlot for a period of ten years. He determined that the natality averaged 40 per year, the mortality averaged 30 per year, immigration 3 per year, and emigration 8 per year. Was the population increasing or decreasing? Was the area supplying box turtles to other places, or vice versa? What was the average annual change due to immigration and emigration? If the initial population was 15 turtles, what must the population have been at the end of ten years?

2. It is seldom possible to count all the individuals in a natural population. How can the biologist study population densities without such data?

3. From *The World Almanac* obtain the total human population of the United States according to each United States census from the first one in 1790. Using as large a scale as possible, graph the data. (a) Which of the population graphs that you have studied does the graph of the United States population most resemble? (b) What hypothesis can you advance for the slight change in the slope of the graph during the decade 1930–1940? (c) On the basis of your present understanding of populations, what can you predict about the shape of the line graph in the future? Explain your prediction in terms of the four determiners of population density. (d) What additional information would you need to convert the census figures to densities? (e) Obtain the necessary information, figure the densities for each decade, and plot a new graph. How is the new graph different from the one based on total population only? (f) Does this new view of the United States population change your predictions about the future? If so, why?

4. Obtain the United States census data for your state. Draw a graph of these data, beginning with the first census after your state entered the Union. Why is it unnecessary (except in the case of Virginia) to refigure these data for density? How does the form of this graph compare with that for the population of the United States as a whole? Try to explain any differences, using whatever knowledge you have of conditions in your state.

5. Some biologists have been studying three populations of frogs. Population $A$ interbreeds with population $B$ under natural conditions. Similarly, population $B$ interbreeds with population $C$. But population $A$ does not interbreed with population $C$. How many species of frogs are involved in this study? How many species would we have if population $A$ became extinct? If population $B$ became extinct?

6. What difficulties may be involved when we use the word "natality" in discussing the population of plants that reproduce by means of seeds?

## SUGGESTED READINGS

BENTON, A. H., and W. E. WERNER. *Principles of Field Biology and Ecology.* New York: McGraw-Hill Book Co., Inc., 1958. Chapter 8. (This describes some methods of population study. Fairly easy.)

BROWNING, T. O. *Animal Populations.* New York: Harper & Row, Publishers, Inc., 1963. (A good, modern discussion. Rather advanced.)

CURRY-LINDAHL., K. "New Theory on a Fabled Exodus," *Natural History,* August, September, 1963. Pp. 46–53.

KENDEIGH, S. C. *Animal Ecology.* Englewood Cliffs, N.J.: Prentice-Hall, Inc., 1961. Chapter 16. (Discusses factors in the regulation of population size. Rather advanced.)

ODUM, E. P. *Ecology.* New York: Holt, Rinehart & Winston, Inc., 1963. Pp. 89–109. (An excellent treatment of growth and fluctuations of populations. Fairly advanced.)

SIMPSON, G. G., and W. S. BECK. *Life: An Introduction to Biology.* 2nd ed. New York: Harcourt, Brace & World, Inc., 1965. Pp. 627–633. (Advanced.)

WYNNE-EDWARDS, V. C. "Population Control in Animals," *Scientific American,* August, 1964. Pp. 68–74.

# 3

# Communities
# and
# Ecosystems

## THE ECOLOGICAL VIEWPOINT

We can group species populations in two ways. One way is to group them according to similar characteristics, which is the method used in the study called *taxonomy*. We shall take the taxonomic viewpoint in Section Two.

taxonomy [tăks ŏn′ ə mĭ; Greek: *taxis*, order, arrangement, + *nomos*, a law]

Another way is to group populations according to their effects upon each other. Then we are led into the study called *ecology*, which investigates the relationships among organisms and between them and the environment. We have been using the ecological viewpoint in Chapters 1 and 2 and shall continue with it in this chapter.

ecology [ĭ kŏl′ ə jĭ; Greek: *oikos*, house, + *logos*, speech, reason]

## THE BIOTIC COMMUNITY

No organism lives alone. This was the first idea we encountered: the rabbit under a raspberry bush. The raspberry bush represented producers; the rabbit, consumers.

Obviously a consumer cannot live alone; it needs something to consume. And a producer? We have emphasized that it is at the center of the food web, getting along on water, carbon dioxide, a number of other inorganic substances, and energy from the sun. But to obtain these things, a producer is dependent upon other organisms. The raspberry plant is rooted in *soil*, which is the product of a long history of interaction between rocks and a host of soil organisms—from earthworms to bacteria. Without saprovores chemical materials needed by producers would remain "locked up" in the bodies of dead organisms; the producers could not live for lack of such materials. The

soil: See further, pages 234–242.

cycles of materials described in Chapter 1 would come to a halt.

## THE CONCEPT

When we say that no organism lives alone, we mean not just individual organisms: no *species* lives alone. In the laboratory it is possible (though not easy) to maintain a population of a single species in a container, isolated from all other species—a *pure culture*. But without the biologist who tends it, the population could not long continue to exist. Thus even in this situation two species are involved: man and the organism in the culture. Perhaps this is the very simplest kind of *biotic community*. However, in nature and even in most laboratory situations, the smallest part of the biosphere that we can conveniently study usually consists of many interacting species.

A single astronaut speeding around the earth in his space capsule is a biotic community. From the moment a person is born (and sometimes before), he begins to acquire populations of microorganisms that ride on and in him for the rest of his life. But the biotic community within the astronaut's capsule cannot survive very long on its own; for one thing, it has no producers. For long voyages into space, more complex biotic communities must be designed. This calls for a thorough understanding of the structure and the interactions in communities.

An understanding of biotic communities is just as necessary for those of us who may never travel in a space capsule—who remain in the biosphere, hurtling along on our own giant spaceship, Earth. Why this is so cannot be explained in a few sentences, but it should gradually become clear as you proceed through this course.

## AN EXAMPLE

You can best begin to understand a biotic community by studying one in the field. You will make such a study in this course. However, because we cannot know just what your class will find in its study, we shall briefly describe a particular biotic community as an example to which we can refer later. (The adjective "biotic" is used merely to show that we are not referring to exclusively human communities, and from here on it will usually be omitted.)

The example is located in the short rivers along the west coast of Florida. Since a community is a web of interactions, it is convenient to begin a description with one species and let its relationships to other species lead us into the community as a whole. We begin with a species known as the river turtle.

You observed only yeasts in Investigation 2.2, but you probably had bacteria in the cultures also; if so, these cultures were not pure.

astronaut [ăs′trə nôt′; Greek: *astron*, a star, + *nautes*, sailor]

Roger Peterson from National Audubon Society

Figure 3 · 1
A west-coast Florida river.

Figure 3 · 2
Map of Florida showing location (*dark green*) of rivers in which the "Florida river community" occurs.

raccoon: Figure 2 · 10

otter: Figure 9 · 6

alligator: Figure 4 · 16

leeches: Figure 4 · 41

Adult river turtles are first-order consumers. They eat many of the species of green plants that grow in the rivers, though they do not eat all species in equal amounts. Perhaps their favorite food is tape grass. When plentiful, some other kinds of plants are eaten, though the mere abundance of a plant does not necessarily make it acceptable turtle food. Further, the abundance of different plants varies with the time of year.

Unlike the adults, young river turtles are not entirely first-order consumers. They eat snails, which are first-order consumers; aquatic insects, many of which are second-order consumers; and worms, some of which may be third-order consumers. Thus, depending on what they eat, young river turtles can be second-, third-, or even higher-order consumers.

We can take a different view of the community by considering river turtles as food for other organisms. The highest mortality probably occurs in the egg stage. Turtle eggs are laid on land, in holes dug by the females. The nests are frequently discovered by skunks, raccoons, or snakes, all of which relish turtle eggs. The unhatched turtles are also killed by molds that live in the soil and grow through the thin shells of the eggs. If the eggs survive, the hatchlings may be picked up by snakes or herons. Once in the water, they may be eaten by some kinds of fish, by otters, or by a species of snapping turtle. When river turtles become larger, however, few organisms can kill them directly. Adults could be attacked by alligators or garfish, but we have little evidence for this.

Leeches attach themselves to turtles and suck their blood but do not kill them. Within the turtles live various "worms" and microorganisms that obtain their food from the turtles, perhaps sometimes killing them. And a turtle that dies becomes food for saprovores, which finally return all of the substances in the turtle's body to the nonliving world.

Plants, besides serving as food, play another part in the river turtle's life. The mats of half-floating vegetation, the tangled tree roots along the bank, the sunken logs—all these provide places for young turtles to hide from their enemies.

Each of the community relationships we have described so far is a *direct* relationship between the river turtle and another organism. River turtles also have many *indirect* relationships with organisms in the community. In the rivers live spiral-shelled snails, which, like the turtle, are very fond of tape grass. The tape-grass population varies greatly; sometimes it is plentiful and sometimes scarce. When tape grass becomes scarce, both the turtles and the snails may continue to use the same food supply for a while. But eventually the snails turn to eating algae, which are tiny green plants that grow on the rocks. They can scrape these off the rocks in a manner that is impossible for the turtles. The turtles, on the other hand, are able to grasp mats of larger plants that have floated away from the land. They can make use of a method of feeding that is impossible for the snails.

Another resident of the river, the musk turtle, eats nothing but snails. By reducing the number of snails, which eat tape grass, the musk turtles have an indirect effect on the river turtles. The musk turtles never eat all the snails, because the snails are not easy to find among the beds of tape grass. Moreover, many animals that kill musk turtles also kill young river turtles. Thus the more musk turtles there are in the river, the less likely it is that young river turtles will be caught.

When tape grass is abundant, another species of turtle, the pond turtle, which does not usually live in streams, enters the rivers and temporarily joins the community. Since the pond turtle leaves as soon as the tape-grass supply begins to decline, it has very little influence on the river turtle.

We have gone far enough in describing this Florida river community to serve our purpose. We have looked at the community as if through the eyes of the river turtle. If we had started with some other organism, we might have developed a somewhat different picture. To understand the community completely, we should have to look at all the relationships of all the organisms. Clearly, the study of

**Figure 3 · 3**

skunk    X 1/20

great blue heron    X 1/25

garfish    X 1/20

snapping turtle    X 1/14

algae [ăl′jē; singular, alga, ăl′gə]: Figure 5 · 30

Figure 3 · 4

Tape grass, spiral-shelled snails, musk turtle (*left*), adult river turtle (*right, above*), and pond turtle (*right, below*). What ecological relationships are shown?

a community—even a small one such as this—is not easy. But without it we can never fully understand the world in which we live, never develop the ecological machinery for voyaging out of this world, never understand any other world on which man might find life.

## INVESTIGATION 3.1

### STUDY OF A BIOTIC COMMUNITY

#### PURPOSE

Reading about a biotic community is not enough. To understand the interrelationships that make a functioning community, you must yourself observe the organisms that live in an active, natural community.

In this investigation you will examine such a community. You will gather as many data as time and opportunity will permit, and then attempt to identify interrelationships between species, to estimate the relative importance of species, and to understand the structure of the community.

### MATERIALS AND EQUIPMENT

The materials and equipment that you need depend upon the kind of community to be studied and the procedures the class chooses to follow.

### GENERAL PROCEDURES

Different schools have different kinds of communities available for study, and these require different study procedures. Therefore, the procedures to be used will have to be worked out by the teacher and the class to fit the community most convenient to your school.

**A. Selecting a study area.** You may not have much choice, but let us examine some alternatives. On land a forest provides the most complex community study. It is the easiest community from which to obtain a wealth of data but the most difficult to picture as a whole. A natural prairie is almost as complex, but a study of it requires fewer procedures. Cultivated areas—such as a cornfield —and pastures are of special interest because so much of the land area of our country now supports communities of these kinds.

Such kinds of communities may be unavailable in cities; however, many city schools have lawns with planted trees and shrubs. Here kinds of organisms may be fewer than in the country, but what is lost in complexity is usually gained in the thoroughness with which such a community can be studied. But suppose there is not even a lawn. Then you must turn to vacant lots and waste spaces between buildings. You can even study the communities that spring up in cracks in sidewalks, in curbs, or in street pavement.

All these are land communities. Water communities can also be studied, but the methods of studying them are not considered here.

In all major communities microorganisms are important. But procedures for studying them are complex and difficult, so we recommend that you do not try to study microorganisms at this time.

**B. Organizing the work.** The first job is to survey the area. Second, the class must decide just what kinds of data to collect. It must decide whether to limit the study to one place or to make it a comparative study. The different parts of the data-gathering will have to be assigned to teams.

Each team should have a leader responsible for directing the work. The more complex the community, the more important it is to have each team do its job well so that all the data will finally fit together.

**C. Collecting the data.** It is easier to handle sheets of paper on a clipboard than to take data books into the field. These sheets can be pasted into the data books when you return. This plan is especially good if the class prepares special forms for recording data.

It is not necessary to be able to identify every species of organism found during the study. Few ecologists can identify every organism they encounter. There are two ways to deal with this problem. One is to identify organisms only by general group terms—for example, "trees," "spiders," "grass," "beetles," "turtles." These are vague identifications, but from them you can still develop ideas about community interrelationships. Another method, used by many ecologists, is to collect a *specimen*—a sample individual of a species or a characteristic part of an individual.

Assign the specimen a letter (*A, B, C*, etc.), and whenever you need to refer to that kind of organism, refer to its letter. Later you may show your specimen to an expert, or you may be able to look up its name after you have returned to the laboratory. When you obtain the name for the specimen, replace the letter with the name.

Perhaps your class will decide to compare two or more communities. If so, you will need *quantitative* data: you will need to determine "how many" or "how much." Even if this aim is not part of your plan, some measurements will be useful. For example, if the density of large trees in a forest is great, this may have an effect on the population density of the smaller plants beneath them. Sometimes, too, the relative numbers of organisms may be a clue to their position in a food web: Insects that are first-order consumers are usually more numerous than the spiders that are second- or higher-order consumers. In any case it is always wise to measure the size of the area being studied. This sets boundaries and allows comparison of data among teams.

## SOME SPECIFIC PROCEDURES

None of the following procedures are complete. All can be greatly expanded, depending upon the wishes of the class. In many cases further procedures can be found in Phillips and in Benton and Werner (for full references see the end of the chapter).

**A. Measuring the area.** In a forest community different organisms must be studied on sample areas of different sizes. These can be set up as in Figure 3·5. Square or rectangular study areas are called *quadrats*. Each team should have its own study area.

Materials needed by each team:

Plastic clothesline or rope, 12 m long, marked off at 0.5 m intervals (use a felt-tip marker with permanent ink), 1

Wooden right triangle, 60 × 80 × 100 cm, 1

Wooden stakes, 8

Hammer or mallet, 1

Drive a stake in the ground. Tie or hold the line to the stake and measure off 10 m. Drive another stake at this point. Place the wooden triangle on the ground, with the right angle at the second stake; use this as a guide to extend the line at 90° to the direction of the first measurement. At 10 m drive a third stake, and continue around the square. Then use the line to mark off the two smaller quadrats, driving a stake at each corner. If the forest is thick, the main quadrat may not be precisely square, because tree trunks and bushes may stand in the way of the line. Be as accurate as possible.

In unforested areas quadrats need not be so large. For example, in cultivated fields quadrats 5 m on a side may

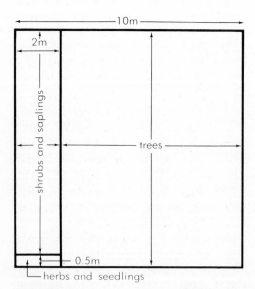

**Figure 3 · 5**

Plan of quadrats for use in the study of a forested community.

be used, with a quadrat 1 m² in one corner. The same measuring procedure may be followed as in the forest. In vacant city lots and other "wastelands" it may be better to have smaller teams and more of them, each working on a 1 m² quadrat (Figure 3·6). If the density of plants is low, the frame may be replaced by a stiff wire bent into a circle with a circumference of 354 cm. Laid on the ground, this circle encloses a study area 1 m² in size.

**B. Gathering plant data.** In a forest community it is convenient to divide plants into three groups: trees, shrubs, and herbs.

A *tree* is a tall woody plant with a single stem (trunk). Trees over 5 cm in diameter (about 16 cm in circumference) are studied in the main quadrat (Figure 3·5). Some attempt should be made to identify the kinds of trees; usually the end of a twig with a few leaves is a sufficient specimen. Trees that form the *canopy* (the forest top, which receives direct

sunlight) should be noted separately from those that do not reach the canopy. If comparisons are to be made between areas studied by different teams, a count of the trees (either by species or just as "trees") should be made. A further refinement may be made by measuring the trees with calipers (for diameter) or with a tape (for circumference).

*Shrubs* are woody plants that branch at or near the ground and therefore lack trunks. *Saplings* are simply young trees with trunks 1–5 cm in diameter. Both shrubs and saplings should be studied in an area smaller than that used for the trees. If the trees have been identified by species, then the saplings should be, too. Counts of the saplings may be made and related to the counts of trees of the same species. Because it is often difficult to distinguish individuals, counts of shrubs may have to be approximate.

*Herbs* (in the ecological sense) are nonwoody plants that die back at least to ground level in winter. (In the tropics they are more difficult to describe.) Tree *seedlings* are very young trees with stems less than 1 cm in diameter. Both herbs and seedlings should be studied on small quadrats, but you may wish to have several of these per team area. A spade may be used to dig a small trench along one side of the "herb quadrat," and the relationships between the underground parts of the plants may be noted. Note, also, the presence of toadstools, mushrooms, and other fungi. Again, if your class is making a comparative study, counts of the different species of herbs and saplings should be made. Finally, the proportion of this quadrat that is covered by moss may be estimated.

In nonforested areas the directions given above can be adapted to the nature of the community. Special problems may arise, however. In a lawn, for example, there is no need to count blades of grass; but a count of the "weeds" might be of

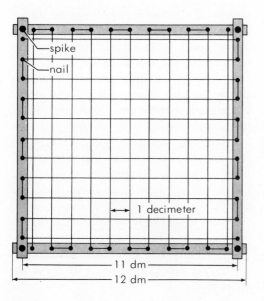

spike

nail

1 decimeter

11 dm

12 dm

**Figure 3 · 6**

Frame for a quadrat in a nonforested community.

some value, especially if comparisons are made between a well-trodden area and a protected one. A frame (Figure 3·6) may be useful for this work.

**C. Searching.** In a forest study this activity should cover the large quadrat. It should be carried on after the studies of plants have been completed, preferably on a later day. Students can best work in pairs—one searching, the other recording. Turn over stones, dead logs, and other cover to find animals. These may be found on plants, too. Look in flowers, especially. Make notes on the kinds of animals and on what they are doing. Specimens may be collected for identification, but all sheltering stones, logs, etc., should be returned to their original positions.

In communities of nonforested areas, searching can be carried on in the same way.

**D. Examining the litter and soil.** To study the smaller organisms that live close to and in the soil, gather samples of the *litter* (loose organic material on the surface of the soil in forests) and of the upper part of the soil. These are to be taken back to the laboratory, where they can be more conveniently examined. Each team will need:

Plastic bags
Rubber bands
Glass-marking crayon
Wire circle, 78.7 cm in circumference,
    enclosing 0.1 m². (This can be made
    from a wire clothes hanger.)
Trowel
Centimeter rule

Before the fieldwork, plastic bags should be labeled with team numbers and date of collection. The wire circle is used to mark out the area from which the loose litter is scraped. Since the area of the circle is known, the density of the organisms in the sample can be computed. Each sample of litter should be placed in a separate plastic bag and the

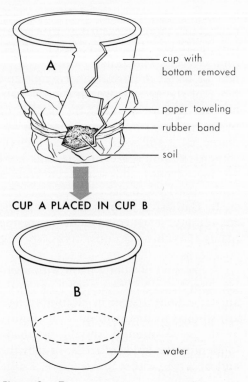

CUP A PLACED IN CUP B

**Figure 3 · 7**
Apparatus for extraction of soil nematodes.

mouth of the bag tightly fastened with a rubber band twisted several times. On the ground from which the litter was removed, mark out a square 10 cm on a side. Using a trowel, remove from the square a sample of soil 10 cm deep. Place each sample in a separate plastic bag, and fasten with a rubber band.

At least two such pairs of samples (litter and soil) should be taken from different places in the large forest quadrats. On smaller quadrats in other kinds of communities, one soil sample per quadrat may be enough. If you are working in cracks in a paved area, there may be no possibility of a measured soil sample.

In the laboratory you will need the following:

Ether or chloroform
White-enameled pan or large sheet of
    white paper

Light source

Forceps, 1 per student

Bottles or jars, with caps, several per
  student

Alcohol or formalin, 50 ml per bottle

Nematode extraction device (Figure
  3 · 7)

Microscope

Berlese apparatus (Figure 3 · 8)

Glass-marking crayon

Place a few drops of ether or chloroform in the bags containing the litter.
Wait five minutes. Then empty the contents into a large, white-enameled pan or
onto a table covered with white paper. A
strong light should shine on the litter,
but not into the observer's eyes. Pick
through the litter carefully with forceps
and put all organisms found into a small
jar of alcohol or formalin.

Small worms called nematodes are
abundant in most soils. To find them,
make a simple extraction device from
two paper cups (Figure 3 · 7). Remove
the bottom from cup A and replace it
with a "wet-strength" paper napkin se-
cured with a rubber band. Place about
10 cubic centimeters (abbreviated cc) of
your soil sample in cup A. Into cup B
pour about 1/3 cup of lukewarm water.
Lower cup A gently into cup B. Let the
setup remain undisturbed for 24 hours,
then very slowly and gently remove cup
A with its soil contents from cup B. Nematodes should be found (when you look
through a microscope) in the water in
cup B.

The remainder of each soil sample
should be loosened and, if very dry,
moistened—but you do not want mud!
Then place the samples in the Berlese
apparatus. The heat and light from the
bulb cause small organisms to crawl
downward and fall into the preservative.
Label the vials with the team number
and the date of collection. Leave the
Berlese funnel in operation about five
days.

**E. Netting insects.** In thick forest it
is difficult to catch flying insects, but the
vegetation can be beaten with a stout net.
This will recover many insects and spiders that would be overlooked in hand-
picking. In open fields nets swept
through the vegetation are more effective. After a series of sweeps, the net can
be placed in a large plastic bag containing several drops of chloroform. After a
few minutes the organisms can be sorted

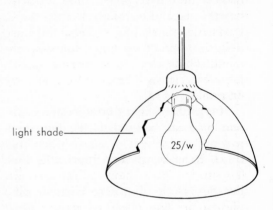

light shade

25/w

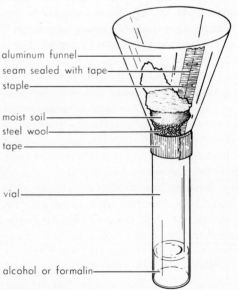

aluminum funnel

seam sealed with tape

staple

moist soil

steel wool

tape

vial

alcohol or formalin

Figure 3 · 8

Berlese funnel.

out, placed in jars of alcohol or formalin, and labeled with the team number and the date. The drawback to this method lies in the fact that it is difficult to tell what organisms are doing or even just where they live.

**F. Studying the larger animals.** To study amphibians, reptiles, birds, or mammals, it is usually necessary to cover much larger areas than the ones we have been considering and to observe for longer periods of time. The searching method described above may uncover amphibians and reptiles. Unless there is some good reason to keep the animals, they should be noted but not collected. These organisms may be found far inside cities, in large vacant lots or old cemeteries.

It is probable that no major land community exists without birds, but they may not be present or active when the class is collecting data. A few of the students in the class may want to take on the special job of noting birds at different times over a period several days long.

Most mammals cannot be observed as easily as birds. The most convenient way to begin a study of smaller mammals is to trap them alive and unharmed. There are several good traps for small mammals; but unless the community you study is fairly large, or unless some members of the class are especially interested in mammals, it will not be worthwhile to construct the traps. However, even if trapping is not attempted, do not overlook animal tracks. In cities keep in mind the possible presence of rats, mice, stray dogs, and alley cats as members of the community. And be sure not to forget man!

## STUDYING THE DATA

The data gathered by each team must be exchanged with other teams. This can best be done by placing team data on stencils from which copies can be made for all members of the class. Team leaders should devise a form that will permit easy comparison.

Here is a sample of questions you should consider:

1. What producers are in the community? This can be answered by using general terms like "trees," "shrubs," etc., or by naming the various species in your list.

2. Are producers abundant or rare? This may be answered in general terms or with density figures.

3. If there are different groups of producers, which one of them seems to contribute the most toward producing food?

4. Are there layers of producers? If so, what relationships can you find between producers in different layers?

5. Does the community produce all its own food, or is food carried in from beyond the community boundaries? What evidence do you have for your answer?

6. What consumers are in the community? This, too, may be answered with such general terms as "insects," "spiders," "birds," etc., or with names of identified species.

7. Which consumer orders (first, second, etc.) are represented? What evidence can you point out that supports your answer?

8. If some quantitative data have been obtained, what relations can you find between the numbers of a particular organism and the numbers of another organism that eats it?

9. Besides evidence of food relationships, what evidence do you have that any one species in the community affects another?

A survey of a community should raise more questions than answers. In studying the data, part of the job is to look for questions that need answering.

## COMMUNITY STRUCTURE

Most telephone books consist of two parts: The first, usually printed on white paper, lists names alphabetically. Studying it would tell us little about the human community. The second, usually on yellow paper, lists people and organizations by occupations, by the services they perform. Studying the yellow pages of a telephone directory might tell us quite a bit about a human community. Likewise with a biotic community: merely listing the names of organisms tells us little. What we need to know is how each organism gets its living and how, in doing so, it affects other organisms.

Without a supply of energy no living thing and no community of living things can function. Therefore, in studying communities the ecologist should first face the basic question: How is energy transferred through the community? From your study of Chapter 1 you can see that this question concerns food webs.

Ecological relationships, however, involve more than "who eats whom." The *way* in which an organism obtains its food is important. Both the river turtle and the spiral-shelled snail eat tape grass, but they eat it in different ways. The snail rasps off bits of the plant to which it is clinging; the river turtle bites off much larger pieces with its horny beak. These two methods of feeding affect the tape grass in different ways.

Obtaining energy is the basic activity of life, but not the only one. The tape grass is important to the spiral-shelled snail as a place to hide—a shelter, a home. This relationship has nothing to do with food. Yet it is an important feature of community structure.

An ecologist may discover a long list of relationships and still not understand the community. A community is not a mere collection of interacting species; it has organization. It has length and width and depth. Some species are

Figure 3 · 9
Lion at its kill and vultures waiting. What ecological relationships are shown?

abundant in one part of the community, others abundant in other parts. And some species are more abundant than others in the community as a whole.

Finally, a community has a history. An ecologist cannot clearly understand a present community unless he gains some understanding of its past. Hopefully, he may then be able to predict certain things about its future.

### KINDS OF ECOLOGICAL RELATIONSHIPS

In the Florida river community you easily recognize that the tape grass, algae, and other green plants are producers. You also see without difficulty that the river turtle and spiral-shelled snail are first-order consumers, herbivores. Now let us look at some relationships that may require further explanation.

predation [prī dā'shən; Latin: *praeda*, prey]

**Predation.**   In the Florida river community, snapping turtles eat young river turtles; musk turtles eat snails; snakes swallow turtle eggs. In other communities, eagles catch jackrabbits; robins catch earthworms; house cats catch mice. A consumer that kills another living organism and eats it, regardless of whether it kills it before or during the eating process, is a *predator*. The organism that is eaten is called the *prey*.

Sometimes organisms that are normally saprovores act as predators, probably from impatience. In the southeastern states vultures may find an animal injured by an automobile and not wait for it to die before beginning to eat. On the other hand snapping turtles are predators most of

Figure 3 · 10

Smut ( a fungus) growing on corn. What ecological relationship is shown?

Department of Plant Pathology, University of Minnesota

the time, but if they find something edible that is already dead, they will not hesitate to eat it. So it is often difficult to decide whether to call a particular species predator or saprovore.

**Parasitism.**   In the river community, leeches cling to a turtle where its skin is soft, usually under the legs, and suck the turtle's blood. Within the blood of turtles lives a kind of microorganism that absorbs food directly from the blood. In other communities, ticks and mites live on larger animals and suck their blood. In aquariums goldfish are sometimes attacked by molds that may eventually kill them. Plants as well as animals may be inhabited by molds or microorganisms. And larger microorganisms may have smaller microorganisms within them. Organisms that live on or in other living organisms and obtain their food from them are called *parasites*. Organisms from which parasites obtain their food are called *hosts*.

**Difficulties.**   How long does an organism have to live on or in another before we call it a parasite? Once tuberculosis microorganisms get into the body of a host, they stay there, and a great many generations may spend their whole lives there. On the other hand, though a leech may stay attached to its turtle host for long periods of time, it does not spend its entire life there. Most biologists would agree to call a leech a parasite. But what about a mosquito? It consumes its victim's blood, just as the leech does, but it stays only long enough to obtain one meal — often a rather short one.

Predators kill their prey; parasites *may* kill their hosts. But the death of the host is always a disadvantage and often a disaster for the parasite. When parasites kill, they usually kill indirectly, by producing substances that are in some way poisonous to their hosts. Of course the host is just as dead when killed by poison as it would be if it had been killed by a predator.

Further, we have seen that some consumers may act as saprovores in one case and as predators in another.

Obviously the terms we have been using are not precise. This does not mean that they are useless; it merely means that their usefulness is limited to cases where their lack of precision does not matter. For example, it is quite safe to say that snapping turtles are predators on young river turtles, even though snapping turtles also eat dead flesh.

**Benefit to one — harm to the other.**   Ecologists now have much precise information about some kinds of communities, and they are developing some new approaches to the study of community relationships.

One such approach is to consider the benefit or harm that the relationship brings to the organisms involved. The

edible [ĕd'ə bəl; Latin: *edere*, to eat]

parasitism    [păr'ə sī'tĭz əm; Greek: *para*, beside, + *sitos*, food]

ticks: illustration, Appendix II, Figure A·124; mites: Figure 3·11

But it would *not* be safe to use any of the foregoing terms for a mosquito!

benefit [bĕn'ə fĭt; Latin: *bene*, well, + *facere*, to do]

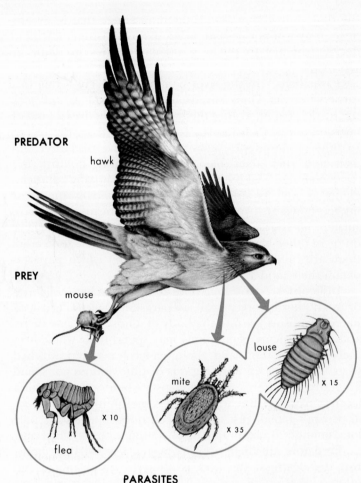

**PREDATOR**
hawk

**PREY**
mouse

louse

X 15

mite

X 35

X 10

flea

**PARASITES**

Figure 3 · 11

Some ecological relationships. Could the flea population have any effect on the hawk population?

relationship between predator and prey seems to be beneficial to the predator and harmful to its prey. The relationship between parasite and host seems to be beneficial to the parasite and harmful to its host. Ecologically, then, predation and parasitism are similar.

Adult river turtles usually eat only part of tape-grass plants; in this they resemble leeches, which we have called parasites. But sometimes a river turtle might eat a whole tape-grass plant, killing it; then its behavior would resemble that of musk turtles, which we have called predators. Like river turtles, most herbivores—such as cattle, horses, sheep—do not usually kill the producers on which they feed but leave part to continue growing. The relationship here is clearly of the same kind as that between predator and prey or parasite and host: beneficial to the one, harmful to the other. As yet, however, ecologists do not have any one term to apply to this kind of relationship.

Douglas P. Wilson

**Figure 3 · 12**
**Sea turtle shown with two remoras.**

**Commensalism.**    A remora is a fairly small fish that has a kind of suction disk on the top of its head. By means of this disk, it attaches itself to some large sea animal, most often a shark. The effect on the shark is probably neutral. But the remora benefits: first, it uses very little energy in moving about, because it is carried by the shark; second, it swallows pieces of the shark's prey that float by. This kind of relationship—in which one organism is benefited and the other is unaffected—is called *commensalism*.

Most of the holes used by bluebirds for nesting are chiseled out by woodpeckers. Bluebirds never use a hole made by a woodpecker unless the woodpecker has abandoned it. Thus, the presence of bluebirds has no effect on woodpeckers, but the presence of woodpeckers is beneficial to bluebirds—a relationship similar to that between the remora and the shark. In recent years some ecologists have broadened the usage of the term "commensalism" to include relationships like that of the bluebird and woodpecker, even though such relationships do not involve food.

**Mutualism.**    Clinging tightly to rocks or sometimes to the bark of trees can be found small plants that have no roots, stems, or leaves. Unlike the mosses often found in the same places, they are never bright green. Instead, they are a dull gray-green, or they may even appear yellow or

remora [rĕm′ə rə]

neutral [nū′trəl; Latin: ne-, not, + uter, one or the other]: here means neither benefit nor harm

commensalism    [kə mĕn′səl-īz′əm; Latin: cum, with, together, + mensa, table]

X 1/4

**Figure 3 · 13**
**Bluebird.**

lichens [lī'kənz]: See Figure 5·33.

orange. These organisms are called *lichens*. Actually, each lichen is composed of two different plants living in very close association. One is an alga, a producer that makes food by photosynthesis. The other is a fungus, a consumer that obtains its food from the alga. Without the fungus the producer probably could not long survive in the places where lichens grow; the consumer protects the tiny producer plants from drying out. Thus both organisms benefit. A relationship such as this—one that is mutually helpful—is called *mutualism*.

mutualism [mū'chŏŏ əl ĭz'əm; Latin: *mutuus*, exchange]

competition [kŏm'pə tĭsh'ən; Latin: *cum*, with, together, + *petere*, to seek]

**Competition.** Both the spiral-shelled snail and the river turtle eat tape grass; the tape grass that the turtle eats is clearly not available for the snail to eat, and vice versa. Thus the presence of the turtle can be harmful to the snail, and the reverse. Another case: Both bluebirds and starlings nest in holes in trees, poles, and fence posts. Neither species is able to dig holes for itself, so both are dependent upon holes already available. Thus the presence of bluebirds may be harmful to starlings and the presence of starlings harmful to bluebirds.

intraspecific [Latin: *intra*, within, + *species*]

interspecific [Latin: *inter*, between, among, + *species*]

The relationships just described are examples of *competition*. This term was used in Chapter 2 (page 48), but we were then discussing competition among individuals that belong to the same species—*intraspecific* competition. Here we are describing *interspecific* competition—competition between individuals belonging to different species. It is necessary to distinguish between these two kinds of competition. Though the importance of intraspecific competition in regulating species populations is well established, the importance of interspecific competition is a matter of disagreement among ecologists.

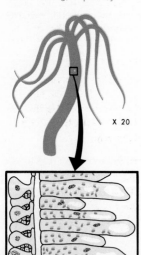

**Evaluating relationships.** A danger lies in any set of scientific terms, for we may mistake our ability to use the terms for an understanding of the things to which we have applied them.

The terms we have been discussing are based on the idea that some ecological relationships are beneficial, others harmful, still others neutral. Now what do we mean by this? Clearly, when a fox kills and eats a rabbit, that individual rabbit is harmed. But in the study of communities the ecologist is not concerned with individuals; he is concerned with species. His question is: Does the fox population harm the rabbit population?

**Figure 3 · 14**

Green hydra. The green color in this small animal comes from the presence of hundreds of microscopic green plants growing within it. What kind of ecological relationship might this be?

To investigate this problem, the ecologist must define "harmful" in such a way that he can look for evidence concerning it. If "harmful" means that an increase in the fox population brings about a decrease in the rabbit population, then the ecologist can obtain definite numerical data by measuring the sizes of the populations over a period of time. "Beneficial" then means that an increase in one population brings about an increase in another population, and "neutral" means that a change in one population has no effect on the population of the other. The preferred evidence in science is always quantitative (numerical data) — so these meanings of "harmful," "beneficial," and "neutral" are, in fact, the ones ecologists use.

Here is an example of the kind of evidence the ecologist seeks: We can observe that lynxes eat snowshoe hares. But does the abundance of hares affect the abundance of lynxes? We have already seen graphed data for the Canadian snowshoe-hare population (Figure 2·19); Figure 3·16 adds data on the Canadian lynx population. This allows us to consider this predator-prey relationship quantitatively. Because the graph shows that the population of the lynx goes up and down, closely following the ups and downs in the population of the hare, it provides evidence that the abundance of hares is an important factor in the abundance of lynxes. Note well, however, that we did not say we had *proved* this. It is perfectly possible that some unknown third factor was affecting both the hare and the lynx populations in the same way.

Obviously, the measurement of natural populations — particularly of animal populations — is difficult; as a result, knowledge of most community relationships is still very imperfect.

From what you have learned about the nature of science, why do you think scientists prefer numerical data?

lynxes [lĭngks′əz]

Figure 3 · 15
Starling.

For some methods by which ecologists measure natural populations, see the book by Phillips (listed on page 101).

Figure 3 · 16
Population fluctuations of lynx and snowshoe hare in Canada, according to the records of the Hudson's Bay Company.

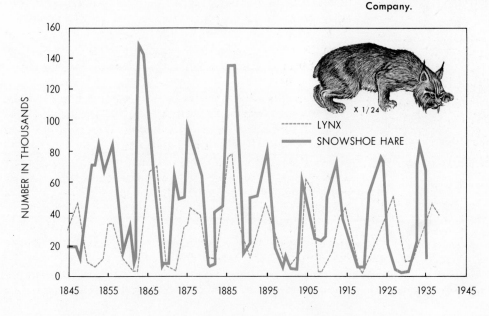

## SPECIES STRUCTURE OF COMMUNITIES

In describing the Florida river community we named more than a dozen species of organisms and referred to many more in general terms. A careful biologist undoubtedly could find hundreds of other species there. The community that you yourself studied in Investigation 3.1 surely had many more species than you were able to find.

Whatever the number of species may be, the ecologist usually finds (and probably you did, too) that some species are represented by many individuals and other species by only a few. In most communities of the middle latitudes, the great majority of individuals belong to a small number of species. When we consider the energy that passes through such a community—and this is a basic concern in any ecological study—we discover that most of it passes through these few species. On the other hand, there is

**Figure 3 · 17**

How many examples of interrelationships between communities can you find in this picture?

George Silk from *Life* Magazine

usually a large number of "rare" species—that is, species having so few individuals that specimens are seldom encountered. Only a small part of the community's energy supply passes through these species.

The species structure characteristic of communities in the middle latitudes does not prevail elsewhere. In most tropical communities no species are represented by very large numbers of individuals; all species are "rare." In contrast, in communities of Antarctica, the Arctic Ocean, and other severe environments—such as rivers in which man has dumped poisonous wastes—only a few species can exist. These have all the energy supply to themselves, and among them the number of individuals per species is comparatively great.

Tropical communities are very stable, while those of severe environments are characterized by wide fluctuations in population densities. It seems, then, that the greater the number of species—and the greater the number of links in the food web—the greater is the homeostasis in the community.

### STRUCTURE IN DEPTH

The community in your classroom aquarium obviously has length, breadth, and depth. The Florida river community likewise has structure in three dimensions: Some of its species are usually found floating near the surface; others swim deep in the water or crawl over the bottom. In water the idea that a community has volume is easy to see.

On land, however, ecologists usually measure out study *areas*, as you probably did in Investigation 3.1. In this case, it may be possible to overlook the dimension of depth. But land communities always have a volume, just as do water communities. In forests a community may be many meters in depth, stretching from the canopy of the trees down through shrubs, herbs, moss, and into the soil. Other communities—a pasture, for example—may be much more shallow, but every community exists in three dimensions.

### COMMUNITY BOUNDARIES

What are the limits to a community? Consider the Florida example again. We would have rather neat boundaries for the community if it could be limited to the water. But the turtles crawl onto the banks to lay their eggs, which then serve as food for land animals. Herons get almost all their food from the river but nest in tall trees. Frogs spend much time in the river, where they are food for snapping turtles, but while on the banks, frogs may also be caught and eaten by raccoons, which are land animals. Frogs eat insects, which they catch outside the river, and the insects, in many cases, spend their early lives in the river.

The example is not a special case. All communities have relationships with others around them. Ecologists set boundaries primarily for convenience of study; they cannot expect the organisms to recognize them! Of course, some boundaries make more ecological sense than others. There are probably more relationships among the organisms that spend most of their time in the river and more among the organisms that spend most of their time on land than there are between the set of "land organisms" and the set of "river organisms." Therefore, the edge of the river waters makes a boundary that is not only convenient but reasonable.

### STRUCTURE THROUGH TIME: SUCCESSION

In all biological studies there is a basic difficulty: Even as we are observing them, living things are changing. We determine the density of the turtle population in a stream, but by the time we finish gathering our data, the density has probably changed. We saw in Chapter 2, however, that such changes are likely to be fluctuations. If we make many measurements, at various times, we can calculate an average density that is likely to be a more reliable indication of population density than any single measurement. Thus, an average may reflect a steady state over a period of time.

reliable [ri li' ə bəl; Latin: re-, back, again, + ligare, to bind]: trustworthy

On the average the Florida river community has probably changed very little for many centuries. Sometimes tape grass is abundant, sometimes not, and this brings about changes in the population of other organisms. But tape grass, river turtles, musk turtles, alligators, and all the rest have been there, interacting, for a long time. From geological evidence we know that Florida was once beneath the sea. At that time, certainly, no river community existed there. In future ages Florida may rise much higher above sea level than it is at present; then the slow-moving streams of today may become rushing rivers. Under such conditions most species now living in the streams could no longer exist. A very different community would appear.

The process by which a community gradually changes over a period of time until we must recognize it as a different community is called *succession*.

succession [sək sĕsh'ən; Latin: sub, under, after, + cedere, to go]

Living things already occupy every place on earth where existence is possible, so only when some event destroys an existing community can succession be easily observed. For example, in the summer of 1959, an earthquake in Montana tumbled tons of rocks into the Madison River, damming it and forming a lake where a valley had once been. The land community that had occupied the valley was drowned, and a water environment favorable to other kinds of organisms was formed. On the slopes, areas of bare rock were left by the landslide—areas where new communities could develop. Whenever a volcano erupts, old communities are destroyed and new areas for occupation by living things are formed. Less dramatic than earthquakes and volcanoes are river floods, which often leave bare sand and gravel bars when they recede. The communities of organisms that invade such "new" living spaces may develop a steady state; but usually they exist only a short time and are replaced by other communities in succession.

recede [rĭ sēd'; Latin: re-, back, again, + cedere, to go]

We shall consider one example of succession and, to simplify the description, emphasize plants, though each community, of course, contains other organisms. The surface of a rock bared by a landslide is hot by day and cold at night. Water cannot soak in, so that shortly after a rain the rock is dry. Under such conditions few producers can exist—lichens are the only ones visible to the naked eye. Land snails may consume these producers, and microscopic saprovores decay them when they die. Thus the first community to appear on bare rock is very simple.

Lichens produce acids that gradually make cavities in the rock surface. Dust and decaying lichen collect in these cavities, forming a simple soil that holds small quantities of water after a rain. Mosses, which cannot survive on the solid rock surface, take hold in these small quantities of soil. Mosses are usually larger than lichens; they trap more windblown dust, and they form more soil when they die. Because mosses carry on photosynthesis more effectively than lichens, the mosses eventually overgrow most of the lichens. Consequently, a "moss community" succeeds a "lichen community."

In the steadily accumulating soil among the mosses, seeds of grass, shrubs, or trees are able to germinate. These larger plants do not necessarily displace the mosses, but as they grow upward, they hide the mosses from view. Being larger, they contribute more to the developing soil; and having roots, they push down into cracks in the rock, forming ever deeper pockets of soil on the rock surface. In many parts of the United States, succession thus continues until a forest community develops, though the process may require hundreds of years. The forest community, once it is formed, may then persist for tens of thousands of years, in steady state. This long-enduring steady-state community is known as a *climax community*.

accumulating [ə kū′myə lāt′ing; Latin: ad, to, + cumulare, to heap]

persist [Latin: per, through, + sistere, to stand, to be fixed]

Thus we see that communities change through time —through only a few years in some cases, through several hundred or a few thousand years in our example, or more slowly, through millions of years, in the geological history of the earth. When does one community succeed another? It should be clear that there is no moment in time when a lichen community suddenly becomes a moss community. Rather, such changes in communities come about gradually, little by little.

*How would succession on a river sandbar differ from that on bare rock?*

Neither in time nor in space can we mark off clear boundaries between communities.

## ECOSYSTEMS

The biotic community is a system of ecological relationships among organisms. But every biotic community exists in an abiotic environment. We can study the relationships between organisms in a community without paying much attention to the abiotic environment, but we can never really ignore it.

### THE STUDY OF ECOSYSTEMS

It is certainly important for the Florida river community that the water does not freeze; if it did, many of the species of organisms we have described could not exist. And of course the river community depends upon energy and materials from the abiotic environment. When we relate the abiotic environment to the community of organisms, we are studying an *ecosystem*.

*ecosystem [ē′kō sĭst′əm]*

An ecosystem is not just the organisms of a biotic community plus the associated abiotic environment. Rather, the word also includes the give-and-take—the whole network of relationships—of each and every part, living and nonliving. Study of an ecosystem involves not only the measurement of populations of organisms but also the measurement of factors in the abiotic environment. It is not enough to know that cold weather kills tomato plants; the ecologist wants to know at what temperature they are killed. Oysters do not grow in fresh water, but at just what *salinity* (proportion of salt to water) do they grow best? The ecologist who studies ecosystems not only must know organisms—biology; also, he must have a knowledge of physics and chemistry and of the methods of measuring physical and chemical factors in the environment.

*salinity [sə lĭn′ə tĭ; Latin: sal, salt]*

### EFFECTS OF ORGANISMS ON THE ABIOTIC ENVIRONMENT

The current in the Florida rivers is not very strong; if it were, tape grass would not grow. But the tape grass—especially when it is abundant—clogs the rivers and makes the current even slower than it would be otherwise. Thus the

A                                    Haven Kolb

B                                    Haven Kolb

Figure 3 · 18

A succession on rock. *(A)* Lichens only. *(B)* Mosses in a small crack. *(C)* Grasses growing up through a mat of moss. *(D)* Aspen and pines.

Paul Pearson

C                    Paul Pearson

D

interaction between abiotic environment and community operates in both directions.

Of all organisms, man has by far the greatest ability to affect the abiotic environment. Very early in history, man covered himself with clothes and built houses warmed by fires; thus he extended a bit of the tropical climate pole-ward. With the invention of agriculture, man had much greater effect on the abiotic factors of ecosystems. He cleared and plowed the land. He spread the waters of rivers onto parched land. Since the invention of power machinery, man has become a force upon the landscape equal to earthquakes and hurricanes. And now, because of his ability to release atomic radiation in vast amounts, he is probably in a position to make the entire earth impossible for life.

### ECOLOGICAL NICHES

niche [nĭch]

The sum of all the relationships between any species of organism and its environment is its ecological *niche.* In describing the niche of a river turtle, for example, we must include all the relationships we mentioned in discussing its place in the Florida river community. We must also include all the ways in which the abiotic environment affects it—the temperature of the water, the flow of the current in the river, the clearness of the water, the nature of the soil in which the turtle digs its nests, and so on. Further, we must include all the ways in which it affects the abiotic environment—these are probably rather few for the turtle, in contrast to man.

Another example: Christmas ferns obtain their energy from sunlight by photosynthesis. They are able to make use of the small amounts of sunlight that filter through the leaves of taller neighbors. Other plants can make use of low illumination, but Christmas ferns are evergreen, so they can use light energy on warm days in fall and winter when the leaves of most other plants are dead. In these seasons their leaves spread out on the ground; under them the temperature remains higher than in the open air. Here small insects and spiders find protection during cold weather. These relationships sketch out the niche of the Christmas fern.

Most dictionary definitions of "niche" stress *location;* the ecological definition concerns a *way of living.* Of course, any particular way of living must occur in a suitable place. Neither river turtles nor Christmas ferns could carry on their ways of life in a desert. But in describing the niche of an organism, the ecologist does not tell *where* it lives; he tells *how* it lives.

X 1/3

Figure 3 · 19
Christmas fern.

## CONTINUITY OF THE ECOSYSTEMS

Biotic communities are linked to the others around them; in the same way, all ecosystems are linked to other ecosystems around them. A forest ecosystem connects with a river ecosystem; a river ecosystem blends gradually into the saltwater ecosystem of the sea—all ecosystems on Earth are connected to one another. We can, then, think of one great world ecosystem—and this is the biosphere.

Ecosystems thus have continuity in space. They also have continuity in time. We can recognize producers among the early traces of organisms preserved in ancient rocks. We can find fossils of extinct organisms that, from their structure, must have been first-order consumers; and we can find others that were clearly predators on these. All these ancient organisms lived in the water; they undoubtedly felt the effects of currents, received energy from the sun, and otherwise responded to their abiotic environment much as modern organisms do.

Organisms have changed greatly. Climate, rivers, rocks, and landscapes have changed. But the system of interactions among organisms and environment appears to have remained much the same. Man has always lived within this system of interactions—within the biosphere. He has learned how to escape from the earth's gravity, but he has not learned how to free himself from the earthly environment. So now, as he ventures out into the universe, he must carry with him a fragment of this ancient world ecosystem.

Figure 3 · 20

A city is an ecosystem that depends upon other ecosystems for its energy. Here are two steps in supplying biotic energy for a city's human population: left, a wholesale market; right, a retail market. Suggest some places where the energy in this food will go.

A. Devaney

**INVESTIGATION 3.2**

## ABIOTIC ENVIRONMENT: A COMPARATIVE STUDY

### PURPOSE

You will measure two abiotic environmental factors that are important considerations in distinguishing between ecosystems.

### BACKGROUND INFORMATION

The abiotic factors to be measured are temperature and relative humidity. Temperature requires no explanation. *Relative humidity* is a measure of the moistness of air. It is defined as the water vapor in the air at a given temperature compared with the maximum amount of water vapor that the air *could* hold at that temperature. Mathematically, it is a ratio and is expressed as a percentage. In general, organisms lose water faster in an atmosphere with low relative humidity than in an atmosphere with high relative humidity. Therefore, an abiotic factor that is of special importance to land organisms is relative humidity.

Any particular kind of environment is a *habitat*. This term—unlike "niche" —implies nothing at all about ecological relationships; it refers only to surroundings.

### MATERIALS AND EQUIPMENT
#### (per team of 6 students)

Watches, 3

Metersticks, 3

Thermometers (0°–100°C), 3

Thermometers (of same range, with
cotton sleeves over the bulbs), 3

Bottles (with screw tops) containing
30–50 ml distilled water, 3

Stiff pieces of cardboard for fanning, 3

Umbrellas for shading, 3

Table of relative humidities, 1

### PROCEDURE

A team consists of six students working in three pairs. One member of each pair reads the instruments; the other fans the thermometer and records the data. Before starting, the three recorders synchronize their watches and agree on the time at which each measurement is to be made. These times should be recorded in a data form similar to this:

| Location _____ | | | | |
|---|---|---|---|---|
| | **HEIGHT** | | | |
| | 0 cm | 30 cm | 90 cm | 150 cm |
| **TIME** | | | | |
| **DRY-BULB TEMPERATURE** | | | | |
| **WET-BULB TEMPERATURE** | | | | |
| **RELATIVE HUMIDITY** | | | | |

Measurements will be made to compare three kinds of environment—three habitats. One pair of students will take measurements in a dense cover of vegetation—a woods (preferable), a thicket, or a mass of shrubbery in a park. A second pair will take measurements in a place that has a single layer of herbaceous vegetation (vegetation composed of herbs)—a meadow or a lawn (preferably not cut close to the ground). A third pair will take measurements in a place that has no vegetation—bare ground or a tennis court. The three habitats should be as close together as possible. In each, four sets of measurements will be taken: the first at ground level, the second at 30 cm above the ground, the third at 90 cm above the ground, and the last at 150 cm above the ground.

Readings on both types of thermometers should be taken at the same time. Thermometers should be in their proper positions (see preceding paragraph) for at least five minutes before readings are taken. Thus, if the first reading is to be taken at 1:30 P.M., both thermometers should be in the first position at 1:25 P.M. The wet-bulb temperature is obtained by soaking the sleeve of a thermometer in water and fanning it vigorously for at least two minutes before making the reading. For the first reading, the wet-bulb thermometer should be fanned from 1:28 to 1:30. At least eight minutes should be scheduled between readings so that there is time to move both thermometers to the next position and leave them there for five minutes. Use the umbrellas to shield the thermometers from the direct rays of the sun.

The reading from the dry-bulb thermometer is the air temperature. The relative humidity must be obtained from a table that will be supplied by the teacher. To find the relative humidity on the table, you need both dry-bulb and wet-bulb thermometer readings. When these two measurements are known, it is possible to determine the amount of water vapor actually in the air compared with the amount that the air *could* hold — the relative humidity. The necessary calculations were made at the time the table was constructed.

### STUDYING THE DATA

• At ground level which habitat — dense cover of vegetation, single layer of vegetation, or bare ground — is coolest and most humid?(1) • At ground level which is warmest and least humid?(2) • How do these two habitats compare in temperature and humidity at higher levels above the ground?(3) • At which level above the ground are all three habitats most alike in temperature and humidity?(4) • How does the greatest temperature difference in the *same* habitat compare with the greatest temperature difference *between* habitats?(5) • What differences among the three habitats may account for differences in the temperature and relative humidity?(6) • How does this show the interaction of biotic and abiotic factors in an ecosystem?(7) In weather forecasts, temperatures predicted for the center of a city often differ from those predicted for the suburban areas. • Relate this fact to the situations you have been observing.(8)

You have been examining the differences among habitats. Now turn to differences *within* a habitat. • How does the temperature in each habitat vary with respect to elevation?(9) • Is the variation the same for each habitat? If not, in which is the variation greatest?(10) • What differences in temperature and humidity would be experienced by a beetle crawling on the ground in a meadow and a gnat hovering at 1.5 m above the meadow?(11) In a general sense we may say that the beetle and the gnat are in the same habitat, but small differences within a habitat are often important to the existence of some organisms. We can therefore distinguish *microhabitats* (small habitats within larger ones) on the basis of measurements such as those you have made in this investigation. • Would it be useful to measure factors in microhabitats if you were studying the ecological relationships among cows in a meadow? Explain.(12) • What other abiotic environmental factors might vary in the microhabitats just discussed?(13)

We know of no species that exists independently of all other species, and it seems that such a situation is impossible. Species interact with each other. The ecological relationships between species are the basis for our concept of the biological community.

Our understanding of any community depends upon how well we have worked out the relationships among all the species. Much of our present knowledge of community relationships rests on plain observational evidence. Ecologists are working at present to describe these relationships quantitatively.

Communities have a definite structure but no definite boundaries. Whatever boundaries we set, some species cross them and link the described community to others. In time, also, there are no boundaries between communities. Over short periods we observe changes that may be thought of as fluctuations in a steady state. Over longer periods we know from indirect evidence that successions of communities occur.

The concept of an ecosystem involves all the relationships within a community and, in addition, all the relationships between a community and its abiotic environment. Within an ecosystem every species has an ecological niche; that is, it has a characteristic way of living. It also lives where there is a characteristic set of environmental factors—a particular habitat. Just as community boundaries are blurred in space or time, so, also, are the boundaries of ecosystems.

## GUIDE QUESTIONS

1. What is meant by the statement "No organism lives alone"?
2. In a diagram summarize the interrelationships in the river-turtle community.
3. For an understanding of any community, what kind of relationship between species is of basic importance?
4. A predator is a factor in determining the population density of the species it eats, but a saprovore is not. Explain.
5. How do a predator and a parasite differ?
6. Distinguish between commensalism and mutualism.
7. How might an ecologist determine whether a relationship between two species is harmful, beneficial, or neither?
8. How is the number of species in a community related to its stability?
9. Why is it impossible to draw sharp boundaries between communities?
10. What is meant by ecological succession?
11. What is the distinction between a community and an ecosystem?
12. What are some ways in which man has changed ecosystems?
13. How can organisms living in the same place be said to occupy different niches?

## PROBLEMS

1. Rivers that run underground through caves (as in Kentucky) contain communities consisting of few species, none of which are producers. Explain why producers are lacking and how a community exists without them.

2. Ecologists usually describe interspecific relationships that tend to increase a population as "positive" and those that tend to decrease a population as "negative." Use the story of the Kaibab deer (Simpson and Beck, *Life: An Introduction to Biology*, pages 669–670) to show how a negative ("harmful") effect on a population may actually benefit the population in the long run.

3. In the *Scientific American* of September, 1962, two articles describe communities

in the Antarctic (Murphy, R. C., "The Oceanic Life of the Antarctic," pages 186–210, and Llano, G. A., "The Terrestrial Life of the Antarctic," pages 212–230). Read these articles. Then contrast land and water communities in the Antarctic, accounting for the contrast by describing the environmental factors in the two ecosystems.

4. Compare the system of biological energy in a cave community with that in a deep-sea community and with that in a city community.

5. Here are two parasite-host relationships: (a) The fungus called *Endothia parasitica* is the parasite; the chestnut tree is the host. The effect on the host is called "chestnut blight." (b) The bacterium *Bordetella pertussis* is the parasite; man is the host. The effect on the host is called "whooping cough." Investigate these two parasite-host relationships —especially their history, the effects on the host populations, the effects on the parasite populations, and the efforts of

man to control the relationships. Then compare the two relationships and attempt to explain any difference you find.

6. In a modern city man is the dominating organism, but he is never the only organism. Investigate the biotic community in a city, gathering evidence to support tentative answers to such questions as these: (a) To what extent is the biological energy in this community derived directly from the photosynthetic activity of its producers? (b) How does the community obtain the rest of its biological energy? (c) Which organisms in the community obtain their energy through the first source? Which organisms obtain it through the second source? (d) Which organisms are present because man is a member of the community? In what way does their existence depend upon the presence of man? (e) Which organisms are encouraged by man? Which organisms exist in spite of man's activities? (f) Which organisms would there be whether man were present or not?

## SUGGESTED READINGS

BATES, M. *The Forest and the Sea.* New York: Random House, Inc., 1960. Chapter 10. (As good a statement of the biological community as can be made in 13 pages. Rather easy, but don't glide over the important points.)

BENTON, A. H., and W. E. WERNER. *Workbook for Field Biology and Ecology.* Minneapolis, Minn.: Burgess Publishing Co., 1957. (Ideas for the design of Investigation 3.1.)

BOOLOOTIAN, R. A. *Biology of Coral Atolls.* (BSCS Pamphlet 10.) Boston: D. C. Heath & Co., 1963. (Excellent description of an ecosystem. Rather easy.)

LESHAN, E., *et al.* "Sabino Grove Ecology Study," *Natural History,* May, 1965. Pp. 14–23. (Report of a study made by high school students in California.)

ODUM, E. P. In Collaboration with HOWARD T. ODUM. *Fundamentals of Ecology.* Philadelphia: W. B. Saunders Co., 1959. Chapters 7 and 8. (A systematic consideration of possible interrelationships between species. Advanced.)

PHILLIPS, E. A. *Field Ecology.* (A BSCS Laboratory Block.) Boston: D. C. Heath & Co., 1964. (Ideas for the design of Investigation 3.1.)

SIMPSON, G. G., and W. S. BECK. *Life: An Introduction to Biology.* 2nd ed. New York: Harcourt, Brace & World, Inc., 1965. Pp. 642–663. (Illustrates how ecological terms are used in slightly different ways by different biologists. Fairly advanced.)

SWAN, L. W. "The Ecology of the High Himalayas," *Scientific American,* October, 1961. Pp. 68–78.

WOODWELL, G. M. "The Ecological Effects of Radiation," *Scientific American,* June, 1963. Pp. 40–49.

# Section Two   DIVERSITY AMONG LIVING THINGS

Every day of the week, and especially on holidays, crowds of curious people throng to zoos in all the large cities of the world. They come to watch lions and elephants, owls and eagles, snakes and turtles. Only a little less popular than zoos are aquariums, where hundreds of kinds of animals that live in water—sharks and whales, eels and starfish, crabs and clams—can be studied under more or less natural conditions. Equally fascinating to many people are botanical gardens, where living plants from all parts of the world are grown—some in the open, others in huge greenhouses.

Of course, you don't have to live near a zoo, an aquarium, or a botanical garden to learn a great deal at first hand· about many different kinds of living things. You may find it easier to visit a forest, a meadow, or a pond to see grasses, shrubs, and trees, caterpillars, beetles, and worms, songbirds and hawks, snakes and mice. Even in a backyard in the suburbs of a large city, hundreds of different kinds of plants and animals can be found.

As you observe living creatures in whatever setting you find them, you are sure, sooner or later, to get an impression of overwhelming diversity. For the casual visitor to the zoo on a Sunday afternoon, this may be only an impression and nothing more. But for one who has caught the spark of science, this impression of diversity will arouse questions.

The biologist knows of greater diversity than can be seen in any zoo. He knows that almost one and a half million species of living organisms have been described and that more are discovered every year. How can he keep track of such a tremendous assemblage? When the species of organisms far outnumber all the words in any language, how can he even find names for them all? And why are there so many kinds of living things?

These questions provide the framework for Section Two. We are not setting out to describe every kind of organism; that is, of course, impossible. But we may be able to see how the biologist keeps track of so many different species; we can look for ways to put some order into this diversity; we can look into the way in which biologists name organisms. We may even *begin* to find clues to the way in which so many different kinds of living things have appeared on the earth.

# Animals

## THE PRINCIPLES OF CLASSIFICATION

One and a half million species of living things! Almost a million of them animals! How can the biologist possibly keep track of such an enormous number of organisms?

This is not a new problem. Even in earliest times men faced it. Before the beginning of agriculture, they roamed far and wide searching for game and for edible or medicinal plants. The ability to distinguish useful kinds of organisms from those that were predatory, poisonous, or otherwise dangerous was necessary for survival. By mentally grouping organisms as "good," or useful, and "bad," or harmful, early man took the first step in solving the problem. But what about organisms that seemed neither useful nor harmful? This question probably had no meaning for the primitive mind.

Curiosity about things for their own sake, rather than for the sake of what they do *to* man or for the sake of what man can do *with* them, marked the dawn of science. By the fifth century B.C. a simple form of science had begun in the lands around the eastern end of the Mediterranean Sea. A little later Aristotle and his pupils attempted to classify all the living things they knew of—about one thousand kinds. To do this, they had to invent new ways of grouping organisms. Before this time men had recognized the groups "animal" and "plant." Under these first-level groups second-level groups were set up. Plants were divided into "trees," "shrubs," and "herbs." Animals that live in the sea were all grouped as "fish." Even today people who are not biologists find use for such groupings.

medicinal [mə dĭs′ə nəl; Latin: *medicus,* a physician]

Aristotle [ăr′ə stŏt′əl]: 384–322 B.C. Greek philosopher and naturalist. He made many investigations, but his reputation in science suffered because later men accepted his writings, not his example.

After the time of Aristotle, knowledge of living things increased rather slowly in Europe; but by the beginning of the eighteenth century A.D., about ten thousand species of organisms were known. A century later the number had risen to more than seventy thousand, and since that time the total has increased more than twenty-fold. Older systems of classification became inadequate to cope with such large numbers of organisms. During the last three centuries an elaborate system of classification has necessarily developed. And in the last hundred years an entirely new purpose has been added, making taxonomy an important specialization within the field of biology.

From these data you can construct a graph to illustrate the increase in man's knowledge of the species of organisms.

## TWO METHODS OF CLASSIFICATION

The basic idea of classification is not difficult to grasp. We all do some informal classifying, and almost anything may be classified—coins, stamps, clouds, stars, rocks, even the kinds of weather. The words in a dictionary are classified. They are classified according to their spelling—that is, alphabetically. Words in an index are classified the same way. In sorting objects rather than words, we could use the same method: we could classify them according to their names, in alphabetical order. But this is seldom done when large numbers of objects are classified.

Suppose the supermarket manager arranged his merchandise alphabetically. Refrigerators for perishable groceries would have to be scattered throughout the store. Think of the varied array of goods to be found under the letter *A*: abalone, allspice, almonds, apples, apricots, artichokes, avocados, and many more. These would be followed by bacon, baking powder, beans, beef, beets, blackberries, bread. . . . Imagine the practical difficulties in such a system! Actually, in any supermarket we find that the merchandise has been grouped according to the nature of the product. In one section we find various kinds of canned goods; in another, fresh fruits and vegetables; in a third, meats; in a fourth, dairy products. Moreover, each of these sections may be further divided. The meat section, for example, may be subdivided into sections for pork, beef, lamb, fish, and poultry—each has an assigned space. Familiarity with this system of classification enables the shopper to locate groceries easily and quickly.

Thus we can classify in either of two ways: according to likenesses in names or according to likenesses in objects themselves. In biology, names are certainly of much less importance than the characteristics of the living things themselves, so we need not consider the alphabetical method of classification any longer.

| LEVEL | DOG | WOLF | MAN | LOBSTER | DAISY | PARAMECIUM |
|---|---|---|---|---|---|---|
| Kingdom | Animalia | Animalia | Animalia | Animalia | Plantae | Protista |
| Phylum | Chordata | Chordata | Chordata | Arthropoda | Tracheophyta | Ciliophora |
| Class | Mammalia | Mammalia | Mammalia | Crustacea | Angiospermae | Ciliata |
| Order | Carnivora | Carnivora | Primates | Decapoda | Campanulales | Holotricha |
| Family | Canidae | Canidae | Hominidae | Homaridae | Compositae | Parameciidae |
| Genus | Canis | Canis | Homo | Homarus | Chrysanthemum | Paramecium |
| Species | familiaris | lupus | sapiens | americanus | leucanthemum | caudatum |

Figure 4 · 1

Classification of a few common organisms. In addition to the seven principal levels, intermediate levels are often used. For example, a *subphylum* level may be placed between phylum and class.

## A BASIS FOR BIOLOGICAL CLASSIFICATION

As we look about us at the great number of kinds of organisms, we are first impressed by the differences between them—by their *diversity*. But as we look at them more closely, we begin to see likenesses—many kinds of likenesses. What kind of likenesses shall we choose as a basis for classifying organisms?

For the sake of the present discussion, let us assume that we have already found a way to separate animals from other organisms. What kind of likenesses may we use in classifying animals?

First, we might decide to look for likenesses in color. So we lump together all the animals that are blue: bluebirds, bluejays, blue whales, bluefish, blue crabs, blue-tailed flies. Or we might pick out likenesses in the number of legs and lump together all animals with four legs: frogs, alligators, mice, goats, lions, elephants. Or we might classify animals according to where they live, lumping together animals that are found in human households: cats, dogs, canaries, mice, bedbugs, lice, fleas—an embarrassing company. These and the many other kinds of likenesses we might use have a basic disadvantage—they do not lead to a consistent *series of subdivisions*. For example, after we have grouped all blue animals together, we cannot use color for subdividing the group. We must turn to some other characteristic. At least the alphabetical system is consistent—its basis is always the order of letters in the alphabet.

structure [strŭk′chər; Latin: *struere*, to heap together, arrange]

Some organisms are very similar in structure, and others are much less similar, just as the words "comb" and "come" are more similar than the words "comb" and "cast." Thus we can first sort organisms on the basis of similarities that we consider most important. But the point we want to

X 1/30

coyote

X 1/27

wolf

X 1/18

fox

X 1/10

weasel

X 1/36

bear

Figure 4 · 2

Some common animals in the order Carnivora. Which two look most alike?

make here is that structure provides a consistent basis for classification. There is a further reason for such a basis. Taxonomists usually work with the preserved remains of dead organisms. The structure of these materials can easily be studied, but behavior or other characteristics of *living* animals or plants cannot be determined. So taxonomists have come to rely upon structural characteristics as a basis for classification.

Each sorting of known organisms gives us a new level in the system. The first sorting results in the establishment of the *kingdom* level. In the scheme of classification adopted in this book, the first sorting gives us three kingdoms, which we can call the animal kingdom, the plant kingdom, and the protist kingdom. The groups that result from the second sorting make up the *phylum* level. This sorting may result in a different number of phyla (plural of "phylum") for each kingdom. Further sortings provide *class, order, family, genus,* and *species* levels. The last level is already familiar to you.

Figure 4 · 1 shows how several familiar organisms fit into this system of classification. (Do not worry about the strange form of some of the group names. Get classification straight first; then you can tackle the problem of naming.) The only thing that *all* the organisms in the table have in common is life. As we read down through the levels, we find that the organisms included in any given group are more and more alike. At the bottom of the table, all the individuals in a species group are similar in a great many ways.

On the other hand, as we go up the table, we find an increasing diversity within groups at each level. Species with somewhat similar characteristics are put into the same genus. Dogs, coyotes, and wolves go into the genus *Canis.* The foxes make up the genus *Vulpes.* This tells us that biologists think there are more important structural similarities between wolves and coyotes than between wolves and foxes.

Similar genera (plural of "genus") are grouped together in a family. *Vulpes* goes with *Canis* in the family Canidae. Bears are put in a separate family (Ursidae), and weasels in still another (Mustelidae). These three families (Canidae, Ursidae, Mustelidae) are grouped with others into the order Carnivora. Certainly these animals have more likenesses among themselves than they have with members of other

protist [Greek: *protos*, first]: here, most primitive. See Chapter 6.

phylum [fī'ləm; Greek: *phylon*, tribe]

genus [jē'nəs; Greek: *genos*, race]

*Canis* [kā'nĭs; Latin: dog]

*Vulpes* [vŭl'pēz; Latin: fox]

Canidae [kăn'ə dē]

Ursidae [ûr'sə dē; Latin: *ursa*, a bear]

Mustelidae [mŭs tĕl'ə dē; Latin: *mustela*, weasel]

Carnivora [kär nĭv'ə rə; Latin: *carnis*, flesh, and *vorare*, to devour, eat]

Primates [prĭ mā′tēz]

Rodentia [rō děn′shĭ ə; Latin: *rodere*, to gnaw]

mammal orders, such as the Primates, to which man belongs, or the Rodentia, to which rats and mice belong. This way of reasoning can be continued up through the table; as we move to higher levels, likenesses between the members of a group decrease.

scheme [skēm; Greek: *schema*, shape]

While all biologists frame their classifications on a system of levels, there is no general agreement about the way in which organisms should be fitted into the scheme. A classification is not a fact. It results from the interpretation of facts; it shows what the facts mean to the classifier. That cats and eagles and alligators have claws is a verifiable fact. But whether or not these three kinds of organisms should therefore be grouped together and, if so, at which level —these are matters of opinion.

The more a taxonomist knows about organisms and the methods of classification, the better his opinions will be. But it can easily happen that taxonomists of equal knowledge and experience will differ greatly in their views. Therefore, even at the very top level, at the kingdom level, you can find different schemes in different books.

A four-kingdom scheme can be found in *A Guide to the Natural World*, New York: Time, Inc., 1965.

For a long time all classification schemes included only two kingdoms—plant and animal. Many biologists still classify all organisms in this way. In the past century, however, some biologists have favored three kingdoms. A three-kingdom scheme is outlined in Appendix II.

## INVESTIGATION 4.1

### THE LEVELS OF CLASSIFICATION

#### PURPOSE

In this investigation you will discover some of the structural characteristics that zoologists use in separating groups at different levels of classification. Because you will be using the observations of other persons (recorded as drawings), your conclusions can be no *more* valid than those drawings. How much *less* valid your conclusions will be depends upon your own thinking.

#### PROCEDURE

Prepare four forms like the one at the right.

Label the first form "Table 1." In the spaces under the heading "Characteris-

tics," copy the italicized words in each of the following questions. (These words should be sufficient to remind you of the full questions when you review the table.)

| Table _____ | | | |
|---|---|---|---|
| **CHARACTERISTICS** | **ANIMALS** | | |
| | 1. | 2. | 3. |
| a. | | | |
| b. | | | |
| c. | | | |
| d. | | | |
| e. | | | |
| Classification level _____ | | | |

a. How does the *length of the arms* of the animal compare with the length of its legs?

b. Is there an *opposable first toe on the foot?* (An opposable toe is one that can be pressed against all the others, as your thumb can press against your other fingers.)

c. Is the *brain case* of the skull relatively *large* or is it *small* as compared with the brain cases of the other organisms shown on the chart?

d. Are the *canine teeth* relatively *large* or are they *small* as compared with the other teeth of the same organism?

e. How many *incisor teeth* are present in the upper jaw?

Study Figure 4·3. For each of the animals, fill in the spaces in Table 1

Figure 4 · 3

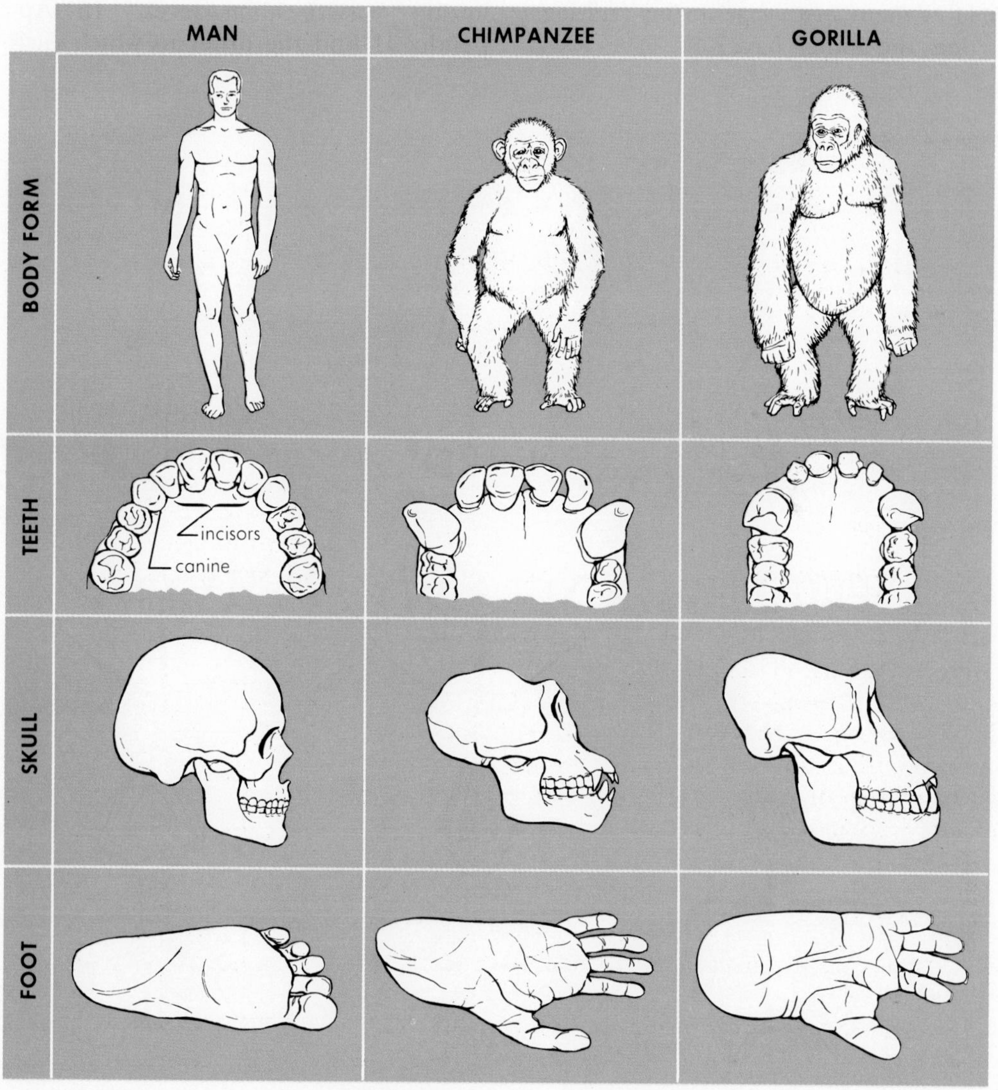

| | MAN | CHIMPANZEE | GORILLA |
|---|---|---|---|
| BODY FORM | | | |
| TEETH | incisors / canine | | |
| SKULL | | | |
| FOOT | | | |

with your answer to each question. Then write the word "Family" in the space following "Classification level." In Appendix II find the family to which each of these animals belongs. In the spaces at the bottom of the table, write the information you have found.

Now fill in the second form and label it "Table 2." In the spaces under "Animals," list "Man," "Dog," "Cat." Under the heading "Characteristics," copy the italicized words in each of the following questions:

a. How many *appendages* (arms and legs) does the animal have?

b. Are *nails* present *or* are *claws* present on the toes of the foot?

c. To what extent is the *clavicle* (collarbone) developed?

d. How does the size of the *canine teeth* compare with that of others in the lower jaw?

e. How many *incisor teeth* are present in the lower jaw?

Study Figure 4·4. For each animal fill in the spaces in Table 2 with your answers to the questions. Then write the word "Order" in the blank space following "Classification level." In Appendix II find the order to which each

Figure 4 · 4

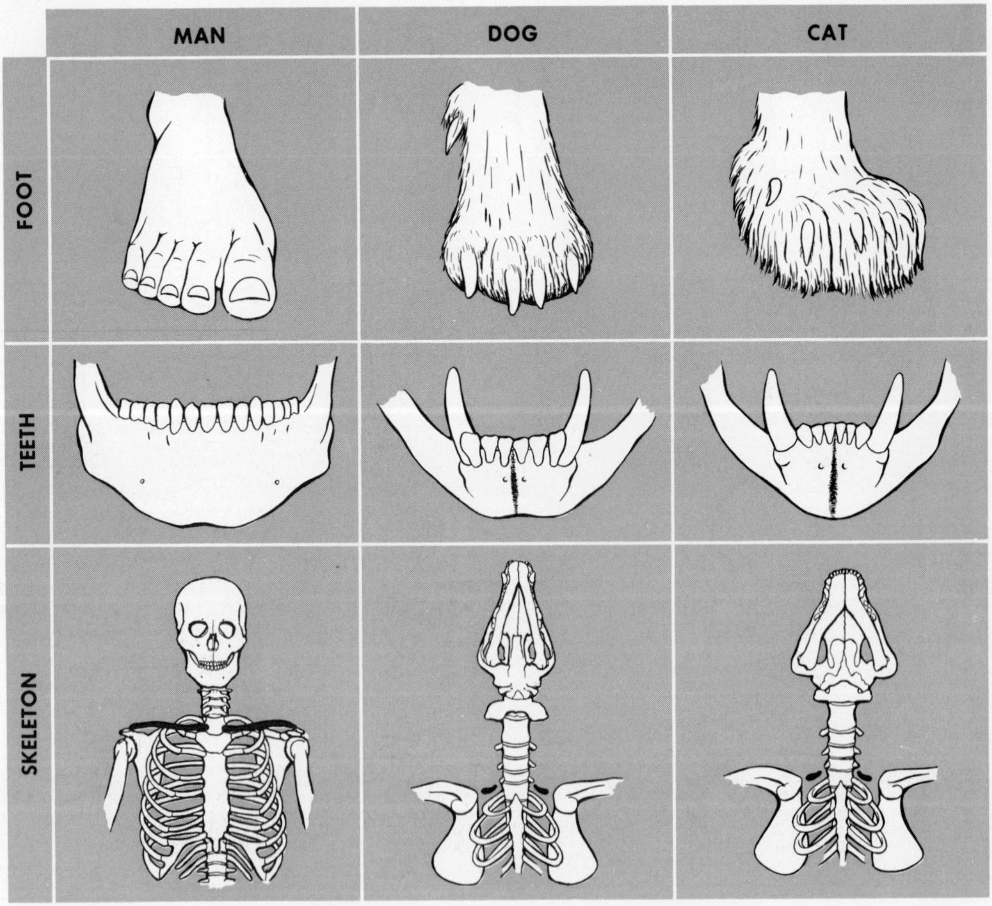

of these animals belongs. Write this information in the spaces at the bottom of the table.

Use the same procedure to fill in the other two forms.

For Table 3 use the information in Figure 4·5 and the following questions:

a. What kind of *body covering* (hair, feathers, scales, none) does the animal have?
b. How many *appendages* (arms and legs) does the animal have?
c. How many *ventricles* are present *in the heart*?
d. Do the *ears* project from the surface of the head?
e. How stable is the *body temperature*? Is it similar to the temperature of the environment, or is it quite different?

Write the word "Class" in the space following "Classification level" and add the name of the class to which each animal in Figure 4·5 belongs.

For Table 4 use the information in Figure 4·6 and the following questions:

a. What kind of *skeleton* (internal or external) does the animal have?
b. Is the *position* of the *nerve cord* along the back or along the belly?
c. Compared with the rest of the nervous system, is the *brain* large or small?
d. Are *paired appendages* present or absent?
e. Are there *grooves behind the head region* of the very young animal?

Write the word "Phylum" in the space following "Classification level" and

Figure 4 · 5

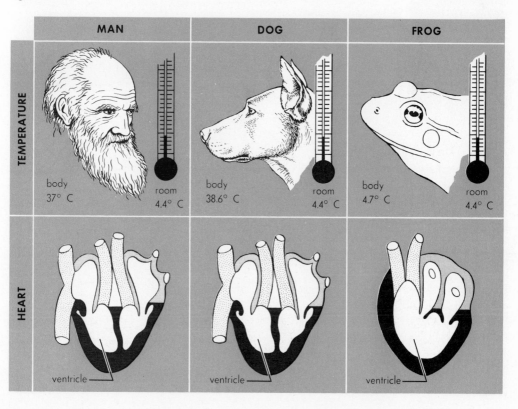

Figure 4 · 6

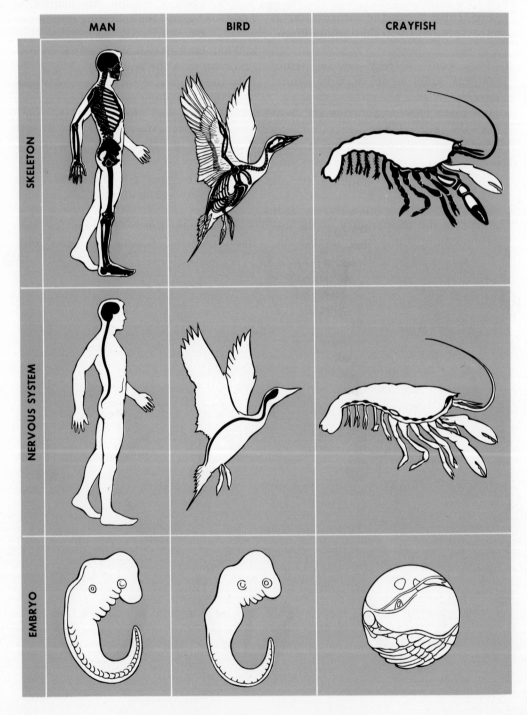

add the name of the phylum to which each animal in Figure 4·6 belongs.

## CONCLUSIONS

• How does the system of classification express the fact that there are more structural similarities:

*a.* between chimpanzee and gorilla than between chimpanzee and man?(1)

*b.* between dog and cat than between dog and man?(2)

*c.* between man and dog than between man and frog?(3)

*d.* between man and bird than between man and crayfish?(4)

*e.* between man and chimpanzee than between man and dog?(5)

• If you are told that species A and B belong to the same kingdom but different phyla and that species C and D belong to the same phylum but different classes, what general statement can you make about similarities between species A, B, C, and D?(6)

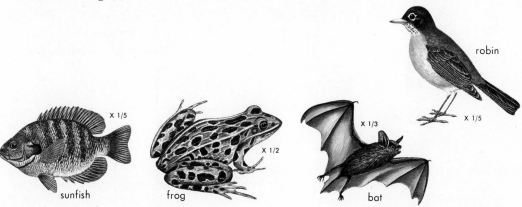

## THE ANIMAL KINGDOM

Now let us see how this scheme of classification can guide us through the diversity of animals. At this time we shall not attempt to define what we mean by "animal," that is, to explain the characteristics we use to distinguish animals from plants and protists. We shall be in a much better position to do this after we see what organisms taxonomists have grouped into the three kingdoms.

## THE CHORDATES

Let us look at a set of six selected animals: a sunfish, a frog, a bat, a robin, a rattlesnake, and a small shark. Can we unite these in one phylum? If so, we must find some structural likenesses among them. The bat and robin have wings, the shark and the sunfish have fins, the frog has legs. Perhaps we can group wings, fins, and legs as similar structures, calling them *appendages*. But on this structural basis the snake would obviously not belong to the group.

**Figure 4 · 7**

What characteristics do all these animals share?

appendage [ə pĕn′dĭj; Latin: *ad*, to, + *pendere*, to hang]

**Figure 4 · 8**

Lancelet. This animal lives partly buried in the sand of ocean shallows.

Lorus and Margery Milne

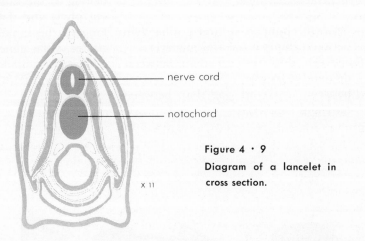

nerve cord

notochord

X 11

**Figure 4 · 9**

Diagram of a lancelet in cross section.

zoologist [zō ŏl'ə jĭst; Greek: zoion, an animal, + logos, word, speech, reason]

vertebra [vûr'tə brə; Latin: vertere, to turn]

lancelet [lăns'lĭt; Latin: lancea, a spear]

notochord [nō'tə kôrd'; Greek: noton, the back, + chorde, string of a musical instrument]

embryo [ĕm'bri ō'; Greek: en, in, + bryein, to swell]

If we sought help from a *zoologist*—a biologist specializing in the study of animals—he would point out that all these animals have similar internal skeletons. Each has a backbone made up of pieces called *vertebrae*—some separate, others fused in groups, but all making up a more or less flexible spine and enclosing a tubular nerve cord, the *spinal cord.*

Having helped this much, the zoologist might then show us a small, fishlike animal called a lancelet, stating that in his opinion it should be added to the group we already have. But close examination shows that the lancelet has no vertebrae. Instead, it has a kind of flexible rod, called a *notochord,* in nearly the same position as the backbone in the other animals. Just above this (closer to the surface of the back) is a nerve cord that seems much like the spinal cord in the other animals in our group.

Then, after a bit of dissection, the zoologist might point out a large number of paired slits located along both sides of the lancelet's body just behind its mouth. When water containing suspended particles of food is taken into the mouth, the food is retained and passed along to be digested; the water flows out through these slits. In the throat region of the lancelet *embryo,* the stage in development before hatching, a series of paired pouches grow outward, and a corresponding series of paired grooves push inward from the body surface. When the pouches and the grooves meet, paired slits are formed. Both the shark and the sunfish have similar slits. But what about the frog, bat, robin, and snake? The zoologist tells us that in the tadpole stage, such slits are present in the frog—but they disappear before the individual becomes an adult. In the case of the bat, robin, and snake, *pharyngeal* pouches and grooves are formed early in development; but they fail to meet, so no openings are ever formed. Here, then, is a new idea: To detect the basic structure of an organism, we may have to study not only its adult form but its embryonic stages as well.

pharyngeal [fə rĭn′jĭ əl; Greek: *pharyngos*, of the throat]

Turning now to Appendix II, we find that in the classification scheme used there, animals with the characteristics we have been discussing are placed in the phylum Chordata, the *chordates*. If we leaf through Appendix II, we find sixteen other animal phyla. In each phylum all the animals have one basic pattern of structure in common—just as the chordates have a basic structural pattern. But there is far less agreement among zoologists about these other phyla than there is about the chordates.

Chordata [kôr dā′tə]
chordate [kôr′dāt]

In this chapter we shall consider only nine phyla, but these will include the kinds of animals most of us are likely to meet. Appendix II includes additional phyla; this, plus the references at the end of this chapter, will guide you to further information.

While we are looking at Appendix II, we can notice that the phylum Chordata is divided into *subphyla* (see caption to Figure 4 · 1) before it reaches the class level. The lancelet is

Russ Kinne from Photo Researchers

Figure 4 · 10

Sand shark. How many pharyngeal openings does this chordate have?

Cephalochordata [sĕ f'ə lō kôr-
dā'tə; Greek: kephale, the
head, + chorde]

vertebrate [vûr'tə brāt']

placed in one of these—Cephalochordata; all the other
animals we were discussing are placed in the subphylum
Vertebrata. This last subphylum, the *vertebrates*, contains
most of the more familiar animals—animals that have backbones of vertebrae. So let us look at the diversity of animals
within this group.

**Mammals.** At present all zoologists probably agree on
which animals should be called mammals. From a tiny field
mouse to a giant blue whale more than 30 meters long (the
largest animal that has ever lived), all mammals share two
characteristics. First, all have hair, although it is sometimes
not very evident and, in some whales, is completely absent
after birth. Second, all species of mammals feed their

Figure 4 · 11

Diversity among mammals.

Aardvark  x 1/25  New York Zoological Society

Pangolin  x 1/10  New York Zoological Society

Gerenuk  x 1/25  John H. Tashjian

Marmot  x 1/12  David Muench

Dolphin  x 1/35  Marineland of Florida

young with milk, a fluid secreted from special glands in the skin called *mammary* glands. These glands function only in females, but they are present in males as well. From "mammary" comes the name "mammal." Hair and mammary glands, and some less obvious characteristics of the skeleton, separate mammals from all other groups of animals.

In addition to these distinctive characteristics, others are often useful to the taxonomist. The hearts of all adult mammals have two *ventricles*—muscular, thick-walled pumping chambers. And mammals are usually "*warm-blooded*"—able to maintain their bodies at a specific temperature regardless of that of the environment. These two characteristics are shared with birds. Further, *most* mammals have a means of nourishing the young within the body of the mother during the early stages of development. The exception involves only two genera, in which the young hatch from eggs laid by the female (see *Monotremata* in Appendix II).

Although they have many characteristics in common, mammals show great diversity. The mammalian structural pattern is found in a giraffe galloping in East Africa, in a seal swimming in the cold water off Greenland, in a bat swooping upon insects over an Ohio lake, in the student reading this paragraph.

The modifications of form that enable an organism to function in a particular niche in the ecosystem are called *structural adaptations*. For example, mammalian hair may be greatly modified—it appears as quills in porcupines; as horns in rhinoceroses; as odd, flattened plates in pangolins; as wool in sheep. We know that these are adaptations of hair from studies of the way in which the structures are formed during embryonic development of the organisms.

**Birds.** All birds have feathers, and all chordates with feathers are birds. No other major group of animals is quite so easy to characterize. All birds have wings, too, though in the kiwi of New Zealand, they are small and hidden in the body. But animals in other groups have wings, so this is not a completely distinctive characteristic.

Many structural adaptations are found in both feathers and wings. Feathers form the soft down of geese and ducks, the long ornamental plumes of ostriches, and the broad, strong flight feathers of eagles. Wings vary from the short, broad ones of chickens—which seldom fly, and then only for short distances—to the long, slim ones of albatrosses—which spend almost all their lives gliding on air currents. And in penguins wings have been modified into flippers, and feathers into a soft, waterproof covering.

spoonb...

X 1/2

crossbill

X 1/5

eagle

X 1/6

X 1/3

robin

pelican

X 1/6

Figure 4 · 12

Diversity in the beaks of birds. How is the structure of each beak adapted to the bird's way of life?

ventricle [věn′trǝ kǝl]:  See Figure 4 · 5.

porcupine [Latin: *porcus*, pig, + *spina*, spine, thorn]: In Appendix II, see Figure A · 179.

rhinoceros [rī nä̌s′ǝ rǝs; Greek: *rhinos*, nose, + *keras*, horn]: See Figure A · 189.

ostrich: See Figure 8 · 35.

albatross [ăl′bǝ tròs′]:  See Figure A · 162.

Figure 4 · 13
Diversity of color and body
form among birds.

quetzal          X 1/5

man-of-war
X 1/3

X 1/10

flamingo

X 1/3

Steller's jay

penguin

X 1/10

Yet diversity among birds is not so striking as it is among mammals. The difference between a hummingbird and a penguin is great, but hardly as startling as that between a bat and a whale. Perhaps birds show the greatest diversity in the forms of their beaks and feet. Diversity in color is also striking. It is variation in details rather than in basic patterns that has been important in the adaptation of birds to many kinds of ecosystems.

New Zealand Government Travel Commission

Figure 4 · 14

Kiwi, a flightless bird native to New Zealand.   x 1/12

**Reptiles.**   Turtles, snakes, lizards, alligators—all these are reptiles. But it is rather difficult to see just what the taxonomist means by a reptile. Reptiles have no obvious characteristics that immediately separate them from other vertebrates. They have skin outgrowths called scales (basically unlike the scales of fish), but so do birds and some mammals. They breathe by means of lungs all their lives; so do birds and mammals. Though their hearts, like those of mammals and birds, have two ventricles, in most species there is an opening in the wall between them. Their body temperatures vary with the environmental temperature —that is, like amphibians and fish, they are "*cold-blooded.*"

reptile [Latin: repere, to creep]

By using a combination of these characteristics, we can obtain some idea of the reptile class without resorting to a study of skeletal characteristics, which taxonomists find very useful.

**Tortoise**    x 1/12       Roy Pinney from Photo Library

Figure 4 · 15

Diversity among reptiles.

**Skink**    x 1/6      Hal Harrison from Grant Heilman

**Southern ribbon snake**    x 1/4
Leonard Lee Rue from Annan Photo Features

**Chameleon**    x 1/3                John H. Tashjian

tortoise [tôrt'əs]

agile [ăj'əl; Latin: agere, to move]: quick and nimble

alligator: See Figure A · 160.

chameleon [kə mēl'yən; Greek: chamai, on the ground, + leon, lion]

amphibian [ăm fĭb'ē ən; Greek: amphi, both, + bios, life]

None of the reptiles living today can really fly, though a lizard of the East Indies can glide by means of membranes stretched between its front and hind legs. On land and in the waters of warmer parts of the world, however, reptiles show great diversity. Contrast the slow and heavily armored tortoises with the slim and agile skinks. Or compare the alligator, crawling through the mud, with the African chameleon, far out on a limb in a tall tree, grasping a twig with its tail. And most extreme in structural adaptation are snakes, some of which are adapted to burrowing, some to climbing, and some to swimming—all without appendages.

**Amphibians.** For a long time amphibians were confused with reptiles—some amphibians are indeed shaped like some lizards. There are, however, differences between the two groups. Unlike most reptiles, very few amphibians have either claws or scales. The amphibian heart has only one ventricle. Further, the eggs of amphibians never have shells, so they must be laid in water—or in places where moisture is available. Young amphibians, such as the tadpoles of our common frogs and toads, may live in the water, but almost all adult amphibians are air-breathers. Most have lungs, but all can breathe through the moist surfaces of their skins. The common kinds of frogs will quickly die if their skins dry out, but they cannot be easily drowned.

Although the amphibian class is rather small in number of species, it shows considerable diversity. Some amphibians climb in trees by means of pads on the toes—structural adaptations that act like suction cups. On the other hand, many burrow in the loose upper layer of the soil or under rocks and dead logs. A few have no appendages—an adaptation that favors burrowing.

How might lack of appendages favor burrowing?

**Fishes.** Most people know more about catching or eating fish than about classifying them, so it may be surprising to learn that living fishes are distributed among three classes instead of being in one (see Appendix II). This means that taxonomists think the differences between a minnow (Osteichthyes) and a shark (Chondrichthyes) are just as important as those between a snake (Reptilia) and a rabbit (Mammalia).

Osteichthyes [ŏs' tē ĭk'thĭ ēz; Greek: osteon, a bone, + ichthyes, fish]

Chondrichthyes [kŏn drĭk'thĭ- ēz; Greek: chondros, cartilage, + ichthyes]

A fish, like an amphibian, has a heart with but one ventricle and is "cold-blooded." Unlike animals in the other classes we have been discussing, almost all fishes, both young and adult, obtain their oxygen supply only through gills. Notable exceptions are the lungfishes. They have a kind of air sac that they use to breathe air when oxygen becomes scarce in the muddy ponds where they live.

Almost all fishes you are likely to know, especially if you do not live near the ocean, are "bony fishes" (Osteichthyes).

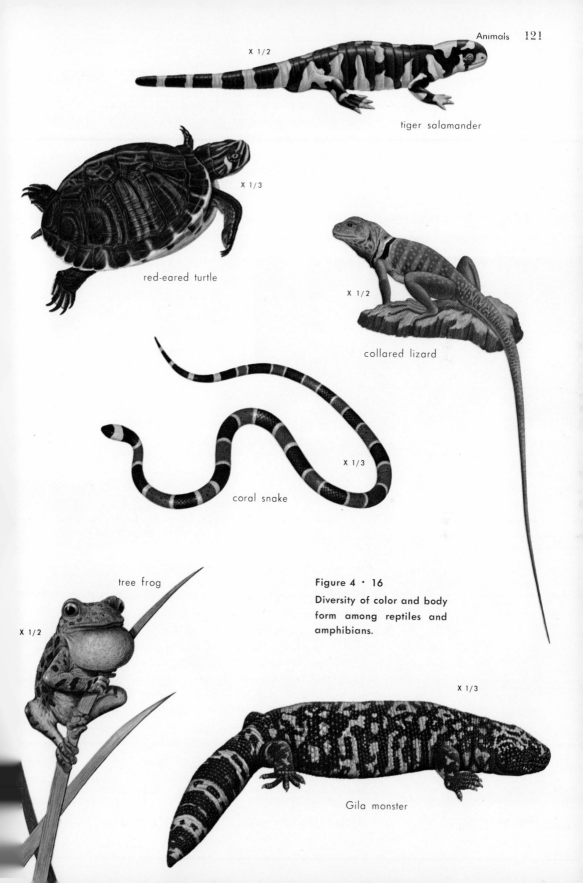

X 1/2

tiger salamander

X 1/3

red-eared turtle

X 1/2

collared lizard

X 1/3

coral snake

tree frog

X 1/2

Figure 4 · 16
Diversity of color and body
form among reptiles and
amphibians.

X 1/3

Gila monster

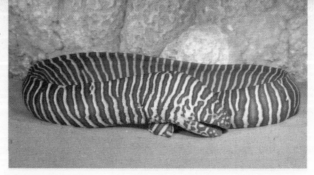

**Moray eel**    x 1/7

All four photographs, John H. Tashjian for Steinhart Aquarium

Figure 4 · 17
Diversity of color and body
form among bony fishes.

**Turkey fish**    x 4/5

**Blue parrot fish**

**Sea horses**    x 1

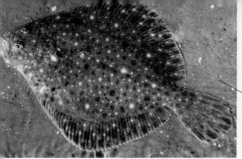

A  **Flounder** x 1/5

B  **Stingray** x 1/8

**Figure 4 · 18**

Species from three verte-
brate classes. (A) A bony
fish that lies on sandy bottoms; note that both eyes
are on the left side of the
body. (B) A cartilaginous
fish that uses its broad fins
somewhat like wings. (C) An
agnathan attacking a trout
(a bony fish). The trout died
in fourteen hours.

C  **Lamprey** x 1/5

This simply means that these vertebrates have skeletons
made of the hard substance we call bone. In number of
species the Osteichthyes are the largest class among the
vertebrates. They display an amazing diversity of form.
There are tiny guppies in aquariums and minnows in
brooks—and, in the open ocean, there are tuna several
hundred times as long as these. There are round, thin sunfish and there are long, slim eels. There are flying fish,
which can glide through the air on expanded fins, and
toadfish, which lie half-buried in the muddy bottom of a
bay. There are trout in cold, freshwater brooks and parrot
fish in warm, salty lagoons. The bony fishes have invaded
almost all the waters on earth, from the sea with its great
depths to small ponds and underground streams.

How does the shape of a fish
relate to the manner in which
it swims? What structural adaptations do bottom-living fish
have? You may be able to answer these questions by carefully observing fish in an
aquarium.

Almost everyone knows something *about* sharks, but
not many people know sharks at first hand—or wish to,
perhaps. At first glance a shark seems to be as much a fish
as a trout is. However, some basic structural differences
have led biologists to place sharks in a separate class, Chondrichthyes. First, sharks have skeletons made up of *cartilage* rather than bone. Cartilage is the substance that gives
shape to your ears and nose; it is stiff enough to give support, but it is more flexible than bone. Second, the cartilaginous fishes have gill systems that differ from those of the
bony fishes. Besides the sharks, the class contains the rays,
which have oddly flattened bodies that seem to be an adaptation for feeding on the bottom of the sea.

cartilage [kärt'əl ij, kärt'lij]

cartilaginous [kär'tə lăj'ə nəs]

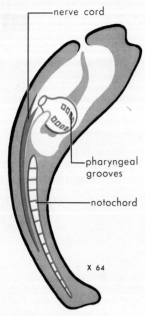

nerve cord

pharyngeal
grooves

notochord

X 64

**Figure 4 · 19**

**Diagram of tunicate larva.**

lamprey [lăm′prē; Latin: *lam-
bere*, to lick, + *petra*, rock (so
called because many cling to
rocks with their mouths)]

tunicate [tŭ′nə kĭt, tŭ′nə-
kăt′; Latin: *tunica*, a Roman
outer garment]

larva [lär′və; Latin: *larva*,
ghost (because the appearance
is very different from that of
the adult)]

Ward's Natural Science Establishment
**Figure 4 · 20**

**Adult tunicate.**    X 2/5

**Figure 4 · 21**

Comparison of arthropod
and chordate structure.

During the last twenty years the fish population of the Great Lakes has been greatly reduced by a slimy, eel-shaped creature that originally came into the lakes from the Atlantic Ocean. An example of the class Agnatha, it is called a lamprey. A lamprey attaches itself to a fish, rasps a hole in the body, and sucks out the body fluids, usually killing its victim. The great increase of lampreys in the Great Lakes has attracted attention, but there are a number of seldom-seen Agnatha, all feeding by suction. This method of feeding is necessary because—unlike other vertebrates—the Agnatha have no jaws.

**Chordates without vertebrae.** So far we have been considering animals with backbones—vertebrates. Reference to Appendix II (a habit that should be well developed by this time) will show that there are other groups (subphyla) in the phylum Chordata. The lancelet, which we briefly discussed earlier in this chapter, is placed in one of these groups. Like the vertebrates, each of these animals has, at some stage in its development, pharyngeal pouches, a notochord, and a tubular nerve cord above the notochord.

All of these non-vertebrate chordates live in the ocean. People who live along the seacoast sometimes notice them, though most are rather inconspicuous. The tunicates are likely to draw attention, for many species are abundant on pilings and other firm underwater surfaces. The adults, permanently attached to a sunken boat or an oyster shell, do not appear to be chordates at all. But the *larvae* (the very young) swim around like miniature tadpoles and clearly show the three chordate characteristics.

### THE ARTHROPODS

Lobsters and bedbugs, spiders and houseflies, grasshoppers and scorpions—all these are usually classified as arthropods. What combination of characteristics do these animals have in common?

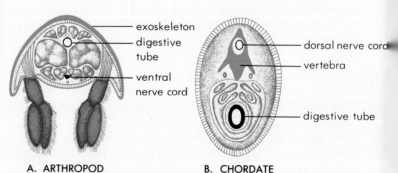

exoskeleton
digestive
tube
ventral
nerve cord

dorsal nerve cord
vertebra
digestive tube

A. ARTHROPOD                    B. CHORDATE

Figure 4 · 22
Diversity of form among
arthropods.

John H. Tashjian

**Praying mantis** x 4/5

**Woolly aphids** x 4 Hugh Spencer

**Silverfish** x 3 Lester Brubaker

**Scorpion** x 1 Paul Knipping

**"Sow bug"** x 4 William H. Amos

**Horseshoe "crab"** x 1/6 American Museum of Natural History

**Swallowtail butterfly**   x 1/2

Herbert Lanks from Black Star

John H. Tashjian

**Garden spider on its web**   x 1

Roy Pinney from Photo Library

**Figure 4 · 23**
Diversity of color among arthropods.

M. Woodbridge Williams

**Millepede**   x 4

Charles E. Lane

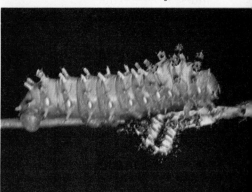

**Larva (caterpillar) of Cecropia moth**   x 1

Thompson from FPG

**Centipede**   x 1

**Fiddler crabs, male (large claw) and female**   x 1

The easiest way to understand basic arthropod structure is to compare it with basic chordate structure, which we already know. From an arthropod's point of view, a chordate is upside down. The arthropod's main nerve cord is close to its *ventral* body surface—the surface that is usually toward the pull of gravity. In chordates the main nerve is close to the *dorsal* surface—the surface that is usually away from the pull of gravity. Moreover, the chordate nerve cord is a hollow tube; the arthropod nerve cord is solid and often double. We might also say, again from the arthropod's point of view, that chordates are inside out. In arthropods the skeleton is outside the muscles—an *exoskeleton.* In chordates the skeleton is inside the muscles—an *endoskeleton.* Further, the body of an arthropod is usually made up of a series of more or less similar *segments*, or sections, to which jointed appendages of various kinds—legs, paddles, mouthparts, antennae—are usually attached. Segments can be detected in the bodies of young chordates, but they are not associated with appendages.

Although they are constructed on a pattern very unfamiliar to us (who are chordates), arthropods are at least as widespread in the world as chordates. This means that arthropod structure has been adaptable to many kinds of environments.

**Insects.** Most people are more interested in vertebrates than in insects; yet in any place you may mention, insects are usually much more abundant. A picnic almost always provides proof of this.

Anyone can find hundreds of species in or around his home if he looks for small insects as well as large and showy ones. Within a house—from roof to cellar—may be found flies, ants, carpet beetles, silverfish, and moths, not to mention the unpleasant possibility of bedbugs, fleas, or lice. Many insects live close to man—some very close indeed! Grass, flowers, and trees provide living places for many more species of insects. On the plants, in the soil that supports them, and flying in the air about them, are found grasshoppers, aphids, scale insects, beetles, butterflies, bees, wasps, and many more. If fresh water is available (ponds, streams, or even a little water collected in a tin can), many immature forms of such insects as dragonflies, mayflies, mosquitoes, and caddis flies may be found. Insects walk, fly, burrow, and swim. Of all the major habitats on earth, only the oceans, which support so much other life, are almost completely lacking insects.

Besides having all the arthropod characteristics, insects have characteristics of their own. An insect's body is divided into three regions: a *head,* bearing a pair of *antennae,*

arthropod [är'thrə päd'; Greek: *arthron,* a joint, + *pous,* foot]

ventral [Latin: *venter,* belly]

dorsal [Latin: *dorsum,* the back]

exoskeleton [ĕk'sō skĕl'ət ən; Greek: exo-, outside]

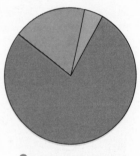

● INSECT ARTHROPODS
◕ NONINSECT ARTHROPODS
● NONARTHROPODS

Figure 4 · 24
Relative numbers of living animal species.

Dr. Frank Lutz, of the American Museum of Natural History, wrote a book (*A Lot of Insects*) about the 1402 species he found on a suburban lot in New Jersey. How many can you find?

For illustrations of insects, see Figures 4 · 22, 4 · 23, 4 · 25, 4 · 26, 9 · 5, and A · 128 through A · 142.

antenna [ăn tĕn'ə]

thorax [Greek: the chest]

abdomen [ăb'də mən]

"feelers"; a middle part, the *thorax*, bearing three pairs of legs; and a rear section, the *abdomen*, which is usually clearly segmented. In most adult insects one or two pairs of wings are attached to the thorax. Some insects, such as fleas, aphids, and silverfish, never develop wings.

Although only the more common insects have been mentioned, many of the names may be unfamiliar. The illustrations on these pages and in Appendix II will help you to visualize the diversity of insects. And what diversity! Figures 4 · 25 and 4 · 26 show various structural adaptations in wings and mouthparts. By studying the illustrations, you should be able to detect some clues about the niches occupied by these insects.

**Arachnids.** Although not as numerous in species as the insects, arachnids are often abundant as individuals. In Appendix II find and note the characteristics of the Arachnida.

arachnid [ə răk'nəd; Greek: *arachne*, a spider]

Arachnida [ə răk'nəd ə]

Spiders are the most familiar arachnids. Housewives are often unhappy about them, and wanderers through the woods sometimes blunder into their sticky webs. Yet the web-building activity of spiders is fascinating—even to persons who dislike the builders. The garden spider's web is a striking example of design. Many spiders, however, construct irregular webs, and some, such as the wolf spiders, make no webs at all.

All spiders have poison glands, used in capturing and killing their prey, but only a few (the black widow and brown recluse, in the United States) are dangerous to man.

Figure 4 · 25

Diversity of wing structure among insects. How do the forms of these wings relate to the ways in which the various species fly?

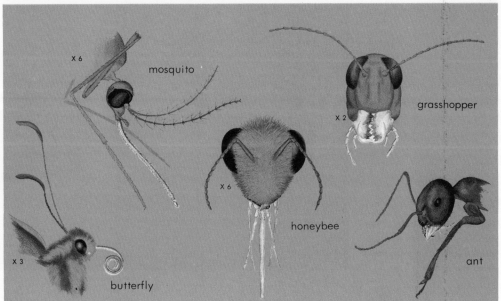

Figure 4 · 26
Diversity of mouth structure among insects. How do these structures relate to the ways in which the various species feed?

Scorpions, which are fairly common arachnids in the Southwest, are also poisonous. Two or three of our native species are really dangerous, particularly to young children.

Some less familiar arachnids are actually much more dangerous than spiders and scorpions—mites, for example. In the United States they merely cause irritating skin rashes. But in parts of the Far East and in the South Pacific region, certain species of mites carry the microorganisms of scrub typhus, a serious disease. Ticks, better known than mites because they are larger, not only annoy our dogs—they may pass to us microorganisms of spotted fever, which is sometimes fatal.

One of the most unusual living arachnids is the horseshoe "crab," a marine animal common along the eastern coast of the United States. It is well adapted to the muddy and sandy bottoms of shallow waters. Such habitats have been available on earth for a long time, and this arachnid has changed only slightly in two hundred million years! Some zoologists do not consider it an arachnid and place it in a separate class.

**Millepedes and centipedes.** Both centipedes and millepedes are elongated, conspicuously segmented animals with large numbers of paired legs. Although at first glance they appear much alike, closer study shows fundamental differences between the two groups. A centipede ("hundred legger") is flattened and has a pair of long antennae, a pair of poison glands behind the head, and one pair of rather long, jointed legs attached to each body segment. A millepede ("thousand legger"), by contrast, is round in cross

centipede [sĕnt′ə pēd′; Latin: *centum*, hundred, + *pedes*, feet]
millepede [mĭl′ə pēd′; Latin: *mille*, thousand, + *pedes*]

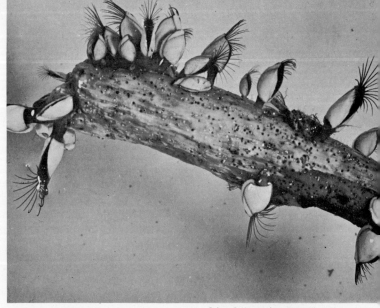

**Figure 4 · 27**
Gooseneck barnacles. The feathery structures are appendages that gather food from the water. x 1/3

How might other zoologists support a classification that placed centipedes and millepedes in a single class?

These crabs breathe by gills. What adaptations might allow them to live on land?

section and usually curls into a ring when disturbed. Its antennae are short, and it has no poison glands. Each of its body segments bears two pairs of short legs.

These differences in structure are adaptations to entirely different ways of life. Centipedes are second- or higher-order consumers — predators that use their long legs to pursue prey (mostly insects) and their poison to kill. Millepedes are saprovores that eat dead plant materials, such as leaves on the forest floor. To most zoologists, these differences in structure and behavior are just as important as those that separate insects from arachnids, so they place centipedes and millepedes in separate classes.

**Crustaceans.** Most people know at least a few of the more than twenty-five thousand different species of crustaceans, especially the kinds that are good to eat — lobsters, crabs, and shrimps. But most crustaceans are small — almost microscopic — animals. In ecosystems of ponds and lakes and especially of the oceans, teeming multitudes of these animals are the principal first-order consumers. They, in turn, form the basic food supply for animals ranging from tiny fish to some of the giant whales.

Just as some species of mammals — a primarily terrestrial group — have adapted to life in the ocean, so a number of crustaceans — a primarily aquatic group — have adapted to a terrestrial life. In the humid tropics of the Pacific, certain large crabs live most of their lives on land, climbing coconut palm trees and breaking open the coconuts with their stout claws. They do, however, return to the sea to lay their eggs. In the United States the "sow bugs" are crustaceans that lead an entirely terrestrial existence. They are small, grayish creatures that often roll up into balls when disturbed. Although they may be found far from water, they live in damp places.

Barnacles are so unlike other crustaceans that they were once classified with the mollusks. Although the larvae are free-swimming, they soon settle down and become permanently attached to some solid surface in the ocean—a wharf piling, the bottom of a boat, or even the back of some animal, such as a sea turtle. There each one develops a limy skeletal cup, into which it seals itself tightly at every low tide.

barnacle [bär'nĭ kəl]

mollusk [mäl'əsk; Latin: *mollis*, soft]

## ANNELIDS, OR SEGMENTED WORMS

Both the biological and the common names of this phylum refer to a conspicuous feature of the animals included in it. The annelid body consists of a series of similar segments. We have already seen segmentation in the arthropods, but in annelids it is developed much further: each external groove marks the location of an internal partition, so that the worm consists of a series of compartments that are more or less similar.

Many of the internal body organs are repeated in one compartment after another. Running through the center of each partition from front to back is a food tube, in which digestion takes place. The annelids usually have appendages, but these are not jointed as in the arthropods. The annelid nerve cord is ventral in position, solid, and often paired—just as in the arthropods. It is difficult to escape the impression that annelids and arthropods are more alike than arthropods and chordates.

The majority of annelids are aquatic. Some marine species reach a length of nearly a meter; swimming around on the surface of the sea, annelids like this may have given rise to stories of sea serpents. But many marine annelids burrow in the sand or mud. From these hiding places they reach out and seize small passing animals with their sharp

marine [mə rēn'; Latin: *mare*, the sea]

Figure 4 · 28

Sandworm, a type of marine annelid.    x 1

Hugh Spencer

jaws. Some burrowing forms have beautifully colored, feathery gills, the only part visible to passing prey.

All this is in sharp contrast to the best-known annelids, the earthworms. Earthworms are one of the extremes of diversity among annelids. Their appendages are merely small bristles. They have no gills; they absorb oxygen from air spaces in the soil through their moist skin. They have no jaws. They produce a slimy substance that helps to smooth their way through the soil. All in all, earthworms show many adaptations to their life in the soil.

Leeches illustrate another extreme of annelid diversity. All live in the same manner as the ones we encountered in Chapter 3 (page 74). They have the usual annelid segmentation, but they have no appendages and their bodies are flat. An obvious structural adaptation of a leech is a pair of suction disks, one at each end, with which it clings to its host.

## MOLLUSKS

Half-buried in reefs of the South Pacific live giant clams, over a meter in diameter and weighing as much as

Hugh Spencer

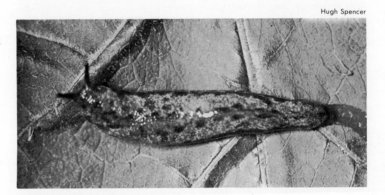

**Figure 4 · 29**
Slug, a terrestrial mollusk that lacks a shell.   x 1

Douglas P. Wilson

**Figure 4 · 30**
Octopus, a marine mollusk that lacks a shell.   x 1/12

Figure 4 · 31
Starfish from beneath. x 1/3

Russ Kinne from Photo Researchers

Russ Kinne from Photo Researchers

Figure 4 · 32
Sea cucumber. x 1/3

300 kilograms (abbreviated 300 kg). In the South Atlantic are giant squids up to 20 meters in length. Both of these animals certainly are quite different from the snails living in your laboratory aquarium. All three, however, are representatives of the great phylum Mollusca, second only to the Arthropoda in number of known species.

Mollusks are not segmented. But like members of other phyla we have discussed, a mollusk has a nervous system, a heart that pumps blood, and a tubular digestive system—an *alimentary canal.* In addition, a mollusk has an organ that, in most species, secretes a hard shell.

Within this structural pattern mollusks show great diversity. Some mollusks are single-shelled, some have shells in two sections, some have many-jointed shells, and some lack shells. Some glide over solid surfaces, others inch their way laboriously through sand or mud, while still others use jets of water for propulsion. Rasping small plants off rocks is a common method of feeding among mollusks. Clams and oysters filter food particles from the water as it passes over their gills. An octopus pounces on its prey, holds it with tentacles, and tears it to pieces with sharp jaws.

Although most mollusks are aquatic, many snails live completely terrestrial lives. Their coiled shells, into which they may retreat, enable them to withstand dry periods; and they have lunglike cavities in their bodies that enable them to get oxygen from the air.

### ECHINODERMS

In all the phyla considered so far, each animal (except for some mollusks) has a "front end," that is, an end of the body that usually points in the direction of movement—an *anterior* end. The opposite end—the end that usually trails along behind—is the *posterior* end. If we divide such an animal as shown in Figure 4·33, we have right and left sides that are very much alike. This kind of body design is called *bilateral symmetry.*

squid [skwĭd′]: See Figure 9·22.

Mollusca [mə lŭs′kə]

alimentary [Latin: *alere,* to nourish]

Figure 4 · 33
Bilateral symmetry.

echinoderm [ĭ kī′nə dərm′; Greek: *echinos,* hedgehog (a spiny-skinned animal), + *derma,* skin]

anterior [ăn tîr′ē ər; Latin: *ante,* before]
posterior [päs tîr′ē ər; Latin: *post,* behind]
bilateral symmetry [bī lăt′ər əl sĭm′ə trĭ; Latin: *bis,* twice, doubly, + *latus,* a side; Greek: *syn,* together, + *metron,* a measure]

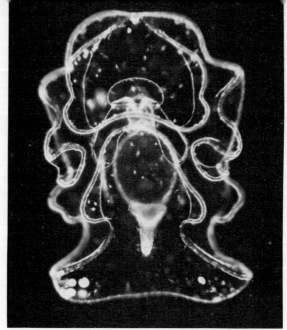

**Figure 4 · 34**
Larva of an echinoderm.
x 150

Douglas P. Wilson

radial [Latin: *radius*, a rod, spoke (of a wheel)]

crinoids [krī′noidz, krĭn′oidz; Greek: *krinon*, lily, + *eidos*, like]: See sea lily, Figure A · 143.

Beowulf [bā′ə woolf′]

In echinoderms the body has a different kind of symmetry. A starfish is a well-known echinoderm, and it shows this symmetry well (Figure 4 · 31). We immediately see that a starfish has no anterior and posterior ends and no definite left and right sides. There are many ways that you could cut through a starfish and get approximately equal halves. This body design is termed *radial symmetry* because the parts radiate from a center as spokes radiate from the hub of a wheel. Oddly enough, however, the larvae of starfish are bilaterally symmetrical and somewhat resemble the larvae of some of the non-vertebrate chordates.

Just beneath its skin, an adult starfish has a hard skeleton with many little bumps and projections. In many echinoderms these are long spines, but in sea cucumbers the skeleton is reduced to a few small, hard particles in the leathery skin.

No echinoderms are found on land or in fresh waters. But echinoderms live in every part of the marine environment, from shallow shores to the greatest depths. We find the delicate sea lilies (crinoids) and the brittle stars in the still, dark waters far beneath the surface; we find the sea cucumbers plowing through muddy bottoms of both deep and shallow waters; and we find sea urchins, with their long spines, on reefs and rocky coasts. Structural adaptations should not be difficult to discover here.

### SOME PHYLA OF "WORMS"

In Old English "worm" meant any creeping or crawling animal. The hero Beowulf fought a "great worm," which

does not sound so heroic to modern ears until it is trans-
lated more accurately as "dragon." Today the word implies
something rather small and lowly. In ordinary language it
is applied quite carelessly to many very different animals.
In biology, also, "worm" has no clear-cut meaning, but,
with various adjectives, it is used to refer to various groups
of animals.

**Rotifers.**    Also called "wheel worms," these tiny animals are likely to be among the first organisms a curious
student equipped with a microscope will find. They are
bilaterally symmetrical, with tufts of tiny, hairlike structures
(*cilia*) at the anterior end. These cilia beat so rapidly that
early observers thought they were structures rotating like
wheels—hence the name of the group. Rotifers are not
segmented, though they often have some external divisions
that resemble segments. Their body plan differs from the
body plans of all other phyla we have met thus far in that it
lacks a *circulatory system*—that is, rotifers have no hearts, no
veins, not even anything we could call blood.

There are no really terrestrial rotifers, but the many
species show adaptations to different kinds of water life.
Some even inhabit the drops of water that collect among
the leaves of mosses. This water may not last long, but
before it dries, the rotifers produce eggs with thick shells
that resist evaporation. These survive until the next rain
wets the moss again. Only a few kinds of rotifers live in the
sea. Some rotifers remain attached to solid objects in the
water and use their cilia to wash food particles into their
mouths. Others use their cilia both for feeding and for
swimming.

**Roundworms.**    Many kinds of wormlike animals are
round in cross section, but this is the only group distinguished as "roundworms" (written as one word). Roundworms are slender and bilaterally symmetrical. They vary
from about 0.5 mm to more than 1 m in length, though
most are nearer the first extreme. Like the rotifers, they
have no circulatory system, but they have a fluid that is
squeezed about in their bodies as they wriggle.

X 125

Figure 4 · 35
A rotifer, or "wheel worm."

rotifers [rō′tĭ fərz; Latin: *rota*,
a wheel, + *ferre*, to bear]

cilia [sĭl′ĭ ə; Latin: *cilium*, eyelid, eyelash]

circulatory [sûr′kyə lə tôr′ĭ]

Ward's Natural Science Establishment

Figure 4 · 36
*Trichinella*, a roundworm
parasite of pig and man.
This photomicrograph shows
larvae in the muscle of a
host.    x 20

Figure 4 · 37
Hookworm, a roundworm
that uses its hooks to attach
itself to the intestinal lining
of a dog or cat.    x 8

Ward's Natural Science Establishment

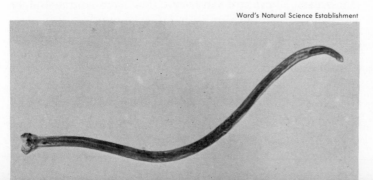

Figure 4 · 38
A marine flatworm.    x 3

William H. Amos

Roundworms are very abundant in soil. Many species are saprovores, but some of these may become parasites, especially on plant roots. Many more species are always parasitic. About thirty species have been found in man. Finding a host is a hazardous business for a parasite, and one of the most common roundworm adaptations is an enormous development of the egg-producing organs. A species that sometimes lives in the intestine of man may lay two hundred thousand eggs a day!

nematodes    [něm′ə tōdz′;
Greek: nema, thread, + eidos,
like]

In Appendix II roundworms (nematodes), rotifers, and four other groups are listed as classes in one phylum. Many zoologists place each group in a separate phylum.

**Flatworms.** One of the main characteristics of the body plan in this phylum is indicated by the name, but this is not sufficient to distinguish the phylum. Flatworms have no circulatory system; in fact, they do not even have any space within their bodies for a fluid. They differ from all the phyla we have discussed so far in having no digestive tube. The "mouth" of a flatworm opens into a kind of sack, and undigested food particles leave by the same opening through which food entered.

There are free-living flatworms in fresh water and in the ocean. There are flatworms that have commensal or mutualistic relationships with other organisms. But most flatworms are parasitic. Some species have a striking adaptation to the parasitic life: living inside the digestive systems of other animals, they completely lack digestive systems of their own. Tapeworms are an example. They simply absorb the digested food that surrounds them and never really "eat" in the sense that most animals do.

## COELENTERATES

coelenterates    [sĭ lĕn′tə rāts′;
Greek: *koilos*, hollow, + *enteron*, intestine]

An actively growing coral reef, fringing an island in the
South Pacific, is a habitat where the water is usually clear
and always warm. The uniformity of the abiotic factors in
this environment contrasts sharply with the diversity of the
animals living in it. Brightly colored fish swim through the
waters; annelids, snails, starfish, sea urchins, crustaceans in
great variety of form and color, crawl or slither or creep
about. But the reef itself is fashioned by still other organisms—for the most part, by corals, which taxonomists place
in a phylum we have not yet examined, the coelenterates.

The body of a coelenterate is little more than a bag, and
digestion occurs in the central cavity. Food is taken in and
undigested particles are thrown out through the same
opening. In this respect a coelenterate resembles a flatworm. But the coelenterate body is radially symmetrical
instead of bilaterally symmetrical. Around the "mouth," a
coelenterate has tentacles that bear many small stingers;
these can paralyze small organisms and, in some cases,
quite large ones—even man. Stinger-bearing tentacles are
the most distinctive characteristic of the phylum.

If flatworms are considered structurally simple, coelenterates are even simpler. Nevertheless, there is considerable
diversity in the details of the coelenterate body plan. The
kinds that live permanently attached to each other—such as
the corals—are fastened at the ends opposite their tentacles. Those that do not live in colonies may glide slowly
from place to place. Still others, such as jellyfish, swim or
float about in the water. These are—from the point of view
of a coral—upside down. The mouth opening points
downward, and the tentacles hang beneath.

**Figure 4 · 39**
A jellyfish that stings swimmers along the Atlantic
coast—often called "sea
nettle."    x 3/4

William H. Amos

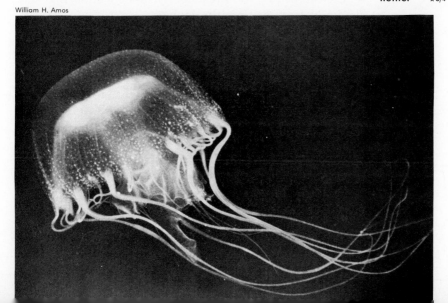

Ralph Buchsbaum

Elephant-ear sponge     x 1/4

Figure 4 · 40

The horny skeleton of an elephant-ear sponge *(above)* and the glassy skeleton of another sponge, Venus's-flower-basket *(left)*.

American Museum of Natural History

Venus's-flower-basket     x 3/8

## SPONGES

It is difficult to think of sponges as animals. This is not merely because they stay in one place, attached to some solid support — corals, oysters, and even the tunicates in our own phylum live this way. And sponges do move around through the water for a time early in their lives, just as do the other *sessile* (attached) animals. But sponges lack all structural systems we normally associate with animals. Of course, we have been pointing out how animals in different phyla lack this or that system. However, even the coelenterates can be said to have a nervous system and a digestive system of sorts. But not the sponges.

Basically the sponge body is a thick-walled bag that is pierced by many *pores* (holes). Through these pores water is pushed inward by the action of *flagella* — hairlike projections that are similar to cilia, but longer and less numerous. The water flows out of the body cavity through an opening that is misnamed a "mouth." The body wall is supported by a mass of hard or tough material — a kind of skeleton.

Sponges as a group show a considerable range of diversity. Some have single body cavities; others have complicated networks of body cavities. Some have skeletons of hard materials chemically similar to glass or to the shells of mollusks; others have skeletons of a tough substance similar to that in a cow's horn. A few sponges have radially symmetrical shapes; most are quite unsymmetrical.

sessile [sĕs′ĭl; Latin: *sedere*, to sit]

flagella [flə jĕl′ə; singular, flagellum; Latin: *flagellum*, a little whip]

## INVESTIGATION 4.2

### STRUCTURAL CHARACTERISTICS IN THE IDENTIFICATION OF ANIMALS

#### PURPOSES

Your purposes in this work are (*a*) to obtain direct experience with the diversity of structure in the animal kingdom, and (*b*) to learn some of the methods used in identifying animals.

#### MATERIALS AND EQUIPMENT

Labeled specimens of animals, living and preserved
Hand lenses or stereomicroscopes

#### PROCEDURES

**A. Observing animal specimens.** Before the laboratory period begins, draw two charts in your data book similar to the ones on page 140. The teacher will tell you how many columns you should draw on the right side of each chart.

You will find several numbered stations arranged around the classroom. At each station will be one or more specimens of an animal species and a label giving its common name. Both living and preserved specimens may be found at some stations. Some of the preserved specimens may be partially dissected so that you can make certain observations. The teacher will announce the total number of stations and assign a starting station to each student. Then follow the procedure given in Investigation 1.1 (page 7).

Begin work at each station by deciding whether the kind of animal you are studying has a backbone and is therefore a vertebrate or does not have a backbone and is therefore an invertebrate. If it is a vertebrate, record its common name on Chart 1 in one of the spaces under the heading "Name of Animal." If it is an invertebrate, follow the same procedure but use Chart 2.

At the left side of each chart is a list of the characteristics to be observed. Each of the sections includes two or more characteristics. After studying the specimens, indicate the presence of the characteristics you observed by placing a check (✓) in the appropriate box.

Let us suppose that the first specimen you study is a cat. Because a cat has a backbone, you write "Cat" in the space at the top of the first vertical column in Chart 1. Now look at the four choices indicated in the section "Skin Structures." Only one of the choices applies to the cat: "Hair present." Therefore, you put a check in the box that is under "Cat" and to the right of "Hair present." Next look at the choices in the section "Appendages." Again there is only one choice that applies to the cat, so you check the box under "Cat" and to the right of "Legs present." Proceed down the column in this manner. When you think your observations are insufficient to make a decision on any point, leave the space on the chart blank.

**B. Using a key.** The process of identifying organisms is difficult because there are so many of them. One tool used in biological identification is called a *key*. There are several different kinds of keys; the kind you will use is called a *dichotomous* key. The word "dichotomous" means "separating into two parts," and it describes the kind of choices you make in using such a key.

The information you have recorded in Chart 1 is used in Key 1 (page 141) and enables you to determine the *class* to which each of the animals you have studied belongs. Begin at the top of the key with Item 1, having the choices 1a and 1b. If the animal you are considering has hair, your choice is 1a. Follow

**Chart 1**

| | | NAME OF ANIMAL | | |
|---|---|---|---|---|
| **SKIN STRUCTURES** | Hair present | | | |
| | Feathers present | → | | |
| | Scales present | | | |
| | None of the above present | | | |
| **APPENDAGES** | Wings present | → | | |
| | Legs present | | | |
| | Fins present | | | |
| | None of the above present | ↳ | | |
| **SKELETON** | Bony | | | |
| | Cartilaginous | | | |
| **TEETH** | Present | → | | |
| | Absent | | | |
| **JAWS** | Present | → | | |
| | Absent | | | |
| | | Class | Class | Class |

**Chart 2**

| | | NAME OF ANIMAL | | |
|---|---|---|---|---|
| **EXOSKELETON** | Present | | | |
| | Absent | | | |
| **BODY SYMMETRY** | Radial | | | |
| | Bilateral | → | | |
| | Part bilateral, part spiral | | | |
| **JOINTED WALKING LEGS** | 3 pairs present | | | |
| | 4 pairs present | | | |
| | More than 4 pairs present | → | | |
| | Absent | | | |
| **BODY SEGMENTATION** | Present | | | |
| | Absent | | | |
| **TENTACLES** | More than 4 present | → | | |
| | 4 or fewer present | | | |
| | Absent | | | |
| **ANTENNAE** | 2 or more pairs present | → | | |
| | 1 pair present | | | |
| | Absent | | | |
| | | Phylum | Phylum | Phylum |

the first line over to the right side of the key and you will find that it belongs to the class Mammalia. If the animal does *not* have hair (choice 1b), follow the second line over to the right and you will find that you are to go to Item 2 in the key. There two more contrasting characteristics are indicated, 2a and 2b. By again making a choice and following numbered items, you will eventually arrive at the name of the class in which the animal belongs. Write the name of the class in Chart 1. Repeat the process for each animal.

After you have determined the class for each vertebrate in Chart 1, use Key 2 to determine the *phylum* for each invertebrate in Chart 2. Record the phyla in the columns at the bottom of Chart 2.

Finally, use Key 3 to determine the *class* to which each of the animals included in the phylum Arthropoda belongs and record this information following Chart 2 in your data book.

A key is obviously a convenience in making identifications. Keys can be made to carry identifications all the way down to the species level. But you must not assume that the simplified keys in this exercise will indicate the correct classification for *any* animal. A key will give you a correct identification *only* if it is used with the group of organisms for which it was constructed. If, for example, you attempt to classify a squid or a slug by using Key 2, the key will indicate

---

### KEY 1
#### DICHOTOMOUS KEY TO CLASSES OF THE SUBPHYLUM VERTEBRATA

1a. Hair present . . . . . . . . . . . . . . . . . . . . . . . . . . . . . . Class Mammalia
1b. Hair absent . . . . . . . . . . . . . . . . . . . . . . . . . . . . . . go to 2

2a. Feathers present . . . . . . . . . . . . . . . . . . . . . . . . . . Class Aves
2b. Feathers absent . . . . . . . . . . . . . . . . . . . . . . . . . . . go to 3

3a. Jaws present . . . . . . . . . . . . . . . . . . . . . . . . . . . . . go to 4
3b. Jaws absent . . . . . . . . . . . . . . . . . . . . . . . . . . . . . Class Agnatha

4a. Paired fins present . . . . . . . . . . . . . . . . . . . . . . . . . go to 5
4b. Paired fins absent . . . . . . . . . . . . . . . . . . . . . . . . . go to 6

5a. Skeleton bony . . . . . . . . . . . . . . . . . . . . . . . . . . . . Class Osteichthyes
5b. Skeleton cartilaginous . . . . . . . . . . . . . . . . . . . . . . Class Chondrichthyes

6a. Skin scales present . . . . . . . . . . . . . . . . . . . . . . . . . Class Reptilia
6b. Skin scales absent . . . . . . . . . . . . . . . . . . . . . . . . . Class Amphibia

---

### KEY 2
#### DICHOTOMOUS KEY TO SELECTED INVERTEBRATE PHYLA

1a. Body symmetry radial . . . . . . . . . . . . . . . . . . . . . . . go to 2
1b. Body symmetry not radial . . . . . . . . . . . . . . . . . . . . go to 3

2a. Tentacles present, body soft . . . . . . . . . . . . . . . . . . Phylum Coelenterata
2b. Tentacles absent, body hard and rough . . . . . . . . . . Phylum Echinodermata

3a. Exoskeleton present . . . . . . . . . . . . . . . . . . . . . . . . go to 4
3b. Exoskeleton absent . . . . . . . . . . . . . . . . . . . . . . . . . go to 5

4a. Jointed legs present . . . . . . . . . . . . . . . . . . . . . . . . Phylum Arthropoda
4b. Jointed legs absent . . . . . . . . . . . . . . . . . . . . . . . . . Phylum Mollusca

5a. Body segmented . . . . . . . . . . . . . . . . . . . . . . . . . . . Phylum Annelida
5b. Body not segmented . . . . . . . . . . . . . . . . . . . . . . . . Phylum Platyhelminthes

KEY 3

DICHOTOMOUS KEY TO SELECTED CLASSES OF THE PHYLUM ARTHROPODA

1a. Walking legs, more than 5 pairs . . . . . . . . . . . . . . . . . . . . go to 2
1b. Walking legs, 5 or fewer pairs . . . . . . . . . . . . . . . . . . . . . go to 3

2a. Legs, 1 pair for each body segment . . . . . . . . . . . . . . . . Class Chilopoda
2b. Legs, 2 pairs for each body segment . . . . . . . . . . . . . . . . Class Diplopoda

3a. Antennae present . . . . . . . . . . . . . . . . . . . . . . . . . go to 4
3b. Antennae absent . . . . . . . . . . . . . . . . . . . . . . Class Arachnida

4a. Antennae, 1 pair . . . . . . . . . . . . . . . . . . . . . . . . Class Insecta
4b. Antennae, more than 1 pair . . . . . . . . . . . . . . . . . . . Class Crustacea

that these animals belong to the phylum Platyhelminthes; but both are actually mollusks. Unless you use a key to unlock only the series of doors for which it was designed, you will almost certainly end up in the wrong house!

Therefore, you must check the correctness of your identifications. You can do this by referring to Appendix II. If the characteristics of an animal match the Appendix description of the group indicated by the key, you can feel reasonably confident that your identification is correct. For even greater confidence, you can check your identification with one of the references at the end of this chapter.

### FOR FURTHER INVESTIGATION

1. Having classified all the animals of your laboratory study, refer again to Charts 1 and 2. Once you know that an animal is a vertebrate, you need only determine a single characteristic—possession of hair—to place it in the class Mammalia. Is there any other *single* characteristic that will enable you to place a vertebrate in its class at once? If so, state what that characteristic is and in which class a vertebrate having it should be placed. Is there any single characteristic that will enable you to place an invertebrate you have studied in its phylum? If so, what is the characteristic and which phylum does it indicate? Is there any single characteristic that will enable you to place an arthropod in its class? If so, what is the characteristic and which class does it indicate?

2. Select ten students, including yourself. Construct a dichotomous key, using characteristics that will enable another person to identify each student in the group.

## THE MEANING OF BIOLOGICAL CLASSIFICATION

By the middle of the eighteenth century, the scheme of classification levels given at the beginning of this chapter had been generally adopted by biologists. Before the middle of the nineteenth century, most of the animal phyla that we have discussed were recognized. But the goal of the taxonomist of that time was still the goal we mentioned at the beginning of this chapter: to arrive at a convenient way to catalogue species, to keep track of them. Biological classification was not supposed to *mean* anything. In this respect it was like the listing of words in a dictionary: "Burmese" and "burn" may be next to each other, but they are entirely unrelated otherwise.

We have put organisms at different levels not alphabetically, but according to their structural characteristics. When we look over the result of this classification, some questions arise. Isn't it strange that *every* animal with a dorsal, tubular nerve cord also has pharyngeal pouches and a notochord (even though it may lose them as it grows up)? Isn't it strange that *every* animal with an exoskeleton and jointed appendages also has a ventral nerve cord? Isn't it strange that *no* animal with a saclike digestive system ever has a circulatory system? Why do animals with the annelid body plan *always* lack skeletons? Why do animals with the mollusk body plan *always* lack segmentation?

All of these questions add up to one big question: By arranging organisms into groups according to their structural likenesses, have we revealed some hidden meaning? In the early nineteenth century "revealed" would have been too strong a word. But at least there was a hint. And even though most biologists of that time failed to understand the hint, they probably sensed it unconsciously. Did they not call one of their levels of classification a "family"?

Why do all eight Wu children in Hong Kong have a fold in the upper eyelid and none have blond hair? Why do all eight Pedersen children in Copenhagen have blue eyes and none have straight hair? Why do all eight Perez children in Guatemala have hair that is both black and straight? In all three cases, of course, the characteristics go together because they are family characteristics—they have "run in the family" for many generations. They have been *inherited* together.

This is an analogy. An analogy is useful for explanation if it is not carried too far. If all the families moved to, say, Chicago or Honolulu, the characteristics might get mixed up in a few generations.

A reasonable answer to the questions we raised about the animal phyla is the same answer we gave to the questions about the children. The patterns of likeness are shared because the organisms are related—not in the ecological sense we used in Section One, but in the kinship sense. All chordates have dorsal, tubular nerve cords, pharyngeal pouches, and notochords, because all are descended from ancestors that had these characteristics. All insects have three pairs of legs and one pair of antennae, because all are descended from ancestors with these characteristics. We have based our classification on structural characteristics, and structural characteristics are inherited.

Scallop  x 1/2

Figure 4 · 41
Colorful aquatic animals. In
Appendix II find the phylum
and class in which each is
classified.

Sea slug  x 1/2

Feather worm  x 1/10

Leech  x 3/4

Sea urchin  x 2/5

Portuguese man-of-war  x 1/3

Sea anemone  x 2/5

This reasonable view did not come directly from a study of classification, however. Two centuries ago biologists were just as intelligent as those today. But scientists, like everyone else, may be blinded to new thoughts by the ideas they have grown up with—ideas that have become fixed. Actually this view came from other kinds of evidence, particularly from the evidence of fossils and later on from the evidence of experimental studies on heredity. About a century ago most biologists became convinced that the different kinds of organisms are related through ancestry. Ever since, taxonomists have tried to express the evidences of relationship in classification.

The modern taxonomist, therefore, does not look merely at structural characteristics in organisms he is classifying. He looks for *any evidence of relationship*. Such evidence may be in the way the individual develops during its early life, in the chemical materials in its body, or even in its behavior. The job of the modern taxonomist is much more complicated than that of the eighteenth-century taxonomist.

Two factors, however, still give structural characteristics particular importance. The first we have already mentioned —structural features are easy to observe and to demonstrate to others from preserved specimens (and for many organisms we still know little more than the nature of their structure). Secondly, structural evidence is all we are ever likely to have for studying organisms known to us only from fossils. We can make some good guesses about the life activities of such organisms, but the evidence is still based primarily on structure. And these organisms are important in figuring out the relationships of living ones, because they may be the ancestors of the living ones.

specimen [Latin: *specimen*, a token, example]

Let us return to an example of classification used in the early part of this chapter (page 107 and Figure 4 · 1). We read, "As we go up the table, we find an increasing diversity at each level." Now we can say, "As we go up the table, we find a series of levels in which the organisms are less and less closely *related*." Let us go on from this point without directly comparing statements. Individual dogs are all so closely related that they form an interbreeding population, a species. Dogs and wolves do not ordinarily interbreed, but it is not impossible; from structural and behavioral evidence most zoologists believe that they had a common ancestry not so long ago—in other words, that they are closely related. The taxonomist expresses this belief by putting them in the same genus (*Canis*), as Figure 4 · 1 shows. By adding coyotes to this genus, he shows that he believes dogs, coyotes, and wolves to be equally related. By placing foxes in a separate genus (*Vulpes*), he shows that he

common: Here this word means "shared by two or more individuals or groups," as we speak in mathematics of a "common denominator."

believes foxes to be less closely related to dogs, coyotes, and wolves than these are to each other. And by placing the genus *Canis* and the genus *Vulpes* in the same family, he shows that dogs are related to foxes—but less closely than to wolves.

This is somewhat similar to saying that you are closely related to your sister (you and your sister have the same mother and father), but you are less closely related to your first cousin (you and your first cousin have only one pair of grandparents in common). By placing the "dog family" (Canidae) and the "bear family" (Ursidae) and the "weasel family" (Mustelidae) in the order Carnivora, the taxonomist is implying that all of these animals descended from a common ancestral group—but probably long, long ago. As we continue up the list of levels, the relationship becomes less and less close. Thus, when we say that a dog and a goldfish belong to the same subphylum, we are talking about a very distant relationship indeed.

Have we abandoned the original purpose of classification—to catalogue organisms for convenient reference? Not at all. The modern taxonomist has *two* aims: (1) to arrange organisms in a way that will allow most convenience in referring to them, and (2) to arrange organisms in a way that will show their relationships. Of course, when we try to do two things at once, we usually get into trouble. The more evidence we obtain, the more complex the relationships of organisms appear to be. Moreover, as we pointed out on page 108, taxonomists differ in how they interpret the evidence. Therefore, there are many existing schemes of classification, all designed within the same framework of levels. Classifications used to arrange specimens in museums often lean toward convenience and neglect relationships. In contrast, classifications in advanced and specialized textbooks usually lean toward relationships and neglect convenience. Classifications in general use are often compromises between the two aims. They are neither as convenient as they might be if we did not have to worry about relationships nor as expressive of relationships as they might be if we did not have to worry about convenience. The classification in Appendix II is of this kind.

## INVESTIGATION 4.3

### DIVERSITY IN THE ANIMAL KINGDOM: A COMPARATIVE STUDY

#### PURPOSE

Our purpose is to compare structure and function in living animals representing five different phyla.

#### MATERIALS AND EQUIPMENT

*Station 1*
Living hydras, 6 to 12
Stereomicroscopes or hand lenses, 3
Watch glasses, Syracuse form, 3
Culture of small crustaceans such as brine shrimp or *Daphnia*
Medicine droppers, 3
Monocular microscopes, 3
Prepared slides of hydras (longitudinal sections), 3
Camel-hair brushes, 3

*Station 2*
Living planarians, 6 to 12
Stereomicroscopes or hand lenses, 6
Watch glasses, Syracuse form, 3
Fresh, raw liver, small pieces, 6 to 12
Camel-hair brushes, 3
Monocular microscopes, 3
Prepared slides of planarians: cross sections, 3; whole mounts, 3

*Station 3*
Large, living earthworms, 6 to 12
Hand lenses, 3
Paper towel, moistened
Boxes containing damp soil, 3

Monocular microscopes, 3
Prepared slides of earthworms, cross sections, 3

*Station 4*
Living crayfish, 3
Aquarium
Camel-hair brushes, 3
Finger bowls (20-cm diameter) or other glass dishes, 3
Fresh, raw liver, small pieces, 6 to 10
Preserved crayfish, 2
Dissecting needles, 3

*Station 5*
Prepared frog skeleton
Live frogs, 3
Battery jars, 3
Freshly dissected frog
Medicine droppers, 2
Dissecting needles, 3
Aquarium

#### PROCEDURE

#### A. General directions

Before coming to the laboratory, make an enlarged copy of the chart shown below. It should extend across two facing pages; each of the thirteen spaces should allow for several lines of writing. Copy the following questions—each in a separate space—in the column headed "Characteristics." (If more than one question follows a number, copy only the first. The thirteenth space is to use for any additional observations that you may make.)

| CHARACTERISTICS | HYDRA | PLANARIA | EARTHWORM | CRAYFISH | FROG |
|---|---|---|---|---|---|
| 1. | | | | | |
| 2. | | | | | |
| 3. | | | | | |
| ↕ | ↕ | ↕ | ↕ | ↕ | ↕ |
| 13. | | | | | |

1. What is the habitat of the animal? Does it live in water, on land, or both in water and on land?
2. Is the symmetry of the body radial or bilateral?
3. Does the animal have a skeleton? If it has, is it an endoskeleton or an exoskeleton?
4. Is the animal's body segmented or unsegmented?
5. Which does the animal have—a digestive tube or a digestive sac? (If it has a tube, there will be *two* openings, a mouth and an *anus*.)
6. Does it have paired appendages?
7. How does the animal obtain oxygen? (Through lungs, gills, skin, or a combination of these?)
8. Are any sense organs visible? If so, what kinds are they, and where are they located?
9. How does the animal move from one place to another?
10. What kinds of movement does it make while it remains more or less in one spot?
11. How does the animal capture and take in food?
12. How does it react when touched lightly with a dissecting needle or camel-hair brush?

All the specimens of one species of animal and the materials and equipment needed for observing them are arranged at one station. There are five species —therefore five stations. Each team will have a turn at each station.

Following are directions for the observation of each species. Some will help you make the observations needed to answer the questions; some will direct attention to additional observations that should be recorded in the thirteenth space of the chart. You may find some observations impossible to make with the material available. Therefore, there may be blank spaces on your chart. Do the best you can. Remember that you are recording your *observations*, not what you have read or heard about.

**B. Observing hydras**

1. Food-capture and feeding in hydras should be observed under a stereomicroscope or hand lens. Place a single starved hydra in a small watch glass that contains some of the same water in which the hydra has been living. Wait until the animal attaches itself to the dish and expands its tentacles. Then slowly add a few drops of the concentrated culture that contains small crustaceans.

2. Try to determine the presence or absence of a skeleton, mouth, and anus in this animal by examining prepared, stained slides of longitudinal sections, using a monocular microscope.

3. Through a hand lens or stereomicroscope, observe the hydra's reactions when it is gently touched with the tip of a dissecting needle or a camel-hair brush.

**C. Observing planarians**

1. Feeding should be studied under a stereomicroscope or hand lens. Place one or two starved planarian worms in a small watch glass that contains pond or aquarium water. Add a small piece of freshly cut liver.

2. Presence or absence of a skeleton, mouth, and anus may be determined by examining prepared slides of cross sections of specimens with the monocular microscopes and whole mounts with the stereomicroscopes.

**D. Observing earthworms**

1. Pick up a live earthworm and hold it gently between your thumb and forefinger. Observe its movements as it attempts to escape. Are there any regions on the body surface that feel rough? If so, examine them with a hand lens and record your observations.

2. Watch the worm crawl about on the slightly moistened tabletop until you have determined which is the anterior

end. Examine both ends of the animal with a hand lens. How does the anterior end differ in structure from the posterior end?

3. Place an earthworm on the surface of some loose soil and observe its movements as it burrows.

4. Using a monocular microscope, examine a prepared, stained slide of cross sections of the body under low power and high power. Try to determine whether a skeleton is present.

**E. Observing crayfish**

1. Observe the movements of the appendages and the pattern of locomotion of a live crayfish in an aquarium. Observe the movements of the antennae. Touch them gently with the tip of a camel-hair brush and note the animal's reaction.

2. Put a small piece of liver in a dish and observe how the crayfish secures and eats its food.

3. Examine a preserved crayfish in which part of the exoskeleton has been removed to expose the gills.

4. Locate the position of the mouth and anus in a preserved crayfish that has been dissected so as to expose these openings.

**F. Observing frogs**

1. Examine a prepared skeleton of a frog. Compare it with a dissected, preserved specimen to determine the position of muscles and other soft tissues in relation to the bones.

2. Study the breathing movements of a live frog that is not moving about. To do this, observe from the side, with your eyes at the level of the animal.

3. If hungry frogs are available, your teacher may be able to show you how the tongue is used to capture food.

4. The lungs of a frog are relatively inconspicuous, but in a freshly killed and dissected specimen they can be inflated with air. The teacher will show you how this is done.

5. Observe the movements of a frog swimming in an aquarium. How do these movements compare with those of a frog hopping and moving about on a laboratory table? The teacher will show you how to catch and hold a frog so it will not be injured.

When you have completed your observations and recorded the data, review what you have learned about each of the items in the chart. By reading across the chart, you should be able to compare and contrast the characteristics you have studied in the five animals.

Optional: Using yourself as the animal being observed, answer each of the questions in the chart.

**SUMMARY**

One of the most important ideas in biology is the principle that the way in which an organism is constructed is related to the way it functions. Organisms living in a particular environment often show special structural adaptations that permit them to carry on these functions. For each animal you have studied, select five functions that the animal performs as part of its way of life and indicate how, in each case, its structure enables it to perform these functions.

Almost a million species of living animals have been discovered by zoologists. Even a brief look at some of these impresses us with the great diversity of structure and function to be found among animals.

Confronted with this diversity, men have attempted since early times to classify living things by separating them into groups according to their similarities and differences. Originally organisms were classified merely for convenience in organizing information about them. Within the past hundred years, however, taxonomists have developed classifications in an attempt to indicate degrees of kinship among different kinds of organisms. For both kinds of classification, structural characteristics have been chiefly considered, though chemical and functional characteristics are now becoming increasingly important.

All evidences of relationship may be interpreted in various ways; moreover, the amount of evidence is increasing every year. Therefore, complete and lasting agreement on any particular plan of classification is not likely to be achieved. One scheme of classification is set forth in Appendix II. In this scheme animals are grouped together as one of three kingdoms of living things. The animal kingdom is then divided into a number of phyla. Each phylum is divided into classes, and these, in turn, into orders, families, genera, and, finally, species. We have looked at the characteristic body plans of nine animal phyla. While doing so we have also examined the diverse structural adaptations associated with different ways of life in different kinds of environments.

## GUIDE QUESTIONS

1. Why is it necessary to classify organisms?
2. What is the basis for biological classification? What advantages does it have over other possible bases?
3. The vertebrates were once grouped as a phylum. Why are they now classified with such animals as lancelets and tunicates?
4. At what level of classification are man, dog, and cat placed together? What characteristics do they share at this level?
5. Fish and most amphibians live in or near water; most reptiles live on land. What reptilian characteristics make this difference possible?
6. How can arthropod structure be considered "upside down" and "inside out" from the chordate viewpoint?
7. What structural adaptations have made it possible for insects to function in so many different niches?
8. How has the annelid body plan been adapted to a life in the soil?
9. How is diversity shown in the mollusk phylum?
10. In which animal phyla is the adult body plan radially symmetrical?
11. Compare and contrast flatworms with roundworms and with coelenterates.
12. Which animal phyla would most probably be represented in a small-stream habitat?
13. The more kinds of structures an animal has, the more complex it is said to be. From this viewpoint what phylum of animals is simplest?
14. What precautions must you observe in using a taxonomic key?
15. What new aim has the taxonomist adopted within the last century?

## PROBLEMS

1. Using Appendix II, look up the derivations of these names for animal groups: Diptera, Agnatha, Polychaeta, Chiroptera, Diplopoda, Gastropoda, Osteichthyes, Proboscidea, Lepidoptera. How appropriate do you consider each name?

2. Some apparently similar vertebrates are usually placed in separate classes. What characteristics would enable you to distinguish between these animals: (a) An eel and a lamprey? (b) An eel and a snake? (c) A lizard and a salamander? (d) A turtle and an armadillo? (e) A bat and a bird?

3. Disregarding relationships but still using structure as a basis, devise a new classification of vertebrates that will make sense for all the vertebrates you know.

4. Suppose that by 1985 every kind of living organism on Earth will have been discovered, described, and classified. Do you think the development of taxonomy will then end? Explain.

5. How can you explain the fact that many sessile or slow-moving animals are radially symmetrical, while, on the other hand, unattached, fast-moving animals are bilaterally symmetrical?

6. The Onychophora are listed in Appendix II as a class. These animals are sometimes grouped as a phylum. This is a good example of a difference of opinion among taxonomists. Collect evidence supporting each opinion and present arguments for and against using the phylum Onychophora.

7. Suppose someone challenged the separation of whales and sharks in classification. Present evidence to support the classification given in this book.

8. Twenty years ago all living species of mollusks could be classified in one or another of four classes. In 1957 a deep-sea dredge brought up some mollusks so different that taxonomists had to place them in a separate class. Look up the story of this discovery. During the last century what other major changes in classification have resulted from the finding of previously unknown organisms?

9. Obtain several college textbooks of zoology. Compare and contrast the classification schemes they use.

## SUGGESTED READINGS

BUCHSBAUM, R. M. *Animals without Backbones*. Rev. ed. Chicago: University of Chicago Press, 1948. (Well-illustrated introduction to the invertebrates. Fairly easy.)

FLEAY, D. "Strange Animals of Australia," *National Geographic Magazine*, September, 1963. Pp. 388–411.

HANSON, E. D. *Animal Diversity*. 2nd ed. Englewood Cliffs, N.J.: Prentice-Hall, Inc., 1964. (A small book that stresses the aims of the modern taxonomist. Somewhat difficult.)

SIMPSON, G. G., and W. S. BECK. *Life: An Introduction to Biology*. 2nd ed. New York: Harcourt, Brace & World, Inc., 1965. Chapters 18, 21, and 22. (Good short discussion of the principles of taxonomy and the major groups in the animal kingdom.)

STORER, T. I., and R. L. USINGER. *General Zoology*. 3rd ed. New York: McGraw-Hill Book Co., Inc., 1957. (College textbook that stresses zoological classification.)

YAPP, W. B. *Vertebrates; Their Structure and Life*. New York: Oxford University Press, Inc., 1965. (Good general account of animals with backbones. Rather difficult.)

ZAHL, P. A. "Giant Insects of the Amazon," *National Geographic Magazine*, May, 1959. Pp. 632–669.

Each of the following is a series of books that treat the classification and identification of certain parts of the animal kingdom.

"Golden Nature Series." Edited by H. S. Zim. Published by Simon and Schuster, Inc., New York. Includes volumes on reptiles and amphibians, fishes, mammals, birds, insects. (Simple, many colored pictures.)

"Pictured Key Nature Series." Edited by H. E. Jaques. Published by Wm. C. Brown Co., Publishers, Dubuque, Iowa. Volumes on flatworms, land snails, insects, spiders, freshwater fishes, birds, mammals. (These books make extensive use of keys for identification.)

"World of Nature Series." Published by Doubleday & Co., Inc., Garden City, N.Y. Volumes on invertebrates, fishes, amphibians, reptiles, birds, mammals. (Large, beautifully illustrated books that emphasize the lives of animals rather than their structures.)

# Plants

## PLANT CLASSIFICATION

To a person who has no interest in automobiles, the flow of traffic along a highway is monotonous. But traffic holds great interest for most high school boys, whose ability to recognize at a glance the make and model of any car is impressive. Most girls have a similar ability when it comes to clothes and hair styles. Interest in automobiles or fashions, in birds or plants, is in part a measure of the extent to which a person has developed his powers of observation. The more we use our eyes and minds to observe differences in the things around us, the more we see and the less we find monotonous.

Until we become interested in plants, we tend to take for granted their presence in the landscape. We may recognize some large plants as trees, take a certain amount of pride in the grass of our lawns, and perhaps know a fern when we see one. But being acquainted with trees, grass, and ferns is only a beginning, for there are approximately three hundred fifty thousand species of plants!

For many centuries the classification of plants was based on Aristotle's divisions: tree, shrub, and herb. These seemed to be sensible and natural divisions. But as botanists (biologists who study plants) learned more, they found that such a simple system of classification was neither convenient nor a good indicator of relationships. It was inconvenient because the same kind of plant might have the form of a tree in one climate and that of a shrub in another. It was not a good expression of relationship because some trees and shrubs seemed to be closely related to some herbs.

What structures in plants should be used as the basis for classification? Early in the eighteenth century part of the

monotonous [mə nät′ən əs; Greek: *monos*, single, + *tonos*, tone]: tiresomely the same

herb [ûrb, hûrb]
botanists [Greek: *botane*, a plant, herb]

The Bettmann Archive

**Figure 5 · 1**

Carolus Linnaeus [kăr′ə ləs lĭ nē′əs]:    1707–1778. Swedish botanist. As a young man Linnaeus journeyed to the far north of Sweden to study the plants of Lapland. He is shown here in the costume of the Lapps, holding a plant that was named after him — *Linnaea borealis.*

nomenclature    [nō′mən klā′chər; Latin: *nomen*, name, + *calare*, to call]

answer to this question came from a young botanist named Carolus Linnaeus. His idea was to use the reproductive parts — flowers, in the more familiar plants — as a basis. This greatly simplified identification of plants and revolutionized plant taxonomy.

Simple ideas have a way of developing complications as new information is obtained. So it was with Linnaeus' idea. Today plant taxonomists still consider reproductive structures as important for classification, but they do not neglect other structures. And like animal taxonomists, they take into consideration characteristics other than structure — such as the kinds of chemical substances found in plants — whenever they have sufficient information to do so. Their task today is, of course, more difficult; their system of classification must express relationships as well as be convenient.

Linnaeus was also responsible for bringing into wide use the scheme of classification by levels that we described in Chapter 4. Although we introduced it in discussing animals, Linnaeus, a botanist, first applied it to the classification of plants. Eventually, however, he extended this scheme to include not only all living things but also nonliving things, such as minerals. It is still the framework for all biological classification, but it has been abandoned by mineralogists.

## A PROBLEM: NOMENCLATURE

In Chapter 2 we ran into our first taxonomic problem: What is a species? In Chapter 4 we brought up two more taxonomic problems: How can we classify organisms? How can we combine convenience with an expression of relationships in classifications? So far, we have ignored the problem of how a name is given to a particular kind of organism.

### DEVELOPMENT OF NAMES

Long before scientists got around to naming plants and animals, men applied so-called common names to organisms that were important to them. These common names are still very useful. If you go into a lumberyard and ask for some *Sequoia sempervirens* fence posts, you are not likely to succeed in getting what you want — a request for redwood posts works much better. Why, then, do biologists need any other names than the ones in common use? Where do these biological names come from? Why do they seem so strange to us? A little history may help us answer these questions.

The first attempts to give names to all known organisms, and not just to those of immediate interest, were probably made by the Greeks. These names became incorporated into Latin, which endured in western Europe for over a thousand years as the language of communication between educated men. Only these men—scholars, clergymen, physicians—were interested in all organisms, not merely those familiar to the farmer or the hunter. Thus "scientific" names were necessarily Latin names.

endure [ĭn dyū′ər]

During the Middle Ages efforts were made to fit the names used by the Greeks and Romans to the plants and animals of the rest of Europe. But this did not work. The plants of England and of Germany were often different from those of Greece and of Italy. The differences in newly discovered organisms had to be recognized; this was usually done by simply attaching a new adjective to the old name of a similar plant or animal.

Then came the Age of Exploration. Year after year explorers sent back strange new plants and animals to the scientists of Europe—from Africa, South America, North America, the East Indies. By the beginning of the eighteenth century, names had become unmanageable. Here is the name that was used at that time for the carnation plant: *dianthus floribus solitariis, squamis calycinis subovatis brevissimis, corollis crenatis*—"the pink [a general name used by botanists for the carnation and its relatives] with solitary flowers, the scales of the calyx somewhat egg-shaped and very short, the petals scalloped."

Imagine writing about organisms when you had to refer to them in such a cumbersome way! But at the time there was no other way to be exact. For Europeans had no "common" names for foreign organisms—except names from the native languages of Africa, the Americas, and India, and these were meaningless to Europeans.

Bad situations do not correct themselves overnight; for many years both botanists and zoologists fumbled toward a more workable system of nomenclature. The solution to the problem was developed by the same Linnaeus who had done such remarkable things for botanical classification a few years before. His system, at first designed as a shortcut in especially difficult cases, was well developed by 1753. With this date modern biological nomenclature begins.

## THE BINOMIAL SYSTEM

Linnaeus' system was simple. He restricted the name of each group that he thought of as a species to just two words. The first word indicated a group of similar species. Linnaeus called this larger group a genus—one of the levels in the scheme of classification we discussed in Chapter 4. Thus, all species of pinks were called *Dianthus*. (Having "promoted" the word to generic use, we capitalize it.)

2 *Caryophyllus fylueftris fimplex, fuaue rubens.* Single red Pinks.

Victor Larsen

**Figure 5 · 2**
Woodcut from the *Herball* of John Gerard (1545–1612). This was an early English book on botany. Note the length of the biological name.

binomial [bī nō′mĭ əl; Latin: *bis*, twice, + *nomen*, name]

*caryophyllus*   [kăr′ĭ ō fĭl′əs]

The first rule of the system decreed that *Dianthus* could never be used for any other genus—only for pinks. The second word was usually an adjective. For the common carnation, formerly referred to by the long name given on page 155, Linnaeus picked the word "*caryophyllus.*" The second rule of the system decreed that *caryophyllus* could never be used for any other species in the genus *Dianthus*. It might be used with some other genus; this would not create duplication, since the scientific name was always to consist of two words, and neither word was, by itself, the name of a species. Thus the name of the carnation became *Dianthus caryophyllus;* as long as Linnaeus' rules are followed, no other species can have this name.

With these two rules a sound binomial (two-word) system of naming was established. It has now been used for more than two hundred years, and though there have been many refinements, the two basic rules remain unchanged. Hundreds of thousands of new organisms have been discovered and easily named.

A few common misunderstandings about scientific names need to be cleared up before we go on. First, the

**Figure 5 · 3**

Title page from Linnaeus' *Species Plantarum* (1753), the first book in which binomial nomenclature was consistently used. With it, all modern plant nomenclature began. Animal nomenclature dates from the tenth edition of Linnaeus' *Systema Naturae* (1758).

Victor Larsen

CAROLI LINNÆI
S:æ R:giæ M:tis Sveciæ Archiatri; Medic. & Botan.
Profess. Upsal; Equitis aur. de Stella Polari;
nec non Acad. Imper. Monspel. Berol. Tolos.
Upsal. Stockh. Soc. & Paris. Coresp.

# SPECIES PLANTARUM,

EXHIBENTES

PLANTAS RITE COGNITAS,

AD

*GENERA RELATAS,*

CUM

Differentiis Specificis,
Nominibus Trivialibus,
Synonymis Selectis,
Locis Natalibus,
Secundum

*SYSTEMA SEXUALE*

DIGESTAS.

Tomus I.

*Cum Privilegio S. R. M:tis Sueciæ & S. R. M:tis Polonicæ et Electoris Saxon.*

*HOLMIÆ,*
Impensis LAURENTII SALVII.
1753.

words used may seem strange, but they are not necessarily long (*Mus*, mice; *Poa*, blue grasses). Many words for genera have been absorbed into English and are properly spelled without capitalization in common usage (iris, petunia, aster). The strangeness of words disappears as we use them.

Second, using scientific names is not a way of showing off; it is necessary for scientific exactness. For one thing, there is no other single set of names available for all organisms. We have English names for the things we know; Malayans have Malay names for the things they know; no language includes names for all known organisms. Further, the same things not only have different names in different languages—as "oak" in English, "*roblé*" in Spanish, and "*chêne*" in French—but even in the same language. For example, the plant that Americans call "corn" is termed "maize" in England and "mealies" in South Africa. Worse still, the same word may refer to different organisms: in Florida "gopher" refers to a turtle; in Kansas, to a rodent.

Third, the names are not a part of the Latin language. They started out as Latin simply because Linnaeus wrote in Latin. Although Latin and Greek word roots are frequently used, the complete words may be from any language or be entirely manufactured. "*Tsuga*" (the hemlocks) comes from Japanese, and "*Washingtonia*" (a genus of palms) is obviously not Latin. The names must, however, be written in the Latin alphabet. Thus, in a Russian or Chinese biology book, biological names are printed in the Latin alphabet ("our" alphabet).

Finally, there is nothing wrong with using common names when you do not need to be exact. Up to this point in our biology course, we have managed to get along without biological names. But sometimes it is necessary to say "*Rubus occidentalis*" instead of "raspberry." There are many species of plants called raspberries, and the biologist frequently needs to specify exactly *which* species he is referring to. From now on we will not hesitate to use scientific names.

*Rubus occidentalis* [rōō′bəs ŏk′sə dən tāl′əs]

## TRACHEOPHYTES

tracheophytes [trā′ki ə fīts]

Roses and grasses, pines and tulips, ferns and carrots—the chances are very good that almost all the plants you can name belong to the phylum Tracheophyta. (Refer to Appendix II as you study the rest of this chapter.)

How can you tell a tracheophyte when you see one? Any land plant that stands as much as a meter high is almost certainly a tracheophyte. Every tracheophyte has a continuous system of tubes (a *vascular system*) extending through its roots, stems, and leaves. By means of this con-

Tracheophyta [trā′kē äf′ə də; Greek: *tracheia*, windpipe, + *phyton*, a plant]: Botanists often use the term "division" in place of "phylum."

vascular [vǎs′kyə lər; Latin: *vasculum*, a little container]

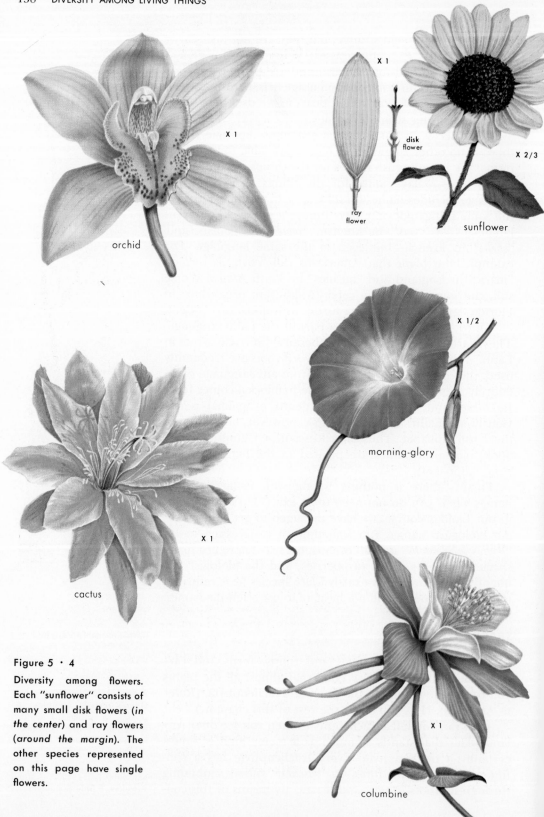

orchid

X 1

X 1

disk
flower

ray
flower

X 2/3

sunflower

X 1/2

morning-glory

cactus

X 1

columbine

X 1

**Figure 5 · 4**
Diversity among flowers. Each "sunflower" consists of many small disk flowers (*in the center*) and ray flowers (*around the margin*). The other species represented on this page have single flowers.

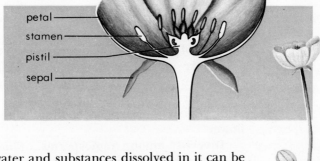

petal

stamen

pistil

sepal

ducting system, water and substances dissolved in it can be moved from one place in the plant to another. Only a land plant that has a vascular system can efficiently move water upward and away from its source, the soil. Of course, the possession of a good conducting system does not mean that a plant *must* grow tall; many tracheophytes are less than 1 m high.

### THE FLOWERING PLANTS: ANGIOSPERMS

Of the more than two hundred thousand kinds of tracheophytes living in the world today, over 95 percent bear flowers at some time during their lives. Yet the flowering plants make up only one class in one subphylum of the tracheophytes. These are the angiosperms.

Not all flowers are brightly colored. Some are so small and inconspicuous that it is hard to believe that they are flowers at all. Grass flowers would not make an acceptable corsage. The flowers of oaks certainly do not get the attention that cherry blossoms do each spring.

**The flower.** What, then, is a flower, this characteristic structure possessed by most of our familiar plants? Botanists think of it as a short branch that bears groups of specialized leaves. Some of these leaves may resemble the ordinary leaves of the plant, but others are so different in structure that it is hard to think of them as leaves at all. If we examine the flower of a buttercup (Figure 5 · 5), for example, we can see a number of green, leaflike structures — *sepals* — on the underside. Before the flower bud opened, the sepals enclosed the other parts of the flower. The most conspicuous flower parts in the buttercup are the *petals*, which are also more or less leaflike in shape but of a quite different color. Attached just above the base of the petals are a number of *stamens,* each having an enlarged, lobed tip. And grouped together in the center of the flower are numerous small, rounded structures called *pistils*, each with pointed tip. Despite their shape both stamens and pistils are believed to have originated from leaves. All these flower parts are attached to the expanded end of the branch, the *receptacle.*

Figure 5 · 5

Buttercup plant (*right*) and diagram of its flower structure (*left*).

X 1

angiosperms [ăn′jĭə spûrmz′; Greek: *angeion,* a small container, capsule, + *sperma,* seed, germ]

sepals [sē′pəlz]

petals [pĕt′əlz]

stamens [stā′mənz; Latin: *stare,* to stand]

pistils [pĭst′əlz]

receptacle [rĭ sĕp′tə kəl; Latin: *recipere,* to receive]

pollen [päl'ən; Latin: *pollen,* a dust]

The flower is a reproductive structure. The stamens produce *pollen* grains, and when these are transferred to the tips of the pistils, seeds may develop. The sepals and petals are not directly involved in seed formation, so a flower can function without them. In fact, in a few plants the flower may consist of only a single stamen or a single pistil. This is sufficient to fit the botanist's definition of a flower.

**Diversity among angiosperms.**    Much of the diversity shown by the angiosperms lies in their flowers. There is no better way to appreciate this than to examine the various kinds of flowers you can find in a greenhouse, a field, or even your front lawn.

Diversity in flower structure is related to the way a flower functions. Flowers in which pollen is transferred from stamen to pistil by insects are often large and conspicuous. Many have brightly colored petals, and some have colored sepals as well. The petals, moreover, often have small glands that produce nectar, a sugar solution. These adaptations probably attract pollinating insects. Flowers in which pollen is transferred by the wind usually have small sepals and petals or none at all. They are often located high up on the plant and produce an abundance of pollen. Their pistils commonly have large, long, or feathery structures at their tips, which are covered with a sticky fluid. Such structural adaptations probably increase the likelihood of wind pollination.

nectar [nĕk'tər; Greek: *nectar,* the drink of the gods]

The base of a pistil encloses developing seeds and is called an *ovary.* As development proceeds, the ovary is transformed into a fruit. Seeds and fruit show as much diversity as flowers. In many cases part of the ovary wall becomes thick and fleshy, as in the fruits of peach, plum, and tomato. Other fleshy fruits, such as apples and pears, include parts of the flower's receptacle as well as the ovary wall. Fleshy fruits are often eaten by animals. The seeds in many such fruits have thick coats that permit them to pass through an animal's digestive tract unharmed, later to be dropped at some distance from the parent plant. Many fruits are

ovary [ōv'ə rē; Latin: *ovum,* egg]

**Figure 5 · 6**

Diversity among pollen grains. By these, taxonomists can identify most angiosperms and gymnosperms to the genus level and often to the species level.

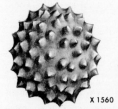

X 1560

tall ragweed

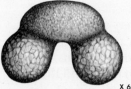

X 680

Austrian pine

X 1080

dandelion

X 600

black walnut

Figure 5 · 7

Stages in the development of tomato fruit from the flower.

not fleshy but have other adaptations that aid in dispersing their seeds (Figure 5 · 8).

Angiosperms also show great diversity in size and in the life-span of the shoot—the part that appears above ground. Some species are trees. The tree form enables the plant to bear its leaves well above the surface of the ground, where they are likely to receive more light than the shorter species growing beneath them. Because of their size, trees can store large reserves of food in trunks and roots, allowing survival through a series of several bad years. Trees have relatively long life-spans; this increases the probability that a tree species will survive even though the entire seed crop of any one year may be destroyed. But most species of angiosperms are not trees. Some, such as lilacs, roses, and raspberries, are woody shrubs. Others, such as ivy, grapes, and hundreds of tropical species, are *lianas*—woody vines —which rely on rocks, walls, or other plants for support. Most, however, are neither shrubs nor vines, but herbs.

Many of these herbaceous plants have roots or stems that remain alive in the soil during winter and send up new shoots in the growing season year after year. These are the *perennial* herbs, such as goldenrod, alfalfa, and asparagus. Other kinds, called *annuals*, such as garden beans, sun-flowers, and crab grass, produce their seed and die after growing for only one season. Still others have life-spans intermediate between those of the perennials and annuals.

Angiosperms are found in all but a very few of the different kinds of land habitats. A limited number live in fresh water, but in all the oceans there are only about thirty species.

**Monocots and dicots.** Further diversity in the angiosperms can be seen by comparing and contrasting the two

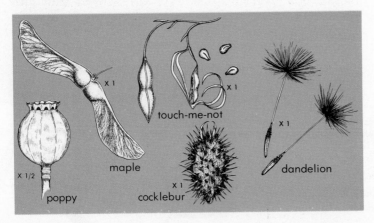

X 1

touch-me-not

X 1

X 1

X 1

maple

X 1/2

poppy

X 1

cocklebur

dandelion

lianas [lĭ ăn′əz, lĭ än′əz]

herbaceous [hûr bā′shəs]

perennial [pə rĕn′ĭ əl; Latin: *per*, through, + *annus*, a year]

goldenrod: See Figure 2 · 5.

Figure 5 · 8

Diversity among fruits. How does each of the structural adaptations shown here provide for seed dispersal?

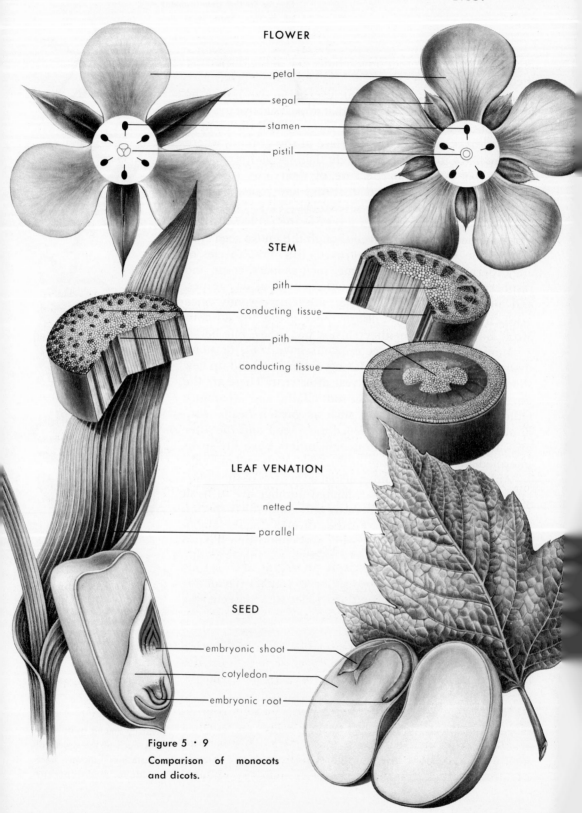

MONOCOT                                                      DICOT

FLOWER

petal

sepal

stamen

pistil

STEM

pith

conducting tissue

pith

conducting tissue

LEAF VENATION

netted

parallel

SEED

embryonic shoot

cotyledon

embryonic root

Figure 5 · 9
Comparison of monocots
and dicots.

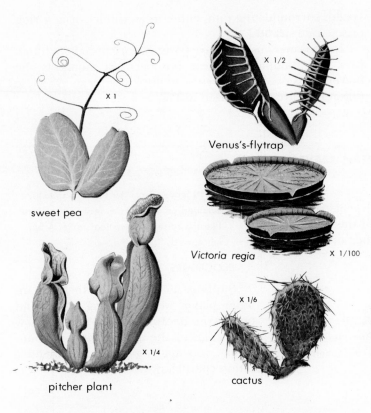

X 1

X 1/2

Venus's-flytrap

sweet pea

Victoria regia                    X 1/100

X 1/6

X 1/4

pitcher plant                    cactus

**Figure 5 · 10**

Diversity among leaves. How do the structural adaptations shown here relate to the life of each kind of plant? (Caution: The broad structures of the cactus are stems.)

subclasses that make up the class. The seed of a flowering plant contains a tiny new plant—the embryo. Part of the embryo consists of one or two modified leaves called *cotyledons*. In the subclass Monocotyledoneae ("monocots") only one of the "seed leaves" is present. In germinating seeds of monocots, such as corn, this single cotyledon digests and absorbs food stored in a region called the *endosperm* and transfers it to the developing young plant. In the subclass Dicotyledoneae ("dicots") the seed contains two cotyledons. In some dicots the endosperm is present in the mature seed. In others—a bean plant, for example—the endosperm is completely absorbed during seed development and food is stored in the cotyledons themselves, which become thick and fleshy.

Monocots usually have leaves in which the main veins are almost parallel. This arrangement differs from the branched and netted veins and veinlets usually found in leaves of dicots.

In the majority of monocots, most of the stem consists of pith surrounded by a harder outer layer. The vascular system is made up of strands extending up and down the stem. In cross section the vascular strands look like islands scattered through the pith. In a dicot stem the vascular

cotyledons    [kŏt′ə lē′dənz; Greek: *kotyle*, anything hollow]

Monocotyledoneae    [mŏn′ə-kŏt′ə lē′də nē; Greek: *monos*, single, + cotyledon]

endosperm    [Greek: *endon*, within, + *sperma*, seed, germ]

Dicotyledoneae [dī kŏt′ə lē′də-nē; Greek: *dis-*, two, double, + cotyledon]

system surrounds the pith, either as a cylinder or as a ring of separate strands.

Dicot flowers usually have parts that are present in fours, fives, or multiples of these numbers. In monocots the flower parts occur in threes or multiples of three. All these differences are summarized in Figure 5 · 9.

## INVESTIGATION 5.1

### DIVERSITY IN ANGIOSPERM LEAVES

#### PURPOSE

You will observe a diversity of forms in angiosperm leaves and then use your observations to extend your understanding of identification keys.

#### MATERIALS
(for each student)

Set A: 10 angiosperm leaves, 1 each from 10 plant species, mounted on cards. The cards, numbered 1–10, are labeled with the plant names.

Set B: 10 leaves, from the same 10 species, mounted on cards. Each leaf is numbered like the corresponding leaf in Set A but not named.

#### PROCEDURE

Suppose a visitor to Earth from another planet were spending a weekend on a farm. Because he does not yet know the names of the animals he is encountering, you might give him the identification chart shown below.

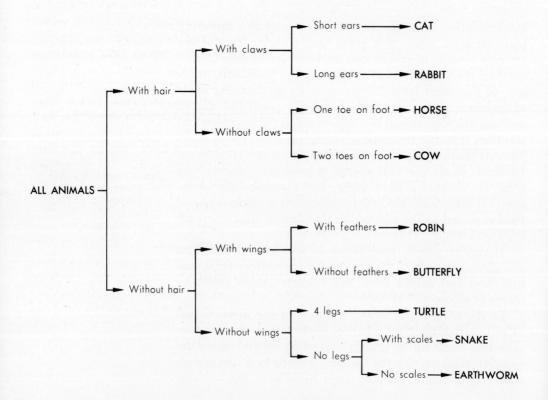

Study this chart and try to determine the principles used to construct it. You will probably recognize quickly that it is a kind of dichotomous key. Such a key is designed so that the group of objects to be classified can be repeatedly divided into smaller groups. Each division is based on sharply contrasting characteristics. Wherever possible, the characteristics used at any point in the key lead to a division into two subgroups of approximately equal size.

Keeping the above points in mind, construct a dichotomous identification chart for the leaves in Set A. Begin by spreading all the leaves on the table in front of you. Study each leaf: In what ways does it resemble the others in the set, and in what ways does it differ? What kinds of characteristics should you look for? Here are a few suggestions:

Are there two distinct regions in the leaf—a stemlike portion (*petiole*) and a flattened part (*blade*)?

Is the blade all in one piece, or is it divided into separate leaflets?

Is the edge of the blade smooth, or is it notched?

Is the blade uniformly green, or are other colors present?

Is the blade heart-shaped, oval, or spear-shaped?

Now select two clearly contrasting characteristics, one of which is possessed by about half the leaves in the set and the other by the remaining half. Following the same arrangement as that used in the chart, draw a box at the left margin of a left-hand page in your data book and label it "All Leaves in Set." (You will probably need both the left-hand and the right-hand pages for the complete chart.) Draw two more boxes to the right of the first box and label them to indicate the characteristics used in making your first division into two groups. Draw

lines to show the division of one group into two. Next study one of the two subgroups. Again find a pair of contrasting characteristics that enable you to divide the group into two subgroups of approximately equal size. Using labeled boxes and lines, place these characteristics in the appropriate position on your chart. Then do the same for the other group. Continue this process until you have completed a key in which there is a final branch for each of the ten kinds of leaves. Label each of these branches with the name of the plant from which the leaf was obtained but do *not* include the identifying number.

Next, turn to Set B and use your chart to identify each of the leaves included in it. Since no two leaves are identical, it is possible that some characteristics used in your chart will need to be changed or modified so that it will work with both sets of leaves.

Now exchange with another student the chart and Set B (but *not* Set A). Using his chart, identify the leaves in his set. Write the number of each leaf next to the name of the species indicated. When you have finished, obtain his Set A (which includes both names and numbers) and check your identifications. If you have not achieved complete success, the fault lies either in his key or in your use of it. Repeat the keying-out process. If differences still turn up, return his key, indicating where you think it needs correction.

### FOR FURTHER INVESTIGATION

Go back to the dichotomous keys in Investigation 4.2 (page 141). In these keys each pair of contrasting characteristics is identified by a number-letter combination. Determine the principle used in this arrangement, and then convert your leaf key from chart form to the number-and-letter system.

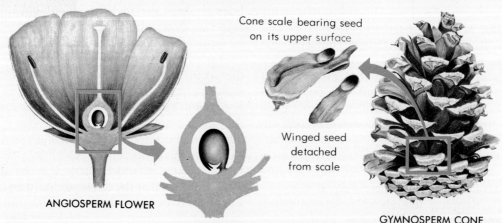

Cone scale bearing seed
on its upper surface

Winged seed
detached
from scale

**ANGIOSPERM FLOWER**

Ovary enclosing
developing seed

**GYMNOSPERM CONE**

**Figure 5 · 11**

Comparison of the seed-bearing structures in angiosperms and gymnosperms.

gymnosperm [jĭm′nə spûrm′]

Gymnospermae [jĭm′nə spûr′-mē; Greek: gymnos, naked, + sperma]

**Figure 5 · 12**

Diversity among conifers. Each illustration shows a twig with leaves and one or more cones.

## GYMNOSPERMS

The class Gymnospermae includes some six hundred species of tracheophytes. Like the angiosperms, they produce seeds. But their seeds do not develop within an ovary; instead, they are attached to the upper surfaces of flat, exposed scales. In most cases a gymnosperm has these seed-bearing scales grouped together in the form of a cone. A seed developing in a cone may be covered by the scales, somewhat as a small coin may be concealed between the pages of a book; or other structures may grow up around

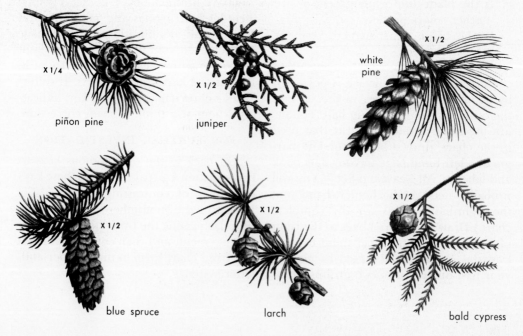

X 1/4

piñon pine

juniper

X 1/2

X 1/2

white
pine

X 1/2

blue spruce

X 1/2

larch

X 1/2

bald cypress

Figure 5 · 13
Diversity among
gymnosperms.

Field Museum of Natural History

*Cycas media,* an Australian cycad. Seed-bearing structures are in the center of the plant. × 1/50

Josef Muench

Robert J. Rodin

*Welwitschia mirabilis,* a gymnosperm of Southwest Africa. A pair of split and twisted leaves spread out over the ground. Many small cones rim the top of the flat stem. × 1/50

The "General Grant" tree, in California. This giant sequoia is a veteran of several thousand winters. × 1/500

the seed before it is mature. The term "gymnosperm" is therefore somewhat misleading.

Almost all gymnosperms are trees or shrubs. Those that bear their seeds in conspicuous cones are called conifers. These cone-bearers—the pines, spruces, and firs—are probably the most familiar gymnosperms. Most conifers are evergreen, but larch and bald cypress are *deciduous*—that is, they lose all their leaves at the end of each growing season.

Although the conifers are the most abundant of present-day gymnosperms, there are other species in the class. In Florida we find cycads—shrublike plants that have leaves like palms, but reproductive structures that clearly show they are gymnosperms. Most cycads are found in the tropics, but they are often grown in large greenhouses in colder regions.

Compared with the angiosperms, there is but a handful of modern gymnosperm species. In some parts of the world, however, much of the vegetation is made up of conifers. The species may be few, but the number of individuals is enormous; the greater part of our lumber supply comes from the conifers.

The oldest living *individual* organisms are gymnosperms. For a long time some of the sequoias of the Sierra Nevada in California were thought to be the oldest living things. Recently, however, it has been shown that some bristlecone pines, a species of the Southwest, are older (about forty-six hundred years old).

## FERNS

Our ancestors found it difficult to believe that ferns have no seeds, and they created much nonsense about the mysterious midnight hours when wise old magicians were thought to collect fern seeds. Although ferns indeed lack seeds, they do have other reproductive structures. At certain times of the year (depending upon the species), small golden or brown spots develop on the undersides of the leaflets or on special leaves that are different from the others on the plant. Each spot consists of a group of knob-shaped cases containing large numbers of tiny *spores*. Spores are almost microscopic. And they are far simpler than seeds; within a spore there is no embryo and only a small amount of food. When the spore case of a fern is ripe, it opens and throws the spores out into the air. If a fern spore falls in a suitably moist place, it germinates and develops rapidly into a thin, green, heart-shaped plant with none of the familiar features of ferns. Rarely over 1 cm in diameter, it is seldom noticed in the woods. A fern plant of the familiar and conspicuous spore-bearing type develops from it.

conifers [kō′nə fərz, kŏn′ə-fərz; Latin: *conus*, a cone, + *ferre*, to bear]

deciduous [dĭ sĭj′oo əs; Latin: *de*, off, down, + *cadere*, to fall]

cycads [sī′kădz]

sequoias [sĭ kwoi′əz]

How can the age of a tree be determined?

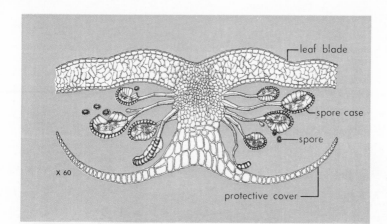

Figure 5 · 14

A section through a fern leaf, showing one of the clusters of spore cases.

leaf blade

spore case

spore

X 60

protective cover

Hugh Spencer                     A      × 7

Figure 5 · 15

Cinnamon fern: (A) Upper surface of the plant that develops from a fern spore. (B) Lower surface of the same plant, showing rhizoids through which it obtains water and minerals from the soil.

Philip Gendreau

B      × 7

Figure 5 · 16

Tree fern on the island of Java. × 1/50

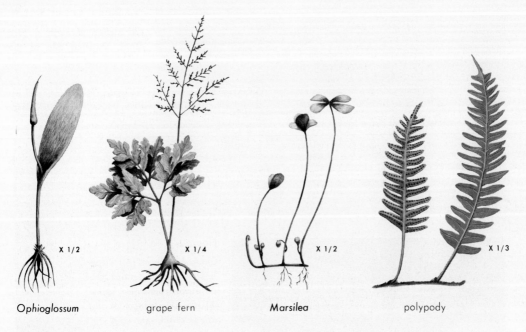

X 1/2    X 1/4    X 1/2    X 1/3

*Ophioglossum*        grape fern        *Marsilea*        polypody

**Figure 5 · 17**

Diversity among North American ferns. Clusters of spore cases are shown on the polypody leaves.

The ferns native to most of the United States are perennials with underground stems. From these stems a new set of leaves appears above ground each spring. In the state of Hawaii and elsewhere in the tropics, many species of ferns have stems that grow upright above the ground —trees that may reach a height of 20 m.

### OTHER TRACHEOPHYTES

In cool woodlands, in tropical forests, and along the sides of railroad tracks, we find still other tracheophytes —species that do not fit into any of the groups we have discussed so far. Most of these are small green plants—perennials without very much woody material in their stems. On the basis of differences in structure and methods of reproduction, taxonomists place them in three separate subphyla.

Lycopsida [lī kŏp′sə də; Greek: *lycos*, wolf, + *opsis*, appearance (because the roots of a lycopod were thought to resemble a wolf's claw)]

Club mosses (subphylum Lycopsida) are low-growing evergreen plants, seldom more than 40 cm tall. They spread by means of branching horizontal stems that grow on the surface of the soil or just below it. The most noticeable part of a club-moss plant is an upright branch growing from this horizontal stem. Certain species bear club-shaped cones at the tips of short, straight stems, and from this feature the name "club moss" is derived. They are rather common plants in much of the United States and are often used to make Christmas wreaths and other decorations.

Longwood Gardens

Figure 5 · 18

A club moss, *Lycopodium obscurum*. Spores are produced in the long, conelike structures at the top. × 4/5

Figure 5 · 19

Horsetails: In this species conelike structures produce spores on shoots that lack chlorophyll. × 1/3

Roche Photography

Paul F. White

Horsetails (subphylum Sphenopsida) have hollow, jointed, upright branches that grow from horizontal underground stems. A circlet of tiny leaves and (sometimes) a whorl of smaller side branches are present at each of the joints. Horsetails are harsh to the touch; their tissues contain silica, a compound present in sand. Pioneer women scrubbed pots and pans with them, and they are still sometimes called "scouring rushes." Like the club mosses, they produce spores in cones that develop at the tips of some of the upright branches. In middle latitudes horsetails rarely reach a height of 2 m, but in the American tropics one species grows in thickets up to 12 m high—giants among their kind.

Unless you live in Florida, Georgia, South Carolina, or Hawaii, you are not likely to encounter psilopsids (subphylum Psilopsida) in the United States—except in a few university greenhouses. All three species of these small plants are found in warm parts of the world. They have a simple stem structure, no roots, and no true leaves. They are the most primitive living tracheophytes.

## NONVASCULAR PLANTS

Tracheophytes are so numerous and conspicuous on land that our concept of the word "plant" is built almost entirely on them. But in water, especially ocean water,

Figure 5 · 20

A psilopsid, *Psilotum nudum*. It grows wild along the Atlantic coast as far north as South Carolina.

Sphenopsida [sfĭ nŏp′sə də; Greek: *sphen*, a wedge, + *opsis* (from the shape of the leaves)]

whorl: here, an arrangement around the same point on a stem

silica [sĭl′ə kə; Latin: *silex*, any hard stone]

psilopsids [sĭ lŏp′sĭdz; Greek: *psilos*, bare, + *opsis*]

Psilopsida [sĭ lŏp′sĭ də]

primitive: See Investigation 5.2.

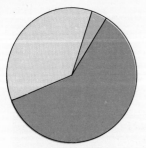

● FLOWERING TRACHEOPHYTES
◐ NONFLOWERING TRACHEOPHYTES
○ NONTRACHEOPHYTES

Figure 5 · 21

Graph showing proportion of plant species in various taxonomic groupings.

X 3

Figure 5 · 22

Moss plant. In nature such a plant does not occur singly but always with others, in colonies.

bryophytes [brī′ə fīts′, Greek: *bryon*, moss, + *phyton*, a plant]

lichen: See page 88.

Bryophyta [brī ə fī′tə]

rhizoids [rī′zoidz; Greek: *rhiza*, a root, + *eidos*, shape]

Marchantia [mär kăn′shĭ ə]

tracheophytes are quite unimportant members of the community. And even on land we can find numerous other plants if we look for them. Nonvascular plants show great diversity, and taxonomists have placed them in many phyla. In the system we are using (Appendix II) there are six.

## BRYOPHYTES

Anyone who has gone on a picnic in the woods has found a moss-covered log or rock that could be used as a soft green seat. The seat is likely to be damp, for mosses grow best in an environment where there is plenty of moisture. Some mosses, however, are rather tough, hardy plants that can survive through dry weather in a dormant condition.

The word "moss" is commonly applied to many different kinds of plants. Spanish moss, for example, is an angiosperm and a rather close relative of pineapples. We have already considered club mosses, vascular plants belonging to the subphylum Lycopsida. Reindeer moss is a lichen. The mosses we are now considering might be distinguished as "true mosses," members of the phylum Bryophyta.

If we separate an individual moss plant from a clump growing on a rock and examine it under low magnification, we find that it consists of an upright stalk with threadlike structures (*rhizoids*) growing out of its base. These help to hold the plant in place and absorb water. A large number of flat, green, leaflike structures are attached along the stalk. If we examine sections of the plant under the microscope, no vascular tissues similar to those in tracheophytes can be found. Therefore, although the moss plant may look somewhat like a tiny tracheophyte with roots, stems, and leaves, these terms are not used because they imply the presence of vascular tissue.

Many people who can recognize a moss have never noticed liverworts. This is not surprising, because these small plants are not nearly so common or widely distributed as mosses. Some look very much like creeping mosses; others resemble branching green ribbons attached to moist soil or wet rocks. The plant body of a liverwort differs from that of a moss in one fundamental respect. The moss plant has its parts more or less regularly arranged around the stalk; like a jellyfish or starfish, it is radially symmetrical. A liverwort has upper (dorsal) and lower (ventral) sides and is either bilaterally symmetrical or asymmetrical.

Not all liverworts are as complicated as *Marchantia* (Figure 5 · 24). In some there are no chambers, no pores, and a less definite pattern of branching.

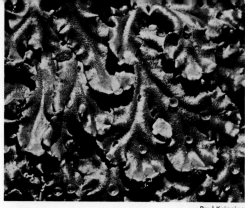

**Figure 5 · 23**

Liverwort (*Marchantia*). Cuplike reproductive structures occur on the upper surface of the plant. × 3/5

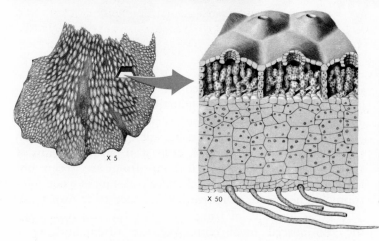

X 5

X 50

**Figure 5 · 24**

Internal structure of *Marchantia*. On the lower surface are rhizoids. On the upper surface are pores through which air passes. Photosynthesis occurs chiefly in the structures within the chambers.

## FUNGI

You may know someone who is enthusiastic about collecting and eating wild mushrooms. Many mushrooms are edible; others are deadly poisonous. The word "toadstool" is commonly used to describe poisonous ones, but only an expert can distinguish "mushrooms" from "toadstools." For eating, the safest mushrooms are those that are grown commercially and sold fresh, dried, or in cans.

Commercial mushroom-growers know there is much more to a mushroom plant than the part we eat. Actually, most of the plant is a mass of slender white threads called *hyphae*. These grow in soil that contains large amounts of dead plant and animal matter—food for the mushroom. The part of the mushroom plant that is eaten is a reproductive structure that grows above the surface of the soil.

hyphae [hī′fē, singular, hypha; Greek: *hyphe*, a web]

Mushrooms—together with plants known by such names as mold, mildew, rust, and smut—belong to the phylum Mycophyta, a group of plants commonly known as fungi (singular, fungus). There is great diversity among fungi. Some are large and conspicuous; others are much

Mycophyta [mī′kō fī′tə; Greek: *mykes*, a mushroom, + *phyton*, a plant]

fungi: For pronunciation, see page 51.

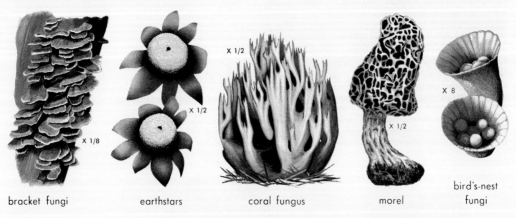

| bracket fungi | earthstars | coral fungus | morel | bird's-nest fungi |

X 1/8    X 1/2    X 1/2    X 1/2    X 8

**Figure 5 · 25**
Diversity among fungi. These are the reproductive structures only.

smaller; many are microscopic. The illustrations (Figure 5·25) emphasize reproductive parts of the plants. The hyphae of most fungi look very much alike.

All fungi have three characteristics: They have no vascular tissues; they reproduce, at least in part, by means of spores; they lack chlorophyll. Some fungi are green, but the color comes from other chemical substances—not chlorophyll. Therefore, fungi cannot produce their own food. The great majority of fungi are probably saprovores like the commercial mushroom. We can often find white hyphae growing among decaying leaves or pieces of rotten wood in a forest. But it is only a short step from feeding on dead organisms to attacks upon organisms that are not yet dead. We might, therefore, expect some fungi to be parasites—and indeed, many are.

The classification of fungi is based upon differences in reproductive structures. Most mushrooms, toadstools, and bracket fungi bear their spores in groups of four at the tips of little club-shaped structures. Such plants are grouped together as club fungi (class Basidiomycetes).

Basidiomycetes [bə sid′ ĭ ō mī-sē′tēz; Greek: *basis*, base, + *myketes*, mushrooms]

**Figure 5 · 26**
Reproductive structure of a field mushroom, a basidiomycete. Where are the spores?

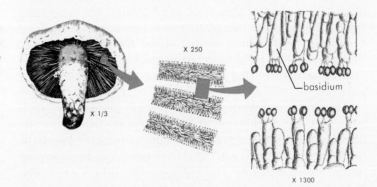

X 1/3    X 250    basidium    X 1300

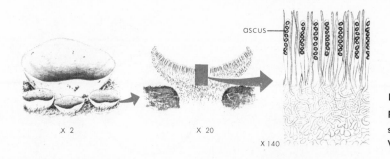

ascus

X 2    X 20

X 140

Figure 5 · 27

Reproductive structures of a sac fungus, an ascomycete. Where are the spores?

Others (class Ascomycetes) as a rule produce their spores in groups of eight, each group enclosed in a sac called an *ascus*. Some of the sac fungi are important in the manufacture of cheeses. The distinctive flavor and appearance of Roquefort cheese is, in part, the result of the growth of an ascomycete, *Penicillium roqueforti.* In Camembert cheese another fungus, *P. camemberti,* is similarly involved. Yeasts also are included in the Ascomycetes, since, under certain conditions, many of them produce spores enclosed in an ascus. Two parasitic ascomycetes are the organisms of chestnut blight and Dutch elm disease, which have destroyed so many trees of these species.

Bread mold and the grayish fungus that grows on drowned flies in an aquarium are members of the class Phycomycetes (alga-like fungi). In this group the hyphae often occur in masses that resemble cotton. Unlike the hyphae of the Basidiomycetes and Ascomycetes, which are divided into separate sections by cross walls, those of the Phycomycetes are continuous, undivided threads. These fungi usually reproduce by means of spores that are formed in large numbers at the tips of hyphae. Parasitic members of this group are involved in many important diseases of grapes, cabbages, onions, cucumbers, and other

Ascomycetes [ăs′kə mī sē′tēz; Greek: *askos*, bag, bladder, + *myketes*]

Roquefort [rōk′fərt]
*Penicillium roqueforti* [pĕn′ə-sĭl′ĭ əm rōk fôr′tī]
*camemberti* [kăm′əm bâr′tī]

Phycomycetes [fī′kō mī sē′tēz; Greek: *phykos*, seaweed, + *myketes*]

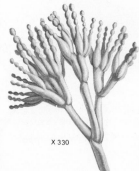

X 330

Figure 5 · 28

Reproductive structures of a species of *Penicillium.*

Figure 5 · 29

*Penicillium notatum,* used in production of penicillin. These are experimental cultures grown in the laboratory of a manufacturing drug company.

Philip Gendreau

X 1/4

Laminaria

X 1/2

Ulva

X 40

X 2

Polysiphonia

X 5

X 165

Enteromorpha

X 1/2

Oscillatoria

X 1/2

Chondrus

X 1/2

X 1/2

Ascophyllum

X 1/2

Fucus

Figure 5 · 30

Diversity among algae. To which phylum does each of these belong?

Victor Larsen

Figure 5 · 31

A phycomycete (*Saprolegnia*) growing on a drowned fly in an aquarium. Only the hyphae, not the reproductive structures, appear here. × 8

crop plants. Occasionally these fungi destroy huge quantities of food crops. For example, in 1845 and 1846 a phycomycete ruined the potato crop in Ireland, resulting in a disastrous famine there.

Much is yet to be discovered about many fungi. In some species the reproductive stages that would enable us to place a fungus in one of the three classes described above have never been found. Such fungi are placed in the class Deuteromycetes (Fungi Imperfecti). Here "imperfect" applies not so much to the plants as to the information we have about them: When the reproductive stages of such a species are discovered, it is placed in another class.

Deuteromycetes [dū′tər ō mī-sē′tēz; Greek: *deuteros*, second, secondary, + *myketes*]

### ALGAE

Aside from swamps, marshes, and shallows, the waters of the world contain few bryophytes or tracheophytes. In aquatic communities the producers are mostly organisms that are much simpler in structure than any we have discussed so far. Some are protists, but most are plants. Although these plants lack stems, roots, and leaves, some grow to enormous size — up to a length of 45 m, though their anchoring stalks are seldom more than 15 cm in diameter. Associated with these giant seaweeds are many smaller plants, the majority of which are microscopic.

Although these plants belong to four distinctly different phyla, all may be referred to as algae (singular, alga). The common names given to the algal phyla are based on color. All algae contain green chlorophyll, but other pigments may also be present, sometimes completely masking the green. Some "green algae" (phylum Chlorophyta) are reddish, some "brown algae" (phylum Phaeophyta) are yellow-green, and at least one of the "red algae" (phylum

algae: For pronunciation, see page 75.

Chlorophyta [klôr′ə fī′tə; Greek: *chloros*, green, + *phyton*, a plant]

Phaeophyta [fē′ə fī′tə; Greek: *phaios*, brown, + *phyton*]

**Figure 5 · 32**
A mass of kelp, one of the large seaweeds, exposed at low tide. × 1/25

Rhodophyta  [rō'də fī'tə;
Greek: *rhodon*, a rose (red), +
*phyton*]

Rhodophyta) is a beautiful violet-green. Thus an apparently convenient way to classify these plants is sometimes very misleading. The characteristics used by plant taxonomists are much less obvious. They include ways in which reproduction is accomplished and the chemical form in which food is stored.

All algae require a moist environment to actively carry on their life processes. Many, however, can become dormant and in this condition remain alive but inactive for long periods of time. Some are even found in deserts. Others live in the water that forms during summer daylight hours on surfaces of snowbanks in high mountains and polar regions. A diversity that allows life on snowbanks, in deserts, on tree bark, in polluted streams and sparkling lakes, on surf-pounded coasts and the broad water of the open oceans—such diversity is as great as any we saw in the animal kingdom. Yet the algae are overlooked by most people.

Most of the algae you are likely to encounter in school aquariums and laboratories are green or golden algae. Unless your school is located near the ocean, you may have little direct experience with living brown and red algae, almost all of which are marine. But most people have indirect contact with them, for much commercial ice cream contains a marine algal product to make it smooth. In some parts of the world—Japan, for example—man is a first-order consumer of the larger marine algae.

## LICHENS

Among the most widely distributed living things are lichens. In a tropical rain forest, on a tombstone in New Hampshire, buried under arctic snow, on the bark of a tree in Arizona—in all these places you can find lichens. In Chapter 3 we discussed the mutualistic relationship of the algae and fungi that make up lichens. Yet, so definite are

A   X 3/5                                    Dennis Brokaw   **B**   X 4/5                    Haven Kolb

the form, color, and other characteristics of each of these
"partnerships" that for several hundred years biologists
described lichens as if they were single organisms. More
than fifteen thousand "species" have been named.

The lichen body has a framework of fungal hyphae. In
its upper layers are many groups of small algae. The algae
will grow independently, and many can be recognized as
species that are also known to live "alone." The fungi, on
the other hand, do not grow well when separated from
their partners. They can be placed in the known classes of
fungi, but they are unlike any species that live "alone."
None of this matters much when we view the world ecologically. But what does the taxonomist do with lichens? If he
describes them as species, where does he put them in the
classification? If he describes the partners separately, are
not his species of fungi rather odd? We are not answering
these questions, but you will notice that we do not have a
place for the lichens in Appendix II.

Figure 5 · 33

Diversity among lichens.
(A) Lichen growing on a
tree branch. (B) Lichen
growing on sterile soil. (See
Figure 3 · 18 for other
kinds of lichens.)

## INVESTIGATION 5.2

### THE CONCEPT OF
### "PRIMITIVE CHARACTERISTICS"

#### PURPOSE

While examining some of the kinds
of structural diversity in the plant kingdom, you will discover the degree to
which various plants of today are thought
to be similar to plants of the past.

**Figure 5 · 34**
**Chart for determining "Advancement Score" for a plant.**

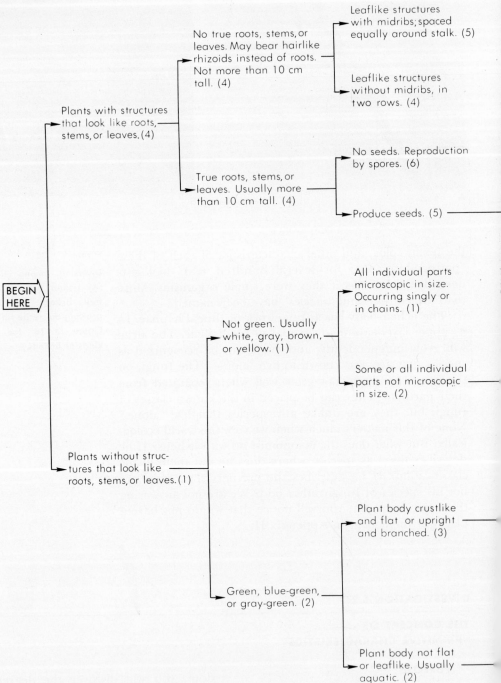

Plants with structures that look like roots, stems, or leaves. (4)

No true roots, stems, or leaves. May bear hairlike rhizoids instead of roots. Not more than 10 cm tall. (4)

Leaflike structures with midribs; spaced equally around stalk. (5)

Leaflike structures without midribs, in two rows. (4)

True roots, stems, or leaves. Usually more than 10 cm tall. (4)

No seeds. Reproduction by spores. (6)

Produce seeds. (5)

BEGIN HERE

Not green. Usually white, gray, brown, or yellow. (1)

All individual parts microscopic in size. Occurring singly or in chains. (1)

Some or all individual parts not microscopic in size. (2)

Plants without structures that look like roots, stems, or leaves. (1)

Plant body crustlike and flat or upright and branched. (3)

Green, blue-green, or gray-green. (2)

Plant body not flat or leaflike. Usually aquatic. (2)

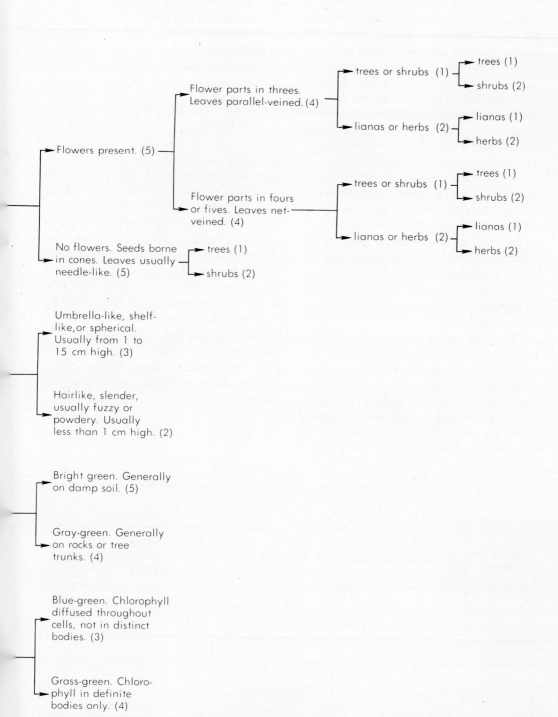

Flowers present. (5)

Flower parts in threes. Leaves parallel-veined. (4)

trees or shrubs (1)

trees (1)

shrubs (2)

lianas or herbs (2)

lianas (1)

herbs (2)

Flower parts in fours or fives. Leaves net-veined. (4)

trees or shrubs (1)

trees (1)

shrubs (2)

lianas or herbs (2)

lianas (1)

herbs (2)

No flowers. Seeds borne in cones. Leaves usually needle-like. (5)

trees (1)

shrubs (2)

Umbrella-like, shelf-like, or spherical. Usually from 1 to 15 cm high. (3)

Hairlike, slender, usually fuzzy or powdery. Usually less than 1 cm high. (2)

Bright green. Generally on damp soil. (5)

Gray-green. Generally on rocks or tree trunks. (4)

Blue-green. Chlorophyll diffused throughout cells, not in distinct bodies. (3)

Grass-green. Chlorophyll in definite bodies only. (4)

## BACKGROUND INFORMATION

Biologists sometimes use the terms "primitive" (for example, on page 171) and "advanced" when discussing diversity among organisms. These terms are linked with the idea developed near the end of Chapter 4: that species existing today are related to each other through their ancestors. From this we can develop the further idea that some of the species living today retain more of their ancestors' characteristics than do other species. An organism that has retained many of the older characteristics – in other words, one that has changed little from its ancestors – is said to be "primitive." An organism that has few of the characteristics of its ancestors is said to be "advanced." Of course, there can be many degrees of advancement, so "primitive" and "advanced" are not absolute terms; they are useful only in making comparisons.

Through many kinds of evidence, but chiefly from the study of fossils, botanists have reached fairly general agreement about which characteristics are very ancient in the history of plants and which characteristics have appeared more recently. The chart to be used in this investigation (Figure 5·34) is based on such studies.

## MATERIALS AND EQUIPMENT

Native plants representing various
    phyla of the plant kingdom,
    10 labeled specimens
Monocular microscopes
Hand lenses
Stereomicroscopes
Microscope slide
Cover slip

## PROCEDURE

You will be provided with labeled specimens of 10 different plants. Determine the "Advancement Score" for each of these as follows: Start at the left of the chart on pages 180–181 (Figure 5·34). Arrows from the starting point lead to two descriptions. Choose the one that fits the plant you are scoring. Proceed across the chart by following the arrows and choosing the descriptions that best fit the plant. Continue as far as the arrows go. The "Advancement Score" for the plant is the *sum* of all the numbers appearing after the descriptions you used in working through the chart. Record these numbers on a table like the following:

| NAME OF PLANT | NUMERICAL VALUES OF CHOICES MADE | TOTAL "ADVANCEMENT SCORE" | RANK |
|---|---|---|---|
| 1. | | | |
| 2. | | | |
| 3. | | | |
| 10. | | | |

When you have a total score for each of the plants studied, give the plant having the highest score a rank of "10" and that having the lowest score a rank of "1." Then rank all the others according to their individual scores. Record the rankings in the column at the right side of the table.

The more alike two plants are, the more alike their scores will be. The greater the degree of difference between two plants, the greater the difference in their scores. Advanced plants will have high scores (maximum, 26), while primitive plants will have comparatively low scores (minimum, 3).

### DISCUSSION

• Assuming that today's plants have developed from simpler, fewer, and older species, would you expect to find less diversity or greater diversity in the plant kingdom as time goes on? Explain.(1)

• Basing your conclusions upon the way the plant score chart was designed, list some of the most important differences among plants.(2)   • What are some of the less important differences?(3)

• On what basis do you distinguish between the important differences and those that are less important?(4)

• Using the information included in the chart, list the characteristics you would expect to find in a primitive plant.(5)   • Do the same for a highly advanced plant.(6)   • In what ways does the plant score chart resemble the dichotomous key constructed in Investigation 5.1?(7)   • How does it differ from this key?(8)

Man probably named many kinds of organisms before he classified them. Organisms *could* be classified without being named. But because our present system of naming organisms developed along with our present system of classification, the two are linked together. An organism's biological name is made up of two words: first, the word that identifies the genus; second, the word that identifies the species within that genus. A species word can be used again and again in combination with different genera.

Diversity in the plant kingdom is less evident to most people than is diversity in the animal kingdom, but plants are just as varied as animals. The obvious difference between trees, shrubs, and herbs has been found to be a misleading basis for a classification designed to show kinship. Botanists have found reproductive structures and life histories reliable evidence of kinship, though modern botanists, like modern zoologists, may also use many other kinds of evidence.

Most land plants—those most familiar to us—are members of one phylum, the tracheophytes. These plants all have vascular systems through which water can easily flow, carrying dissolved substances from the soil to considerable heights above the ground. Plants of other phyla lack such a structural adaptation. They are, therefore, rarely taller than 0.4 m if they grow on land.

Most aquatic plants are members of various phyla generally referred to as "algae." Though many members of these phyla are microscopic, some—the seaweeds—may be rather large.

Besides the plants that dominate the land and waters, there are the bryophytes—small plants, usually of damp habitats—and the fungi. The fungi lack chlorophyll; thus, unlike the great majority of plants, they are consumers.

## GUIDE QUESTIONS

1. From the viewpoint of modern taxonomy, why is a classification of plants that is based on the differences between trees, shrubs, and herbs a poor one?
2. What were Linnaeus' major contributions to taxonomy?
3. What are the basic principles of the binomial system of nomenclature used in biology?
4. Why is it incorrect to think of biological nomenclature as being Latin?
5. What is the chief structural characteristic of the tracheophytes?
6. What does a botanist mean by the word "flower"?
7. What characteristics of a flower would lead you to believe it is probably pollinated by the wind?
8. What structural characteristics of fruits seem to be adaptations related to seed dispersal?
9. In what ways are dicotyledons unlike monocotyledons?
10. What are gymnosperms?
11. What is a spore?
12. Why is the term "moss" rather indefinite?
13. What kinds of characteristics are used in classifying fungi?
14. What plants are the chief producers in the oceans?
15. Why have lichens been given no place in our "Catalogue of Living Things"?
16. What does a botanist mean by a "primitive" plant?

## PROBLEMS

1. People who buy ferns as ornamental houseplants sometimes return them to the florist because there are dark spots on the undersides of the leaves. As a biologist, what explanation would you give such customers?
2. Insectivorous plants are frequently found in regions where the soil is deficient in one or more elements needed by plants. Why?
3. What advantages and disadvantages does a seed-producing plant have compared with one that produces only spores? How do you interpret the words "advantage" and "disadvantage" here?
4. Most plant parts that we use as direct sources of food are either seeds of annual herbs or underground roots or stems of biennial or perennial herbs. Explain this.
5. Criticize the following statement: "All plants that are producers are green, because they contain the green pigment chlorophyll."
6. The classification of plants has been revised by several botanists in the last quarter century. Look up an old classification and a few recent ones in college botany textbooks. (Wilson and Loomis, *Botany*—New York: Holt, Rinehart and Winston, Inc., 1962—is a good beginning.) Compare these classifications with each other and with the one that is used in this book.
7. How many of the taxonomic groups of plants in Appendix II are represented in your locality? Consider wild and cultivated plants, indoor and outdoor plants, aquatic and terrestrial plants.

## SUGGESTED READINGS

AHMADJIAN, V. "The Fungi of Lichens," *Scientific American,* February, 1963. Pp. 122–130+.

BENTON, A. H., and W. E. WERNER. *Principles of Field Biology and Ecology.* 2nd ed. New York: McGraw-Hill Book Co., Inc., 1965. Chapter 3. (An excellent, simple discussion of the problems of taxonomy—the species, classification, and nomenclature. Fairly easy.)

CHRISTENSEN, C. M. *Molds and Man; an Introduction to the Fungi.* Minneapolis: University of Minnesota Press, 1951. (A balanced account of the important relationships between fungi and man. Moderately difficult.)

GROSVENOR, M. B. "World's Tallest Tree Discovered," *National Geographic Magazine,* July, 1964. Pp. 1–9.

HYLANDER, C. J. *World of Plant Life.* 2nd ed. New York: The Macmillan Co., 1956. (A good, simple description of the important plant groups. Fairly easy.)

JAQUES, H. E. (ed.). "The Pictured Key to Nature Series." Dubuque, Iowa: Wm. C. Brown Co. (This series makes extensive use of keys for identification. Volumes, by various authors, have been published on trees, flowering plants, "seaweeds," grasses, mosses and liverworts, cacti, and "weeds.")

LAMB, I. M. "Complex Primitives: The Red Alga Group," *Natural History,* March, 1960. Pp. 16–25.

RAVEN, P. H., and T. R. MERTENS. *Plant Systematics.* (BSCS Pamphlet 23.) Boston: D. C. Heath and Co., 1965. (A clear statement of aims and methods of modern plant taxonomy.)

TIFFANY, L. H. *Algae: The Grass of Many Waters.* 2nd ed. Springfield, Ill.: Charles C. Thomas, Publishers, 1958. (An excellent introduction to this group of plants. Moderately difficult.)

# 6

# Protists

## THE DISCOVERY OF MICROORGANISMS

Behind words like "animal" and "plant" lies a long history. But when we turn from the familiar, visible world to the world revealed by the microscope, we encounter something comparatively new to human experience—so new that we can chart the history of its discovery and exploration.

What do we mean by "discovery"? We say Columbus discovered America in 1492. But it is clear that he did not fully realize what he had discovered; it is also clear that the Vikings had been on the continent before him. And Columbus certainly did not discover America for the American Indians. We are driven to saying that *modern* European knowledge of the New World can be traced back to Columbus' first voyage. But the time was ripe. European knowledge had reached a point where the discovery was inevitable.

### LEEUWENHOEK AND HIS "LITTLE ANIMALS"

Antony van Leeuwenhoek [lā′-vən hōok′]: 1632–1723. Dutch lens-maker and naturalist

We say that Antony van Leeuwenhoek discovered the world of microscopic life in the 1670's. There were no Indians there before him—his discovery was new, not only to Europeans but to all mankind. Yet he (like Columbus) did not—could not—know the full significance of what he had found. And again the time was ripe.

Really, Leeuwenhoek's microscopes were simple lenses, not compound instruments. But so carefully were they ground that he could obtain clear magnifications of 200X.

Leeuwenhoek's discovery resulted from the development of a technique: the grinding of lenses for magnification. It is curious that the discovery came so late, because eyeglasses had been known for several hundred years. But it was not until around 1600 that people started to use lenses as telescopes, to look at distant things, and as microscopes, to enlarge things nearby.

The Bettmann Archive

**Figure 6 · 1**
Antony van Leeuwenhoek. He is holding one of his microscopes in his left hand.

**Figure 6 · 2**
Replica of a Leeuwenhoek microscope, about natural size. The specimen was placed on the metal point in front of the lens. The turnscrews adjusted the focus.

Leeuwenhoek was a cloth merchant of Delft, Holland. His hobby was grinding lenses. He also did metalworking to construct tubes for holding the lenses. After a while he became interested in the things he could see with his instruments. Sometime after the middle of the seventeenth century, Leeuwenhoek began to look at many kinds of small objects. Other men were examining the fine structure of easily visible plants and animals. But Leeuwenhoek alone had the idea of looking at drops of water from rain, wells, the sea, and melting snow. By 1675 he had observed in such water—apparently for the first time by any man—some of the living things that we now call protists. He called them *tierken*, Dutch for "little animals."

Fortunately for the fame of Leeuwenhoek, his observations were communicated in letters to the Royal Society for the Improvement of Natural Knowledge, London. In the Royal Society's *Philosophical Transactions*, the first scientific journal in the English language, a paper appeared (Vol. 11, 1677) with this title: "Observations communicated to the publisher by Mr. Antony van Leeuwenhoek in a Dutch Letter of the 9th of October, 1676, here English'd: Concerning little animals by him observed in Rain-Well-Sea-and Snow water; as also in water wherein Pepper had lain infused." In 1680 Leeuwenhoek also reported seeing organisms that are now called yeasts, and in 1683 he observed bacteria—all "little animals" to him. The world of microorganisms was beginning to unfold.

*tierken*: Leeuwenhoek spelled this Dutch word in more than one way. Spelling in most languages was variable until the nineteenth century.

Such was the fame of the Royal Society—still flourishing today—and so wide the distribution of its *Transactions* that the news was soon spread among natural philosophers. (The word "science" began to replace the term "natural philosophy" only after the beginning of the nineteenth century.) Those who had microscopes or could construct them began making observations of their own. But when we look back now, progress in exploring the world of microorganisms seems remarkably slow. It was hard to get away from the idea that these minute creatures simply came into being spontaneously, when conditions were right, and perhaps vanished as easily. Studying them seemed unimportant. The great classification of all organisms by Linnaeus (in the 1750's) took little notice of the microscopic world.

spontaneously [spŏn tā′nĕ əs lĭ; Latin: *sponte*, of one's own accord]

### THE BEGINNINGS OF MICROBIOLOGY

After 1800, following the Industrial Revolution, the manufacture of microscopes improved rapidly. Thus the study of microscopic organisms increased. But it was not until the middle of the nineteenth century that the attention of biologists focused upon them. At that time a series of discoveries clearly showed the importance of these creatures to man's welfare.

In this period the name of Louis Pasteur stands out because of the variety of the subjects he studied, the ingenuity of his experiments, and the force of his personality. First, Pasteur showed the importance of *microbes* (a general name for microscopic organisms) in the processes by which wine, beer, and cheeses are made. He thus linked the world of microscopic life to commercially important enterprises. Second, he furthered (though he did not originate) the idea that microbes were associated with diseases of larger organisms, including man. Third, he demolished the idea that living microbes might arise of their own accord from dead materials. Microbes, then, had to be studied as visible animals and plants were studied. They became a true part of biology.

Pasteur was trained as a chemist, but his interests were many. Robert Koch was a physician, and he concentrated his attention upon the relationship of microbes to disease. To study this relationship, he had to be able to grow and study the microbes. For nearly forty years he and his colleagues invented methods, materials, and instruments for culturing, handling, and examining microorganisms, especially bacteria. Many of their methods are still used. Koch himself set up the experimental procedure by which a particular microbe could be definitely associated with a partic-

The Bettmann Archive

**Figure 6 · 3**

**Louis Pasteur [lwē päs-toer′]: 1822–1895. French chemist and biologist.**

ingenuity [ĭn′jə nū′ə tĭ]: inventive talent

See Investigation 6.4.

Figure 6 · 4
Robert Koch [kôKH]: 1843 –
1910. The German physi-
cian and microbiologist is
shown here at work in his
laboratory.

ular disease, and he used the procedure to identify the
microbe of tuberculosis. Building on the work of Pasteur,
he founded the science of microbiology.

An old but still excellent book
on the development of microbiology is Paul de Kruif's
*Microbe Hunters* (paperback —
New York: Pocket Books Inc.).

## INVESTIGATION 6.1

### A GARDEN OF MICROORGANISMS

#### PURPOSES

In this investigation you will observe
the growth of some common microorganisms, learn to recognize some groups
of microorganisms *macroscopically* (with
the unaided eye), and observe some microbes under the microscope.

#### BACKGROUND INFORMATION

In modern biology the word "microorganism" does not always mean a
microscopic organism. The methods developed by Koch and his colleagues for
working with bacteria were later found
suitable for working with many other
organisms. Gradually biologists began to
extend the meaning of the term "microorganism" to include any organism
that could be cultivated and handled by
the methods originally developed for
bacteria, whether such organisms were
microscopic or not. Thus, today we can

find in books on "microbiology" much
about organisms that are *not* microscopic
(molds, for example) and little or nothing about some organisms that *are* microscopic (rotifers, for example).

#### MATERIALS AND EQUIPMENT
(for each team)

Glass-marking crayon

Glass finger bowls (about 250 ml) or
any clear plastic containers, 10

Fruit (a plum, an orange, a lemon, an
apple, or similar kinds), very ripe

Ripe grapes, 5 to 10

Water from pond, lake, or river,
containing materials from the
bottom and some surface scum

Hay or dried grass

Dried beans

Cottage cheese or cream cheese

Lettuce

Bread

Filter paper

Garden soil

Cornstarch

Spatula

Peppercorns

Glass covers for finger bowls, 3 or 4

(for each pair of students)

Hand lens or stereomicroscope

Forceps

Dissecting needles, 2

Microscope slide

Medicine dropper

Cover slip

Monocular microscope

## PROCEDURE

**A. Setting up the cultures.** Mark the finger bowls with your team symbol and number them *1* through *10*. Place materials in the bowls as follows:

Bowl 1 — Fruit, cut to fit into bowl if necessary.

Bowl 2 — Slightly crushed grapes, with sufficient water to cover.

Bowl 3 — Water from lake, pond, or river, containing surface and bottom materials.

Bowl 4 — Enough hay to cover the bottom of the bowl, and 200 ml of water.

Bowl 5 — A few dried beans and 200 ml of water.

Bowl 6 — Cottage cheese or cream cheese, spread over bottom of bowl.

Bowl 7 — Lettuce leaves, broken into small pieces, in a little water.

Bowl 8 — Two pieces of stale bread, moistened with water. (Caution: The bread should not be *soaked*.) Expose to air for twenty-four hours before covering.

Bowl 9 — Place a piece of filter paper on the bottom of the finger bowl. Mix 5 g of cornstarch with 95 g of rich soil. While mixing the soil and starch, add enough water to give the mixture a doughlike consistency. Spread the mixture on the filter paper, using a spatula to make a smooth surface. Keep the soil mixture moist throughout the investigation.

Bowl 10 — 1 g of peppercorns and 200 ml of tap water.

Place the bowls in stacks of three or four and cover each stack with a piece of glass or an empty bowl. Do not place in direct sunlight. If any of the bowls fit very tightly together, place the flat end of a toothpick between them. (Be sure to expose Bowl 8 to air, as directed.)

**B. Observation.** Examine the bowls each day. In your data book record (*a*) the date of each observation, (*b*) the number of the bowl you are observing, (*c*) the macroscopic appearance of the bowl's contents, (*d*) the appearance under a hand lens or stereomicroscope, and (*e*) anything else that you can notice with your senses.

In describing growth of organisms in the bowl, consider color first, then size. In recording the appearance of the growths, you may find some of the following terms useful: fuzzy, cottony, powdery, smooth, rough, shiny, glistening, dull, compact, spreading, irregular. You should not, of course, limit yourself to using these terms alone.

After good growth has been obtained, make observations with the monocular microscope as follows: Using forceps or dissecting needles, place bits of the visible growths from the solid media on a clean slide. Where a liquid medium has been used, simply draw up a drop or two of it with a medicine dropper and place on a slide. Then, for either kind of preparation, add a cover slip and observe. Record your observations by making sketches. Using references and help from the teacher, attempt to place organisms in taxonomic groups.

## DISCUSSION

• Is there any evidence that different groups of microbes grow better on one or another kind of food? If so, what is it? (1) • Which group of microorganisms was found in the largest number of dishes? What reason can you suggest for this? (2) In Chapter 3 we encountered the idea of succession. • Have you any evidence for succession within a bowl?(3) • What happens to the food materials as the microorganisms grow? Explain.(4)

### FOR FURTHER INVESTIGATION

1. Some of the things we have used as foods for microorganisms are also foods for us. We have seen what the microorganisms do to them, and clearly it is desirable to prevent such effects.

Choose one food and investigate the growth of microorganisms on it at various temperatures.

2. Chemicals are often added to our foods to discourage the growth of microorganisms. Commercial bread usually contains a "mold inhibitor," and commercial catsup a "preservative." The presence of these substances is mentioned on the label of the product. By comparing microbial growth on commercial bread and catsup with growth on homemade products, you can test the effectiveness of such chemicals.

## THE PHYLA OF PROTISTS

The two aims in classification—convenience and the expression of relationships—often conflict. In classifying microorganisms, no really satisfactory method of avoiding this conflict has yet been found.

The diversity of life may be thought of as an almost continuous band or spectrum, like a section across a rainbow; but instead of different colors, we observe different species as we move across the spectrum of living things. At one end of the diversity spectrum, all organisms are unmistakably animals—such as horses and elephants; at the other end they are just as obviously plants—such as grasses and roses. But what about the central zone? As we move from either end toward the center, a point is reached where the organisms—mostly microscopic forms—are neither clearly animals nor clearly plants. They possess some characteristics of both groups; yet they are different from either group.

As early as 1866 Ernst Haeckel proposed a third kingdom, the Protista. In recent years this suggestion has been revived, and it is used in this book. There is, however, no agreement among biologists on the usefulness of a third kingdom and even less agreement as to which organisms should be placed in it. Certainly size is not the only point to be considered—many microscopic organisms are undoubtedly animals (rotifers), and others are undoubtedly plants (yeasts, many algae). So the Protista are not just all the microorganisms.

Ernst Haeckel [hĕk'əl]: 1834–1919. German biologist

Protista [prō tĭs'tə; Greek: protos, first (here "most primitive")]

The protist kingdom is frankly a grouping of convenience. Many species that have been placed in it combine "animal" characteristics with "plant" characteristics. If we do not place them in a separate kingdom, we must place them in *both* kingdoms. By assigning such puzzling species to one "catchall" group, we can retain better organization in the animal and plant kingdoms.

## BACTERIA

Schizomycetes [skĭz ō mī sēt'ēz; Greek: *schizein*, to cut, split, + *myketes*, mushrooms]

Figure 6 · 5
Diversity among schizomycetes: (A) Spherical bacteria (*Bordetella pertussis*), organism of whooping cough. (B) Rod-shaped bacteria (*Bacillus megatherium*). (C) Spirochete (*Spirochaete recurrentis*). (D) Rickettsia of Rocky Mountain spotted fever.

The phylum Schizomycetes includes the smallest things that can be classified, without uncertainty, as living. Some organisms in the phylum are larger than others, but all are far too small to be seen with the unaided eye. They generally range from 0.001 to 0.005 mm (1 to 5μ) in size. Most species in this size range are called *bacteria*, and we can conveniently use this name for the phylum as a whole, except where noted otherwise.

The great majority of the schizomycetes are consumers —they obtain their energy from foods produced by other organisms. Some are parasites; but many are saprovores, using the materials in dead organisms as food. A few

A   x 19,000                                   Leslie A. Chambers

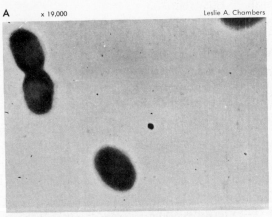

B   x 3000                                     C. F. Robinow

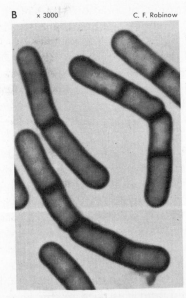

C   x 8000          Carl Struwe from Monkmeyer

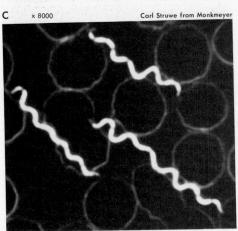

Harry Plotz, Joseph E. Smadel, T. F. Anderson, Leslie A.
D   x 32,000   Chambers, and *Journal of Experimental Medicine*

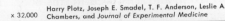
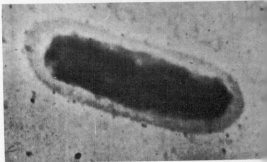

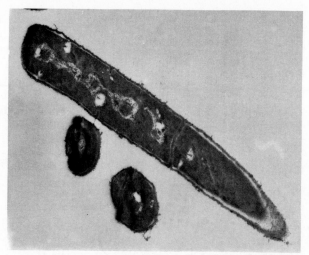

George B. Chapman and James Hillier

Figure 6 · 6
An electronmicrograph reveals the internal structure of a "simple" bacterium, *Bacillus cereus*. In the longitudinal section note the faint new cross wall.

bacteria, however, possess pigments that are chemically similar to chlorophylls in plants. These bacteria carry on a kind of photosynthesis that produces food but differs in some details from plant photosynthesis. A few other bacteria obtain their energy from inorganic substances that contain iron, sulfur, or nitrogen. They are the only known organisms that do not depend, either directly or indirectly, upon radiant solar energy.

Ever since it was first suspected that microbes might be a factor in diseases of man, the parasitic bacteria have received far more attention than the rest. Yet, for man, benefits resulting from activities of nonparasitic bacteria are enormous. Bacteria break down the chemical compounds in dead organisms, making them available to the roots of growing plants. Bacteria serve as food for countless small organisms, including the young of many crustaceans that are important links in food chains leading to man. Man has put bacteria to work in producing alcohols; in tanning leather; in separating fibers from hemp, flax, and other plants; in preparing tea, coffee, and cocoa. Cheese, buttermilk, and yogurt are bacterial products. So are sauerkraut, dill pickles, and silage for livestock.

As ordinarily prepared for microscopic study, bacteria have few visible characteristics besides shape. Early in the history of bacteriology, however, it became clear that there are many more species than shapes of bacteria. Therefore, bacterial taxonomists were among the first to use characteristics other than structure for classification. The kinds of foods bacteria use, the kinds of waste materials they produce, their reactions to various dyes and other chemicals,

Wyeth Laboratories

Figure 6 · 7
Compare this electron microscope with Leeuwenhoek's microscope and with those in your laboratory.

even the macroscopic appearance of bacterial colonies—all of these may be used to identify bacteria.

Besides the "true" bacteria, a number of other small organisms are usually placed in the Schizomycetes. Among these are the spirochetes, which, unlike most "true" bacteria, are flexible and may reach a length of 0.5 mm (though they are invisible because they are very slender). Also, there are the actinomycetes, which form structures somewhat resembling fungal hyphae. And there are organisms still smaller than most bacteria—the rickettsias, among others.

Rickettsias, most of which are rodlike or oval, measure about 0.35 by $0.25\mu$ and are thus barely visible under a light microscope. With the exception of one known species, they can be grown only in living cells. Electronmicrographs indicate that they have an internal structure much like that of bacteria—in fact, some microbiologists think rickettsias may be very small bacteria that became parasitic in the past and can now live in no other way. Many kinds of rickettsias live in the digestive tracts of insects and other arthropods. Several kinds are involved in human diseases, the most important being typhus (carried by lice) and Rocky Mountain spotted fever (carried by ticks).

spirochetes [spī'rə kēts'; Greek: *speira*, a spiral, + *chaite*, hair]

actinomycetes [ăk'tə nō mī'sēts; Greek: *aktinos*, ray, + *myketes*]

rickettsias [ri kĕt'sĭ əz]: named for Howard T. Ricketts, 1871– 1910, American pathologist

electronmicrograph: a picture taken by means of a stream of electrons instead of by rays of light

## INVESTIGATION 6.2

### MICROBIAL TECHNIQUES: POPULATIONS

#### INTRODUCTION

If we have a mixed population of horses, cattle, and sheep in a pasture, it is easy to separate the three kinds of animals and determine the number of each. But if we have a mixed population of millions of invisible microorganisms, how can we separate the kinds into *pure cultures,* and how can we count the individuals? There is a further difficulty: Occasionally horses and cattle may be dangerous, but at least we can see them coming. How can we protect ourselves from dangerous kinds of microorganisms in a mixed population?

Since the days of Koch, methods for studying microorganisms safely have been much improved, and entirely new techniques—some, for example, involving the use of radioactive materials—have been developed. But the beginning microbiologist must still learn the basic microbial techniques.

#### PURPOSES

In this investigation you should learn how to (a) handle microorganisms safely and efficiently; (b) determine the density of a microbial population; and (c) obtain pure cultures from a mixed culture of microorganisms.

#### MATERIALS AND EQUIPMENT
(per team)

Culture tubes, plugged, containing
   15 ml of sterile nutrient agar, 5
Test-tube rack
Beakers, 600 ml, 2

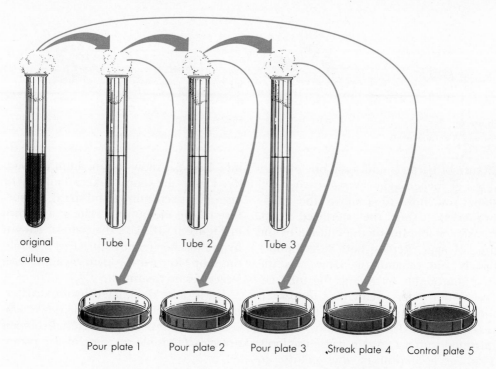

original
culture

Tube 1

Tube 2

Tube 3

Pour plate 1    Pour plate 2    Pour plate 3    Streak plate 4    Control plate 5

Figure 6 · 8
Plan for setting up Investigation 6.2.

Ring stand
Bunsen burner or alcohol lamp
Thermometer, —10°C to +110°C
Sterile petri dishes, 5
Glass-marking crayon
Inoculating loop
Mixed culture of bacteria (*Serratia
    marcescens* and *Sarcina lutea*)
Paper towels

## PROCEDURE

The following directions will be supplemented with demonstrations by the
teacher. As you read the directions and
observe the demonstrations, keep the
following questions in mind: (*a*) How do
these techniques prevent organisms in
dishes and tubes from escaping? (*b*) How
do these techniques prevent organisms
in the environment from entering dishes
and tubes?

**A. The pour-plate method.** Place
your team's five tubes of medium in a
600-ml beaker and add enough water to
fill the beaker above the level of the
medium in the tubes. Place the beaker
on a ring stand and heat. When the
medium in the tubes has melted, transfer the tubes to a second 600-ml beaker
containing water at 44°C. Check the temperature of this water bath carefully with
a thermometer. The beaker will have to
be heated gently from time to time to
maintain the water at approximately this
temperature.

Wipe the top of the laboratory table
with a wet paper towel. Place five sterile
petri dishes on the table. Using a glass-
marking pencil, number them *1* through
*5;* write on the *bottom* of each dish, near
the edge.

Refer to Figure 6 · 8 throughout the
remainder of this procedure.

Sterilize an inoculating loop in the
flame of a Bunsen burner or alcohol
lamp. Remove the plugs from the mixed

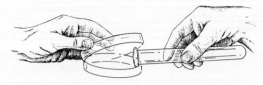

Figure 6 · 9
Pouring a culture plate.

Figure 6 · 10
Streaking a culture plate.

culture of bacteria and from one of your tubes of melted agar. (Your teacher will show you how to remove the plugs properly.) Using the sterilized loop, transfer a loopful of the culture to the tube of agar. Replug both tubes immediately and reflame the loop. Mix the agar thoroughly by rolling the tube between your palms, being careful to keep the plugged end up so that the cotton remains dry. Using the crayon, label this tube with a *1*. Again flame the loop. Transfer a loopful of the mixture in Tube 1 to a second tube of melted agar. Replug the tubes and reflame the loop. Mix in the same way you mixed Tube 1. Label this second tube with a *2*. Return Tube 1 to the 44°C water bath.

Using the same technique, transfer a loopful of material in Tube 2 to a third tube of melted agar. Replug the tubes, reflame the loop, and mix the contents of the tube. Label this tube with a *3*. Return Tubes 2 and 3 to the water bath.

Remove Tube 1 from the water bath, dry it with a paper towel, remove its plug, and flame the mouth of the tube. Pour its contents into Petri dish 1. Do not allow the tube lip to touch the dish (see Figure 6 · 9). Cover the dish (now called a "plate") and swirl it very gently, keeping it on the tabletop. This should distribute the medium in a uniform layer covering the bottom of the plate. Repeat this technique in preparing Plates (Dishes) 2 and 3.

**B. The streak-plate method.** Pour one of the remaining tubes of melted nutrient agar into Dish 4 and the other

into Dish 5. Allow the medium to solidify. Flame the loop. Take a loop of the original mixed culture and streak the surface of the medium in Plate 4, as shown in Figure 6 · 10. Use the pattern chosen by the teacher from Figure 6 · 11. Flame the loop. Record the pattern used. Dish 5 receives no treatment.

In a place designated by the teacher, incubate all the plates upside down. Observe daily until many bacterial colonies are clearly visible in some of the plates.

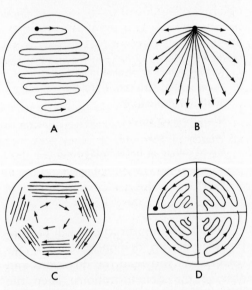

Figure 6 · 11
Four patterns for streaking a culture plate.

**C. Counting the colonies.** Ignoring differences in appearance, count the separate colonies of bacteria that have developed on the medium in each of the pour plates (1, 2, and 3) and record the counts.

In some cases the colonies may be too crowded for counting. In other cases you can estimate the number by using the following sampling technique:

With black ink draw a square 10 × 10 cm on a piece of white paper. Inside this square draw a series of straight lines parallel to its sides, forming a grid of 100 smaller squares—each 1 cm on a side. Position the plate on the paper so the colonies of bacteria can be seen against the background of the grid. Choose five to ten of the small squares at random and count the number of colonies in each. Add all the counts and divide the total by the number of small squares counted. This will give an average count per small square. Next, calculate the *total* surface of the culture medium. To do this, square the radius (in cm) of the plate and multiply by pi ($\pi$; equals approximately 3.14). To obtain an estimate of the number of colonies on the whole plate, multiply the average number of colonies per small square by the surface area (in cm²) of the entire plate.

### STUDYING THE DATA

When you have completed counts of all plates (except the streak plate), you are ready to estimate the population density of organisms (number per cubic centimeter) in the original mixed culture of bacteria. To do this, you need the following information:

The volume of liquid held in your inoculating loop was about 5 mm³. One cm³ contains 1000 mm³. Therefore the loopful of material introduced into Plate 1 contained about $5/1000 = 1/200$ of the number of bacteria in each (average) cubic centimeter of the original culture.

If we assume that each organism in Plate 1 produced a visible colony, the number of colonies in Plate 1 multiplied by 200 gives the number of organisms per cubic centimeter in the original culture.

Before Tube 1 was poured, a loopful of its contents was transferred to Tube 2. Since the volume of medium in Tube 1 was 15 cm³, and that of the loopful of material was 1/200 cm³, the loopful must have contained $1/15 \times 1/200 = 1/3000$ of the number of organisms in Tube 1. But Tube 1 contained only 1/200 of the organisms in the original culture; thus Tube 2 must contain $1/200 \times 1/3000 = 1/600{,}000$ of the number of organisms per cubic centimeter in the original culture. Thus to obtain the number of organisms per cubic centimeter in the original culture, you multiply the number of colonies in Plate 2 by 600,000. • How many organisms per cubic centimeter of original culture does each colony in Plate 3 represent?(1)

From the counts on each of the pour plates, carry out the calculations necessary to estimate the density of the population in the original culture. If it was possible to make estimates for all plates, you now have three separate estimates of the number of organisms present per cubic centimeter in the original culture. • How closely do these compare with each other?(2) It is thought the best estimates can be made when the dilution results in a count of from 30 to 300 colonies per plate. • Do you have a plate that falls in this range? If so, circle the population estimate made from it.(3)

Examine Plate 5 (control). If colonies are present, count them and record the data. • What correction in your original calculations is indicated if colonies are present in this control plate? Make such a correction, if necessary.(4)

Next examine Plate 4—the streak plate. Compare the pattern of colonies with the pattern of streaking that you recorded in your data book. • Are the patterns different or similar?(5) • Are any of the colonies well separated from all others? Suppose that you were to lift a part of *one* such colony with a sterile

inoculating loop and streak it on a plate of sterile medium. How many kinds of colonies would you expect to develop? (6)
• What would you call such a culture? (7)
• How many kinds of colonies have developed? In what ways do they differ? (8)
• How many kinds of bacteria were in the original culture? (9) • What seems to be the principal way in which the colonies of these bacteria differ macroscopically? (10)

• Suggest a method for disposing of the cultures after you have finished studying them.(11)

### SUMMARY

Now look back at the purpose of this investigation. You need to consider each of the three problems raised there.

• From the instructions of the teacher and your own experience, form a set of rules for working with microorganisms.(12)

• Which steps in the procedure are concerned only with a determination of the population density of microorganisms?(13) • Which steps are concerned only with obtaining a pure culture?(14)

### FOR FURTHER INVESTIGATION

1. The procedure for producing a pure culture was not really completed. Carry out the last step. How can you determine that you have been successful?

2. Use the methods of Investigation 6.2 to determine the population density of microorganisms in a sample of stream or pond water. How might the kind of culture medium and the incubation temperature affect your results? The hypothesis that results from this question may be investigated by culturing samples from a single source in various kinds of media and at different incubation temperatures.

---

## INVESTIGATION 6.3

### MICROBIAL TECHNIQUES: MICROSCOPIC STUDY OF BACTERIA

#### PURPOSE

Now you will investigate the technique by which bacteria are prepared for detailed microscopic observation.

#### MATERIALS AND EQUIPMENT

(for each student)

Microscope slide
Bunsen burner or alcohol lamp
Inoculating loop
Mixed culture of bacteria
Beaker
Glass-marking crayon
Medicine dropper
Crystal-violet stain
Paper towels
Glycerin
Cover slip
Monocular microscope

#### PROCEDURE

#### A. Staining bacteria

1. Gently heat a *clean* slide by passing it above the blue cone of a burner flame three times. When the slide is cool, place a loop of the mixed culture of bacteria on it. Use the loop to spread the liquid over an area the size of a nickel. Mark the slide, on the side having the bacteria on it, with a crayon. Let the slide dry in the air; an almost invisible film of bacteria will remain.

2. *Quickly* pass the slide *through* the flame three or four times, film side up. The slide should feel just uncomfortably hot to the back of the hand. Let the slide cool to room temperature.

3. Pour tap water into a beaker until the water is about 3 cm from the top. Place the slide across the top of the beaker with the film surface up, as

shown in Figure 6·12 (A). Cover the film with three or four drops of crystal-violet solution. Allow the dye to remain on the film for fifteen seconds. Then rinse off the stain by pulling the slide gently to one side until one end drops slowly into the water, as shown in Figure 6·12 (B).

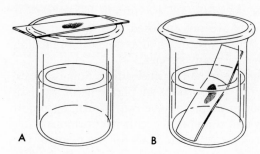

**Figure 6 · 12**
Staining procedure.

4. Remove the slide. Empty the beaker and refill it with clean water. Gently dip the slide in the water several times. Drain the water from the slide by holding it vertically and pressing a lower corner against a paper towel. Remove the remaining water by blotting gently with a folded paper towel, as shown in Figure 6·13. Close the towel upon the slide as you would close a book. Do not *wipe* the slide. When the film is dry, add a drop of glycerin, then a cover slip.

**Figure 6 · 13**
Blotting the stained slide.

### B. Examining stained bacteria

Use the low-power objective to focus on the stained bacteria on the slide. Many species of bacteria can barely be seen with low power. They may appear only as tiny colored specks. Move the slide around until a group of bacteria is located in the central region of the field of view, then swing the high-power objective into place. If necessary, refocus with the fine adjustment.

Bacteria of various kinds should be visible in the field. In your data book draw a circle about 6 cm in diameter to represent the field of the microscope. In the circle carefully draw the organisms you can observe. Try to show accurately their shape, the way they are grouped, and their size in relation to the diameter of the field of view. Refer to Investigation 1.3, subheading G, and to your record of it. Then estimate the sizes (diameter of round organisms, length and width of others) of the smallest and the largest bacteria on your slide. • Record the dimensions in microns.(1) • Do all the bacteria appear to have reacted to the stain in the same way? If not, in what ways do they differ?(2)

### FOR FURTHER INVESTIGATION

1. Observations at a magnification close to 1000× may be made if microscopes with oil-immersion objectives are available. Swing the high-power objective to one side. Put one drop of immersion oil directly on the stained bacterial film. Slowly swing the oil-immersion objective into place, watching the end of the objective from the side. The tip of the objective should dip into the drop of oil but should not be allowed to touch the slide. Using the *fine* adjustment, very carefully focus on the stained bacteria. Caution: Use *only* the fine adjustment, and turn it back and forth only a small fraction of a full turn at a time, until the stained organisms come into clear focus.

2. Because different species of bacteria react to staining procedures in characteristic ways, staining is useful for identification. Perhaps the most-used technique for this purpose involves Gram's stain; the teacher can give you directions for this.

## BLUE-GREEN ALGAE

Myxophyta [mĭk'sō fī'tə; Greek: myxa, slime, + phyton, a plant]

You may be surprised to find a group of algae, the Myxophyta, included in the protist kingdom. In some characteristics, however, the Myxophyta resemble bacteria and actinomycetes. As in the photosynthetic bacteria, their chlorophyll pigments are not enclosed in organized structures. And as in actinomycetes, filamentous or branching colonies are formed by many species.

The term "blue-green" can be misleading. Some species, depending upon the proportions of pigments other than chlorophyll present in them, may be red, brown, or almost black. One species that sometimes occurs in enormous numbers in tropical seas provides the basis for the name of the Red Sea.

The blue-green algae may be found in almost any place where there is liquid water. Ponds, lakes, streams, soil,

Figure 6 · 14
Diversity among
flagellates.

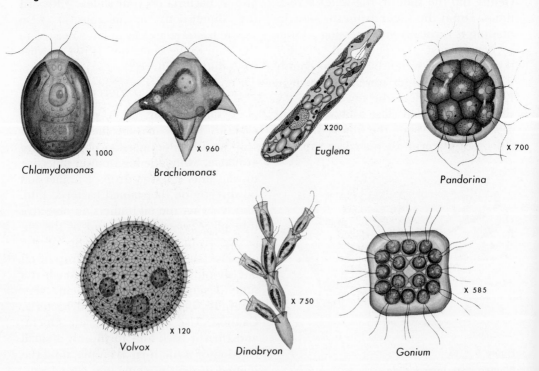

Chlamydomonas    X 1000

Brachiomonas    X 960

Euglena    X200

Pandorina    X 700

Volvox    X 120

Dinobryon    X 750

Gonium    X 585

snow, glaciers, hot springs, mud flats, and tree bark—all of these are habitats for one or more species.

## FLAGELLATES

Among the most puzzling microbes are the flagellates, which move about by making use of flagella. Some flagellates contain chlorophyll, synthesizing their own food when light is present. When light is not present, they may digest food particles in the surrounding water and absorb the products. Other species lack chlorophyll but capture smaller microorganisms and digest them internally. Such a mixture of "plant" and "animal" characteristics has made the classification of flagellates difficult—especially if only two kingdoms are recognized.

Flagellates are abundant in soil, in fresh water, and in the ocean. Among the most common are species of the genus *Euglena*, great numbers of which often tint a pond bright green in late summer. All species of *Euglena* have a flexible outer covering and contractile fibers that permit shortening or lengthening of the body. In moving from place to place, a euglena extends its anterior, whiplike

synthesizing [Greek: *syn*, together, + *tithenai*, to place]

*Euglena* [ū glē′nə]

contractile [kən trăk′təl; Latin: *con*, with, together, + *trahere*, to draw]

**Figure 6 · 15**
**Diversity among dinoflagellates.**

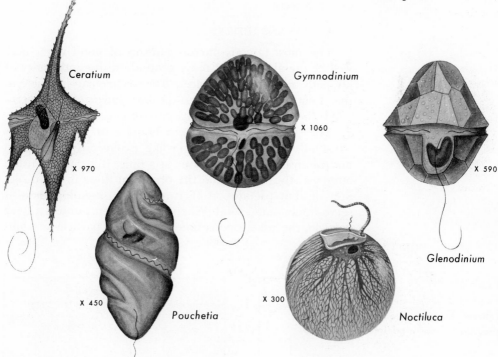

Ceratium

Gymnodinium

X 1060

X 970

X 590

X 450

Pouchetia

X 300

Glenodinium

Noctiluca

flagellum into the surrounding water; then, by quickly curl-
ing the whip, the organism draws itself forward, contracting and elongating its body and revolving on its long axis.

The dinoflagellates inhabit both fresh waters and the
ocean. Sculptured plates of cellulose cover their bodies.
Most dinoflagellates swim in the upper levels of the ocean,
where they can carry on photosynthesis. But many obtain
food from decaying matter, and still others capture and
digest bacteria. One genus of these more animal-like dinoflagellates is *Noctiluca,* which emits a flash of light when
stimulated. Often at night so many *Noctiluca* may be disturbed by a human swimmer or the wake of a boat that the
water glows with their light.

Many flagellates live in close community relationships
with other organisms. These relationships may be parasitic
or mutualistic. For example, some flagellates live in the
intestines of certain cockroaches and termites. There they
digest cellulose, a substance abundant in the wood eaten by
the insects. Without the flagellates, the termites or roaches
would starve to death, just as we would on a cellulose diet;
for neither we nor the insects can digest this material. Thus
the insects obtain food from the digestive activity of the
flagellates, and the flagellates, in turn, get a moist place to
live and a convenient supply of food — the wood chewed up
by the insects.

### AMEBAS AND THEIR KIN

The most famous microorganisms of pond water may
well be the amebas that move around on the undersides of
lily pads and similar surfaces. Amebas are barely visible to
the unaided eye, but under the low power of the microscope they look like granular, grayish masses.

The substance of an ameba is more or less fluid. It is
constantly flowing into finger-like extensions (*pseudopods*)
and often into more than one at a time. But one extension
outgrows the others, and the organism flows in the direction of that pseudopod (Figure 6·16). Pseudopods also
serve in obtaining food. When an ameba encounters a food
particle, the pseudopods flow around the particle and join

dinoflagellates    [dī′nō flăj′ə-
ləts; Greek: *dinos,* a whirling,
+ Latin: *flagellum*]

cellulose [sĕl′yə lōs′]: This substance is found in almost all
plants and in almost no animals. Paper is mostly cellulose,
and so is cotton.

*Noctiluca* [nŏk′tə loo′kə; Latin:
*noctis,* of night, + *lux,* a light]

ameba [ə mē′bə; Greek: *amei-
bein,* to change]

pseudopods    [soo′də pŏdz′;
Greek: *pseudes,* false, +
*podion,* little foot]

Figure 6 · 16

Locomotion of an ameba.
Lettered lines indicate the
progress of the organism.

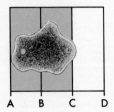 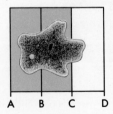 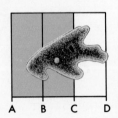

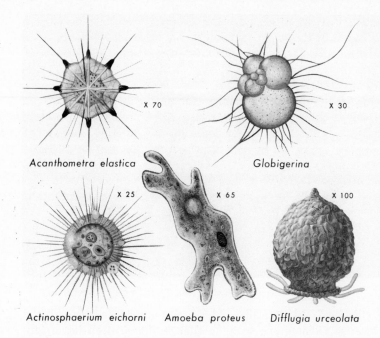

Acanthometra elastica    X 70

Globigerina    X 30

X 25    X 65    X 100

Actinosphaerium eichorni    Amoeba proteus    Difflugia urceolata

**Figure 6 · 17**
**Diversity among sarcodinans.**

together. Then the food lies within the ameba in a little drop of water.

Pseudopods are the characteristic structures of the phylum Sarcodina. In some species, pseudopods are much less numerous than in the ameba; in others, they are more numerous and do not constantly change position. And there also is a kind of flagellate that sometimes loses its flagellum and moves about with pseudopods. Differences between protist phyla are not always clear.

Sarcodina    [sär′kō dī′nə; Greek: sarx, fleshy, + eidos, form]

One group of sarcodinans, the radiolarians, have shells of silica (a substance similar to sand). Many long, stiff pseudopods radiate from the shells. The foraminiferans, another group, build shells of calcium carbonate (chemically, the same as clam shells). Like their makers, most of these shells are very small. During past ages great numbers of such shells have accumulated in the seas and solidified into rock. The famous White Cliffs of Dover (England) are formed from remains of foraminiferans.

radiolarians [rā′dī ō lâr′ī ənz; Latin: radius (so named from the radiating pseudopods)]

foraminiferans [fō răm′ə nĭf′ər-ənz; Latin: foramen, a hole, + ferre, to bear]

Many ameba-like sarcodinans live in ponds, puddles, or damp soil. Most of the shell-bearing kinds live in the seas. Other species live with larger organisms in various kinds of relationships—some as commensals, some as parasites.

## CILIATES

Ciliates (phylum Ciliophora) are microbes that have a multitude of cilia extending from their outer surfaces. The

Ciliophora [sĭl′ē äf′ə rə; Latin: cilium, eyelash, + Greek: -phoros, bearing, carrying]

Figure 6 · 18

Photomicrograph of the shells of foraminiferans.

George Schwartz

cilia beat rhythmically, driving the organisms through the water. Ciliates are so agile that students often have difficulty observing them through the microscope. The instrument, of course, magnifies the rate of movement, just as it does the organism.

*If a ciliate swims across the low-power field of view of your microscope in one second, what is its speed in meters per hour?*

Ciliates are generally larger than other protists (excepting the slime molds). Some pond-dwelling species are 0.25 mm long — visible to the unaided eye when seen in good light against a dark background. Most species are microscopic, but they are large enough to be studied in detail with the high power of a light microscope. In an individual of the genus *Paramecium*, we can find a place where food particles are taken in (a "mouth"), a region through which the food enters the body (a kind of "gullet"), a temporary digestive sac (a "stomach"), and so on. With the electron microscope even more detail can be observed. Further, the way paramecia behave indicates that their tiny bodies are

*Paramecium* [păr'ə mē'shĭ əm; Greek: *paramekes*, oval]

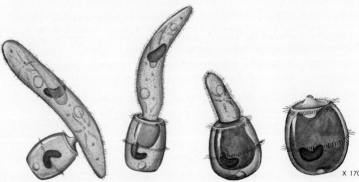

Figure 6 · 19

A predator that is smaller than its prey. From the left, four stages are shown as a species of the ciliate *Didinium* consumes a species of *Paramecium*.

X 170

not really simple. For example, the movements of their cilia are coordinated, so they must be subject to some kind of internal control.

All ciliates have definite shapes. Some species that live attached to solid objects, such as twigs or dead leaves in a pond, tend toward radial symmetry. The many forms that are active swimmers have definite anterior and posterior ends but are usually unsymmetrical.

Some ciliates are parasitic, but a majority are free-living.

### SPOROZOANS

Organisms of the phylum Sporozoa are parasites that may not be closely related to each other. But they do have two things in common. First, they have no means of locomotion (at least, not as adults). Second, a parent sporozoan reproduces by forming large numbers of tiny spores within its body, which then bursts and releases the spores into the environment. There are additional kinds of reproduction in many species. Indeed, the life histories may be very complex.

Some species affect their hosts only slightly, if at all. Others have such a weakening effect that the hosts become ill. Still others frequently cause the death of the hosts. Among these are the best-known sporozoans, the malaria organisms.

Taxonomists who use a two-kingdom system group sporozoans, ciliates, sarcodinans, and most flagellates together as *protozoa*. The protozoa are then placed as a phylum in the animal kingdom.

### SLIME MOLDS

The common English name "slime molds" is a direct translation from Greek of the organisms' phylum name, Myxomycetes. Although slime molds do not have a particularly attractive name, many are rather beautiful during certain stages in their life histories.

These organisms usually grow among damp, decaying leaves and other dead plant material. If you search through a mass of such material soon after a heavy rain, you are likely to come across a slime-mold plasmodium—a glistening sheet or network that may be as much as several centimeters, or even a meter, across. Orange, yellow, white, or almost colorless, such organized living masses crawl slowly from place to place. For food they take in bacteria and other protists, fungal spores, and small bits of dead organic material.

At this stage in its life history, a slime mold's methods of feeding and locomotion closely resemble those of an

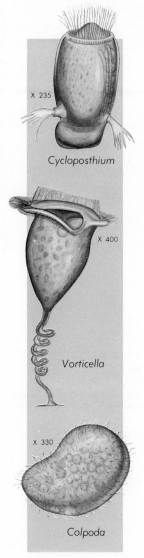

Cycloposthium

Vorticella

Colpoda

**Figure 6 · 20**

**Diversity among ciliates.**

protozoa [prō′tə zō′ə; Greek: *protos*, first, + *zoion*, animal]

Myxomycetes [mǐk′sō mī sē′tēz; Greek: *myxa*, mucus, slime, + *myketes*]

ameba—but one that is thousands or millions of times larger than those in the phylum Sarcodina. After a period of feeding and growth, a plasmodium crawls to a drier, more exposed location and slowly transforms into a number of spore cases. These tiny stalked structures are usually not more than a few millimeters high, and many are brightly colored. Inside each case large numbers of spores are formed. When a case breaks, spores are released; if they land in a suitable spot where water is available, the spores give rise to tiny, flagellated "swarm cells." After swimming about for a brief period, swarm cells lose their flagella, crawl around like amebas, and eventually fuse in pairs. By feeding and growth, each of these develops into a new plasmodium.

Few other organisms have life histories that include such diverse and contrasting stages as the slime molds have. In the flagellated and ameboid stages slime molds move about like animals. Their spore cases and spores, however, are distinctly plantlike in structure. The existence of such "plant-and-animal" organisms is one of the best reasons for a three-kingdom scheme of classification.

## VIRUSES

virus [Latin: a slimy liquid, poison]

Often when a physician isn't quite sure what is wrong with you, he says, "It's probably a virus." And he is probably right. New kinds of viruses, many of them associated with human ailments, are being discovered every year. And many already well-known human diseases—measles, mumps, influenza, polio, yellow fever, smallpox, common colds, and others—result from virus infection.

Dimitri Iwanowski [də mē′trĭ ē′və nŏf′skĭ]: 1864–1919. Russian microbiologist

mosaic disease: a condition in which tobacco leaves become blotched and wrinkled

Martinus W. Beijerinck [bī′ə-rĭngk]: 1851–1931. Dutch microbiologist

Viruses were first recognized toward the end of the nineteenth century. In 1892 Dimitri Iwanowski was studying the mosaic disease of tobacco plants. He forced the juice of diseased plants through porcelain filters, through which bacteria could not pass. When this filtered juice was injected into healthy plants, they developed the mosaic disease. Iwanowski apparently did not realize the significance of this curious result. But six years later M. W. Beijerinck, who was studying the same disease, observed the same thing. Beijerinck repeated the experiment over and over and concluded that the tobacco disease must result from what he called a "contagious living fluid" that was able to pass through porcelain filters.

Since 1900 scientists have acquired an enormous amount of information about viruses. Viruses are too small to be seen with even the best light microscopes, but by using the electron microscope we can obtain pictures of virus particles. They are of many different sizes and shapes,

A  x 82,000    C. E. Schwerdt and R. C. Williams    B    x 61,000    C. A. Knight and R. C. Williams

Figure 6 · 21

Electronmicrographs of two kinds of virus: (A) virus of poliomyelitis; (B) virus of influenza.

but all are extremely small. The smallest are merely giant molecules. This was shown in 1935 by W. M. Stanley, who first succeeded in crystallizing the tobacco-mosaic virus and then demonstrated that it was still capable of infecting tobacco plants.

Viruses grow only within the substance of living things; none has yet been grown in artificial culture media. Like the rickettsias, many viruses are most easily cultivated in developing chick embryos. Viruses, it seems, cannot "live" except in association with some other form of life.

But are viruses alive? They seem to possess two characteristics that we usually associate with living things: first, the capacity to reproduce, and second, the ability to undergo changes in hereditary characteristics. Yet what we call reproduction in the virus is really not that, for the virus cannot independently produce copies of itself; it can do so only in association with a living organism. For example, a particle of the virus called "bacteriophage" attaches itself to a bacterium; then part of the virus moves inside. Less than half an hour later the bacterium falls apart, releasing approximately two hundred new virus particles.

While inside the living bacterium (or other organism), the virus behaves as though it were alive; but crystallized, it can be stored on the laboratory shelf like a jar of salt. Thus viruses might seem to be a link between the living and nonliving worlds.

In classifying living things, we have seen cases in which organisms do not fit neatly into our groupings. Viruses

Wendell M. Stanley: 1904———. American biochemist

hereditary [hǐ rĕd′ə tĕr′ǐ]: carried from parent to offspring

bacteriophage [băk tĭr′ǐ ə fāj′; Greek: bakterion, + phagein, to eat]

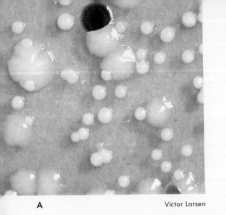

A

B    x 2

C    x 3

Figure 6 · 22

A. Colonies of four kinds of bacteria growing on agar.

B. The creeping stage of a slime mold, *Physarum*.

C. Spore cases of the slime mold *Stemonitis*.

D. Spore cases of the slime mold *Leocarpus*.

E. Effects of a virus infection on a squash plant.

D    x 3

E

present a similar problem. Man likes to put things in order; he likes to have clear-cut answers to his questions. But the universe about him does not seem very neat, and the answers to man's questions are often ambiguous.

ambiguous: having two or more possible meanings

Of course, it is not necessary to decide whether viruses are alive in order to study them. Many virologists have started as physicians, studying disease; others have started as biochemists. All, however, probably regard themselves as biologists of one kind or another. Perhaps this answers the question in a way. But you will notice that viruses have not been put into the "Catalogue of Living Things."

## INVESTIGATION 6.4

### EXPERIMENTS ON SPONTANEOUS GENERATION

#### INTRODUCTION AND PURPOSE

Throughout the eighteenth century there was a growing belief that microbes are connected with the putrefaction (rotting) of meat and meat broths. There was much speculation about the origin of the microbes that could be observed in putrefying broths: Do microbes arise without ancestors from the nonliving materials; that is, do they appear spontaneously? Or do they come from preexisting microbes that can somehow get into the broth? These questions led scientists into heated controversy. Many believed in the theory of *spontaneous generation* of microbes—that is, the theory that microbes arise of their own accord, without parents, from nonliving materials. A few denied the theory.

At the time of the American Revolution, an Italian, Lazzaro Spallanzani, conducted experiments in an attempt to settle the matter. His results cast doubt upon the theory, but he failed to convince those who believed in it. Later, in the middle of the nineteenth century, Pasteur carried out more carefully designed experiments that led biologists to general agreement.

In this investigation you will perform experiments similar to those of Spallanzani and Pasteur. You will use some techniques developed since their day, but the principles involved in your procedure will be the same as theirs.

#### MATERIALS AND EQUIPMENT
(per team)

Straight glass tubes (7–8 mm diameter, 30 cm long), 2

Bunsen burner with wing top

Triangular file

Stoppers or corks to fit flasks, one hole, 3

Stoppers or corks to fit flasks, without holes, 2

Straight glass tube (7–8 mm diameter, 8–10 cm long)

Bouillon cube

Beaker, 1000 ml

Stirring rod

Glass funnel

Ring stand (to fit funnel)

Filter paper

Graduated cylinder

Erlenmeyer flasks, 250 ml, 7

Heat source, for boiling broth

Autoclave or pressure cooker

Paraffin or sealing wax

Beaker, 250 ml

Forceps and wad of cotton

Figure 6 · 23

Completed setup for Investigation 6.4.

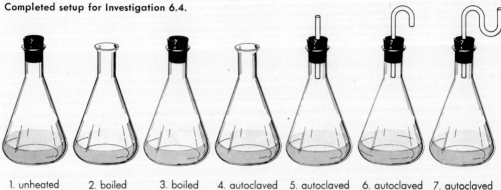

1. unheated    2. boiled    3. boiled    4. autoclaved    5. autoclaved    6. autoclaved    7. autoclaved

## PROCEDURE

Using the wing-top burner, bend one of the 30-cm lengths of glass tubing into a J shape, the other into an S shape (see Figure 6·23). Trim the tubes to the lengths of those in the illustration. Insert them into one-hole stoppers. Insert the straight piece of glass tubing into the third one-hole stopper.

Dissolve one bouillon cube in 500 ml of warm water. When cool, filter. The broth must be sparkling clear. Pour 70 ml of the clear broth into each of seven flasks. Number the flasks with a lead pencil. Treat them as follows:

Flask 1 — Overall Control
Plug with a solid stopper. Do not heat.

Flask 2 — Spallanzani's Control
Add 10 ml of water. Boil gently for fifteen minutes. About 10 ml of water will boil off, making the level approximately the same as in the other flasks. Leave open.

Flask 3 — Spallanzani's Experiment
Add 10 ml of water. Boil gently for fifteen minutes, with the solid stopper resting at an angle in the mouth of the flask. At the conclusion of boiling, plug immediately with the stopper. To seal, melt wax or paraffin in a beaker; apply with a wad of cotton held in a forceps.

Flask 4 — Pasteur's Control
Heat in a pressure cooker or autoclave for fifteen minutes at 15 lb pressure. Leave open.

Flask 5 — Modified Pasteur's Control
Plug with the stopper through which a straight glass tube was inserted. Heat as for Flask 4. Then seal with paraffin around the neck of the flask and around the tube where it comes through the stopper.

Flask 6 — Pasteur's First Experiment
Plug with the stopper through which the J-shaped glass tube was inserted. Heat as for Flask 4. Seal as for Flask 5.

Flask 7 — Pasteur's Final Experiment
Plug with the stopper through which the S-shaped glass tube was inserted. Heat as for Flask 4. Seal as for Flask 5.

Put all flasks on a laboratory table (not in direct sunlight or over a radiator).

Record the date on which the experiment is set up. Look for changes in the flasks each day for one week, then weekly for five weeks. Record any changes in the clearness of the broth, noting the number of the flask and the date. Other observed changes in the broth (appearance of scum, mold colonies, etc.) should also be recorded. At the end of the experiment, open the flasks and note the odor of the broth in each.

## STUDYING THE DATA

Flasks 2 and 3 represent Spallanzani's experiment. • What differences did you observe in these flasks during the five weeks?(1) • How can you explain the differences?(2) In your experiment Flask 3 may or may not have developed turbidity (cloudiness). Spallanzani's sealed flask developed no turbidity or putrid odor. But biologists of his day denied that this showed microbes had to get into the broth from outside; they clung to the theory of spontaneous generation. • How do you think they defended their point of view in the face of Spallanzani's evidence?(3)

Flasks 4 to 7 represent some of Pasteur's work. • In the experimental set-up, what is the function of Flask 4?(4) • Why did Pasteur provide openings in his flasks?(5) • How do you explain the result obtained in Flask 7?(6)

• Compare your observations of Flask 1 with those of Flasks 2 and 4. Explain any likenesses and differences in these results. (7)

## CONCLUSIONS

• In the light of the results of these experiments, discuss the questions that were raised in the introduction to this exercise.(8)

---

The world of microscopic living things was discovered about three hundred years ago, when the art of lens-making developed instruments of clear and adequate magnification. The understanding of this world has continued to depend largely on improvement of instruments and techniques used in its exploration.

Microscopes reveal a great variety of living things. Some of these are, obviously, very small relatives of visible animals and plants; some are early stages in the development of larger organisms; some are quite different from anything seen with the unaided eye. Efforts to classify many of these as either animals or plants have not been very satisfactory. In this book most of them are assigned to a third kingdom, the Protista.

Protists show as great diversity among themselves as visible plants and animals. The phyla of this kingdom include bacteria, blue-green algae, flagellates, sarcodinans, ciliates, sporozoans, and slime molds (though these last are not really microscopic).

Below the range of light microscopes, but visible with electron microscopes, are the viruses. Whether we call viruses alive or not depends somewhat on our point of view. But since viruses grow at the expense of things that are undoubtedly alive, they are important in the study of biology.

## GUIDE QUESTIONS

1. Why was progress in studying microorganisms very slow for a century and a half after Leeuwenhoek's discovery?
2. Why is the science of microbiology dated from Pasteur and Koch rather than from Leeuwenhoek?
3. What are the reasons for establishing a third kingdom? What are some difficulties with placing organisms in the kingdom Protista?
4. Long before man knew microorganisms existed, he learned to use them for his own benefit. Give some examples.
5. What are the differences between the "true" bacteria and the rickettsias?
6. What steps are necessary in preparing a pure culture of microorganisms?
7. Why are the blue-green algae placed in the protist kingdom in our classification?
8. In what ways are euglenas plant-like? In what ways are they animal-like?
9. Why is it somewhat misleading to speak of protists such as *Paramecium* as "simple"?
10. In what kind of habitat would you look for slime molds? Why do they usually occur in such habitats?
11. Which characteristics of slime molds are animal-like? Which are plant-like?
12. Give examples of diversity in the ways protists obtain food.
13. Compare and contrast the ways in which flagellates, amebas, and ciliates move about.
14. Why might we consider viruses living things? Why might there be disagreement with this view?
15. What evidence led biologists to discard the theory of spontaneous generation?

## PROBLEMS

1. Explain the statement "All bacteria are the direct descendants of other bacteria that never died but never lived at the same time as their offspring."
2. Under favorable environmental conditions individual bacteria of some species divide once every twenty minutes. Suppose we begin with one bacterium at noon on a certain day. Assume that no bacteria die and each divides every twenty minutes. How many bacteria will there be at noon on the next day?
3. Why will food in cold storage usually remain unspoiled longer than it will at ordinary temperatures?
4. The rickettsias are smaller than the "true" bacteria, and the viruses are smaller than the rickettsias. Certain other organisms in the size range between bacteria and viruses share various combinations of characteristics with bacteria, rickettsias, and viruses. Investigate the characteristics of the pleuropneumonia organisms (PPO) and the characteristics of pleuropneumonia-like organisms (PPLO), and write a report comparing and contrasting these very small things.
5. Pasteur, with the help of other early microbiologists, established the idea that microorganisms and other forms of life arise only from similar living things. There is evidence, however, that at first the earth was without life. If life began once, why does it not begin again?

## SUGGESTED READINGS

ALEXOPOULOUS, C. J., and J. KOEVENIG. *Slime Molds and Research.* (BSCS Pamphlet 13.) Boston: D. C. Heath & Co., 1964. (Recent results from experiments on the biology of these large protists. Fairly easy.)

ALLEN, R. D. "Amoeboid Movement," *Scientific American*, February, 1962. Pp. 112–120+.

BURNET, F. M. *Viruses and Man.* Baltimore: Penguin Books, Inc., 1953. (The viruses and their role in disease, written by the winner of the 1960 Nobel Prize in medicine.)

DOBELL, C. (ed.) *Antony van Leeuwenhoek and His Little Animals.* New York: Dover Publications, Inc., 1960. (Translations of the letters in which Leeuwenhoek described his discoveries. Fine description of his microscopes and his methods of work.)

ECHLIN, P. "The Blue-Green Algae," *Scientific American,* June, 1966. Pp. 74–81.

JAHN, T. L., and F. F. JAHN. *How to Know the Protozoa.* Dubuque, Iowa: William C. Brown Co., 1950. Pp. 3–38. (The introduction to this identification book contains some excellent material on the biology of those protists that are often placed in the animal kingdom. Easy.)

MOMENT, G. B. *General Zoology.* 2nd ed. Boston: Houghton Mifflin Co., 1967. Chapter 4. (Standard college-textbook account of protists that may be classified in the animal kingdom. Advanced.)

MOROWITZ, H. J., and M. E. TOURTELLOTTE. "The Smallest Living Cells," *Scientific American,* March, 1962. Pp. 117–126.

RAHN, O. *Microbes of Merit.* New York: The Ronald Press Co., 1945. (Stresses the benefits man obtains from microscopic organisms. Fairly easy.)

WILSON, C. L., and W. E. LOOMIS. *Botany.* 3rd ed. New York: Holt, Rinehart & Winston, Inc., 1962. Chapters 21–22. (Standard college-textbook account of bacteria and their relations with man. Somewhat advanced.)

# Section Three    PATTERNS IN THE BIOSPHERE

In the preceding sections we saw how individual organisms may be grouped as populations. From an ecological viewpoint, populations may be studied as parts of communities. From a taxonomic viewpoint, populations may be considered as species, and from this kind of grouping a classification may be constructed. Now we turn to another aspect of biology—to the distribution of organisms in the biosphere.

No species lives everywhere. Some species are widespread, and some are found only in a few places; some are living on the earth today, and some have become extinct. Nor are species scattered helter-skelter over the earth. Different species live in different places. That whales do not occur in Nebraska today, that echinoderms occur only in the seas and apparently never occurred elsewhere, that palms once occurred in Greenland, that the bacterium of tuberculosis lives in man and cows but not in dogs—all these are facts of distribution. Some are obvious facts; some are facts that have been established only after much patient searching for evidence. But do these facts make any sense?

Cyril N. Hinshelwood, a British scientist, has said, "Science is not the mere collection of facts, which are infinitely numerous and mostly uninteresting, but the attempt of the human mind to order these facts into satisfying patterns." In Section Three we shall attempt to find some satisfying and meaningful patterns within the multitude of facts about the distribution of organisms in the biosphere.

# Patterns of Life
# in the
# Microscopic World

## MICROORGANISMS
## IN SCHOOL ENVIRONMENTS

### PURPOSE

You will investigate the relative numbers of airborne microorganisms present at different places in your school.

### MATERIALS AND EQUIPMENT
(per team)

Petri dish containing sterile nutrient
agar, 1

Glass-marking crayon, 1

### PROCEDURE

Caution: Do not remove the cover from the petri dish until directed to do so in the procedure.

Each team will try to trap a sample of microorganisms from the air. This is done by exposing to the air a sterile petri dish filled with nutrient agar (a plate). Each team will be assigned a location where its plate is to be exposed. Some suggestions: a laboratory, industrial arts shop, English room, auditorium, gymnasium, lunchroom, corridor, washroom.

On the bottom half of your petri dish, write your team's number and as-signed location. When your plate is in its location, remove the cover and expose the agar to the air for exactly six minutes. • Why must all teams be very careful to expose their dishes for the same length of time? (1) Replace the cover and return the dish to the laboratory. Turn it upside down (to prevent water that might condense inside the cover from dripping on the growing colonies) and incubate in a place designated by the teacher.

After three or four days count and record the number of colonies of microorganisms in your plate. You can distinguish mold colonies by their cottony or fuzzy appearance and their large size as compared with bacterial colonies. Place your count on the class chart that includes counts from all teams.

### DISCUSSION

• According to the data collected by your class, which location had the largest population of microorganisms? (2) • Which location had the smallest population of microorganisms? (3) • Coughing or sneezing may spread droplets of materials from the mouth and nose to a distance of 3 m or more. The water in these droplets evaporates rapidly, leaving bits of dry materials (dust particles) that contain dormant bacteria. Dormant microbes derived from many other sources may also be carried on dust particles. • How can you use this information to help interpret the class data? (4) • Did the location with the largest population of microorganisms also have the largest number of different kinds, as indicated by macroscopic appearance of colonies? (5) • Where would you be more likely to pick up the microorganisms of disease—in an environment with large populations of a few kinds of microorganisms or in an environment with small populations of many different kinds? Explain. (6)

• How *reliable* do you think the results of this experiment are? In other words, do you think it likely that repeating it would give the same results? (7) • Depending on your answer to the preceding question, suggest factors that may have made the results reliable or unreliable. (8) • Why is it especially important to use proper bacteriological techniques in disposing of these plates? (9)

### FOR FURTHER INVESTIGATION

Does the kind of medium used in the petri dishes affect the count obtained at any one location? Does the temperature at which the plates are incubated affect the count? Design and carry out experiments that test hypotheses based on these questions.

## THE ECOLOGY OF MICROORGANISMS

You have just seen that microorganisms occur in all parts of your school environment. From this it should be reasonable to assume that they occur in all natural ecosystems. Research by microbiologists completely supports this idea. Microorganisms grow on snowbanks in polar regions. They thrive in hot springs that would scald larger organisms. In the depths of lakes and seas, microorganisms live without free oxygen. They survive also when carried high into the stratosphere. But no individual species grows everywhere.

When we look at biotic communities, we are likely to be most conscious of the macroscopic plants and animals. We are likely to forget the millions of microorganisms busily carrying on their important community functions. It is misleading to separate the distribution of microorganisms from the distribution of macroorganisms, for any natural ecosystem consists of both. But the distribution of macroorganisms is greatly affected by geography; the distribution of microorganisms is not. For example, pond fishes in any one region tend to be different from those in other parts of the world; pond microorganisms are likely to be much the same wherever they may be. Therefore, for convenience, ecologists sometimes study the distribution of microorganisms separately from the distribution of larger organisms. In this chapter we consider two sets of community relationships in which microorganisms are especially important—those of disease and those in soil.

## MICROBES AND DISEASE

We use the words "disease" and "health" easily—and know what we mean. But as words, they are not easy to define. Dictionaries are likely to note that disease is a departure from a state of health and that health is the absence of disease—which makes a nice circle.

"Health" and "disease" are words like "hot" and "cold": each has little meaning without reference to the other. The physicist has a standard for absolute cold (absence of all heat), but "hot" is a matter of degrees, to which there is no reasonable limit. Likewise we might consider absolute disease to be death (the absence of all health), but is there any limit we can put on health? Many useful words are difficult to define with scientific precision, so we shall continue the discussion of disease without any further attempt at definition.

### DISEASE: ORIGIN AND KINDS

Anyone who has a pet dog, a cat, or even an aquarium with tropical fish knows that many kinds of animals get diseases. And every person who has kept potted plants knows that they can become diseased. Diseases occur in protists, too—not just in the larger protists, but even in the tiny bacteria. All diseases are of interest to biologists, and

pathology [Greek: *pathein*, to suffer, + *logikos*, art ("science") of reasoning]

the principles of *pathology* (the science of disease) are similar for all organisms. But since we are naturally most interested in human diseases, we shall center our discussion on them.

**Some history.**   An early and widespread idea among men was the notion that illness came from an evil spirit that had entered the body. Obviously, then, the cure was to get the spirit out by frightening or coaxing it. This became the function of witch doctors, with their masks, rattles, and charms. Even ancient peoples, however, did not rely entirely upon magic. It was all right for the witch doctor to call upon the toothache demon to depart; but in the meantime, a soothing application of coca leaves was not rejected.

Thus, primitive tribes and peoples discovered practical remedies for various kinds of illness. In fact, many of the drugs we use today have long histories. Aspirin is a nice example. This modern drug had its origin in an extract of willow bark that was long used in folk medicine. The pain-relieving substance in the willow bark was synthesized

synthesized [Greek: *syn*, together, + *thesis*, an arranging]: here, meaning to form a more complex chemical substance from simpler substances

by a German chemist in 1835 and named salicylic acid. Another German chemist discovered later that for unknown reasons the salicylic acid was more effective in a chemical combination called acetylsalicylic acid, and this product was marketed under the name Aspirin. It is our most common drug, but we still don't know much more than our ancestors did about how it works.

salicylic [săl'ə sĭl'ĭk]

acetylsalicylic    [ə sē'təl săl'ə-sĭl'ĭk]

Much folk medicine was (and is) pure superstition. Scientific studies have been needed to sort the sense from the nonsense. Today it is more likely that theories about the causes of disease will lead to improved treatments than it is that treatments will be improved independently of theory. This is just another way of saying that some current theories of disease are better than primitive ones. The "evil-spirit" theory led to very little improvement in treatment.

Physicians of ancient Greece developed some theories that did lead to better treatment. For example, they developed the idea that the health of the body is related to the food we eat, and they investigated the effects of various diets in illness. But there was little progress in the centuries that followed. Two hundred years ago physicians were not much further along in understanding and treating human illnesses than they had been fifteen centuries earlier.

That many diseases are "catching" has long been known, but for centuries no one guessed that the thing "caught" was a microorganism. Leeuwenhoek started writing to the Royal Society about his "little animals" in 1676,

**Figure 7 · 1**

Navajo healing ceremony. The medicine man (*right*) and his helper construct a design with colored powders. The young patient will sit in the middle of the design when it is finished.

Josef Muench

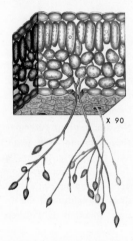

X 1

X 90

**Figure 7 · 2**

Late blight of potato.
*Above:* Infected leaflet.
*Below:* Section through the
leaflet with hyphae of the
pathogen growing from it.
The hyphae bear spore
cases.

Heinrich Anton De Bary
[dĕ bä rē′]: 1831–1888. German botanist

infectious [ĭn fĕk′shəs; Latin:
*infectus,* tinge, stain]

scurvy: characterized by weak-
ness, spongy gums, bleeding
from the mucous membranes

rickets: a softening and bending of the bones, particularly
in childhood

allergies [ăl′ər jēz; Greek:
*allos,* other, + *ergon,* work]

but the first clear evidence that disease might be the result
of the activities of microorganisms did not come until the
nineteenth century.

Oddly enough, this evidence did not involve a human
disease or even a disease of animals. It grew from the study
of a plant disease. Late in the summer of 1845, potato
plants throughout northern Europe were struck by a blight
that turned whole fields almost overnight into black masses
of rotting plants. In Ireland the consequences were disastrous, because most of the population depended on potatoes as the main source of food. During the next two years
nearly half a million Irish died of famine, and two million
emigrated to America. Crop failures and famine had occurred many times in the past, but this time a scientific
investigation of causes could be made. It was soon found
that the dying plants were full of fungal hyphae. But was
the fungus present because the plant had died, or was the
plant dead because the fungus was present?

Early in the nineteenth century a French scientist had
shown a close connection between another fungus and a
disease of wheat. He had thought that the fungus brought
about the disease. But his evidence was not strong, and few
people knew of his work. The observations made on the
potato blight, however, could not be ignored. By 1861
another scientist, Heinrich Anton De Bary, had gathered
enough evidence to convince most biologists that the blight
was a result of the fungus observed in the plants. By the
end of the nineteenth century, the idea that microorganisms "cause" disease was thoroughly established — not
merely among biologists but also in the mind of the public.

**Kinds of disease.**   We still do not have any generally
accepted classification of diseases, though a few broad
groups are usually distinguished. First, we have the *infectious diseases,* which are associated with germs. By "germs"
we mean living organisms. Or at least we mean things that
can reproduce: viruses are certainly disease germs, whether
we call them "living" or not.

Just as it had once been thought that all disease is
caused by evil spirits, so in the late nineteenth century it
appeared that all disease might be caused by germs. But
disease is not so simple. We now realize that many factors
are involved. There are *deficiency diseases,* which develop
when some necessary substance is lacking in the diet.
Scurvy, for example, is caused by the lack of a substance
called vitamin C, rickets by the lack of vitamin D, and in
plants disease may be caused by the lack of nitrogen compounds in the soil. There are *allergies,* which are brought
about by substances in the environment that are irritating

to an organism. The organism reacts in various ways, and disorders that range from skin rashes to asthma result. There are *mental illnesses*, troubles that come from the mind but that are far from imaginary. There are *hereditary diseases*, such as hemophilia, a condition in which the blood in a wound fails to clot. And there are the *degenerative diseases*, such as arthritis and "hardening of the arteries," which usually come with old age.

Most diseases are rather easy to classify, but others present difficulties—cancer, for example. Some kinds of cancer are associated with infection by viruses, some with factors in the abiotic environment, and some with heredity. One type of cancer in mice arises from the combined actions of a virus, a hereditary factor, and a certain kind of body chemistry. Thus, the various kinds of cancer do not fit readily into a system of classification.

### INFECTIOUS DISEASES

In this chapter we are concerned with microorganisms, and only the infectious diseases involve them. So, having pointed out the existence of other kinds of disease, we now focus attention on the infectious kind.

An infectious disease is an interaction of two organisms, a *pathogen* and a host; it is a kind of ecological relationship. We might suspect that "pathogen" is a synonym for "parasite," but such is not the case. We cannot say that all parasites are pathogens. An organism may live at the expense of another without causing obvious damage—without producing *symptoms* (signs of illness). On the other hand, an organism that is not a parasite may be involved in a disease. The fungi that are associated with athlete's foot and ringworm are saprovores, living on the dead outer layers of the skin. Yet athlete's foot is certainly an uncomfortable condition, a disease. But because most infectious diseases are associated with the presence of parasites, we refer to the diseased organism as the "host," even though this is not always accurate.

**Transmission of infections.** Because an infectious disease is a *condition* that results from the association of pathogen and host, the disease itself cannot be transmitted (carried). The thing that actually is transmitted is the pathogen. However, physicians are not always careful to make this distinction, so "pathogen" and "disease" are sometimes used interchangeably when transmission is discussed.

For some purposes it is convenient to divide pathogens into two groups according to the way they get from one host to another. Let us look at two extreme cases.

Syphilis is a disease that results from infection of a

S. R. Aldrich, Univ. of Illinois

Figure 7 · 3

Deficiency diseases occur in plants as well as animals. This corn plant lacks a sufficient supply of nitrogen.

asthma [ăz′mə, ăs′mə; Greek: *azein*, to breathe hard]

hemophilia [hē′mə fĭl′ĭ ə]

arthritis [är thrī′tĭs; Greek: *arthron*, joint, + *-itis*, (now) inflammation of]

pathogen [păth′ə jən; Greek: *pathein*, + *-genes*, born]

symptoms [sĭmp′təmz]

syphilis [sĭf′ə ləs]

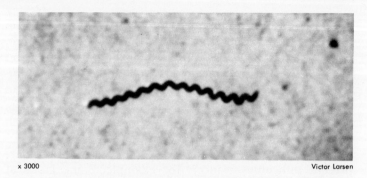

Figure 7 · 4
The spirochete of syphilis.

x 3000                                    Victor Larsen

*Treponema pallidum* [trĕp'-
ə nē'mə păl'ĭ dŭm]

*Plasmodium vivax* [plăz mō'-
dē əm vē'văks], *P. falciparum*
[făl sĭ'pər əm], and *P. malariae* [mə lĕr'ĭ ē]: See Figure
A · 16.

human host by a corkscrew-shaped protist called *Treponema pallidum*. This organism dies in seconds when exposed to light and air, but within the human body it not only survives; it multiplies and eventually may inhabit every part of the host. The disease may go through three stages, each of which can be quite variable in time of onset and kinds of symptoms. The usual first symptom of the first stage is a small open sore at the point of original infection. Treponemes from this sore are easily transmitted if the sore touches any moist membrane of another person. Usual symptoms of the second stage, which may begin from two to six months after the appearance of the first sore, are rashes, blotches, and sores on the skin and mucous membranes. Symptoms of the disease may then disappear for a period of ten to twenty years, while the treponemes attack internal body parts, especially nerves and brain. Eventually the third stage becomes evident, resulting in blindness, deafness, or insanity.

Human malaria is a disease that results from infection by protists of the phylum Sporozoa (*Plasmodium vivax, P. falciparum*, and *P. malariae*). For infection to occur, the

Man with male and
female forms of
parasite in his blood.

Uninfected female **Anopheles**
bites man, withdrawing
blood and parasites.

About 2 weeks

Infectious parasites
have developed and
migrated to mosquito's
salivary glands.

pathogen must enter the host's bloodstream. Through the bloodstream it travels to the liver and multiplies. The offspring move back into the blood, where they enter red blood cells, continue to multiply, and in doing so, destroy the cells. This destruction of blood cells takes place at definite intervals, depending upon the species of *Plasmodium.* At these times the host experiences alternating violent chills and high fever that greatly weaken him.

From time to time special forms of the parasite that can be called "male" and "female" are produced. If the infected person happens to be bitten at such a time by a mosquito of the genus *Anopheles,* the male and female forms may be picked up by the insect. In the mosquito's stomach the male parasite unites with a female parasite, forming a single new individual. This new form then squeezes through the stomach wall of the mosquito and starts to divide, eventually forming a cluster of hundreds of individuals within the insect. These individuals presently burst free from the cluster and migrate through the mosquito's body to the salivary glands. When the mosquito "bites," it injects saliva into the blood of its victim. If the mosquito has malarial parasites in its salivary glands, these are injected along with the saliva, and the parasite has found a new, human host.

Syphilis is strictly a *contagious* disease. Because treponemes do not survive drying, they must be transmitted directly from a moist surface of one person to a moist surface of another. Normally such contacts occur only in the regions of the mouth and the sexual organs. Malaria, on the other hand, is strictly a *vector* disease; that is, the pathogen can get from one human host to another only when some other thing—in this case a living thing, a mosquito—carries it.

*Anopheles* [ə nŏf′ə lēz′]

salivary glands [săl′ə vĕr′ĭ]: Saliva produced by these glands prevents the blood of the mosquito's victim from clotting.

contagious [kən tā′jəs; Latin: *cum,* together, + *tangere,* to touch]

vector [Latin: *vector,* a carrier]

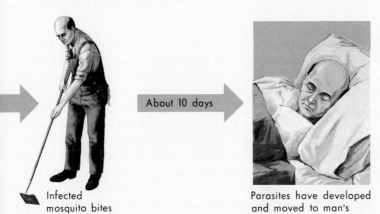

About 10 days

Infected mosquito bites healthy man.

Parasites have developed and moved to man's blood.

**Figure 7 · 5**
Transmission of malaria. What would be the best way to stop the spread of this disease?

In these examples, the meanings of "vector" and "contagious" are clear. But very few human diseases are strictly contagious. The germs of smallpox may be acquired by contact with a blanket used by a smallpox victim; the germs of tuberculosis may be acquired from breathing in dust particles that carry microbes coughed up by a tuberculosis victim. Even though the blanket and dust particles are vectors, smallpox and tuberculosis are often described as contagious. On the other hand, typhoid fever germs are carried in drinking water or on the feet of flies and then on food—typhoid is usually described as a vector disease even though the means of transmission are very different from the bite of a mosquito.

smallpox: disease in which the human host has a fever, develops sore spots on the skin, and often dies

tuberculosis: disease in which tissues of the host—most often in the lungs—are destroyed

typhoid fever: disease centered in the digestive system of the host

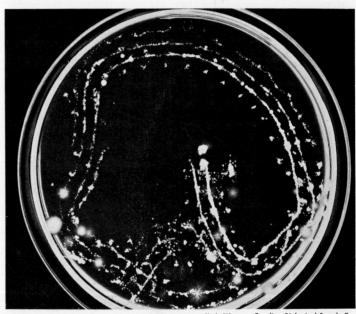

K. A. Wagner, Carolina Biological Supply Co.

Figure 7 · 6
A housefly walked over the nutrient medium in this petri dish before incubation. How do you explain the results?

For transmission to be effective, a pathogen must enter the living substance of the host. Undoubtedly many potentially pathogenic microbes exist on the human skin, and any break in the skin may be a dangerous entryway for such germs. Other microbes are able to penetrate the mucous lining of the digestive system once they get into the mouth. Many microorganisms, however, normally inhabit the digestive system without penetrating the body. Your intestines contain enormous numbers of bacteria, particularly the kind called *Escherichia coli*. But under some circumstances *E. coli* produces illness; then the commensal has become a pathogen.

potentially: refers to something that is possible

*Escherichia coli* [ĕsh′ər ĭk′ĭ ə kō′lī]

Why is *E. coli* referred to here as a commensal?

When a vector is a living thing that becomes a host for the parasite it transmits—as in malaria—the use of the word "vector" implies a point of view: for man, mosquitoes are the vectors of malaria parasites; but the mosquitoes, if they worried about the matter, would probably consider man to be the malarial vector. From the biological point of view, it is preferable to think of such relationships as an *alternation of hosts.*

Alternation of hosts is far from unusual. The hosts for yellow fever are mosquitoes and man (or monkeys); hosts of Rocky Mountain spotted fever are ticks and man (or rodents); African sleeping sickness involves tsetse flies and man (or cattle). Details vary greatly from one disease to another, and there may be more than two kinds of hosts. Human diseases with alternate-host transmission are unfamiliar to us in the United States today, because it has been possible to control most of them through sanitary measures directed at the alternate hosts. But such diseases are still important in many parts of the world.

**Host specificity.** Some pathogens are highly *host-specific;* that is, they infect only a few kinds of organisms. Where there is an alternation of hosts, the pathogen may be highly specific for both hosts. For example, the pathogen that causes human malaria infects only man among the vertebrates and only mosquitoes of the genus *Anopheles.*

Diseases of man that are specific for man alone are particularly difficult to study because it is impossible to use other animals in investigating them. If we could infect rats or guinea pigs with the pathogens of leprosy or the common cold, we might know a great deal more about these diseases.

Many pathogens, on the other hand, are not highly host-specific; they will infect a variety of organisms. There is no way to predict whether a given pathogen will infect a given host. In general, the more closely two organisms are related (in the taxonomic sense), the more likely they are to be infectible by the same pathogens. Monkeys can often be used in the experimental study of human pathogens that do not infect common laboratory animals such as dogs or rats.

**Virulence and resistance.** Every infectious disease involves the interaction of a pathogen and a host. The extent to which a pathogen is capable of affecting its host is called its *virulence.* And the ability of a host to cope with a pathogen is termed *resistance.* A pathogen with high virulence may cause death in a host with low resistance, severe illness in a host with medium resistance, and perhaps not even symptoms in a host with high resistance.

yellow fever: a chiefly tropical fever disease. See Figure 7 · 10.

Rocky Mountain spotted fever is actually most common in the Atlantic coastal states; it has caused many deaths.

African sleeping sickness affects the nervous system of the mammalian host.

tsetse [sĕt′sē]

leprosy [lĕp′rə sĭ; Greek: *lepros,* rough, scaly]: characterized by nodules, open sores, scabs, and a wasting away of tissues—at first, those of the skin and nerves

virulence [vĭr′yə ləns, vĭr′ə ləns; Latin: *virus,* a poison]

Corynebacterium diphtheriae
[kə rī″nə băk tir′ i əm dĭf thĭr′ ĭ ē]

U.S. Dept. of Agriculture

**Figure 7 · 7**

Black stem rust of wheat. The pathogen, a fungus, has barberry as an alternate host. Some varieties of wheat have an inherited resistance to the disease.

x 1

immunity [ĭm yōō′nət ē]

poliomyelitis    [pō′lē ō′mī′ ə-
līt′əs]: a disease in which a virus pathogen attacks nerves of
the host, frequently leaving
him crippled

What determines the virulence of a pathogen? This is a complex problem, but consider some evidence. In diphtheria, damage to the host is the result of a poison produced by the pathogen *Corynebacterium diphtheriae*. The ability of this bacterium to produce the poison can be determined by growing it in a petri dish and measuring the quantity of poison produced. But different *strains* of *C. diphtheriae* — that is, pure cultures of bacteria obtained from different sources — produce different amounts of poison even though grown under identical conditions. In other words they have different virulences. Evidently virulence (at least in *C. diphtheriae*) is a characteristic that is inherited. This, of course, is only a first step in investigating the problem of virulence.

**Immunity.**    Why do different individuals of the same host species have different degrees of resistance? This is another complex problem. We know that we can develop breeds of domestic plants and animals that are more resistant to particular diseases than are other breeds. Some human diseases seem to "run in families," though it is difficult to obtain convincing evidence of this. It seems, therefore, that the resistance of a host involves inherited characteristics.

On the other hand much resistance is not inherited, but *acquired*. When a human host is invaded by a pathogen, the host reacts by producing substances called *antibodies*. Antibodies combat the pathogen or the poisons produced by it. If the host survives the infection, its body retains the ability to produce antibodies. Then if a new infection by the same kind of pathogen occurs, the host can act immediately against it. Such resistance is called *immunity*.

Antibodies may be produced even though there are no symptoms of disease. Thus a person may be immune without knowing it. By the time they reach adulthood, many people have had some contact with the pathogens of poliomyelitis and tuberculosis and have acquired some immunity to these diseases.

Each kind of antibody is effective only against the kind of pathogen that brought about its production or occasionally against very similar pathogens. An antibody produced as the result of an infection by the mumps virus has no effect on the organism of diphtheria.

There is great variation in the length of time immunity lasts. Sometimes immunity is very short, as with the common cold. Sometimes it is lifelong, as with yellow fever. The strength of immunity to a disease may vary, too. Though able to ward off an attack by a weakly virulent strain of the pathogen, it may have little effect on a strong strain.

The immunity discussed so far is *natural;* it occurs as a result of chance infection. Fortunately, we do not have to depend on natural immunity or on inherited resistance. We can produce *artificial* immunity in various ways.

In the late eighteenth century Edward Jenner observed in England that milkmaids and other workers associated with cows seldom had smallpox—at that time a common and often fatal disease. However, such workers usually had been infected at one time or another by a mild disease of cattle, cowpox. From these observations Jenner concluded that a person might become immune to smallpox by deliberately infecting himself with cowpox. This idea led him to develop the practice of vaccination more than half a century before the development of the germ theory of disease.

**Figure 7 · 8**

A cartoonist of Jenner's day shows the fears that vaccination aroused. Are all fears of new medical treatments as unreasonable as these?

vaccination    [văk′sə nā′shən; Latin: *vacca,* cow]

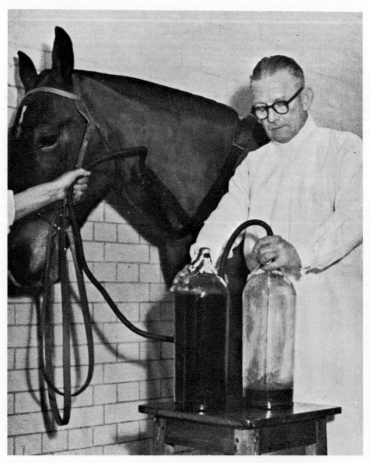

**Figure 7 · 9**

Horses are used in the production of antibodies because they can contribute large amounts of blood.

CIBA Pharmaceutical Products, Inc.

Today several ways of bringing about artificial immunity are known. The kind of antibody formed depends on the kind of pathogen rather than on the kind of host. Therefore it is possible to inject a pathogen into an animal host, where antibodies are then produced. Removed from the blood of the animal host, these antibodies may then be injected into a person. Sometimes the pathogens themselves, weakened or even dead, may be injected into a human being, where they stimulate the production of antibodies without producing symptoms of disease. This method is used in immunizing against poliomyelitis. However, for some diseases—such as leprosy and syphilis—no effective artificial immunity has been developed.

**Environment and disease.** During most famines more people perish from disease than from starvation. This illustrates how important the environment is in a biological consideration of disease.

Environmental factors may affect the host, the pathogen, or both. For example, if the environment is such that the host is vigorous and relatively free from other diseases, then the host will be more able to resist infection by (say) tuberculosis organisms than it would be otherwise. A host that is poorly nourished and already defending itself against other germs will have much less resistance.

Environmental factors may also have effect on the ability of a pathogen to infect its host. For example, fungi that attack the human skin are favored by a warm, moist atmosphere. In some parts of the tropics, these pathogens are very active in producing disease. In much of the United States, they usually find such favorable conditions only inside shoes and stockings—where they cause the disease called "athlete's foot."

It should now be evident that combating infectious disease involves much more than the killing of pathogens. It is a complex ecological problem involving three major factors: the nature of the pathogen, the nature of the host, and the nature of the environment in which pathogen and host interact. The modern physician realizes his work is basically ecological.

## EPIDEMIOLOGY

The science of *epidemiology* is concerned both with the ways in which diseases are transmitted and with the frequency with which they occur. The name of the science comes from the word *epidemic,* an unusual or severe outbreak of disease. Epidemics usually (though not always) involve infectious disease, and in this discussion we shall consider only such diseases.

epidemiology [ĕp'ə dē'mĭ ŏl'ə- jĭ; Greek: *epi,* on, upon, + *demos,* the people, + *logikos*]

The unusual, the epidemic, situation always attracts attention, causes alarm and panic; but it cannot be understood except in relation to the usual, the *endemic,* situation. In the endemic situation a pathogenic species lives in a steady state with its host species. There are always a few cases of measles present in the child population. But in the fall, when the opening of schools brings large numbers of children into close contact, there is frequently a sudden increase in the number of cases. Endemic measles become epidemic.

**Causes of epidemics.** Many infectious diseases exist in the endemic state, often at a very low density but ready to break forth as epidemics, given the right conditions. The "right conditions" generally mean either low resistance in the host population or increased chances for transmitting the pathogen from one host to another. Perhaps epidemics also occur because the virulence of the pathogen increases,

influenza [ĭn'flōo'ĕn'zə]: Many forms of this disease, having quite different pathogens, exist.

*Salmonella typhi* [săl'mə nĕl'-ə tī'fī]: the pathogen of typhoid fever; not related to typhus fever, in which the pathogen is a rickettsia

but this is difficult to show. In 1918 an epidemic of influenza swept the world, killing a great many people. This event has sometimes been attributed to an increase in virulence. But at that time much of the world had been engaged for four years in a great war, and it is certainly reasonable to suppose that resistance was low in many human hosts.

Perhaps the most spectacular epidemics, however, have occurred when diseases were introduced into populations that had no hereditary resistance. Measles, which seldom kills Europeans (except for infants), was a deadly disease when introduced among island people in the Pacific.

In modern times epidemics may occur when control methods break down. Typhoid fever is infrequent in the United States, but we have no reason to think that *Salmonella typhi* is an extinct organism. Any relaxation in the care with which water is treated or in sewage disposal would certainly result in a major typhoid epidemic in our crowded cities. This is not the least horrifying of the consequences that result from bombing attacks in war.

**The geography of disease.**    People about to travel to distant lands are likely to get a series of "shots" (immunizations) protecting them from this or that strange disease; and they are likely to ask physicians about precautions to be taken with food and drink. Disease, then, is not the same everywhere.

Through history the geographical patterns of human diseases have shifted greatly. We know that many contagions of the Old World were absent from the New at the time of its discovery by Europeans. It is also possible that the New World contributed diseases to the Old. Syphilis became suddenly prominent in Europe about 1500 A.D., and some medical historians have supposed that it was brought back by the sailors of Columbus, but this is by no means certain. Old descriptions of diseases and epidemics are usually incomplete or difficult to interpret.

The common human contagions—influenza, measles, colds, tuberculosis, and the like—are now almost worldwide. They have been carried everywhere by modern transportation, and they persist wherever the population is dense enough to support them. Diseases that have a limited infection period of a few days or weeks and that leave the host temporarily or permanently immune to a second attack cannot persist among small or scattered human populations. To survive, the pathogens of such diseases need a steady supply of new hosts. The common cold is one of these diseases. Often when a ship visits a small Pacific island, everyone on the island will, within a few days, come

down with a cold, brought in by some visitor. When everyone has acquired a temporary immunity, the colds disappear, and there will be no more until another ship turns up. Most contagious diseases follow such a pattern.

On the other hand, a pathogen that requires an alternation of hosts for survival can only occur in places where both hosts are present. African sleeping sickness, for instance, is transmitted by the tsetse fly, so the disease is found only where these flies live. It is thought that yellow fever also originated in Africa. The vector of this disease is the mosquito *Aedes aegypti*. Breeding in the water kegs of sailing ships, it was carried from Africa to the New World. With modern air transportation it is easy to see how the tsetse fly might today be carried from Africa. Constant vigilance is necessary to prevent this.

**Figure 7 · 10**

Yellow fever in the American tropics. Forest mosquitoes (*shown on white*) transmit the pathogen from monkey to monkey. A man working in the forest may acquire the pathogen from these mosquitoes. In town this man may be the source of infection for other persons if *Aedes* (on orange) is not controlled.

*Aedes aegypti* [ā ē′dēz ē jĭp′tī]

**Figure 7 · 11**

Distribution of tsetse flies in Africa. Into what parts of the world is a spread of African sleeping sickness most to be feared?

## INVESTIGATION 7.2

### INVESTIGATING AN INFECTIOUS DISEASE

#### PURPOSE

In this investigation you will develop evidence to link the presence of a specific microorganism with the symptoms of an infectious disease.

#### BACKGROUND INFORMATION

One of the first steps in controlling an infectious disease is to determine what specific organism must be present in the host to produce the symptoms of the disease. Robert Koch (see page 189) was the first biologist to set forth a method for determining that a *particular* disease results from the presence of a *particular* microorganism. This method is embodied in the following set of tests (known as Koch's postulates):

1. The organism suspected of producing the disease symptoms must be found constantly associated with those symptoms.

2. The suspected organism must be grown outside the host and in a pure culture.

3. When organisms from this pure culture are inoculated into a healthy individual of the host species, the symptoms of the disease in question must appear in the individual.

4. The suspected organism must then be taken from the experimental host, grown again in pure culture, and identified as the species present in the original culture.

Koch's postulates cannot be used to establish the cause of *every* type of infectious disease, because some microorganisms cannot be grown outside the body of the host (thus making Postulates 2 and 4 impossible). Nevertheless, the postulates are still considered to be the basic tests for determining the pathogens of most infectious diseases.

#### MATERIALS AND EQUIPMENT
(for each team)

Potted plants of bean, tomato, or sunflower, 2
Dissecting needle
Bunsen burner
Culture of *Agrobacterium tumefaciens*
Inoculating loop
Microscope slides, 3
Beaker, 5 to 7 cm in diameter
Crystal-violet solution
Medicine dropper
Paper towels, 3
Monocular microscope
Glass-marking crayon
Scalpel (or razor blade)
Forceps
Sodium hypochlorite solution, 1%
Container for disposal of gall tissue
Sterile distilled water in plugged test tube
Petri dish, sterile
Tube of sterile dextrose agar

#### PROCEDURE

Caution: *Agrobacterium tumefaciens* does not infect man, but it is a dangerous plant pathogen. Be sure to maintain sterile laboratory conditions!

Choose two plants of approximately the same size and age. Using lead pencil, label their pots *A* and *B;* then write your team's symbol on both pots.

Sterilize a dissecting needle by heating it in a flame. Allow the needle to cool. Locate a portion of the stem that is about 4 to 6 mm in diameter. With the needle make several punctures (about 2 mm apart) on one side of the stem of Plant A, midway between two points at which leaves are attached.

Again sterilize the dissecting needle. Allow it to cool. Dip the tip of the needle into the culture of *Agrobacterium tumefaciens*. Using the needle, puncture the stem of Plant B just as you did that of Plant A. Sterilize the needle. Place the plants in a well-lighted part of the laboratory, and keep them well watered.

Prepare a stained microscope slide of *A. tumefaciens*, using the method given in Investigation 6.3. Examine under high power of a monocular microscope. Sketch a few of the bacteria, showing both their shapes and their arrangement. With a glass-marking crayon label the slide *1* and store it for later use in this investigation.

Observe the potted plants every two or three days for a period of four or five weeks. Record all changes and the dates on which they were first observed.

A knotlike growth, or *gall*, may appear on one of the plants. If this occurs, use a sharp scalpel to remove it. Wash the gall thoroughly. Using forceps, dip a clean microscope slide into a 1% solution of sodium hypochlorite for about twenty seconds. Rinse in sterile distilled water. Place the slide on a paper towel on the laboratory table and cover with the top of a sterile petri dish. Do not touch the upper surface of the slide, and do not allow it to touch anything in the laboratory.

Again using the forceps, dip the plant gall into the solution of sodium hypochlorite. Rinse in distilled water and place on the sterile microscope slide near one end. Using a sharp scalpel sterilized in a flame, cut the gall in half. Cut a small piece (about 2 mm in diameter) from the center of the gall and place it in the middle of the slide. (Important: Discard the remaining gall tissue into the container provided for this purpose.) Crush the small piece of tissue with the flat side of the scalpel blade. Sterilize the scalpel blade.

With a sterile inoculating loop, transfer some of the juice from the crushed gall tissue to a sterile tube of dextrose agar. Label the tube and store it in a place designated by your teacher.

Examine the tube four or five days later. If colonies of microorganisms are present, take material from one of the colonies and prepare a slide as you did before. Label the slide *2*.

Compare Slides 1 and 2 under high power of a monocular microscope. Draw a few of the organisms observed on Slide 2.

## DISCUSSION AND CONCLUSION

• Did either of the two plants develop crown gall? If so, which one? (1) • Which of the two plants was the control? (2) • Why was a sterile needle used to puncture Plant A? (3) • On the basis of your visual comparison of Slides 1 and 2, what conclusion may be drawn about the identity of the organisms in Slide 2? (4) • Why is similarity of appearance not sufficient evidence for concluding that the bacteria on the two slides are of the same species? (5)

• Do you believe that this experiment provides proof that *Agrobacterium tumefaciens* is the "cause" of crown gall? If so, explain how each of Koch's postulates is fulfilled in the experiment. If not, what additional steps should be taken to fulfill them? (6)

### FOR FURTHER INVESTIGATION

1. Determine whether or not bacteria taken from your cultures will produce new galls when inoculated into other plants of the same species.

2. The plants suggested for use in this experiment are dicots. Are other dicots susceptible to infection by *A. tumefaciens*? Are monocots susceptible?

## THE SOIL ECOSYSTEM

There is a living world beneath your feet. It is a world made up of mineral and organic matter, water, and air. It has length, breadth, and depth, and it harbors populations of organisms large and small—all bound together in complex community relationships.

Farmers are well acquainted with this ecosystem. They will often pick up a handful of soil and let it trickle through their fingers. From its feel, odor, and appearance, they can tell a great deal about its condition and the kinds of crops for which it might be suitable. They know that they hold in their hands the source of their livelihood. The city dweller often forgets that he, too, depends on the soil, even though his dependence is by way of the supermarket.

components [Latin: *cum*, together, + *ponere*, to put, place]: a substance that is part of a more complex substance

### COMPONENTS OF A SOIL

A heap of builder's sand is not soil, nor is a lump of sticky clay in the brickworks. Soil consists of a group of interacting organisms living in a special sort of inorganic environment. It is an ecosystem. The soil ecosystem is a complex mixture—substances derived from rocks and air, substances derived from the dead bodies of living things, and, of course, living things themselves.

**Mineral components.** Heating and cooling, freezing and thawing, wetting and drying, all tend to weaken the structure of rocks. Minerals in rocks react with the water and air that enter through tiny cracks and crevices. These forces cause the rocks to break up, and the loose, weathered material becomes the basic ingredient of soil. Coarse

Charles E. Kellogg, U.S. Dept. of Agriculture

Figure 7 · 12
Boulder weathering into mineral soil particles.

rock particles are called sand, intermediate-size particles are called silt, and "clay" refers to very fine particles.

Each rock particle holds a thin layer of moisture. In the spaces between particles are tiny pockets of gases, mostly the gases of the atmosphere—air. If the soil is very wet, many of the spaces between particles may be filled with water and the amount of air correspondingly reduced. Many substances that soil organisms need are dissolved in the soil water. Some of these substances are organic and some are inorganic. From rock particles come compounds containing phosphorus, sulfur, calcium, potassium, iron, magnesium, and other elements mentioned in Chapter 1.

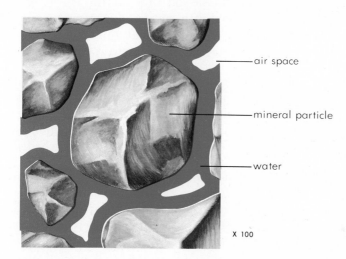

air space

mineral particle

water

X 100

Figure 7 · 13

The relation among in-organic substances in soil. Water adheres to the mineral particles. Usually, the larger the particles, the larger the air spaces. Dissolved substances are not visible at this degree of magnification.

Most of the mineral compounds in soil water are not present as molecules. Magnesium sulfate, for example, is shown in symbols by the chemist as the molecule $MgSO_4$, but particles with this structure do not occur. Magnesium sulfate consists of the electrically charged particles $Mg^{++}$ and $SO_4^{--}$. Such charged particles are called *ions*. The charges cause the chemical characteristics of the particles to be quite different from what they would be without the charges. For example, an uncharged magnesium atom (Mg) is very unlike a magnesium ion ($Mg^{++}$). Mg and $MgSO_4$ particles are *not* present in soil water; $Mg^{++}$ and $SO_4^{--}$ ions *are*.

Water, on the other hand, occurs chiefly as molecules —$H_2O$, also written HOH. But at any given moment a few water molecules in any sample ionize, forming hydrogen ions ($H^+$) and hydroxyl ions ($OH^-$). When a water molecule ionizes, just one hydrogen ion and one hydroxyl ion are formed; in pure water the two kinds of ions are equal in

ions [ī′ənz, ī′ŏnz]

hydroxyl [hī drŏk′sĭl]

acid [Latin: *acidus*, sour]

alkaline [ăl′kə lĭn′, ăl′kə lĭn]

humus [hū′məs; Latin: ground, soil]

decompose: to separate a thing into its parts. Rotting is a decomposing process.

alpine [Latin: *Alpes*, the Alps Mountains]: now, of mountain areas above the level of tree growth

bog: wet, spongy ground

reservoir [rĕz′ər vôr′, rĕz′ərvwär′]: a store, reserve

number. In soil water, however, ions from other substances are always present. Some of these substances also produce hydrogen ions. This results in a greater number of hydrogen ions than are present in chemically pure water. Water with more hydrogen ions than hydroxyl ions is said to be *acid*. Other substances in soil reduce the number of hydrogen ions. When hydroxyl ions are more numerous than hydrogen ions, the water is called *alkaline* (or basic). The acidity or alkalinity of the soil water is an important limiting factor in the distribution of soil organisms.

**Humus.**    From the viewpoint of the microbiologist, the soil is a huge digestive system into which all kinds of organic materials descend. Land plants, land animals, even we ourselves, return to the soil. Much of the activity of soil organisms is concerned with getting the remaining energy out of these dead materials. Through this activity the materials are returned to an inorganic state as minerals, gases, and water.

The decomposing process occurs most rapidly under warm, moist conditions that favor the growth of microorganisms. However, in all climates some time is required, so organic substances in various stages of decomposition usually occur in soils. When decomposition has reached the point where the original organisms can no longer be distinguished, the remains are called *humus*. In general, the darker a soil, the larger the proportion of humus it contains. The proportion of humus in soils varies from about 1 percent in desert soils to more than 70 percent in some alpine and bog soils.

Humus acts as a reservoir of materials needed by the organisms living in the soil. It increases the water-holding ability of the soil and, to some degree, the amount of air space. It moderates extremes in soil temperature. These

James H. Wells, Forest Service

Conservation and Survey Division, Univ. of Nebraska

**Figure 7 · 14**

Sections through soils. *Left:* A forest soil (North Carolina). *Right:* A prairie soil (Nebraska). Which appears to have the larger proportion of humus?

functions of humus tend to improve the soil as a habitat for living organisms. But there can be too much of a good thing—humus increases the acidity of soils, and this makes many bog soils unfavorable to most organisms.

**Soil organisms.** To the soil scientist, at least some of the living organisms in the soil are part of the soil. Of course, which organisms are part of the soil and which are not is a matter of definition. Prairie dogs dig into the soil; earthworms plow through it. Both affect the soil in various ways, but are they both part of it? Whatever the answer, there is no question about microorganisms being a part of the soil.

*prairie dogs: See Figure 8 · 26.*

Bacteria are probably more widely distributed in the biosphere than are any other organisms. They are abundant in all soils. In the relatively dry and alkaline soils of grasslands, they are the chief agents of decay.

The importance of actinomycetes in the soil was first pointed out in 1900 by Martinus Beijerinck, but it was not until the 1920's that soil microbiologists began to take much interest in them. Then it was found that when we culture soil samples in the laboratory, from 30 to 40 percent of the colonies that appear are actinomycetes. Some of these decompose cellulose, one of the most abundant materials in the remains of plants. Others act on the substances that result from this decomposition. But usually our only acquaintance with these organisms is their pleasant, earthy smell in freshly turned soil.

If a forest soil is overturned to a depth of a few inches, an irregular network of delicate gray or white filaments is usually exposed. These are bundles of fungal hyphae. Although fungi occur in many soils, they are particularly important as agents of decay in forest soils. This is probably because they have a better tolerance of the acid conditions that occur in such soils than have bacteria. Soil fungi are as active as actinomycetes in decomposing cellulose. They also use as food *pectins* and *chitins*. Pectins are common substances in plants; some of them help to hold plant tissues together. Chitins are found principally in the exoskeletons of insects.

*tolerance: in ecology, the ability to endure an environmental condition*

*chitins [kīt′ənz]*

Ordinarily, we think of algae as producers that are abundant in bodies of water. But more than sixty different species have been found in soil samples. Under appropriate conditions they will develop on the surface of soil as green, slimy growths. Algae are important inhabitants in paddy soils used for cultivation of rice; by contributing to the nitrogen and oxygen content of the soil, they increase crop yields. In desert soils algae may help to control soil erosion by forming surface crusts.

*Why would algae be unlikely to grow deep in soil?*

Everyone knows earthworms. These are among the larger soil animals. Just as important are smaller and less-known soil animals such as centipedes, millepedes, mites, and many small insects. Nematodes are among the most abundant animal groups in soils. They are particularly important in agricultural soils because of their relationships to crops.

*If you have forgotten what some of these animals are, consult Appendix II.*

## INVESTIGATION 7.3

### A CHEMICAL CHARACTERISTIC OF SOILS

#### PURPOSES

This investigation (*a*) shows a method by which acidity-alkalinity may be measured, and (*b*) uses this method in an investigation of soil pH.

#### BACKGROUND INFORMATION

The degree of acidity-alkalinity of a solution is indicated by a series of numbers from 1 to 14 called the *pH scale*. In chemically pure water there are equal numbers of hydrogen and hydroxyl ions; such water is neither acid nor alkaline. It is *neutral* and has a pH of 7. If the amount of liquid remains constant and the number of hydrogen ions is increased tenfold (that is, if the *concentration* of the hydrogen ions is multiplied by 10), the pH is 6. If the concentration of hydrogen ions is multiplied by 100, the pH is 5, and so forth. On the other hand, if the concentration of hydrogen ions is reduced to 1/10 of that in pure water, the pH is 8; if reduced to 1/100 of that in pure water, the pH is 9, and so on. The pH numbers below 7 indicate acid solutions (the smaller the number, the greater the acidity); pH numbers above 7 indicate alkaline solutions (the larger the number, the greater the alkalinity).

The pH of a solution is measured most accurately by means of electrical instruments. You will use a less accurate but quite satisfactory method. Many soluble *pigments* (coloring substances) change chemically when there is an increase or decrease in the pH of the water in which they are dissolved. Often the chemical change in the pigment involves a loss of color or a shift to a different color. For many such pigments the pH range in which the color change occurs is known. Therefore, if both the pigment and the pH range within which it changes color are known, the pigment can be used as an indicator to determine the pH of an unknown solution. One such indicator, bromthymol blue, was used in Investigation 1.5.

#### MATERIALS AND EQUIPMENT
(per team)

*For Procedure A*

    Beakers, 50 or 100 ml, 6

    Glass-marking crayon

    Graduated cylinder, 25 ml

    Distilled water, 100 ml

    Glass stirring rods, 6

    Dropping bottles, 10 ml, 1 for each of the following:

        Methyl red solution

        Bromthymol blue solution

        Phenolphthalein solution

        Hydrochloric acid

        Sodium hydroxide solution

*For Procedure B*

    Soil samples, 3 or more

    Mortar and pestle

    Graduated cylinder, 25 ml

    Distilled water

    Test tubes, 1 per soil sample

    Test-tube rack

Glass-marking crayon

Microscope slides, 1 per soil sample

Wide-range pH test paper, 1 cm per soil sample

Glass stirring rods, 1 per soil sample

### PROCEDURE A:
### THE ACTION OF INDICATORS

Mark six beakers as follows: *1-A, 1-B, 2-A, 2-B, 3-A, 3-B*. Into each beaker pour 15 ml of distilled water and add a stirring rod. To Beakers 1-A and 1-B add a drop of methyl red solution; to Beakers 2-A and 2-B add a drop of bromthymol blue solution; to Beakers 3-A and 3-B add a drop of phenolphthalein solution. Record the color in each beaker.

To each of the three A beakers add a drop of hydrochloric acid and stir; to each of the B beakers add a drop of sodium hydroxide solution (an alkaline solution, or base) and stir. Keep each stirring rod in its own beaker. If no color changes occur, repeat the procedure. Continue in this way, alternating additions of acid to A beakers and base to B beakers.

### STUDYING THE DATA

• According to the background information given above, approximately what pH should distilled water have? (1) • As acid is added to the A beakers, what happens to the pH value? (2) • As base is added to the B beakers, what happens to the pH value? (3) • Keeping these ideas in mind and referring to your data, arrange the indicator colors in order of increasing pH. (4) The teacher will then give you the pH range in which each indicator changes color.

### PROCEDURE B:
### THE pH OF SOIL SAMPLES

With a large enough series of indicators, the approximate pH of solutions can be worked out. Often it is more convenient to use indicator paper than a pigment solution. Indicator paper is prepared by soaking porous paper in a pigment solution and then allowing it to dry. A number of pigments may be combined in the same paper so that different ones do not have to be tried separately. This part of the investigation makes use of such an indicator paper.

Obtain soil samples from different environments. Place about 10 g of soil in a mortar, add 10 ml of distilled water, and grind. Pour the mixture into a test tube labeled with the name or number of the soil sample. Wash the mortar and pestle and rinse with distilled water before preparing the next sample. Repeat this procedure for each sample prepared. Permit the tubes to stand for ten minutes.

Place one microscope slide in front of each test tube. Place a small piece of test paper on each slide. Dip a glass stirring rod into the first sample and transfer a drop of the liquid to the test paper. Note the color of the test paper where the drop has been placed and compare it with the color scale that comes with the paper. Record the pH of the sample. Repeat this procedure for each sample, using a different stirring rod and slide in each case.

### SUMMARY

• What is the pH range of your samples? (5) • According to your evidence, what types of soils are most likely to be acid? Which are most likely to be alkaline? Which are most likely to be neutral? (6) • Suggest some reasons for the differences (or similarities) in pH. (7) • This method provides a comparison of the pH of the samples, but it does not give the true pH. Why? (8)

## COMMUNITY RELATIONSHIPS IN SOIL

**Saprovores.** Except for the algae, which live near the surface where light is available, soil microorganisms are consumers, and most of these are saprovores. Many do not consume the entire body of a dead organism but use only certain substances in it.

In a dead leaf lying on the surface of the soil, there are relatively large amounts of complex organic substances— cellulose, pectins, and *lignins.* Some soil organisms can use these substances as food but leave as waste products simpler organic substances that still contain energy. Other soil organisms then use these waste products. Even they may not extract all the energy but leave still simpler substances—such as sugars—that still another group of organisms may use. Thus, one organism depends on another for its food supply. Such a food chain is like an assembly line in reverse. Instead of building step by step from simpler to more complex things, the food chain breaks down organic substances in an orderly sequence until only inorganic substances—carbon dioxide, water, and mineral compounds—remain.

Before the final inorganic substances are reached, a large number of intermediate organic substances are formed. These not only serve as food for various organisms; they affect the whole soil environment. For example, many organisms form acids. When these accumulate, as they do in many forest soils, the pH of the environment becomes unfavorable for many bacteria. But many fungi can tolerate a low pH and thus thrive in forest soils.

Other substances produced not only by soil microorganisms but also by the roots of plants do not merely change the nature of the environment; they are actively harmful to other organisms. Such an *antibiotic* substance, when accumulated in the soil around the organism that

lignins [lĭg'nənz; Latin: *lignum,* wood]: a group of substances abundant in wood

Figure 7 · 15

Some soil saprovores. Hyphae of most fungi are much alike; these drawings show spore cases. Only generic identification is given.

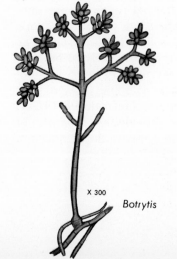

X 300

*Botrytis*

X 300

*Alternaria*

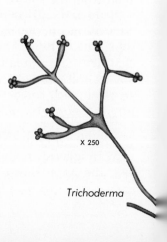

X 250

*Trichoderma*

forms it, reduces growth of competing organisms. Some of these have been found useful for combating bacterial infections in man; the drug Aureomycin, derived from an actinomycete, is an example.

On the other hand, a number of soil organisms produce substances that seem to *promote* the growth of other organisms in their environment. Some yeasts, for example, apparently increase the growth of certain neighboring bacteria. We have mentioned that soil bacteria are more abundant around the roots of plants than elsewhere in the soil. Such a pattern of distribution seems to be (at least in part) the result of substances given off by the roots. Much work remains to be done on the biochemistry of the growth-promoting substances, which are not as well known as the antibiotics.

**Mycorrhizae.**    If we trace fungal hyphae in loose soil, we often find that some of them lead to the roots of trees, shrubs, and other plants. There the fungi form feltlike sheaths around knobby branches of the roots. Microscopic examination shows that some of the fungal hyphae penetrate the outer parts of the roots and form complicated interweaving masses of tissue. These associations of fungi and roots are referred to as *mycorrhizae.*

Numerous experiments have been conducted to determine the extent to which the root-bearing plants are benefited by the mycorrhizal relationship. In a comparison of mycorrhizal pine seedlings with non-mycorrhizal seedlings of the same species growing in the same kind of soil, it was shown that the mycorrhizal seedlings took up almost twice as much nitrogen and potassium and more than three times as much phosphorus.

In some plants the mycorrhizal relationship is essential. Many conifers and orchids either do not grow or show only limited growth if their mycorrhizal fungi are not present. On the other hand, mycorrhizal fungi probably absorb food from the roots.

**Parasites and predators.**    If the fungi in mycorrhizae harmed instead of benefited the plants whose roots they inhabited—and it is quite possible some soil fungi do this—then they would be parasites. It is easy for a saprovore to shift from living on dead organisms to living on live organisms—to parasitism. So the parasite-host relationship is quite frequent in soil communities.

Predator-prey relationships also occur among soil organisms. Centipedes and many beetles prey on smaller animals. Rotifers prey on protists. Slime molds, amebas, and ciliates feed on bacteria. The predatory protists are probably one of the chief biotic factors influencing the popula-

antibiotic [Greek: *anti,* against, + *bios,* life]

Aureomycin [ôr′ē ō′mĭ′sĭn]

mycorrhizae [mī′kə rī′zē; Greek: *mykes,* fungus, + *rhiza,* root]

What kind of ecological relationship would you say mycorrhizae represent?

242

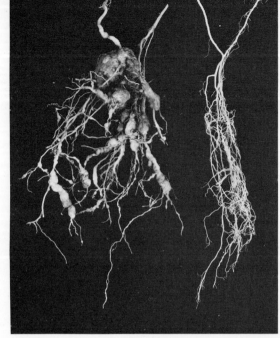

**Figure 7 · 16**

Nematode infection of tomato roots; undamaged roots are shown on the right. Infected roots form masses of tissue that hinder conduction of soil water and minerals.

How are the words "good" and "bad" being used here? Would this statement still be true if the insects attacked by the nematodes were honeybees?

adjacent [Latin: *ad*, toward, near,+ *jaceo*, to lie]

tions of soil bacteria. Nematodes are particularly important in the ecology of agricultural soils, for they attack the root systems of many commercially important plants. On the other hand, some nematodes parasitize other animals that damage crops—for example, insects. In these cases the parasite-host relationships are similar; but from the viewpoint of man, one is good and the other is bad.

One of the strangest community relationships in the soil is one in which a plant acts as a predator. Several species of soil fungi form hyphae with stout lateral branches that curl about in semicircular loops. The tips of the loops from adjacent hyphae intermesh, forming a network. The network produces a sticky fluid. Nematodes are caught in this "trap," and despite violent struggles, they are held fast. Then other hyphae of the fungi grow into the bodies of the captive nematodes and consume them.

**Figure 7 · 17**

A nematode trapped in fungal hyphae.

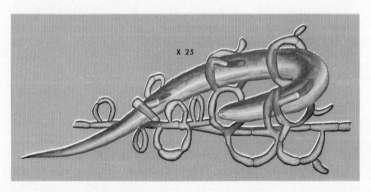

X 25

## THE NITROGEN CYCLE

Soil microorganisms are essential in the chemical cycles of the biosphere. The nitrogen cycle will serve as an example. Nitrogen gas (the uncombined element nitrogen, $N_2$) makes up about 78 percent of the atmosphere; yet the great majority of organisms can make no use of it. We ourselves take it in at every breath and breathe it out unused. Likewise, elemental nitrogen in air or dissolved in water enters most other plants and animals and comes back out again without taking any part in their life processes.

Nitrogen compounds, however, occur in the living substance of all organisms. The percentage of nitrogen is sometimes small, but it is very important. Nitrogen is a part of proteins, and proteins are one of the most important classes of substances found in organisms. Therefore a source of nitrogen is necessary for all organisms.

Where do *we* get our nitrogen? We get it from various nitrogen-bearing compounds in the things we eat. All our

**Figure 7 · 18**
Diagram of the nitrogen cycle.

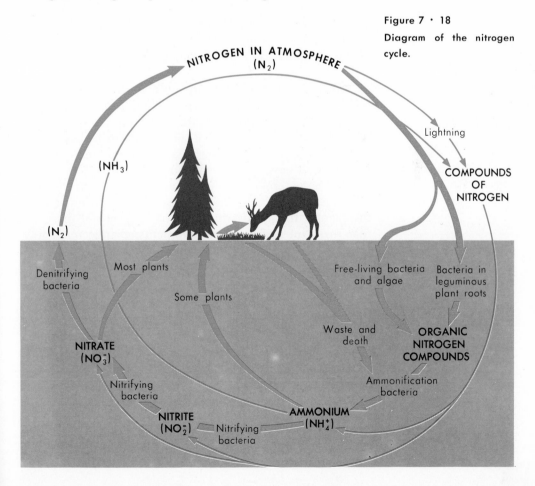

food, of course, can be traced to plants. And where do plants get their nitrogen-bearing compounds? From the soil (or the water) in which they grow. This brings us to a general question: How is nitrogen involved in the soil community?

We have just pointed out that all organisms contain proteins. Many soil microorganisms can decompose proteins, extracting some of the energy from them and leaving simpler substances. Among these simpler substances the chief one that contains nitrogen is ammonia ($NH_3$). Ammonia is a gas, but it dissolves readily in water. In soil water, ammonia reacts chemically with hydrogen ions to form ammonium ions ($NH_4^+$). In the form of ammonium ions, nitrogen may be absorbed by the roots of plants and built into proteins again. When this occurs, we have a short nitrogen cycle.

However, other things may happen. Two groups of bacteria in the soil are called nitrifying bacteria. One group changes the ammonium ions ($NH_4^+$) to *nitrite* ions ($NO_2^-$). Then another group rapidly converts the nitrite ions to *nitrate* ions ($NO_3^-$). In general, plants cannot use nitrites, but nitrates are the main source of nitrogen for most plants. From nitrates plants build proteins, and this completes a second nitrogen pathway.

Nitrifying bacteria operate only under *aerobic* conditions — that is, when oxygen is available in the soil water. Oxygen dissolves into soil water from the air spaces that normally occur in soil. But if all the spaces become filled with water, leaving no room for air, then the soil water has no source of oxygen — the soil conditions are *anaerobic*.

Under anaerobic conditions nitrifying bacteria cannot carry on their activities. Even worse (from the viewpoint of the plants), the *de*nitrifying bacteria, a group of microbes that thrive in anaerobic environments, change remaining nitrates to nitrogen gas. This gradually escapes into the atmosphere, where it is lost to the great majority of organisms.

But, fortunately, it is not lost to *all* organisms. Although lightning changes a small amount of gaseous nitrogen to nitrogen compounds, this process is of very little importance to the biosphere. Much more important is the action of *nitrogen-fixing* organisms — organisms that can change elemental nitrogen ($N_2$) to nitrogen compounds.

Centuries ago man discovered that soils in which clover has been grown produce better crops of other kinds of plants than do soils in which clover has not been grown. Early in the nineteenth century a French chemist showed that this is the result of an increase in the amount of nitrates in such soils. And not only clover but most of the members

extracting [Latin: *ex*, out, + *trahere*, to draw]

nitrifying [nī′trə fī″ing]

nitrite [nī′trīt]

nitrate [nī′trāt]: Caution: Do not confuse these closely similar words.

aerobic [â rō′bĭk; Greek: *aer*, air, + *bios*]: In biology the term is applied specifically to oxygen, not to air in general.

anaerobic [Greek: *an-*, without, + *aer*, + *bios*]

of the family Leguminosae—beans, alfalfa, vetch, etc.—have
this effect. Still later it was found that nitrogen-fixing is not
performed by the legumes but by bacteria that live in the
roots of the plants. There they form easily visible swellings
called nodules. This discovery was another scientific contribution by the great Dutch microbiologist Martinus Beijerinck. Under favorable conditions root-nodule bacteria
can fix as much as 225 kg of nitrogen per hectare (about 200
pounds per acre) per year.

Leguminosae [lə gyū′mə nō′sē′]

nodules [näj′ōō əlz; Latin: *nod-
ulus,* small knot]

How these bacteria of the genus *Rhizobium* get into the
roots of the plants Beijerinck did not discover. Since his
day we have learned something of this process. We now
know, also, that different species of *Rhizobium* live in different kinds of legumes. And recently microbiologists have
found that some actinomycetes have a similar relationship
with roots of some shrubs and trees—alders, for example.

*Rhizobium* [rī zō′bē əm]

While nitrogen-fixing in the mutualistic relationship
between *Rhizobium* and legumes was being studied, it was
discovered that nitrogen-fixing also is carried out by a few
free-living soil bacteria. Even some of the blue-green algae
were found to be nitrogen-fixers. Which is more important—the free-living or the mutualistic method of nitrogen-
fixing? For the farmer who uses legumes in rotating his
crops, there is no question about the answer: only about 5
percent of the nitrogen fixed in a hectare of cultivated soil
comes from the free-living forms. But in forests and natural grasslands the relative importance of the two processes
is unknown.

The Nitragin Co.

Figure 7 · 19

Soybean roots that have
abundant nodules formed
with a species of *Rhizobium.*
Why are these root out-
growths considered mutualistic, but those of Figure
7 · 16 infectious?

## INVESTIGATION 7.4

### DECOMPOSING ACTION OF SOIL MICROBES

#### PURPOSES

The purposes of this exercise are to compare (*a*) the decomposing effects of soil microorganisms on different organic substances, and (*b*) rates of decomposition in different soils.

#### MATERIALS AND EQUIPMENT
(for each team)

Flowerpots, 4 inches in diameter, 4

Washed sand

Dead leaves, 2

Dead insects, 2

Dead twigs, 2

Cotton string or twine, 2 pieces

Rolled oats, about 4 cm³

Nylon fabric, 2 cm × 2 cm, 2 pieces

Deep dishes, 4

Rich garden soil

#### PROCEDURE

Cover the drainage holes in the flowerpots with small stones or pieces of broken pots. Fill two flowerpots with moist, washed sand. Press the sand down firmly to within 1.5 cm of the top. In both pots mark off the surface of the sand into three equal sectors. In the middle of one sector of the first pot, place a piece of dead leaf that has been soaked in water until it is pliable; in a second sector place a dead insect; in the third, place about 2 cm³ of rolled oats. In the middle of one sector of the second pot, place a dead twig; in a second sector, a piece of cotton string; in the third, a piece of nylon fabric.

Using a pencil, mark the rim of each pot with your team's symbol. Cover the materials with a petri-dish lid (open side downward), gently but firmly pressing the edge of the lid into the sand. Set the pots in deep dishes and fill each dish with water. The water will rise through each pot until its contents are moist.

Repeat this procedure with the two remaining pots, using rich garden soil instead of sand. Put all four pots in a warm, dark place. *Keep the soil moist at all times* by adding water to the dishes in which the pots were placed.

#### OBSERVATIONS

Make two copies of the chart shown below. The charts should extend across facing pages to allow wide columns under "Changes Observed." Label one chart *Sand* and the other *Garden Soil*. Make observations at the times indicated on the chart. Continue the experiment as long as you feel necessary to obtain valid results.

Note any odors. Compare the appearances of the materials. Look for masses of mold hyphae. Test the strength of the twine by pulling on it.

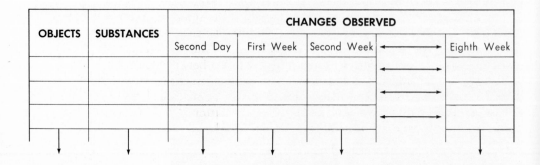

| OBJECTS | SUBSTANCES | CHANGES OBSERVED | | | | |
|---|---|---|---|---|---|---|
| | | Second Day | First Week | Second Week | ← → | Eighth Week |
| | | | | | ← → | |
| | | | | | ← → | |
| | | | | | ← → | |

## STUDYING THE DATA

• What are the principal substances in each of the objects you tested? (Use clues in preceding text.) (1) • On the sand which *substance* decomposed most rapidly? (2) • Most slowly? (3) • On the garden soil which substance decomposed most rapidly? (4) • Most slowly? (5) • What kinds of organisms were you able to observe during the experiment? (6)

## CONCLUSIONS

• What statement can you make about the rate at which different substances are decomposed by soil organisms? (7)

• Do your data show any general difference between rates of decomposition on sand and those on garden soil? If so, what hypothesis can you suggest to explain the difference? (8)

## FOR FURTHER INVESTIGATION

1. In the light of the results of this experiment, discuss problems involved in the preservation of fiber and wood products.

2. What effect would the warmth of a climate have on the formation of humus? You might investigate this problem experimentally.

Microorganisms are probably found in all biotic communities. In this chapter we have considered two situations in which they are especially important: disease and soil.

We tend to think of microorganisms in connection with disease, but only the infectious diseases are associated with microbes—with "germs." Each infectious disease is a complex ecological situation that depends on the interaction of pathogen, host, and environment. Pathogens may pass directly from one host to another of the same kind (in contagious disease), or they may be transmitted indirectly by vectors. Some pathogens have an alternation of hosts. The severity of a disease depends upon both the virulence of the pathogen and the resistance of the host. Some kinds of resistance are inherited; some are acquired. Acquired resistance involves the production of antibodies that combat the invasion of a host by a pathogen. Diseases have a geographical distribution. For many diseases of man and his domesticated plants and animals, this distribution has changed greatly during the period of recorded history. Today man's increased ability to move about in the world has greatly extended the distribution of many diseases, but some are still characteristic of particular regions or climates.

All true soils contain populations of living things. Among microbe groups, the true bacteria, the actinomycetes, and the fungi play important parts in forming soil. Many of the community relationships discussed in Chapter 3 are found in soil communities. Such relationships exist not only among microbes themselves but also between microbes and larger organisms—mycorrhizae, for example. The decomposition processes that occur in soil are largely a result of microbial action. These processes are important in the cycles of matter in land ecosystems; we have looked at the nitrogen cycle in detail.

## GUIDE QUESTIONS

1. What does the biologist mean by the term "disease"?
2. What ideas about the causes and treatment of disease did man have before the nineteenth century?
3. How are the infectious diseases distinguished from other groups of diseases?
4. Why are problems concerning infectious disease considered to be ecological problems?
5. Contrast the ways in which the pathogens of syphilis and malaria are transmitted.
6. The environment abounds in pathogens. What must occur if any of these is to infect a host?
7. Why do different host individuals react differently to infection by the same kind of pathogen?
8. How may resistance to a specific infectious disease be acquired?
9. It is often said that a physician must know his patient. To cope with any infectious-disease situation, what other factors must the physician understand?
10. What relationships exist between endemic and epidemic disease situations?
11. Why are some human infectious diseases worldwide and others found only in certain geographic regions?
12. What are Koch's postulates?
13. Why is soil considered to be an ecosystem?
14. What are the nonliving components of the soil?
15. In what chemical form do most dissolved minerals occur in soil?
16. What is humus?
17. What are the principal groups of organisms in a soil ecosystem?
18. How is pH measured?
19. What is the principal part played by microorganisms in a soil ecosystem?
20. What are mycorrhizae? What kind of community relationships is represented by them?
21. Some microorganisms grow best under anaerobic conditions. What does this mean?
22. What roles do soil organisms play in the nitrogen cycle?

## PROBLEMS

1. The following questions are about disease: (a) Why is it inaccurate (though customary) to say that a pathogen *causes* a disease? (b) Do vector-borne diseases necessarily involve pathogens that have alternate hosts? Why or why not? (c) Why are human diseases with low host-specificity likely to be the easiest to study experimentally? (d) What kinds of immunization are required of United States citizens who want to travel to other parts of the world?
2. Investigate an infectious disease, using the following outline of topics: history, symptoms, pathogen, vector (where appropriate), treatment, epidemiology. This outline is suitable for investigating diseases of plants as well as those of man and other animals. Suggested diseases: anthrax, bacterial meningitis, Dutch elm disease, filariasis, tsutsugamushi fever, black stem rust of wheat, hoof-and-mouth disease, brucellosis, fire blight of pears, diphtheria.
3. In recent years epidemics of a virus disease usually referred to as "Asian flu" have spread through the United States periodically. How might you interpret these epidemics in the light of your understanding of endemic disease, pathogens, and acquired immunity?
4. How do antibodies produce immunity? This question is more complicated than it first appears to be. To investigate it thoroughly, you will need to consult books on human physiology.
5. Suppose that some catastrophe completely disrupted a large city's sanitation procedures — water purification, sewage disposal, trash and garbage collection, etc. What diseases would be favored by such a catastrophe? What diseases would be least likely to increase?
6. The following questions are about soils: (a) How does the size of mineral particles in the soil affect its suitability for microorganisms? (b) In what ways may the acidity or alkalinity of soil water affect soil organisms? (c) Desert soils usually contain a relatively low percentage of

humus and have a low density of soil microorganisms. Why are they often very productive of crops? (*d*) Wild plants are often difficult to transplant. List as many reasonable explanations as you can. (*e*) Soils in tropical regions usually contain less humus than do soils in cooler climates. Explain this statement.

7. A farmer owned a field in which the soil seemed to be quite uniform in texture, mineral nutrients, microorganisms, and humus. He divided this field into halves, A and B. He planted rye in plot A. When the rye was almost full-grown, he plowed it under; then he planted potatoes in both plots. More potatoes were produced in plot B than in plot A. Without further treating the soil, he planted potatoes in both fields the following year. In the second year, he harvested more potatoes from plot A than from plot B. Give an explanation for the differences in potato production in the two years.

8. In this chapter some instances are discussed in which practice came before general knowledge of how the practice worked; in other words, technology came before theory. Though the sequence is usually reversed today, the history of science contains many other examples of practice preceding theory. Find several and report on them.

## SUGGESTED READINGS

ALVARADO, C. A., and L. J. BRUCE-CHWATT. "Malaria," *Scientific American*, May, 1962. Pp. 86–96+.

BATES, M. *The Forest and the Sea*. New York: Random House, Inc., 1960. Pp. 125–137. (Parallels the discussion of disease in Chapter 7 but presents some different viewpoints. Fairly easy.)

BURNET, F. M. "The Mechanism of Immunity," *Scientific American*, January, 1961. Pp. 58–67.

FARB, P. *Living Earth*. New York: Harper & Brothers, 1959. (Deals with the soil and organisms that live in it. Rather easy.)

FIENNES, R. *Man, Nature and Disease*. New York: New American Library, 1965. (The infectious diseases of man considered from an ecological viewpoint. Fairly easy.)

FROBISHER, M. *Fundamentals of Microbiology*. 7th ed. Philadelphia: W. B. Saunders Co., 1962. Pp. 311–347. (A technical description of immunity. This book also contains materials on many other aspects of infectious diseases and on soil microorganisms. Very advanced.)

GABRIEL, M. L., and S. FOGEL (eds.). *Great Experiments in Biology*. Englewood Cliffs, N.J.: Prentice-Hall, Inc., 1955. Pp. 119–126. (Original reports by Koch and Iwanowski on infectious diseases. Advanced.)

LANGER, W. L. "The Black Death," *Scientific American*, February, 1964. Pp. 114–118+.

OOSTING, H. J. *The Study of Plant Communities*. San Francisco: W. H. Freeman & Co., Publishers, 1956. Pp. 159–206. (The soil from the viewpoint of the plant ecologist rather than of the microbiologist.)

# Patterns
# of Life
# on Land

X 1/12

**Figure 8 · 1**
Black-tailed jackrabbit.

cottontail rabbit: See Figure 1 · 1.

## MEETING THE ENVIRONMENT

Consider all the species of organisms found within 50 miles of your school. Many you probably know by name. Many you probably know in a general way without being able to name them. And many exist quite unknown to you. Whether you are well or poorly acquainted with the *biota* (all the living things) of your region, you undoubtedly realize that some organisms do not "belong" there. In Kentucky, for example, you expect oaks and maples, cottontail rabbits and woodpeckers—though you might see few of them in downtown Louisville. But you would be surprised to find palm trees or polar bears in the Kentucky woods.

## GEOGRAPHIC RANGE

Palm trees are not a part of the biota of Kentucky; Kentucky is not within the *geographic range* of any species of palm. The cottontail rabbit is a part of the biota of Kentucky. It is also a part of the biota of Texas. But the geographic range of this species does not extend as far west as Nevada, so the cottontail is not a part of the biota of that state. On the other hand, the geographic range of the black-tailed jackrabbit covers both Texas and Nevada but does not extend to Kentucky. Thus, with respect to rabbits, the biota of Texas resembles that of both Nevada and Kentucky. With respect to many other organisms, it is like the biota of neither. Therefore, the basic question about the biota of any particular place is: What determines the geographic range of the species found there?

X 1/2

Figure 8 · 2
Young caiman.

## SURVIVAL

Are there dandelions in your lawn? Are house mice a problem in your neighborhood? These organisms were immigrants to this continent in historical times, just as were European, African, and Asian men. Geographic ranges are not permanent; like everything else in the biosphere, they are constantly changing. That dandelions and house mice exist here today is evidence that they—and man—are able to survive under the conditions of this continent.

Every year visitors to Florida buy small caimans (which resemble alligators) as souvenirs and carry them northward to New England and the Middle West. As the pets grow larger, they become bothersome and are then often dumped into the nearest river or pond. Although this has been going on for many years, the Ohio and Connecticut rivers are as free of caimans today as they ever were. Why? What would happen to corn if man left Iowa? What would happen to sheep if man left Wyoming? What would happen to the monkeys if some last human survivor opened the cages of the St. Louis zoo?

The larger problem behind these questions is: What determines the *survival* of a species in a particular ecosystem? Here "survival" does not mean mere existence in a dormant condition—a Michigan groundhog in its January burrow or a lockjaw bacterium on a rusty nail. Here "survival" means active living—an organism growing and reproducing. One or even several individuals may be able to survive in an environment, but this does not make the species a part of the ecosystem. Only continued reproduction accomplishes that.

## TOLERANCE

If a household geranium is left outdoors in Iowa, it will die during the winter. If a blacksnake is exposed in a shadeless cage to the July sun of Georgia, it will die. If a rancher in western Nebraska plants a beech tree in his upland pasture, he is probably wasting his time. Household geraniums do not tolerate long periods of freezing temperature; blacksnakes do not tolerate high temperatures; beech trees do not tolerate low soil moisture. *Tolerance* is

caimans [kā′mənz]

x 1/4

Figure 8 · 3
Household geranium, a native of South Africa.

tolerate [Latin: *tolerare*, to bear, to endure]

the ability—of either an individual organism or a species—to withstand particular environmental conditions.

Working with any one measurable environmental factor, we can, by experiment, determine an upper (*maximum*) limit and a lower (*minimum*) limit of tolerance in any one species. Likewise we can determine the range of conditions most favorable for growth and reproduction of a species; these are called *optimum* conditions.

This seems clear-cut, but several complications arise. First, the duration of the condition is important, especially in determining maximum and minimum limits. Geraniums can withstand short periods of freezing temperature but not long ones.

Second, there is variation among individuals. An experiment in which 25 domestic pigeons were kept at an environmental temperature of −40°C resulted after four days in 11 of them dying and 14 surviving. Third, there is variation within the same species between populations that come from different parts of the species' geographical range. The optimum temperature for swimming movements in the jellyfish *Aurelia* is between 5°C and 18°C in the population off Nova Scotia, but it is between 28°C and 30°C in the population off the southern tip of Florida.

Finally, there are complications due to the interaction of different factors. When relative humidity is near zero, man can withstand very high temperatures. But when the relative humidity is close to 100 percent, man will die in a few minutes at a temperature between 48°C and 50°C. At an intermediate humidity of 50 percent, the optimum temperature for clothed man is usually put at 20°C to 22°C. For land animals the effects of humidity and temperature are so closely related that there is little point in measuring one without the other.

## MEETING THE ENVIRONMENT AS A WHOLE

Consider now the interaction of tolerances in determining geographic range. Field sparrows (*Spizella pusilla*) of the eastern United States can survive northern winter temperatures if they have an adequate food supply. The food supply required for winter living is greater than that for summer living because heat loss in winter is greater. But sparrows can hunt food only during the day, and during the northern winter the day is short. Which, then, is the tolerance factor that sets the northern boundaries of the winter range of the field sparrow—temperature, length of day, or food supply? To analyze this kind of situation, we need laboratory studies of tolerance to different factors as well as field observations.

duration: here, length of time

*Aurelia:* See Figure A · 89.

relative humidity: See Investigation 3.2.

X 1/3

**Figure 8 · 4**
**Field sparrow.**

Josef Muench

Figure 8 · 5
Bald cypress in an Arkansas swamp.

Environmental conditions within a species' tolerance limits may allow it to survive, but they do not guarantee that the species will be part of a particular ecosystem. The species may fail because it has to compete with other organisms. For example, under natural conditions bald cypresses live in swampy areas near the southeastern coast of the United States and up the Mississippi Valley to southern Indiana. But when planted and tended by man, bald cypresses also grow successfully on hilltops. Evidently they are tolerant of considerably less moisture than that found in swamps. Perhaps cypresses fail to grow naturally on hills because trees that are *more* tolerant of low moisture crowd them out. Or we may look at the matter from the opposite direction. Bald cypresses are tolerant of flooded ground, and few trees of other species are. Perhaps, then, cypresses grow in swamps not so much because they need a swamp environment as because they encounter weaker competition there.

From these two examples, it is clear that the *whole* individual organism encounters the *whole* environment. But

Can you outline a plan for an experimental investigation of this hypothesis?

individual organisms can be observed to respond in certain ways when particular environmental factors are changed experimentally. Therefore, ecologists can gain a partial understanding of the whole situation by studying environmental factors one at a time. This is an aspect of ecology that we have not emphasized previously. It involves the relationships between individuals and environment rather than the relationships between populations and environment. It is an aspect of ecology that is best pursued in the laboratory.

## INVESTIGATION 8.1

### A STUDY OF ENVIRONMENTAL TOLERANCE

#### PURPOSE

You will investigate effects of light and temperature on the growth of several organisms. You will then try to relate your results to the natural distribution of these organisms. • Before beginning work, set up hypotheses on the basis of the experimental design outlined in the Procedure.(1)

#### MATERIALS AND EQUIPMENT
(for each team)

Beakers, 50 ml, 4

Seeds of radish, vetch, tomato, and lettuce, 50 each

Fungicide, about 150 ml

Petri dishes, 5

Pieces of paper toweling, cut to fit petri dishes, 20

Cardboard dividers, cut to fit petri dishes, 20

Forceps, 1

Glass-marking crayon, 1

Clear plastic bags, 5

Rubber bands, 5

Shallow cardboard boxes with covers, 2

Refrigerator, 1

Incubator, 1

Thermometers (−10°C to +110°C), 2

#### PROCEDURE

Label the beakers *tomato, radish, vetch,* and *lettuce*. In each, place 50 seeds of the species named. Add fungicide and allow to soak for the period of time recommended by the teacher.

Place 4 disks of paper toweling in each petri dish. Moisten the paper thoroughly. Divide each dish into quarter sections by inserting cardboard dividers, as shown in Figure 8 · 6.

Pour the fungicide solution from the beakers. Rinse the seeds with water. Using forceps, place 40 seeds in each petri dish—10 of each kind in each quarter section. Label the dishes with the team symbol and number from *1* to *5*. Place each dish in a clear plastic bag and close the bag with a rubber band.

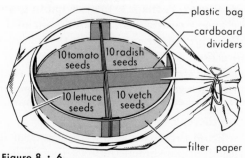

Figure 8 · 6

Place each dish in a different environment, as follows:

Dish 1. Continuous light and cold
Dish 2. Continuous dark and cold
Dish 3. Continuous light and warm
Dish 4. Continuous dark and warm
Dish 5. Variable temperature and light

For Dish 1 use a refrigerator that has the light adjusted to remain on when the door is closed. Place Dish 2 in a light-tight box in the refrigerator. Try to maintain temperatures at 10° to 12°C; check the temperatures with a thermometer. For Dish 3 use an incubator containing a light. Place Dish 4 in a light-tight box in the incubator. Try to maintain temperatures at 30° to 32°C; check temperatures with a thermometer. Place Dish 5 on the windowsill.

Each day count the number of seeds that have germinated. Record the counts in your data book, using the following form (one for each dish):

| Dish No. _____   Environment _____ | | | | |
|---|---|---|---|---|
| KIND OF SEED | NUMBER GERMINATED | | | |
| | Day 1 | Day 2 | ←——→ | Day 10 |
| Tomato | | | ←——→ | |
| Radish | | | ←——→ | |
| Vetch | | | ←——→ | |
| Lettuce | | | ←——→ | |

### STUDYING THE DATA

Combine the data of all teams. • Why?(2)

First, consider the percentage of seeds that germinated. • In which environment did the greatest percentage of tomato seeds germinate?(3)   • Of radish seeds?(4)   • Of vetch seeds?(5)   • Of lettuce seeds?(6)

Second, consider the speed of germination.   • Is there any case in which the seeds of one species germinated more rapidly in one environment but germinated in larger proportion in another? If so, which species and which environments are involved?(7)

Finally, consider the environmental factors separately.   • Which kind of seed has the greatest tolerance for continuous light?(8)   • Which kind has the greatest tolerance for low temperature?(9)   • Does any kind germinate similarly in all the experimental environments?(10)

### CONCLUSIONS

• Compare your results with your hypotheses.(11)

Recall that the establishment of a species in an ecosystem depends on both its tolerances and its competition with other species.   • Which do you think would give a species a greater advantage—ability to germinate rapidly or ability to germinate a large percentage of its seeds? Why?(12)

• On the basis of your experimental results, describe an ecosystem in which each species you studied in this investigation might have an advantage.(13)

### FOR FURTHER INVESTIGATION

In markets it is possible to obtain seeds of plants from many places, such as seeds of avocado, date, grapefruit, orange, pomegranate, lentil, and many kinds of beans. These can be tested for germination in experimental environments, but the time allowed for germination may have to be greatly lengthened.

## ECOLOGICAL DISTRIBUTION OF LIFE ON LAND

Environmental factors, operating through tolerances, sort out the kinds of organisms that are able to live in a particular place. The result is an ecosystem—a community of organisms in a suitable environment.

You can hold a whole ecosystem in your hand: an aging acorn contains a community of molds, bacteria, insects, and nematodes. At the other extreme, the entire biosphere is one big ecosystem. In Chapter 3 we saw that there are no real boundaries, in either space or time, to ecosystems. The acorn is a part of an ecosystem of decaying materials on the surface of the soil, which is a part of an ecosystem that includes the oak tree (from which the acorn came), and the tree, in turn, is part of a forest.

Though there are no real boundaries within the biosphere, biologists, as scientists, must order the facts of geographic distribution into meaningful patterns. One result of their efforts has been the division of the biosphere into large-scale ecosystems based on climate.

### CLIMATES

Climate is a reasonable basis for large-scale ecosystems because it summarizes a number of biologically important

**Figure 8 · 7**

Climatograms. Average monthly temperatures are shown in blue (degrees Celsius); average monthly precipitation is shown in gray (centimeters). Other factors, such as wind and cloud cover, are also important in determining climates.

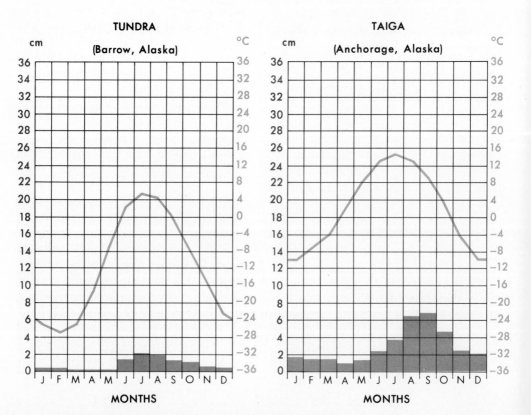

abiotic environmental factors. Solar radiation is the source of biological energy. The shape of the earth and its tilt with respect to its orbit around the sun result in an unequal reception of this energy at different places on the earth's surface. But the earth has an atmosphere, and the atmosphere's circulation helps to distribute that part of the radiant energy that is converted to heat. At the same time, the circulating atmosphere carries water—a substance essential for life—to land surfaces.

Climates occur in broad belts that encircle the earth, but the boundaries of these belts are disrupted by lands and oceans; and they are still further modified by mountains and plains on land, shallows and depths in oceans. It is rather easy to map the distribution of a particular factor of climate: solar energy, winds, temperature, rainfall, humidity, or evaporation rate. However, it is difficult to map a climate as a whole, because the factors in the makeup of climate overlap and mix with one another in complex ways.

World maps showing the distribution of a number of climatic factors may be found in Goode's World Atlas, Edward B. Espenshade, Jr. (ed.), Rand McNally & Co., Chicago.

Because the many climatic factors interact in complex ways, it is also difficult to describe climates quantitatively. In an attempt at a simplified description, ecologists frequently use *climatograms*, which summarize monthly changes in temperature and precipitation. Though radiant energy is more important to ecosystems than temperature, it is also

climatograms [klī mă′tə grămz′; Greek: *klima*, latitude, climate, + *gramma*, writing, record]

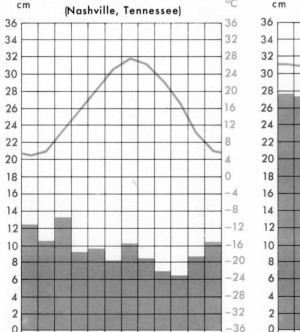

MIDDLE-LATITUDE DECIDUOUS FOREST
(Nashville, Tennessee)

MONTHS

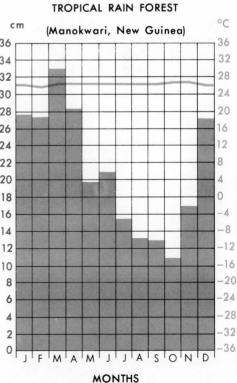

TROPICAL RAIN FOREST
(Manokwari, New Guinea)

MONTHS

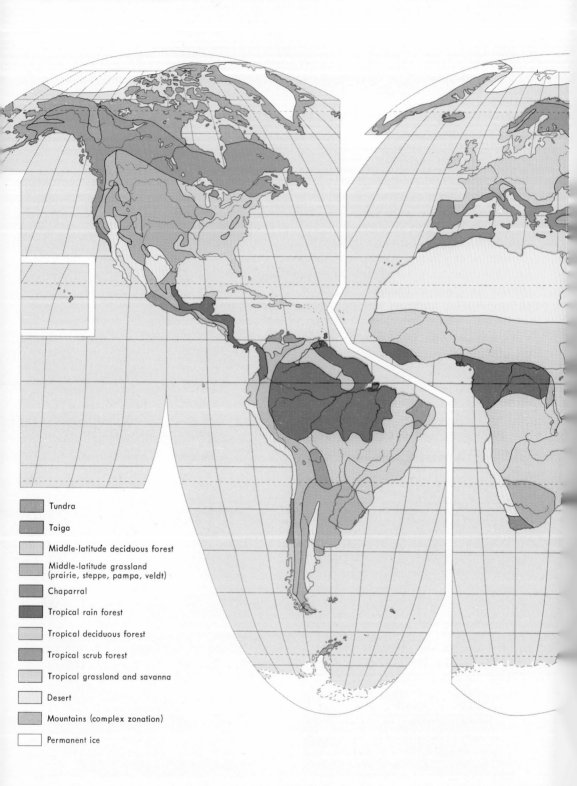

Tundra

Taiga

Middle-latitude deciduous forest

Middle-latitude grassland
(prairie, steppe, pampa, veldt)

Chaparral

Tropical rain forest

Tropical deciduous forest

Tropical scrub forest

Tropical grassland and savanna

Desert

Mountains (complex zonation)

Permanent ice

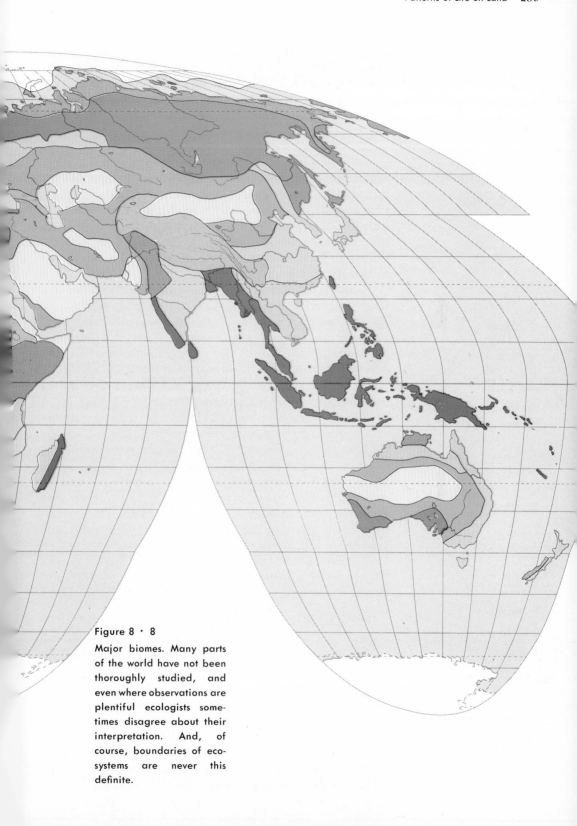

Figure 8 · 8
Major biomes. Many parts
of the world have not been
thoroughly studied, and
even where observations are
plentiful ecologists sometimes disagree about their
interpretation. And, of
course, boundaries of ecosystems are never this
definite.

more difficult to measure. Since temperature changes not only are easier to measure but also roughly reflect changes in radiant energy, temperature rather than radiant energy appears on the climatograms. Likewise precipitation is not a perfect measure of the water available to organisms, but data on precipitation are easy to obtain.

## BIOMES

Each major kind of climate has a characteristic type of vegetation — provided human interference is slight. Warm, arid climates, for instance, are associated with desert vegetation; semiarid climates, with grassland; moist climates, with forest. Because vegetation is so obvious in most natural landscapes, we are likely to think first of plants when studying effects of climate, but animals are also influenced by climatic conditions.

biome [bī′ōm; Greek: *bios*, life, + *oma*, group, mass]

A major climate with its vegetation and animals is a large-scale ecosystem called a *biome*. Within each biome smaller ecosystems exist. Variations in rocks and soils, elevation and topography, cause variations in the biota. Further, in most parts of the world man has modified the effects of climate in many ways and has brought about many other variations in the landscape. But despite this lack of uniformity, most of the biomes described by ecologists are so distinct that even non-biologists can recognize them.

Biomes are not sharply defined; the landscape usually changes quite gradually as one goes from grassland to desert or from grassland to forest. Ecologists do not agree about where boundaries separating biomes should be drawn; this is a matter of opinion, not fact. Nor do they agree about the number of biomes to be recognized. Moreover, many parts of the world have not been sufficiently studied to allow more than rough guesses about the boundaries of biomes. Therefore, the world map of biomes (Figure 8 · 8) must be taken as a very general guide, not to be relied upon for detail.

### BIOMES AND RADIANT ENERGY

We need not study all the biomes represented on the map. We can gain some understanding of the ecological distribution of terrestrial life by looking at certain selected biomes. One series has an *increasing* total annual supply of radiant energy but no lack of water. Such a series begins near the poles and ends near the equator.

tundra [tŭn′drə, to͞on′drə]

### TUNDRA

circumpolar    [sûr′kəm pō′lər; Latin: *circum*, around, about, + Greek: *polos*, a pivot]

The *tundra* biome is circumpolar in the Northern Hemisphere. It lies just south of the ice-covered polar seas. In

A

C. J. Ott from Shostal

**Figure 8 · 9**

(A) Alaska tundra in late August when the growing season has passed.

Tundra flowers: (B) *Geum* (yellow) and *Arenaria* (white) — x 1/3, and (C) *Silene* — x 1. Note the size of tundra flowers in comparison with the size of the rest of the plant.

Haven Kolb

B

Elra M. Palmer

C

the Southern Hemisphere a corresponding biome is not developed—there, north of the ice-covered Antarctic continent, most of the latitudes in which the climate would permit tundra are covered by ocean.

**Abiotic environment.**   Because the angle of the sun's rays is never high, the tundra receives little radiant energy at any time. In summer, however, the long days somewhat make up for the low angle of the sun. Then the top layer of soil thaws, though the ground beneath always remains frozen—the *permafrost*. Melting snow cannot drain into the frozen ground, so water collects on the surface. For about six to eight weeks the tundra is a land of ponds and marshes, even though the yearly precipitation is very small. In this short growing season, plants must synthesize a whole year's food supply.

permafrost [Latin: per, through, + manere, to remain, + frost]

The change from summer to winter is abrupt. Lakes and ponds freeze—the shallower ponds all the way to the bottom. Snowfall is light, and high winds sweep all the more exposed areas free of snow. Days are short and temperatures low. Organisms must survive on stored energy. Few species can tolerate these conditions.

sedges: See Figure A · 73.

**Summer.**   Grasses and sedges dominate tundra landscapes in summer. Extensive areas are covered by low mats of lichens and mosses. The few woody plants, such as willows and birches, grow close to the ground, seldom reaching a height of more than a few centimeters. Leaves of most

Rutherford Platt

Figure 8 · 10

A tundra willow. What environmental conditions limit the growth of this woody plant?

X 1/6

Figure 8 · 11

Ptarmigan in winter (*left*) and summer (*right*). How can you explain the difference in the coloration of the feathers?

plants are small, and many are hairy or have margins rolled inward. Flowers appear rapidly and develop seeds quickly.

These are adaptations—structural and functional—to the abiotic environment. Try to explain them.

During the summer the tundra teems with animal life. Hordes of waterfowl and shorebirds raise their young in the long days that allow around-the-clock food-gathering. Insects are few in species but great in numbers of individuals. Caribou graze on grasses and lichens. Ptarmigan, arctic foxes, and snowshoe hares are present in their brown summer coats. Lemmings scurry along their runways among the plants. When the lemming population is high, predators such as snowy owls and weasels are numerous.

**Winter.**   Winter involves not merely cold but also darkness and, particularly, scarcity of food. The large numbers of waterfowl that use the summer food supply leave the tundra in the winter, flying far to the south. Among mammals the chief migrants are caribou, which return southward to the forests. Some animals, such as gulls and foxes, migrate to the seashores, where they become commensal with seal-hunting polar bears.

Almost all the plants of the tundra are perennials; these are dormant in winter. The invertebrate animals also become dormant. Most insects survive the winter in the egg or

Figure 8 · 12

Tundra mammals: musk oxen (*left*) and caribou (*right*).

hibernation    [hī'bər nā'shən;
Latin: *hibernus,* wintry]

How does a snow cover provide
protection?

taiga [tī'gə]

larva stage. But among the larger animals *hibernation* (winter dormancy) is rare.

Lemmings and other small animals avoid the windswept bare ground and burrow under the snow in sheltered spots. There, protected from the severely low temperatures, they consume underground parts of plants or supplies of seed that they have stored during the summer. Ptarmigan burrow into the snow for protection during storms, but at other times they feed on buds of plants that protrude above the shallow snow.

Musk oxen face the tundra winter's full might. Living on lichens, they seek out bare areas or paw away the snow cover. A few predatory birds either hunt ptarmigan or turn saprovores.

## TAIGA

In the Northern Hemisphere as we travel southward in the tundra, scattered clumps of dwarf trees appear in sheltered places, and presently tundra gives way to a great coniferous forest that extends in a broad zone across Eurasia and North America. This is the *taiga.* In the Southern Hemisphere the climates of the small land areas that exist at suitable latitudes are so strongly modified by the surrounding seas that taiga does not occur.

**Abiotic environment.**   Because it lies closer to the equator, taiga receives more radiant energy both annually and daily than does tundra. Summer days are not so long as those in tundra, but they are warmer and the ground thaws

**Figure 8 · 13**
Taiga in northern Alberta,
Canada.

George Hunter

Weyerhaeuser Company

**Figure 8 · 14**
Shrubs and young conifers
in a burned-over section of
taiga.

completely. Winters are not so long, and few places in taiga
have winter days without sunlight. But snowfall is heavier.

Until ten to twenty thousand years ago, most of the
taiga region was covered by a great sheet of ice. Grinding
its way slowly across the continents, it gouged out depressions. As it melted, it left masses of rubble that often
formed dams across streams. The result is a multitude of
ponds and lakes in the taiga.

rubble: here, masses of loose
earth and rock. "Rubble" is
related to the word "rubbish."

**Summer.**   The taiga forest is composed almost entirely
of coniferous trees, most of which are evergreen.
Throughout the year they keep out the sunlight, so there is
little vegetation near the ground. Thus, though the mantle
of vegetation is deeper than in the tundra, the production
of food takes place mostly in the upper parts of the trees.

Can you think of a coniferous
tree that is *not* evergreen?

Even seedling trees are few in the forest. These get a
chance to grow only when fires or windstorms destroy the
old forest. Then light is let in, and for a few years a dense
growth of herbs and short-lived trees (such as aspens and
birches) springs up. Under this deciduous growth young
conifers begin the new taiga forest.

In summer many insects attack the conifers, and a large
number of small birds live on the insects. Some birds harvest the seeds of the conifers, and a few mammals eat the
needles and twigs. Deer, moose, and beaver live largely on
the vegetation around ponds, along streams, and in burns
and windfalls.

**Winter.**   The low plants along ponds and streams and
in forest openings are well protected by a heavy blanket of

**Figure 8 · 15**

Beaver (*left*) and moose (*right*).

**Figure 8 · 16**

Wolverine.

snow. Needles of the conifers are covered with a waxy coating that reduces water loss when the ground is frozen and water cannot be obtained. The branches bend with the burden of snow until it slips off.

Animals of the taiga meet winter conditions in ways similar to those used in the tundra. Squirrels and bears, though they do not become completely dormant, spend long periods sleeping. Insects hibernate. Insectivorous birds migrate southward. Seed-eating birds wander around until they find places where the crop of cones has been good. Caribou arrive in the autumn from the tundra. With their long legs, caribou and moose wade about in the snow. Snowshoe hares spread their large feet and hop over the snow, avoiding lynxes, wolves, and wolverines, which continue their predatory activities throughout the year.

### MIDDLE-LATITUDE DECIDUOUS FOREST

As we go southward in the taiga in eastern North America, we find more and more trees with broad leaves rather than needles, trees that usually shed their leaves in the fall—that is, deciduous trees. By the time we reach Massachusetts, southern Michigan, or southern Wisconsin, the deciduous trees predominate. We are in the *middle-latitude deciduous-forest* biome.

This biome is not continuous. It is found in the eastern United States, in western Europe, and in eastern Asia. In the Southern Hemisphere a small area of somewhat similar forest occurs in southern Chile.

Because Figure 8 · 8 is much simplified you will find this biome mapped at two other Southern Hemisphere areas, but they are rather different from the biome described here.

In China and Europe the middle-latitude deciduous forest was greatly modified by man long ago, but in North America the Indians had only minor effects upon it. Descriptions of the American forest by early explorers have been valuable as background for modern studies of the scattered bits of forest that remain. The following account applies in general to all of the middle-latitude deciduous-forest biome, but the specifically mentioned organisms are North American.

**Abiotic environment.**   In summer the sun is high in the sky, and days are long. This combination results in the reception of much radiant energy. In June at the latitude of Philadelphia, Indianapolis, and Peking, the daily supply of radiant energy is greater than it is in the tropics at any time of the year. But, of course, in December it becomes low—though never as low as during taiga winters—so the *annual* supply of radiant energy is much less than in the tropics. Precipitation is high enough and steady enough that droughts are infrequent and not severe.

Change is characteristic of weather in this biome. In winter, snow may be heavy, but it often melts rapidly and the ground is seldom snow-covered throughout the season. In summer, heat and humidity may both be high; but at any time cool, dry masses of air may push down from higher latitudes.

**Summer and autumn.**   The middle-latitude deciduous forest is made up of many species of trees. The tallest of these form a canopy, an upper layer of leaves that catch the full strength of solar radiation. But leaves of deciduous trees are rather thin, and much radiation filters through the canopy. Thus there is light enough for another layer of trees—understory trees. But even these do not use up all the light energy. Usually there is a layer of shrubs beneath the understory trees. Finally, close to the ground, mosses and ferns are able to utilize the last remaining light.

This large mass of producers supports a large number of consumers. Squirrels live in the treetops but get much of their food on the ground. Deer mice climb in the shrubs and glean fallen seeds from the ground. White-tailed deer browse on shrubs and lower branches of the trees. Insects are abundant in all layers of the forest, from the canopy down into the soil.

Insectivorous birds prey upon the insects. Red-eyed vireos specialize in consuming the canopy insects. Acadian flycatchers specialize in eating insects of the understory. Ovenbirds search over the ground layer. Woodpeckers extract boring insects from the bark of trees.

Large predators such as bears, wolves, and pumas are now gone, but during the hunting season man takes their place ecologically. Omnivores—animals such as raccoons and skunks—eat fruits, insects, small animals, and many other things.

X 1/4

**Figure 8 · 17**
Red-eyed vireo.

X 1/4

**Figure 8 · 18**
Ovenbird.

deer mice: See Figure 18 · 24.

Acadian flycatcher: See Figure 2 · 31.

How does this paragraph illustrate the concept of "niches"?

puma: See Figure 2 · 9.

omnivores [ŏm′nĭ vŏrz; Latin: *omnis*, all, + *vorare*, to devour]

raccoon: See Figure 2 · 10.

**Summer**

All four photos, William L. Hutcheson Memorial Forest

**Figure 8 · 19**

Seasons in middle-latitude deciduous forest (New Jersey). All of these pictures show the same area. What effects do these changes have on white-tailed deer, which are first-order consumers?

**Autumn**

**Winter**

**Spring**

In the middle-latitude deciduous forest there are four well-defined seasons. This is the biome of flaming autumns, where the leaves of the deciduous trees turn scarlet and orange, golden, copper, and, finally, rich russet brown. Then they drift downward, covering the ground with a thick mass of organic matter. Nuts and acorns fall; berries cover the understory trees and shrubs. Many animals fatten on the abundant food. Deer mice and some other mammals store food. Woodchucks form thick layers of fat and then hibernate in their burrows. Reptiles, much more abundant than in the taiga, also hibernate. Many insectivorous birds migrate to the tropics.

woodchucks: a species of marmot; a related species is shown in Figure 4 · 11.

**Winter and spring.**   Leafless deciduous trees lose little water during periods when soil water is frozen. Without becoming completely dormant, most mammals rest during cold spells and resume activity when warm masses of air push in from lower latitudes. Squirrels then frisk through the leafless branches, gnats dance in swarms above brooks, and even a few butterflies may appear in the weak midday sun. Birds, much more abundant than in the winter taiga, consume seeds and fruits and search out many dormant insects and insect eggs from crevices in tree bark and from dead leaves on the ground.

In spring solar radiation becomes strong before air temperatures are high enough to bring the trees into leaf. A great number of herbaceous plants spring up on the forest floor. They put forth their leaves quickly and flower; and by the time the shade from the trees has closed over them, they have finished photosynthesis for the year. With food stored in roots or underground stems, they disperse their seed and die back to the ground until the next spring.

## TROPICAL RAIN FOREST

In three separate places along the equator we find a biome called *tropical rain forest.* The largest area of this biome is centered in the Amazon Basin of South America; the second, in the East Indies; the smallest, in the Congo Basin of Africa.

**Abiotic environment.**   In tropical rain forest, environmental conditions are favorable for more kinds of organisms than in any other terrestrial biome. The noon sun is never more than $23\frac{1}{2}°$ north or south of the zenith; thus, the energy supply is both large and fairly constant. Rain falls almost every day, and the humidity is always high. Temperatures vary little from month to month. Beneath the upper layer of the canopy, there is not even much change in temperature between day and night. No other terrestrial biome has such a uniform climate.

Ralph Buchsbaum

Carl Gans

Figure 8 · 20

Within tropical rain forest. How can you explain the predominant color of this scene?

Figure 8 · 21

Epiphytes high in a tropical rain-forest tree. In the center is a bromeliad.

**Producers.** Vegetation deeply covers the landscape. The forest canopy reaches an average height of about 50 m, but some individual trees stretch above it to 80 m or more. Thus the layer of vegetation is much deeper than the average of 30 m in middle-latitude deciduous forest, 15 m in taiga, and perhaps 0.1 m in tundra. Beneath the taller trees are shorter ones that are tolerant of shade, and beneath these are still others that are even more shade tolerant. Weaving together the branches in this multistoried forest are many lianas.

The trunks and branches of the trees and the twisting stems of the lianas serve as perches for many kinds of *epiphytes*. These plants get no nourishment from the trees —they simply use them for support. Lichens and mosses grow as epiphytes in other forests, but in the tropical rain forest there is a bewildering variety of such plants—ferns, orchids, peppers, bromeliads (plants of the pineapple family), and even cacti. Since epiphytes have no connection with the ground, they must get their water and minerals elsewhere. Many have roots that absorb moisture from the damp atmosphere in the same way that blotting paper absorbs water. Many obtain water by catching the rainfall, usually in the hollows of specially adapted leaves. Mosqui-

epiphytes [ĕp'ə fīts'; Greek: epi, upon, + phyton, a plant]

bromeliads [brō mē'lĭ ădz]

What abiotic factors make this possible?

USAFSO Tropic Survival School, Canal Zone

**Figure 8 · 22**
In tropical rain forest even anteaters are arboreal: a tamandua, Panamá.

toes, water beetles, many other aquatic insects, and even a species of frog live in such treetop puddles.

The dense layers of the always green canopy absorb most of the light, so few plants grow on the forest floor. The trunks of trees are supported in the damp soil by massive buttresses (Figure 8 · 20). Lianas coil upward into the dim green of the canopy overhead. But the way through the forest—once you are in it—is uncluttered. Only along rivers or at the edges of clearings does a thick wall of vegetation extend down to the ground.

**Consumers.**  All forests have some animals that live in the treetops—*arboreal* animals; in the tropical rain forest the animal life in the canopy is abundant. Dr. Paul Slud, of the American Museum of Natural History, found during a study of rain-forest birds that over 90 percent foraged primarily in the canopy. For winged animals such as birds this may not be surprising, though the percentage is high in comparison with that for birds of other forests. But in the tropical rain forest a large number of mammals also are arboreal—54 percent of the species in one South American study. Moreover, there are many tree snakes and tree lizards as well as tree frogs. And there are untold numbers of arboreal insects.

Overripe fruits drop to the forest floor, forming a food supply for some ground-dwellers. Dead leaves also descend continuously, because the trees release worn-out leaves a few at a time. In the ever-warm, ever-moist environment a

buttresses [bŭt′rĭs əz]

For vivid descriptions of the vegetation of this biome by a non-biologist, see *The Sea and the Jungle*, H. M. Tomlinson, New American Library, New York.

arboreal [är bōr′ĭ əl; Latin: *arbor*, tree]

forage [fôr′ĭj]: to search for food

Can you explain the rarity of large herbivores?

myriad of insects, molds, and bacteria attack this food supply rapidly. Therefore, organic remains do not accumulate on the ground. The consumers on the forest floor are chiefly saprovores. Herbivores, such as hoofed mammals, are rare or live near riverbanks. Predators and parasites are abundant at all levels of the forest.

## BIOMES: A SEQUENCE WITH DECREASING PRECIPITATION

sequence [Latin: *sequi*, to follow]: here, a series of connected things

The principal variable in the preceding sequence of biomes was radiant energy. In each biome the precipitation during the growing season was sufficient for the needs of the plants. In many biomes, however, lack of water is a limiting factor. Here we shall use as an example the middle latitudes of North America. A somewhat similar sequence can be found in the middle latitudes of Asia, Europe, and Australia.

### MIDDLE-LATITUDE GRASSLAND

As we go westward in the deciduous forest, we eventually leave the trees behind. In the great expanse of country stretching roughly from the Mississippi westward to the Rocky Mountains and from central Canada southward to the Gulf of Mexico, grasses are the predominant natural

Figure 8 · 23

Compare these climatograms with those seen in Figure 8 · 7.

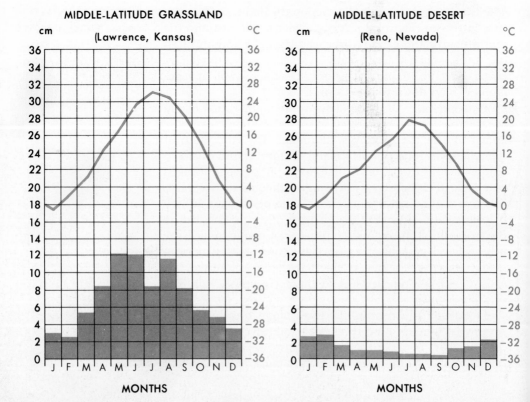

MIDDLE-LATITUDE GRASSLAND
(Lawrence, Kansas)

MIDDLE-LATITUDE DESERT
(Reno, Nevada)

MONTHS

vegetation. The change to grassland occurs gradually; in Illinois much grassland lies east of the Mississippi, but in Missouri and Arkansas much deciduous forest extends farther westward.

**Abiotic environment.** Because this biome stretches through the same latitudes as the deciduous forest described on pages 266–269, the energy supply is similar. Temperature changes between day and night and between winter and summer are somewhat more extreme in the grassland than in the forest. The principal difference, however, is in precipitation. It is consistently less in the grassland than at the same latitude to the east, and droughts are more frequent.

Use the results from Investigation 3.2 to explain this.

**Producers.** The height of the grasses varies from more than 2 m in the east to only 0.5 m in the west. Clearly the depth of the vegetation is less than that in forest. But in those parts of the grassland where moisture is relatively abundant, the vegetation is very thick. And during the summer the leaves of the grasses grow continuously from their bases. Thus, as herbivores consume the tops, the grass crop is renewed from below. Many other herbaceous plants grow among the grasses, but except along watercourses woody plants are rare.

You should now be able to make a generalization about the relationships between production of vegetation (kg/ hectare/year) and the abiotic environment.

**Consumers.** The most conspicuous first-order consumers are hoofed mammals. Bison and pronghorns once thronged the North American grasslands; now they have

Figure 8 · 24

Bison in Arizona, where grassland borders desert. What other first-order consumers might you find here?

Josef Muench

National Park Service

Figure 8 · 25

North American grassland near its center (Kansas). How can you explain the presence of the trees?

been replaced by cattle and sheep. Less conspicuous herbivores are jackrabbits and such rodents as prairie dogs and ground squirrels. And many kinds of insects feed upon the vegetation. At times grasshopper populations reach gigantic size; then the insect swarms may devour the plants down to ground level.

George Porter from National Audubon Society

Figure 8 · 26

Prairie dogs. Try to find how these rodents received this misleading name.

X 1/7

Figure 8 · 27
Meadowlark.

X 1/24

Figure 8 · 28
Pronghorn.

Wolves and coyotes were once the chief larger predators; wolves have been eliminated by man, but coyotes survive. Foxes, rattlesnakes, and badgers are important predators on prairie dogs and ground squirrels. Many insectivorous birds, such as meadowlarks, prey upon insects. Various kinds of hawks and owls prey upon small rodents and birds.

As elsewhere in middle latitudes, winter brings a reduction in plant growth and, with the smaller supply of food, a reduction in active animal life. Most of the rodents hibernate. Insects often overwinter in the egg stage or as dormant, immature forms. Snowfall is not heavy, even in the northern part of the grasslands, but it drifts easily before the strong grassland winds. Thus, though snow may be quite deep in some places, dried grasses are exposed in other places. The remaining herds of pronghorns forage on exposed grass as their ancestors did. In former days great herds of bison migrated into the southern parts of the grasslands each autumn. Insectivorous birds migrate out of the region, but some seed-eating birds move in from farther north.

### MIDDLE-LATITUDE DESERT

In North America the western edge of the grassland is bordered by desert. The situation is complicated by the Rocky Mountains, but between the ranges of the mountains various kinds of desert occur from eastern Washington southward into Mexico.

**Abiotic environment.** The word "desert" is usually associated with low precipitation. Equally important in defining a desert climate is the rate of evaporation. In deserts the evaporation rate is always high compared with the precipitation. This is partly a matter of latitude—the amount of precipitation that produces desert at the equator can support a fine grassland at middle latitudes. When

X 1/12

Figure 8 · 29
Badger.

precipitation does occur in the desert, it is likely to be heavy but brief, and much of the water runs off instead of sinking into the soil.

In all regions of the earth, loss of heat is greatly slowed down by water vapor in the air. Because desert air is very dry, the heat that builds up rapidly during the cloudless days is quickly lost again at night. Although temperatures of the air and of the soil surface vary greatly between day and night, temperatures underground are much more stable.

**Producers.**   Desert plants are widely spaced; there is much bare ground between individuals. Their roots spread far in all directions from the stems. Roots of many desert plants are only a short distance below the ground. When rains occur, these widespread roots soak up the moisture rapidly; the water is then stored in the tissues of the plants. Cacti, for example, store large quantities of water in their thick stems. Thorns and spines are numerous on desert plants. And most desert plants have small leaves or no leaves at all.

**Consumers.**   At dawn and dusk desert animals may seem surprisingly abundant, considering the low density of producers. This impression is due partly to the ease with which the animals may be seen in the sparse vegetation, partly to the ease with which their tracks may be observed on the bare ground.

Here are more statements of fact that require ecological explanations.

Figure 8 · 30

"Cool" desert (Nevada). What environmental factor most probably explains the distance between shrubs?

David Muench

Josef Muench

Woodrow Goodpaster

Figure 8 · 31
"Hot" desert (Arizona) after spring rains.

Figure 8 · 32
Kangaroo rat, a desert rodent.
X 1/2

Few large herbivores occur in middle-latitude deserts, but rodents are rather numerous. Most of these are burrowers. They obtain water in food they eat or from dew. A few—pocket mice—survive with little intake of water because they use water that is produced from the chemical breakdown of foods in their bodies. As in all terrestrial biomes, insect herbivores are abundant.

This chemical breakdown is discussed on pages 415–418.

Many birds and some reptiles, especially lizards, are insectivorous. Scorpions also prey upon insects. Among larger predators are coyotes, hawks, and rattlesnakes, all of which depend primarily upon rodents and rabbits for their food.

### SOME OTHER BIOMES

Our primary purpose in this chapter is to show broad patterns in the biosphere. We make no attempt at completeness. This is impossible, because in many parts of the world, ecologists have not yet studied biomes in detail.

**Tropical deciduous forest.** The seasonless rain forests cover a relatively small part of the tropics. Most tropical regions have seasons; but instead of being warm and cold seasons, they are wet and dry seasons. Just as most of the broad-leaved trees and shrubs of high latitudes are deciduous in winter—the season when frozen soil limits available moisture—so many woody plants in the tropics are deciduous during the dry season. These plants are the basis for distinguishing a *tropical deciduous-forest* biome.

In this biome the canopy is neither as deep nor as dense as in the rain forest. Light filters all the way to the forest

X 1/2

Figure 8 · 33
Pocket mouse.

Use Figure 8 · 8 to locate regions of tropical deciduous forest.

A. W. Kuchler

**Figure 8 · 34**

Tropical deciduous forest (Thailand). In what season do you think this picture was taken?

estivation [ĕs'tə vā'shən; Latin: aestas, summer]

If you traveled from savanna to still drier regions, what changes would you expect to find in the vegetation?

floor, which is therefore covered by a dense mass of undergrowth that man can penetrate only by cutting his way with axes or large knives. It is this biome that best matches the common notion of a "jungle."

Many animals go into a state of dormancy during the dry season. This state is somewhat similar to hibernation in the higher latitudes, but a different word — *estivation* — is used in referring to it. Insects and "cold-blooded" vertebrates, in particular, are likely to estivate.

**Savanna.** Where tropical dry seasons are especially long and severe, trees grow far apart. Between the trees the ground is covered with tall grasses. This is *savanna*, which covers large areas in South America and Africa.

In Africa savanna is the home of big-game animals. These are large grazing and browsing species such as elephants, rhinoceroses, zebras, and many kinds of antelope. These first-order consumers are followed by predators, such as lions and leopards, and the kills made by them are cleaned up by saprovores that range in size from vultures to bacteria.

Figure 8 · 35

Tropical savanna in Africa. Elephants, zebras, and giraffes (background); gnu and ostrich (foreground). What predators might you find here?

**Middle-latitude rain forest.**    In North America from southern Alaska to Oregon, the climate is milder—cooler in summer and warmer in winter—than we might expect at this latitude. In addition, there is much precipitation. These climatic conditions produce a *middle-latitude rain forest.*

The trees are mostly conifers, but they are much larger than those of taiga, some exceeding the height of trees in tropical rain forests. However, the canopy is much simpler than in the tropics, and there are relatively few species of trees. Lianas are uncommon. Epiphytes are abundant, but they are mostly mosses, ferns, and lichens. Shrubs are fairly numerous, but herbs are few. The ground is covered with deep cushions of moss.

Elk and deer browse on the shrubs. Among birds the first-order consumers live largely on conifer seeds, as do many rodents. Compared with the tropical rain forest, this forest has few arboreal vertebrates. Insects are abundant, and there are small invertebrates in the deep layers of humus on the forest floor. These organisms support populations of birds, such as thrushes, that are second-order consumers.

**Chaparral.**    In California most of the precipitation comes in winter; summers are very dry. South Africa, western Australia, central Chile, and the region around the Mediterranean Sea have a similar climate. The biome characteristic of this climate has several names; in America the term *chaparral* is used.

A textbook on North American geography will explain these climatic conditions.

See the cover photograph of this book.

chaparral [chăp′ə răl′]

Figure 8 · 36
Chaparral (California). At what season do you think this picture was taken?

Dennis Brokaw

USAFSO Tropic Survival School, Canal Zone

Figure 8 · 37
Cloud forest (Panamá). Year-round winds from the Caribbean bring moisture that condenses into clouds at an altitude of about 1000 m. How might such conditions affect the biota?

Chaparral is composed of small trees and large shrubs with small, evergreen leaves that are thick and often coated with waxy material. The canopy is low and often discontinuous. Herbaceous plants have thick underground stems that survive the dry summers. Rodents and reptiles are numerous and show some of the adaptations of those in deserts. As in the tropical deciduous forest, estivation occurs in the dry season.

To what environmental condition do you think such leaves adapt a plant?

**Biomes in mountains.** Air is heated by the earth's surface, so the higher we go, the cooler the air becomes. The temperature drops (on the average) about 2.7°C for each 500 m of elevation. Thus, by climbing only a few hundred meters up the side of a mountain we get the effect—as far as temperature is concerned—of going many kilometers poleward. In addition, mountains receive more precipitation than the surrounding lowlands, especially on the windward sides. The intensity and wavelength of radiation are also affected by elevation, although the yearly pattern of radiation is not. Obviously, mountains produce complications in the pattern of biomes.

Because the environment changes with altitude in mountainous regions, the biota also changes with altitude. Therefore, a mountain slope bears a variety of biotic zones in a relatively small area, and these are repeated at equivalent altitudes on each separate mountain or range over a large region. We might consider these zones as discontinuous biomes and attempt to relate them to biomes in nearby regions (Figure 8·38). However, these similarities are somewhat superficial. For example, in the alpine (tundra-like) region of the Rockies, there is no permafrost in the

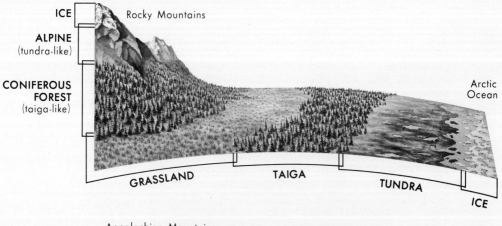

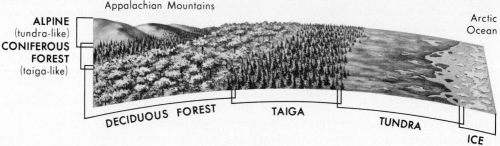

**Figure 8 · 38**

Comparison of effects of altitude and latitude in western (*above*) and eastern (*below*) North America. These are *diagrams*, not pictures; interpret them with caution.

ground; there is no long period of darkness in the winter; the amount of radiant energy received in summer is much greater than that received at any time in the tundra. It seems best, therefore, to think of mountainous regions as exceptions to the patterns of biomes.

## INVESTIGATION 8.2

### TEMPERATURE, RAINFALL, AND BIOME DISTRIBUTION

#### PURPOSE

This investigation provides practice in associating climates (as expressed in climatograms) with biomes.

#### BACKGROUND INFORMATION

Climatograms show monthly variations in only two climatic factors. Other factors may greatly affect climate, but a climatogram does give a rough idea of climate in the location from which the data were obtained.

By daily observation you can easily associate the climate of your own locality with the biome found there. Only by extensive travel, however, can the relationship of particular climates with particular biomes be learned on a worldwide basis. This investigation is a poor substitute for such travel; but if it is carried out thoughtfully and with frequent reference to pictures and descriptions of biomes, it can help you to visualize relationships between the abiotic and biotic features in some of the earth's major ecosystems.

### MATERIALS

Graph paper, 3 to 17 sheets per student

### PROCEDURE

First, obtain monthly averages of precipitation and temperature from the weather station closest to your school. Because the U.S. Weather Bureau is one of the very few still reporting in British units, these data will be expressed as inches of precipitation and as degrees Fahrenheit. Therefore, you will need to convert the data to centimeters of precipitation and degrees Celsius before making comparisons with the data given here. From the local data draw a climatogram. The heading of the climatogram should include the name of the biome in which the data were recorded and the location of the weather station.

Second, draw climatograms from the data in Group 1. When these are completed, you will have eleven climatograms (six being on pages 256–257 and 272 of this book) representing major land biomes.

Third, from the data in Group 2 draw climatograms as assigned by the teacher.

## GROUP 1
$T$ = temperature (in degrees Celsius);   $P$ = precipitation (in centimeters)

**a.** Tropical Deciduous Forest: Cuiabá, Brazil

|   | J | F | M | A | M | J | J | A | S | O | N | D |
|---|---|---|---|---|---|---|---|---|---|---|---|---|
| T | 27.2 | 27.2 | 27.2 | 26.7 | 25.6 | 23.9 | 24.4 | 25.6 | 27.8 | 27.8 | 27.8 | 27.2 |
| P | 24.9 | 21.1 | 21.1 | 10.2 | 5.3 | 0.8 | 0.5 | 2.8 | 5.1 | 11.4 | 15.0 | 20.6 |

**b.** Chaparral: Santa Monica, California

|   | J | F | M | A | M | J | J | A | S | O | N | D |
|---|---|---|---|---|---|---|---|---|---|---|---|---|
| T | 11.7 | 11.7 | 12.8 | 14.4 | 15.6 | 17.2 | 18.9 | 18.3 | 18.3 | 16.7 | 14.4 | 12.8 |
| P | 8.9 | 7.6 | 7.4 | 1.3 | 1.3 | 0.0 | 0.0 | 0.0 | 0.3 | 1.5 | 3.6 | 5.8 |

**c.** Savanna: Moshi, Tanzania

|   | J | F | M | A | M | J | J | A | S | O | N | D |
|---|---|---|---|---|---|---|---|---|---|---|---|---|
| T | 23.2 | 23.2 | 22.2 | 21.2 | 19.8 | 18.4 | 17.9 | 18.4 | 19.8 | 21.4 | 22.0 | 22.4 |
| P | 3.6 | 6.1 | 9.2 | 40.1 | 30.2 | 5.1 | 5.1 | 2.5 | 2.0 | 3.0 | 8.1 | 6.4 |

**d.** Tropical Desert: Aden, Aden

|   | J | F | M | A | M | J | J | A | S | O | N | D |
|---|---|---|---|---|---|---|---|---|---|---|---|---|
| T | 24.6 | 25.1 | 26.4 | 28.5 | 30.6 | 31.9 | 31.1 | 30.3 | 31.1 | 28.8 | 26.5 | 25.1 |
| P | 0.8 | 0.5 | 1.3 | 0.5 | 0.3 | 0.3 | 0.0 | 0.3 | 0.3 | 0.3 | 0.3 | 0.3 |

## GROUP 2

| | | J | F | M | A | M | J | J | A | S | O | N | D |
|---|---|---|---|---|---|---|---|---|---|---|---|---|---|
| **a.** | T | 1.1 | 1.7 | 6.1 | 12.2 | 17.8 | 22.2 | 25.0 | 23.3 | 20.0 | 13.9 | 7.8 | 2.2 |
| | P | 8.1 | 7.6 | 8.9 | 8.4 | 9.2 | 9.9 | 11.2 | 10.2 | 7.9 | 7.9 | 6.4 | 7.9 |
| **b.** | T | 10.6 | 11.1 | 12.2 | 14.4 | 15.6 | 19.4 | 21.1 | 21.7 | 20.0 | 16.7 | 13.9 | 11.1 |
| | P | 9.1 | 8.9 | 8.6 | 6.6 | 5.1 | 2.0 | 0.5 | 0.5 | 3.6 | 8.4 | 10.9 | 10.4 |
| **c.** | T | 25.6 | 25.6 | 24.4 | 25.0 | 24.4 | 23.3 | 23.3 | 24.4 | 24.4 | 25.0 | 25.6 | 25.6 |
| | P | 25.8 | 24.9 | 31.0 | 16.5 | 25.4 | 18.8 | 16.8 | 11.7 | 22.1 | 18.3 | 21.3 | 29.2 |
| **d.** | T | 12.8 | 15.0 | 18.3 | 21.1 | 25.0 | 29.4 | 32.8 | 32.2 | 28.9 | 22.2 | 16.1 | 13.3 |
| | P | 1.0 | 1.3 | 1.0 | 0.3 | 0.0 | 0.0 | 0.3 | 1.3 | 0.5 | 0.5 | 0.8 | 1.0 |
| **e.** | T | −3.9 | −2.2 | 1.7 | 8.9 | 15.0 | 20.0 | 22.8 | 21.7 | 16.7 | 11.1 | 5.0 | −0.6 |
| | P | 2.3 | 1.8 | 2.8 | 2.8 | 3.2 | 5.8 | 5.3 | 3.0 | 3.6 | 2.8 | 4.1 | 3.3 |
| **f.** | T | 19.4 | 18.9 | 18.3 | 16.1 | 15.0 | 13.3 | 12.8 | 13.3 | 14.4 | 15.0 | 16.7 | 17.8 |
| | P | 0.0 | 0.0 | 1.5 | 0.5 | 8.9 | 14.7 | 12.2 | 8.1 | 2.0 | 1.0 | 0.3 | 0.8 |
| **g.** | T | −22.2 | −22.8 | −21.1 | −14.4 | −3.9 | 1.7 | 5.0 | 5.0 | 1.1 | −3.9 | −10.0 | −17.2 |
| | P | 1.0 | 1.3 | 1.8 | 1.5 | 1.5 | 1.3 | 2.3 | 2.8 | 2.8 | 2.8 | 2.8 | 1.3 |
| **h.** | T | 11.7 | 12.8 | 17.2 | 20.6 | 23.9 | 27.2 | 28.3 | 28.3 | 26.1 | 21.1 | 16.1 | 12.2 |
| | P | 3.6 | 4.1 | 4.6 | 6.9 | 8.1 | 6.9 | 6.4 | 6.6 | 8.9 | 5.1 | 5.6 | 4.6 |
| **i.** | T | 23.3 | 22.2 | 19.4 | 15.6 | 11.7 | 8.3 | 8.3 | 9.4 | 12.2 | 15.1 | 18.9 | 21.7 |
| | P | 5.1 | 5.6 | 6.6 | 5.6 | 2.8 | 0.9 | 2.5 | 4.1 | 5.8 | 5.8 | 5.1 | 5.3 |
| **j.** | T | 17.2 | 18.9 | 21.1 | 22.8 | 23.3 | 22.2 | 21.1 | 21.1 | 20.6 | 19.4 | 18.9 | 17.2 |
| | P | 0.3 | 0.5 | 1.5 | 3.6 | 8.6 | 9.2 | 9.4 | 11.4 | 10.9 | 5.3 | 0.8 | 0.3 |
| **k.** | T | −20.0 | −18.9 | −12.2 | −2.2 | 5.6 | 12.2 | 16.1 | 15.0 | 10.6 | 3.9 | −5.6 | −15.0 |
| | P | 3.3 | 2.3 | 2.8 | 2.5 | 4.6 | 5.6 | 6.1 | 8.4 | 7.4 | 4.6 | 2.8 | 2.8 |
| **l.** | T | −0.6 | 2.2 | 5.0 | 10.0 | 13.3 | 18.3 | 23.3 | 22.2 | 16.1 | 10.6 | 4.4 | 0.0 |
| | P | 1.5 | 1.3 | 1.3 | 1.0 | 1.5 | 0.8 | 0.3 | 0.5 | 0.8 | 1.0 | 0.8 | 1.5 |

## STUDYING THE DATA

Compare the climatogram based on data from the weather station nearest your school with the climatogram on page 256, 257, or 272 or from Group 1 that most resembles it. • In what ways are the two climatograms similar? In what ways are they different?(1) • Do they represent the same biome?(2) • If they don't, what climatic differences account for the biome differences? If they do, what characteristics of climate seem to be related to characteristics of living things in your biome?(3)

Now attempt to associate biomes with the sets of data given in Group 2. In doing this, you use generalizations made from studying climatograms of known biomes. Of course, you are working with only two variables; you have no data concerning winds or cloudiness, and you can only judge humidity indirectly. Nevertheless, by careful thinking you can make fairly accurate deductions even from a consideration of these two variables alone.

Write the name of your hypothesized biome at the top of each graph. • For each biome relate the characteristics of its biota to the characteristics of its climate.(4) Afterward the teacher may give you the location of the places from which the data came. You can then check your deductions.

### FOR FURTHER INVESTIGATION

1. No biome is uniform throughout. Within each one you can observe gradual changes in both biotic and abiotic factors. Therefore ecologists distinguish subdivisions of biomes—ecosystems on a smaller scale. These subdivisions can be correlated with slight changes in climate. Consider data from three locations in middle-latitude grassland of North America:

**a. Dubuque, Iowa**

|   | J | F | M | A | M | J | J | A | S | O | N | D |
|---|---|---|---|---|---|---|---|---|---|---|---|---|
| T | −6.7 | −5.0 | 1.7 | 9.4 | 15.6 | 21.1 | 23.9 | 22.2 | 17.8 | 11.1 | 2.8 | −3.9 |
| P | 3.8 | 3.6 | 5.6 | 6.6 | 9.9 | 11.4 | 9.4 | 8.6 | 10.2 | 6.4 | 4.8 | 3.8 |

**b. Kearney, Nebraska**

|   | J | F | M | A | M | J | J | A | S | O | N | D |
|---|---|---|---|---|---|---|---|---|---|---|---|---|
| T | −4.6 | −1.9 | 2.6 | 9.9 | 15.8 | 21.8 | 25.7 | 24.4 | 18.9 | 12.2 | 3.3 | −2.2 |
| P | 1.3 | 1.6 | 2.8 | 6.1 | 9.9 | 10.3 | 6.5 | 5.2 | 6.1 | 3.0 | 2.1 | 1.5 |

**c. Laramie, Wyoming**

|   | J | F | M | A | M | J | J | A | S | O | N | D |
|---|---|---|---|---|---|---|---|---|---|---|---|---|
| T | −6.1 | −5.6 | −1.7 | 3.3 | 7.8 | 12.8 | 16.7 | 16.7 | 11.1 | 5.0 | −1.1 | −5.6 |
| P | 1.3 | 0.8 | 2.0 | 2.5 | 3.8 | 3.1 | 4.3 | 3.0 | 2.5 | 2.3 | 1.3 | 1.3 |

How might the vegetation in these three places differ? You can check your conclusions by referring to Gleason and Cronquist, pages 346–352 (for title and publisher see "Suggested Readings").

2. The *relationship* between temperature and precipitation is more important than the actual amount of either. Draw climatograms from the three sets of data on page 286. How do you explain the presence of middle-latitude grassland in these different climates?

**a.** Coastal Prairie: Galveston, Texas

|   | J | F | M | A | M | J | J | A | S | O | N | D |
|---|---|---|---|---|---|---|---|---|---|---|---|---|
| T | 12.2 | 13.3 | 17.2 | 21.1 | 24.4 | 27.8 | 28.9 | 28.3 | 26.7 | 22.8 | 17.2 | 13.9 |
| P | 8.6 | 7.6 | 7.4 | 7.9 | 8.6 | 10.7 | 10.2 | 11.9 | 14.5 | 10.9 | 9.9 | 9.4 |

**b.** Mid-Grass Prairie: Omaha, Nebraska

|   | J | F | M | A | M | J | J | A | S | O | N | D |
|---|---|---|---|---|---|---|---|---|---|---|---|---|
| T | −5.6 | −3.9 | 2.8 | 10.6 | 17.2 | 22.2 | 25.0 | 23.9 | 18.9 | 12.8 | 3.9 | −2.8 |
| P | 1.8 | 2.3 | 3.3 | 7.1 | 10.4 | 11.9 | 10.2 | 8.1 | 7.6 | 5.8 | 2.8 | 2.3 |

**c.** Prairie-Aspen Border: Winnipeg, Manitoba, Canada

|   | J | F | M | A | M | J | J | A | S | O | N | D |
|---|---|---|---|---|---|---|---|---|---|---|---|---|
| T | −20.0 | −17.8 | −9.4 | 3.3 | 11.1 | 16.7 | 18.9 | 17.8 | 12.2 | 5.0 | −6.1 | −14.4 |
| P | 2.3 | 1.8 | 3.3 | 3.6 | 5.1 | 7.9 | 7.9 | 5.6 | 5.6 | 3.6 | 2.8 | 2.3 |

## EARTH HISTORY AND DISTRIBUTION

In polar regions of the Arctic and Antarctic, climate and other abiotic environmental factors are much the same. Yet only in the Arctic do polar bears roam the ice floes; in the Antarctic they are absent. Only in the Antarctic do penguins waddle about in their dignified way; in the Arctic there are none. Why are there no polar bears near the South Pole, no penguins near the North Pole? In rain forests of South America, we can find tapirs; in rain forests of the East Indies, tapirs—a slightly different species—also occur. But there are no tapirs in the African rain forest. Why not?

Figure 8 · 39

Two kinds of tapirs.

Malayan tapir        X 1/48

American tapir

From these and numerous other examples we must conclude that climates and other environmental factors do not entirely explain geographic ranges of organisms. Because an organism *can* live in a particular place does not necessarily mean that it *does* live there. To understand the geographic distribution of polar bears, penguins, tapirs, and numerous other organisms, we must seek facts in addition to those from ecology.

We can begin with either of two possible assumptions: (1) all species once occurred everywhere and later disappeared from some places; or (2) each species originated in a particular place and then spread into other places. For the first of these assumptions we have little or no evidence; for the second the evidence is strong. Study of fossils from all parts of the world indicates that species populations have developed in rather small areas and have then spread. How does such spreading occur?

### DISPERSAL

If fences aren't kept in good repair, every farmer knows that his cattle will wander out of the pasture. In all populations this tendency of living things to spread from places where they are to places where they aren't may be observed.

In the case of motile organisms, such *dispersal* may be accomplished by flying, swimming, walking, running, crawling, or burrowing. In the case of non-motile organisms, dispersal is passive. Seeds, spores, and eggs remain alive but in a dormant state for long periods. In currents of air, in water, or in mud on the foot of a bird, they may be carried great distances from their original locations. Even motile organisms may be passively transported much farther than they could actively travel. A polar bear may be carried hundreds of kilometers on floating ice. A spider attached to strands of its silk may be blown a long way by air currents. Tornadoes and hurricanes may pick up snails, salamanders, frogs, and fish and later drop them more or less unharmed far from where they started.

By itself, of course, dispersal does not change a species' geographical range. Unless the organism survives and reproduces in the new location, its range has not changed.

### BARRIERS

Since every kind of organism has some way of getting from "here" to "there," it would be reasonable to expect that eventually each species might be found in every place on the earth where conditions ecologically favorable for it occur. Actually, such broad distribution is the exception rather than the rule. What, then, limits the dispersal of

dispersal [dĭs pûr′səl; Latin: *dis-*, apart, + *spargere*, to scatter]

passive: inactive but acted upon

Figure 8 · 40

The thick husk of the coconut is an excellent float. When the fruit is washed onto a beach, the seed may sprout—as here.

Carl Gans

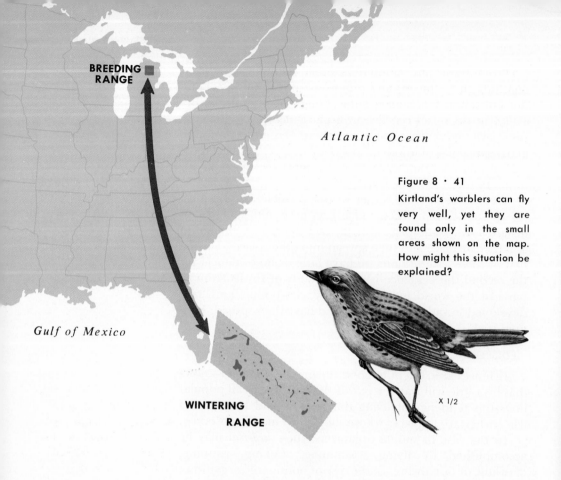

Atlantic Ocean

BREEDING RANGE

Gulf of Mexico

WINTERING RANGE

Figure 8 · 41
Kirtland's warblers can fly very well, yet they are found only in the small areas shown on the map. How might this situation be explained?

X 1/2

organisms? In the case of pastured cattle it is a fence—a *barrier*. In nature, too, barriers of one kind or another are effective, to varying degrees, in preventing dispersal.

What constitutes a barrier depends upon the means of dispersal a species possesses. For most terrestrial animals, large areas of water are effective barriers. For most aquatic organisms, land areas are equally effective. Within a land area mountains are barriers to many organisms.

Besides physical barriers there are ecological barriers. For organisms adapted to life in a forest, a region of grassland or desert may be a barrier. And for grassland species, a forest region may limit dispersal.

Some barriers are best described as behavioral. It seems reasonable to suppose, for instance, that flying birds would be found almost everywhere. But many birds that can fly great distances remain inhabitants of very restricted regions. The Amazon River, in Brazil, serves as the northern or southern boundary of the ranges of many forest birds. Undoubtedly most of these birds *could* fly across the river, but they don't.

What barrier has probably kept tsetse flies from South America?

An increase in the population of a motile species favors emigration into less densely populated areas. When conditions are very favorable, emigration may take place rapidly. But the rate at which a species spreads depends not only upon emigration but also upon the barriers that are encountered. When barriers are great, dispersal may be very slow. If dispersal is passive, the means of transportation may be the decisive factor in determining rate of spread. Populations of trees whose seeds are carried away and buried by squirrels have been estimated to spread about 1.6 km every thousand years. By contrast, organisms swept up in a tornado may be carried 30 km in a few hours.

decisive: here, determining

### CONCLUSIONS

If the reasoning of biologists is correct, we can now explain the absence of polar bears from the Antarctic as follows: Polar bears originated in the Arctic. Their ecological requirements are such that the tropical environment is a barrier to their dispersal. Throughout the existence of the

Philip Gendreau

Figure 8 · 42

A changing barrier. Dispersal of plants at the retreating edge of Mendenhall Glacier, Alaska.

ICE
LIMIT
1916

**Figure 8 · 43**

In many parts of the world man's activities have radically changed natural biomes: (A) In this view (Ohio), little of the deciduous forest remains. (B) In this view (Iowa), little of the grassland remains. Which represents a greater change in the landscape?

Litton Industries—Aero Service Division                          A

Josef Muench

B

polar-bear species this wide barrier has existed, and thus far no part of the population has been able to move across it. So no polar bears are found in the Antarctic.

Similar reasoning can be applied to penguins. The case of the tapirs is more complex, but it involves the same elements: the past history of the organism, dispersal, and barriers.

## MAN'S INFLUENCE ON TERRESTRIAL ECOSYSTEMS

Flying from Cleveland, Ohio, to Louisville, Kentucky, we cross the middle-latitude deciduous-forest biome, but we see only a few traces of it. Flying from Chicago, Illinois, to Lincoln, Nebraska, we cross the eastern part of the North American grassland, but here, too, we see only traces of the original biome. In fact, from the air the landscapes below us in these two flights appear to be remarkably alike.

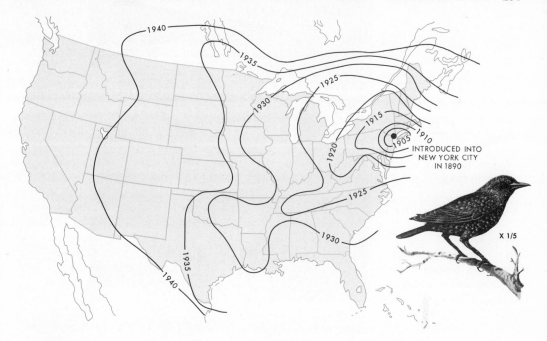

INTRODUCED INTO
NEW YORK CITY
IN 1890

X 1/5

Although in both cases climate remains an important factor in the ecosystems, the chief molder of the present landscape has been man.

### MAN AS AN AGENT OF DISPERSAL

Man has wandered more widely than any other organism. And in his travels he has always carried other organisms with him. At first, perhaps, this meant merely the dispersal of his parasites, such as lice. But since he started the cultivation of plants, at least fifteen thousand years ago, he has become an increasingly important agent of dispersal and one that has carried many organisms over barriers they might never have crossed otherwise.

Oranges and lemons have been taken from southeastern Asia and made an important part of landscapes in all the warmer regions of the earth. Wheat and barley have been taken from southwestern Asia and made to replace thousands of square kilometers once covered by forest. Cattle and horses from Asian grasslands now graze in almost every biome except tundra. These—and there are dozens of other examples—were deliberate dispersals.

Man has also dispersed organisms unintentionally. Dandelions and hundreds of "weeds" have been carried along with the seeds of crop plants. Rats, mice, bedbugs, and other animals have hitched rides in wagons and ships.

It is difficult to determine whether an organism that man carries into a new area will thrive or fail. In some

Figure 8 · 44

Expansion of the range of the European starling in North America. The bird has now reached the Pacific, but it is still rather uncommon in the western third of the continent.

deliberate: with intention, not accidentally

PLANTS-FRUITS-VEGETA L
INSPECTION - ONLY

**Figure 8 · 45**
Plant quarantine: inspect-
ing carrots brought across
the international bridge at
El Paso, Texas.

U.S. Dept. of Agriculture

quarantine [kwòr'ən tēn'; Italian: *quaranta,* forty]: originally, forty-day period during
which a vessel suspected of
carrying disease was detained
in port before landing was
permitted

cases, organisms have become part of the biomes in the
new areas. Wild orange thickets now thrive in many parts
of the tropics. After man introduced a few European rabbits to Australia, rabbits quickly spread over much of the
continent without further help. In fact, they became disas-
trously numerous. Therefore, many governments are
coming to realize that careful studies should be made before plants or animals are deliberately introduced into new
regions. Some governments have set up quarantine services
to inspect automobiles, ships, and planes in hopes of preventing accidental introduction of undesirable organisms.

In other cases, however, the organisms dispersed by
man exist only through man's continued protection. There
has been wheat in England for two thousand years, but it
soon disappears there when it is not cultivated. Dozens of
species of European birds have been transported to North
America, but less than half a dozen have become a real part
of the North American biota. On the whole, success in trans-
plantation of species by man is less frequent than failure.

### CULTIVATION

In many ways, cultivated fields — especially grainfields — resemble grasslands. Thus it can be said that man
has spread the grassland biome; in particular, he has
spread it into the middle-latitude deciduous forest of eastern Asia, western Europe, and the eastern United States.
Into these artificial grasslands have moved organisms of the
grassland biome. In the United States, for example, coyotes
are now found as far east as New York.

In some places man has made agricultural land himself: the Dutch have drained land once covered by the sea, the Filipinos have built terraces for rice, the Rhinelanders have constructed vineyards on steep slopes. In many countries complex irrigation systems have been used to transform deserts into agricultural lands. Today thousands of hectares of irrigated land yield a considerable percentage of the total agricultural production of the United States.

But man has also destroyed ecosystems. Before European man invaded it, the great grassland of the central United States was an ecosystem in homeostasis. There were periodic droughts and strong winds. But the grasses survived the droughts, and their matted roots protected the soil from erosion by the wind. Finding fertile soils here, man rapidly converted the grasslands into plowed and cultivated fields. Gradually cultivation was extended westward into drier and drier regions. Then, in the 1930's, one of the great droughts that are characteristic of grasslands occurred. With the grasses gone and the cultivated crops destroyed by drought, the winds swept up the dry topsoil in great dust storms that left many areas barren. With the return of normal rains, neither the cultivated crops nor the native grasses could be easily reestablished on the remaining soil. With his plow man had created—at least temporarily—a desert.

## SUCCESSION ON ABANDONED LAND

In Chapter 3 we discussed the succession of communities that follow each other when bare areas are formed by

Figure 8 · 46

The difference that irrigation makes (California). Where do you think the water comes from?

Monsanto Magazine

X 1/8

ragweed

**Figure 8 · 47**

You can study succession in your own region in a fairly short period of time by comparing pieces of land that have been abandoned for varying numbers of years.

aggregation [Latin: *ad*, toward, + *gregare*, to collect]: a group that has come together

urban [ûr'bən; Latin: *urbs*, a city]

earthquakes, landslides, or other natural means. In landscapes that are influenced by man, we can also observe succession when, for one reason or another, man abandons his activities on a piece of land. Observation of such a process can tell us much about a biome.

Suppose, for example, a cultivated field is abandoned in Virginia. In the first year, the field is covered with annual weeds, such as ragweed. In the second year, perennial plants—goldenrods, asters, and grasses—become conspicuous. By the third or fourth year, young woody plants—shrubs and tree seedlings—are large enough to be seen among the herbs. Within a decade young trees have shaded out the earlier perennial herbs. As the trees grow larger, their fallen leaves begin to form a humus soil in which seeds of forest herbs and shrubs can germinate. Seeds from the first generation of trees are usually unable to thrive in the shade of their parents. But seedlings of oaks, beeches, and other shade-tolerant trees thrive, and in a century or two, perhaps, the deciduous-forest biome will develop again.

What if the abandoned field is in central Kansas instead of Virginia? Woody plants (if their seeds germinate at all) do not long survive, and grasses soon dominate the scene. If the field is in western Oregon, coniferous trees eventually dominate. And further, if an irrigated field is abandoned in southern Arizona, neither grass nor trees appear; instead, cacti and thorny shrubs reoccupy the ground. Thus, even in regions where man has controlled the landscape, succession on abandoned land produces the biome that the local climate naturally supports.

## URBAN AND SUBURBAN ECOSYSTEMS

The most drastically rebuilt landscape is a city. Here man has smothered the land under roads and buildings. The soil is covered with cement; hills and cliffs are constructed from steel and glass. The streets, to be sure, are sometimes lined with shade trees, and there are parks; but these, like most things in a city, are designed for purely human purposes.

A city is mainly an aggregation of organisms of a single kind—man—rather than a system of interacting populations of many kinds. Biological communities are defined primarily in terms of food relationships among the organisms involved. Urban man gets his food from many places: wheat from Nebraska, sugar from Colorado or Puerto Rico, beef from Texas, bananas from Honduras, potatoes from Maine. His biological community extends to many parts of the world.

Figure 8 · 48
Wild rock doves nesting in the cornices of city buildings. What is their source of energy?

Figure 8 · 49
*Ailanthus,* Asiatic tree tolerating urban environments.

Figure 8 · 50
Man-made "forest" on the naturally treeless Great Plains (Fort Morgan, Colorado). The fields near town are irrigated.

Yet man is not alone in a city. An urban community contains a number of organisms that in one way or another have adapted to urban conditions. The chief requirement is ability to get along with man. Some organisms—dogs, cats, even pigeons—are deliberately cared for by some people. Others—rats, mice, starlings, cockroaches—manage quite well without encouragement. Certain trees and shrubs are planted because they can tolerate the cement-covered soil and poisoned atmosphere; and hardy herbs spring up unwanted and untended in vacant lots and even in the cracks of city sidewalks.

Around all our cities a special kind of ecosystem is being formed that might be called the "suburban forest." The trees are species that for one reason or another are favored by man, and a large proportion of all the vegetation is deliberately planted. Mammals and birds have moved in from the surrounding countryside. Rabbits hop across suburban lawns in the evening, and raspberry bushes are likely to turn up on neglected stretches of roadside. Several species of squirrels thrive in suburbia, but usually only one

Figure 8 · 51
Suburban organisms.

species in any particular town—fox squirrels in one place, red squirrels in another, gray squirrels in a third—for reasons that are little understood. The diversity of birds that can be found in suburbia is great—with or without the encouragement of feeding stations and free housing. In the south, various species of lizards get along nicely in gardens and even in houses. And of course, insects, bacteria, and viruses are ever-present.

dominate [Latin: *dominus*, lord, master]: to rule, control

There is a strange biological sameness in man-dominated communities. It is true that the palms of suburban Los Angeles are missing from the suburbs of Boston, and perhaps crickets do not chirp everywhere between Miami and Seattle. But over wide stretches of the United States, the lawn-owner fights the crabgrass, coddles his azaleas, and admires his wife's African violets, while his cat stalks the fledgling robins. Unlike natural biomes, man's monotonous communities in city and suburb exist in spite of, not because of, the climate.

## INVESTIGATION 8.3

### EFFECTS OF FIRE ON BIOMES

#### INTRODUCTION

Fire is an important ecological factor in terrestrial ecosystems. Some fires start from natural causes—lightning and volcanoes, for example—but many are caused by man deliberately or accidentally. However they begin, fires have many effects upon the organisms in their paths. The most easily observed effects are in the vegetation.

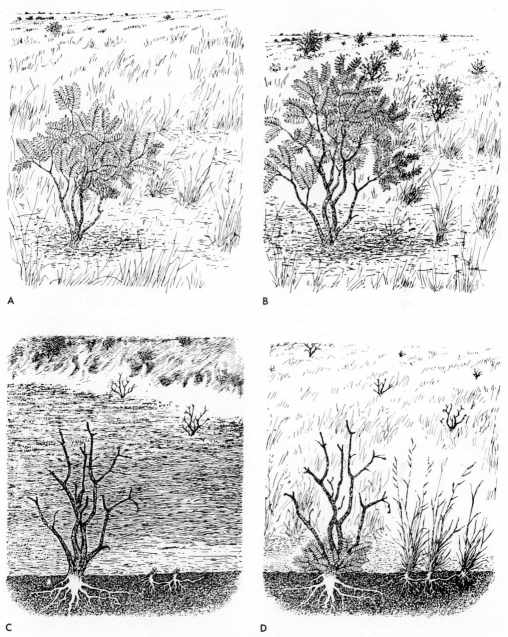

A

B

C

D

Figure 8 · 52

## PURPOSE

In this investigation you will study evidence concerning effects of fires on communities in three ecosystems. This evidence is presented in pictures.

## PROCEDURE

As you read each of the following sections, base your answers to the questions upon study of the pictures in Figures 8 · 52, 8 · 53, and 8 · 54.

**A. Fire in a middle-latitude grassland.** Figures 8 · 52A to 8 · 52D picture a series of events that often occur in the southern part of the North American grassland. Two populations are involved: grasses of various species and a shrub, mesquite. Study Figures 8 · 52A and 8 · 52B. • Which population is increasing in size?(1) Roots of mesquite have been found in mine shafts many meters below the surface of the soil. • What competitive advantage might this give mesquite over grasses?(2) • If the trend shown in these two pictures continued, what kind of community might result?(3)

Now refer to Figures 8 · 52C and 8 · 52D. In these figures the plant parts shown in white at or below ground level represent unharmed tissue. • Do both kinds of plants survive fires?(4) • In which kind has more growing tissue been killed?(5) Grasses usually reach maturity and produce seeds in one or two years; mesquite usually requires four to ten years. • Which kind of plant has lost more in terms of growing time?(6) • In Figure 8 · 52D, which kind of plant occupies most of the land?(7) • What might you expect this area to look like four or five years after a fire?(8)

Now you can make a generalization on the effect of fire in this community. • Describe the probable landscape if fires did not occur at all.(9) • What would be the appearance of the landscape if fires occurred every few years?(10) • What environmental factor seems to be necessary for maintaining grassland in this region?(11)

**B. Fire in a forest of the Great Lakes region.** The Great Lakes region of North America is an *ecotone*—a region of transition, a region in which there is a gradual change from one biome to another. The forests of the Great Lakes region (Figure 8 · 53A) show a mixture of characteristics of middle-latitude deciduous forest and taiga. But early in his settlement of the region, European man brought about a great change in the landscape (Figure 8 · 53B). • What was this change?(12) Following the change, fires had apparently been rare in this region, but they became more frequent. • What might have brought about the increase in the number of fires?(13) • If fire does not occur, what might the area shown in Figure 8 · 53B look like in later years?(14)

Study Figures 8 · 53B, 8 · 53C, and 8 · 53D, which picture jack pine. • What characteristic of jack pine gives that species a competitive advantage when there is a fire?(15) • Describe the probable appearance of the area shown in Figure 8 · 53D five or six years later.(16) Jack pines produce cones in eight to ten years but do not live to a very great age. Their seedlings do not thrive in shade. Suppose no further fires occurred for two hundred years. • What changes in appearance might take place in this area during that period?(17) Suppose fires occurred about once every twenty years. • What might the area look like at the end of two hundred years?(18)

**C. Fire in a forest of the southeastern United States.** In the southeastern United States occur extensive forests in which longleaf pine is almost the only large tree, though seedlings and saplings of deciduous trees often occur. Until they are from three to seven years old, young longleaf pines look somewhat like clumps of grass (Figure 8 · 54A). While in this "grass stage" the young trees develop deep roots in which a reserve supply of food is stored.

Fires in these forests generally are confined to the ground, where they burn grasses and the sparse growth of deciduous shrubs and saplings (Figure 8 · 54B). • What is the effect of fire on young longleaf pines in the "grass stage"?(19) • What is the effect on the deciduous shrubs and saplings?(20)

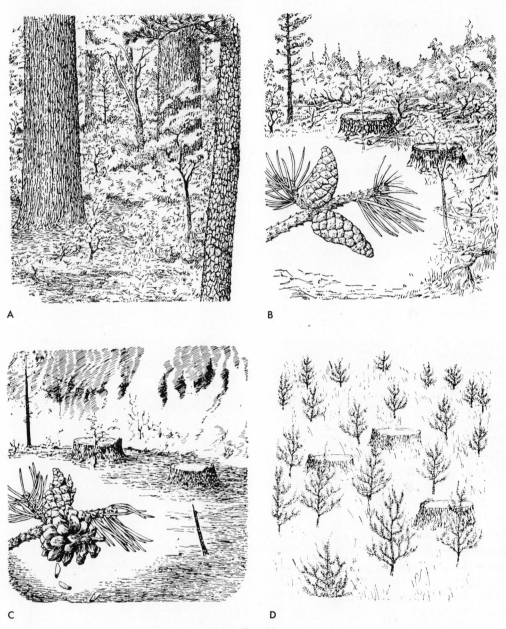

A

B

C

D

Figure 8 · 53

• Which plants have a competitive advantage after a fire?(21) After the "grass stage" longleaf pines grow rapidly in height and develop a thick bark that resists scorching.   • What is the effect of ground fires at this stage in the development of the pines (Figure 8·54C)?(22) • Which plants have a competitive advantage when fires do not occur (Figure 8·54D)?(23)   • What factor seems to maintain a longleaf-pine forest within the deciduous-forest biome?(24)

Figure 8 · 54

## DISCUSSION

Knowledge of ecological effects of fire on biomes can be useful to man. • If you were interested in raising cattle in the region described in Procedure A, would occasional fires be an advantage or a disadvantage? Why?(25) • If you were interested in growing deciduous trees in the region described in Procedure B, would fire be an advantage or a disadvantage? Why?(26) • If you were interested in maintaining a longleaf-pine forest to obtain turpentine (a product of longleaf pines), would ground fires be an advantage or a disadvantage? Why?(27) Suppose you wanted bobwhites (game birds that nest on the ground) in your turpentine forest. • What effect might this have on your management of the forest?(28)

• What things must ecologists know before deciding whether to recommend using fire as a method of management to a landowner?(29)

### FOR FURTHER INVESTIGATION

Investigation 8.3 is based on an article by Charles F. Cooper, "The Ecology of Fire," in *Scientific American*, April, 1961. The article also discusses fire in Douglas-fir forests of the Northwest and in ponderosa-pine forests of the Southwest. Other information may be found in Gleason and Cronquist (see "Suggested Readings") and in books on forestry, range management, and plant ecology. Prepare a comprehensive report on fire as a factor in terrestrial ecosystems.

Organisms are not scattered helter-skelter over the surface of the earth. Each species has a geographic range. In attempting to explain the extent of a geographic range, we may adopt two viewpoints. One is historical: How did the species get to the place where we find it? The other is ecological: How does the species survive in the place where we find it? In any region survival of a species is the result of interaction between environment and the tolerances of the species. Though we can measure an organism's tolerances of particular environmental factors, in nature the organism reacts to the whole environment. Under natural conditions tolerance of any one factor may be modified by other factors in complex ways.

Climatic factors, operating through tolerances, are particularly important in producing characteristic large-scale ecosystems—biomes. In this chapter we have arranged the study of land biomes in two sequences: the first, in order of increasing total annual solar radiation; the second, in order of decreasing total annual precipitation. In the first series, there is a gradual increase in the depth and complexity of the vegetation—the producers. The result is a corresponding increase in the complexity of the consumer system. In the second series, there is a gradual decrease in the depth and density of the vegetation. The result is a corresponding decrease in the complexity of the consumer system. Both of these broad patterns are complicated by seasonal changes and disrupted by mountain systems. Finally, we have seen that the activities of man have greatly modified the pattern of biomes.

## GUIDE QUESTIONS

1. How are the ideas expressed by the ecological terms "biota" and "geographical range" related?
2. What must occur if a species is to survive as a part of a particular ecosystem?
3. Why is it difficult to make precise measurements of an organism's maximum and minimum tolerance for any single environmental factor?
4. What are biomes?
5. What structural and functional adaptations to long, severe winters are found among tundra organisms?
6. If caribou stayed in the taiga during the summer, how would their environment differ from that in the tundra?
7. How do seasons affect the biological characteristics of the landscape in middle-latitude deciduous forest?
8. What are epiphytes?
9. Contrast the vegetation in middle-latitude deciduous forest with that of tropical rain forest and explain the differences.
10. How can we explain the presence of large numbers of arboreal animals in tropical rain forest?
11. What climatic factor is chiefly responsible for the presence of grasslands in the same latitude with forests?
12. Explain the relatively large proportion of grassland animals that have adaptations for running and burrowing.
13. Competition among plants in a forest is different from competition among plants in a desert. What is the difference, and how can it be explained?
14. What environmental factor is associated with estivation?
15. If you went from savanna toward a region of larger precipitation, what changes would you expect in the vegetation?
16. Describe the vegetation in the middle-latitude rain forest by comparing it with that in the middle-latitude deciduous forest and that in the tropical rain forest.
17. What is chaparral?
18. In what ways do conditions in alpine communities on middle-latitude or tropical mountains resemble conditions in the tundra? In what ways do the two sets of conditions differ?
19. In addition to knowledge of biological tolerances, what information is needed to explain the geographic distribution of species?
20. How can a barrier to the dispersal of one species be a pathway of dispersal for another species?
21. How have the activities of man tended to produce "grassland landscapes" in middle-latitude deciduous forests and "deserts" in grassland?
22. How can a study of succession reveal the biome pattern in a region that has been greatly modified by man?
23. What is the principal ability required of a species if it is to adapt to life in cities?
24. Using fire as an example, explain how an abiotic environmental factor can have different effects in biotic communities that differ.

## PROBLEMS

1. Make a list of terrestrial organisms that have been brought into your locality by man. Divide the list into two parts, as follows: (a) organisms that (in your opinion) survive because of man's activities, and (b) organisms that (in your opinion) would survive without man. Give reasons for your placement of each organism on the list.

2. A plant is growing in each of the following cities at the time of year indicated. In each list, arrange the cities in order of decreasing solar energy (from the one in which the plant receives the most solar energy at noon to the one in which it receives the least). (a) At the June solstice (vertical rays of the sun at the Tropic of Cancer): Winnipeg, Canada; New Orleans, Louisiana; Rio de Janeiro, Brazil; Anchorage, Alaska; Havana, Cuba; Caracas, Venezuela; Boston, Massachusetts. (b) At the December solstice (vertical rays of the sun at the Tropic of Capricorn): Singapore, Singapore; Hobart, Tasmania; Tokyo, Japan; Vladivostok, Soviet Union; Manila, Philippines; Brisbane, Australia; Canton, China; Little America, Antarctica. (c) At the equinox (vertical rays of the sun at the equator): Tananarive, Malagasy; Cape Town,

South Africa; Madrid, Spain; Nairobi, Kenya; Murmansk, Soviet Union; Copenhagen, Denmark; Cairo, United Arab Republic. (*d*) To compare the possible amounts of photosynthesis in the plants per day, what additional information would you need?

3. Some problems concerning biomes: (*a*) Present evidence (other than Figure 8 · 8) for identifying the biome of your own locality. (*b*) In middle-latitude biomes many mammals hibernate in burrows; in tundra very few do. Explain. (*c*) Why is estivation unlikely to occur in tropical rain forest? (*d*) Describe some North American ecotones. (*e*) The amount of precipitation in a region does not by itself determine whether the region is desert. Most places in tundra receive less precipitation than do many of the most barren tropical deserts. Investigate the relationships between the climatic factors that produce arid regions.

4. In North America and Europe, a number of species of migratory birds are now seen at much higher latitudes during winter than forty to fifty years ago. How might you explain this?

5. Before Europeans settled the grasslands of Australia, kangaroos were the *ecological equivalents* there of the bison and pronghorns of the North American grasslands. In other words, all these animals played the same part in the community structure of their regions; all were the large first-order consumers, the grazing animals, of the biome. (*a*) What are the ecological equivalents of these animals in most of the Australian and North American grasslands today? (*b*) What were the ecological equivalents of these animals in the steppes of Asia, the pampa of Argentina, and the veldt of South Africa before these regions were

highly modified by man? (*c*) What are the ecological equivalents of these animals in the tundra? (*d*) In the desert of South Africa, what are the ecological equivalents of the cacti of North American deserts? (*e*) In the tropical forests of the Old World, what are the ecological equivalents of the hummingbirds of the New World tropical forests?

6. In this chapter the expansion of the geographical ranges of organisms was discussed. It is clear, however, that complete explanations of present ranges of organisms may depend also on explanations of the contraction of former ranges. What are some of the factors that might bring about contraction of ranges?

7. Some geologists support the theory of *continental drift*, which holds that the present arrangement of continents is different from what it was in the distant geological past. Investigate this theory —especially its use in explaining the geographical distribution of plants.

8. The dispersal of starlings in North America has been shown in Figure 8 · 44. Investigate these additional cases of dispersal: in North America—house sparrows, Japanese beetles, cotton-boll weevils, fungus of chestnut blight, gypsy moths; in Europe—muskrats, the Chinese mitten crab; in the islands of the Indian and Pacific oceans—giant African land snails.

9. Choose some small taxonomic groups (genera or families) that are present in your own state or locality. Investigate their distribution in the world as a whole, and construct maps to show this information. Try to explain the distribution shown on your maps.

10. What factors of the lunar environment must be overcome if man is to become an inhabitant of the moon?

## SUGGESTED READINGS

BARTHOLOMEW, G. A., and J. W. HUDSON. "Desert Ground Squirrels," *Scientific American*, November, 1961. Pp. 107–112+.

BATES, M. *The Forest and the Sea.* New York: Random House, Inc., 1960. Chapters 7 and 8. (A whole chapter on the tropical rain forest; then a contrasting chapter on biomes at middle latitudes. Fairly easy.)

ELTON, C. S. *The Ecology of Invasions by Animals and Plants.* New York: John Wiley & Sons, Inc., 1958. (Includes many examples of dispersal in recent times; explains the ecological principles involved in dispersal and the establishment of organisms in new regions.)

GLEASON, H. A., and A. CRONQUIST. *The Natural Geography of Plants.* New York: Columbia University Press, 1964. (The principles of plant distribution, with examples mostly from North America. Of medium difficulty.)

HAAG, W. G. "The Bering Strait Land Bridge," *Scientific American,* January, 1962. Pp. 112–120+.

HARTESVELDT, R. J. "Fire Ecology of the Giant Sequoias," *Natural History,* December, 1964. Pp. 12–19.

KENDEIGH, S. C. *Animal Ecology.* Englewood Cliffs, N.J.: Prentice-Hall, Inc., 1961. Chapters 22–27. (A thorough description of biomes and their subdivisions. Fairly advanced.)

KILBURN, P. D. "Floras of the Tundra," *Natural History,* August, 1965. Pp. 52–59.

LEOPOLD, A. S., and EDITORS OF LIFE. *The Desert.* New York: Time, Inc. Book Division, 1961. (This book does for deserts what McCormick's does for forests. Easy.)

LÜSCHER, M. "Air-conditioned Termite Nests," *Scientific American,* July, 1961. Pp. 138–145.

McCORMICK, J. *The Life of the Forest.* New York: McGraw-Hill Book Co., Inc., 1966. (Emphasis on North American forests. Abundant illustrations. Easy.)

ODUM, E. P. In Collaboration with HOWARD T. ODUM. *Fundamentals of Ecology.* Philadelphia: W. B. Saunders Co., 1959. Pp. 383–418. (A somewhat less complete coverage than Kendeigh's, but with a broader viewpoint. Fairly advanced.)

PRUITT, W. O. "Animals in the Snow," *Scientific American,* January, 1960. Pp. 60–68.

SIMPSON, G. G., and W. S. BECK. *Life: An Introduction to Biology.* 2nd ed. New York: Harcourt, Brace & World, Inc., 1965. Pp. 705–720. (Brief but well-expressed descriptions of biomes, with some consideration of the principles of biome distribution.)

# Patterns
# of Life
# in the
# Water

## AQUATIC ECOSYSTEMS

Man is a terrestrial organism. Therefore, most of us are better acquainted with other terrestrial organisms than we are with aquatic organisms. But aquatic environments occupy more space on this earth than do terrestrial ones; they greatly influence adjacent terrestrial environments; and they play important parts in the great cycles of chemical substances. So biologists must attempt to understand aquatic environments and the organisms that inhabit them—aquatic ecosystems.

Environmental conditions a thousand meters beneath the surface of the open ocean must certainly differ from those in a roadside puddle that dries up in a few days. Yet there is life in both of these extreme examples of aquatic ecosystems and in a multitude of intermediate ones. To make sense of the many observations that have resulted from studies of diverse aquatic ecosystems, we must again seek patterns—just as we did for terrestrial ecosystems.

intermediate: between extremes

The distinction between ocean waters and inland waters may serve as a beginning. In general, we can think of the ocean waters as those forming the great interconnecting system that surrounds the continents and in which the tides are clearly evident. Inland waters are the waters on the surface of the land and generally above the level of the oceans (though there are some exceptions); they tend to flow downward, to the level of the oceans. Ocean waters usually contain a considerable amount of dissolved minerals; inland waters usually contain very little. But again there are exceptions.

## INLAND WATERS

Inland waters are affected in many ways by the surrounding land, but they also have their own environmental characteristics. Puddles in South Dakota, Germany, and Australia may have very much the same kinds of protists living in them. And though the delta of the Nile is surrounded by desert and the delta of the Mississippi by forest, environmental conditions within the slow-moving, warm, muddy waters of both places are similar. Therefore, ecologists are inclined to consider the ecosystems of inland water separately from the biomes surrounding them.

delta: so called because the deposit of soil at a river mouth is usually triangular, resembling the Greek letter "delta" (see page 41)

### KINDS OF INLAND WATERS

Inland waters may be grouped into two general classes: standing waters and flowing waters. As usual in ecological classification, the boundary between these two classes is not sharp. A pond is an example of standing water. But most ponds are fed by springs or brooks and most have an outlet; so some current of changing water passes through them. On the other hand, a river is an example of flowing water; yet in some places a river may have such a slow current that careful observation is necessary to detect it.

Standing inland waters differ in size, in age, and in many abiotic environmental characteristics. They range in size from roadside puddles to the Caspian Sea. Puddles may last for only a few days or weeks; ponds, for a few hundred to a few thousand years. In general lakes are older, though the waters of some tropical "lakes" disappear completely during each dry season. Standing waters vary from very shallow to very deep, from clear to muddy, and from fresh to salty.

A good atlas will be useful while you study this chapter.

In flowing waters we roughly distinguish between brooks, creeks, and rivers. The size and age of flowing waters are unimportant. Speed of flow, clearness, oxygen content, and other chemical characteristics are used by *limnologists* in studying flowing-water ecosystems.

limnologists [lĭm nŏl' ə jists; Greek: *limne, marsh*]: scientists who study the biology of fresh waters

### PONDS

A pond is a convenient place to begin studying inland waters. In many parts of the United States, no natural ponds can be found. But where natural ponds are fewest, man has been most active in constructing artificial ones. For a general view of inland waters, it does not matter much whether a pond is natural or artificial. As an example, however, we shall look at a natural pond in a region where such ponds are numerous—the northeastern United States. As you read, try to compare this pond with one you know.

Bob and Ira Spring

Figure 9 · 1

A mountain pond (Washington State). Compare and contrast it with the pond in the northeastern United States.

**Approach to the pond.** We are standing on a hill overlooking the pond. The time is midsummer. Surrounding us are trees — mostly oaks, maples, or beeches. As we walk down the slope, mosquitoes start to annoy us. They began their life in the pond. Soon we leave the trees behind and enter a region of low shrubs. As we push our way through willows and alders, the ground becomes wet. Then the last shrubs are left behind and our feet sink into mud. Before us lies a mass of sedges and cattails.

Here land and water are difficult to separate. Dragonflies — lately emerged from the water — dart about; frogs sit on driftwood; a water snake slithers through the mixture of mud and water; a muskrat interrupts his meal of cattail stems, shuffles away, and dives noisily into the water just beyond our view.

With wading boots, we can follow the muskrat. We push on through the cattails and at last see the open-water surface. Here and there it is dotted with leaves of water lilies. With our boots in deep mud and with water lapping at knee level, we now have the pond ecosystem all about us.

**Pond producers.** In studying any ecosystem, the ecologist first looks for its source of energy. The most important producers in ponds are not the most obvious ones. The large emergent plants, such as cattails, that rim a pond are conspicuous. We saw a muskrat eating cattail stems. But these produce little of the food in the ecosystem. Indeed, in some ponds — especially in artificial ones — emergent plants may be scarce or absent.

emergent [ĭ mûr′ jənt; Latin: *ex,* out of, + *mergere,* to dip]: arising out of (here) water

Beyond the rim of emergent plants, we see many plants growing within the water itself — some floating on the surface, some submerged. Though such plants may become so numerous at times that their thick mass hampers human

submerged [Latin: *sub,* under, + *mergere*]

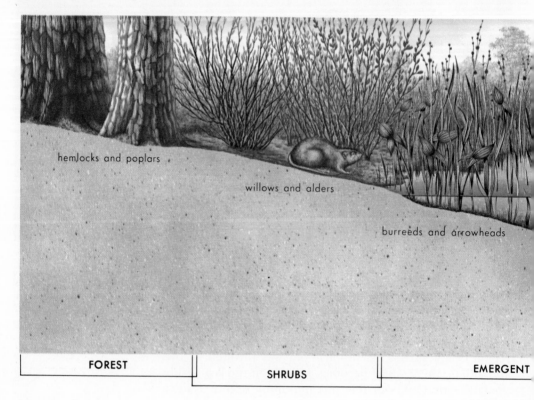

hemlocks and poplars

willows and alders

burreeds and arrowheads

| FOREST | SHRUBS | EMERGENT |

Figure 9 · 2

Cross section through the edge of a natural pond in the northeastern United States.

erratically [ĭ răt′ ĭk lī; Latin: errare, to wander]

swimmers, these are not really important pond producers either.

Rooted seed plants are usually absent from the centers of ponds, where the water may be more than 3 m deep. But in most ponds enough light to support photosynthesis reaches the bottom. There diatoms may become so plentiful that they tinge the mud golden-green. Filamentous algae—mostly Chlorophyta—grow in dense patches, waving back and forth in the currents. The producers on the bottom of the pond are more important than any others we have yet noted, but even they are not the main food source of the pond ecosystem.

Have you ever watched specks of dust dance in a bright beam of sunlight? In a beam of light shining into the waters of a pond, you can see erratically moving specks that resemble specks of dust in a sunbeam. But the specks in the water are not dust—they are living organisms. Among them are the real supporters of the pond ecosystem, the important producers.

If we view a sample of pond water through a microscope, we can see these organisms more clearly. Some are plants, some are protists, and some are animals. All are micro-

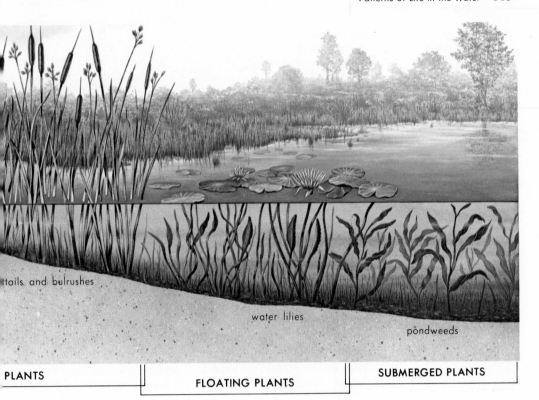

tails and bulrushes

water lilies

pondweeds

PLANTS    FLOATING PLANTS    SUBMERGED PLANTS

scopic or nearly so. And all can stay afloat, though few are really swimmers. They are carried about hither and thither by the currents in the pond—they are drifters. In the late nineteenth century, biologists began to study these drifters in European seas and lakes. From the Greek word for "drifter" or "wanderer," Victor Hensen, in 1887, coined the term by which they are collectively known—the *plankton*. Slowly, early limnologists began to realize that plankton organisms (*plankters*) made up for their smallness by their incredible numbers. Careful quantitative studies eventually showed that most food production in ponds and in most other bodies of water is the result of photosynthesis by plankters.

These producers are referred to collectively as the *phytoplankton*. Many are algae, but some are chlorophyll-bearing protists. The species making up the phytoplankton vary in abundance from one body of water to another, but diatoms are usually the most numerous. In some inland waters dinoflagellates also make up much of the phytoplankton. Neither diatoms nor dinoflagellates are conspicuous, but green algae may become so abundant in summer that a pond's whole surface becomes green. The "green scum" so

Victor Hensen: 1835–1924. German zoologist

incredible [Latin: *in-*, not, + *credare*, to believe]

phytoplankton [fī′ tō plăngk′- tan; Greek: *phyton*, a plant, + plankton]

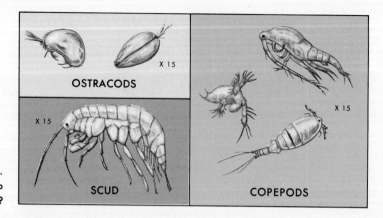

**Figure 9 · 3**

Some pond zooplankters. In what taxonomic group do you think they are placed?

detested by swimmers is only a sign that a pond has reached its annual peak of productivity.

**Pond consumers.** Since the majority of the pond producers are microscopic, we might expect the first-order consumers also to be small. Most of them are, and they form a part of the plankton—the *zooplankton*. There are protists—ciliates and flagellates; there are rotifers, often tiny as the protists; there is a great variety of tiny crustaceans. However, some first-order consumers in pond waters are not part of the plankton—for example, young fish, which are swimmers, not drifters, and mussels, which are bottom dwellers. Moreover, not all zooplankters are first-order consumers. Some small crustaceans eat consumers even smaller than themselves.

Most adult pond fishes are second- and third-order consumers. The smaller kinds, such as darters and sunfish, are

**Figure 9 · 4**

Some pond fish.

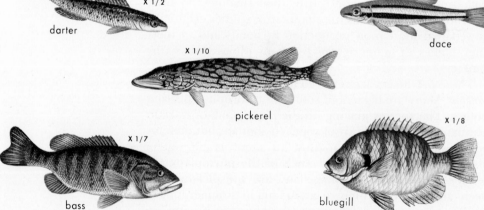

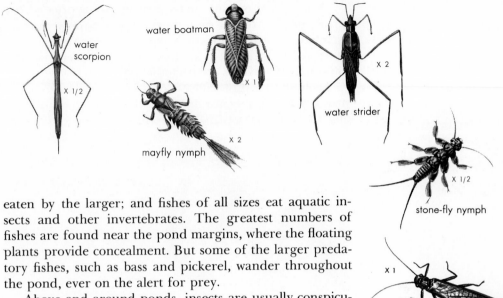

eaten by the larger; and fishes of all sizes eat aquatic insects and other invertebrates. The greatest numbers of
fishes are found near the pond margins, where the floating
plants provide concealment. But some of the larger predatory fishes, such as bass and pickerel, wander throughout
the pond, ever on the alert for prey.

   Above and around ponds, insects are usually conspicuous. Most of these began their lives within the pond, and
many spent most of their lives there. For example, only the
last few hours of a mayfly's life are spent in the air above
the pond. And even an adult mayfly may be returned to the
pond system if it is snapped up by a hungry fish.

**Figure 9 · 5**
**Some pond insects.**

**Figure 9 · 6**
**Terrestrial animals that de-
pend upon aquatic eco-
systems for food.**

   Frogs live largely on the insects that spend their early
lives in ponds. Water snakes consume fish and frogs. Herons and kingfishers among birds and otters among mammals are mostly consumers of fish. Such consumers, though
they spend much of their time on land, are truly part of
pond ecosystems, since their energy can be traced back to
the phytoplankton.

tubifex worms [tū′ bə fĕks; Latin: *tubus,* tube, + *facere,* to do, make]

Dead organisms sink, so large quantities of organic matter accumulate on the bottom of a pond. Saprovores such as tubifex worms (phylum Annelida) burrow in this rich source of energy. As in all ecosystems, however, the most important saprovores are bacteria and fungi.

Such diversity of consumers—from protists to mammals—indicates the vast amounts of energy that are available from the phytoplankton producers.

Figure 9 · 7
Tubifex worm.

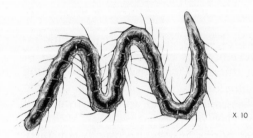

X 10

## INVESTIGATION 9.1

### SUCCESSION IN A FRESHWATER ECOSYSTEM

#### INTRODUCTION AND PURPOSE

In most ecosystems ecological succession occurs so slowly that studying it is difficult. However, in such freshwater ecosystems as puddles and seasonal ponds, succession can be detected in rather short periods of time. And miniature examples of these ecosystems can even be studied in the laboratory. In this investigation you have two problems: (*a*) What successional stages occur in small aquatic ecosystems? (*b*) What effects do differences in the original populations have on the course of succession?

#### MATERIALS AND EQUIPMENT

Wide-mouth jars (about 1-liter capacity), 3
Glass-marking crayon
Debris from ditch or pond
Sterilized pond water, about 6 liters
Aquarium gravel
Pond organisms (algae, small crayfish, snails, water beetles, duckweed, etc.)
Glass plates (somewhat larger than jar mouths), 3
Distilled water, about 1 liter
Microscope slides
Cover slips
Medicine droppers
Monocular microscopes
Stereomicroscopes or hand lenses

A

B

C

D

Figure 9 · 8
Diagrammatic history of a northern pond. Using all of your ecological knowledge, describe the successions of terrestrial and aquatic ecosystems that occur during such a change.

## PROCEDURE

Using glass-making crayon, label three wide-mouth jars *A, B,* and *C.* Place a water-level mark on each jar, at a height equal to two-thirds of the distance from the bottom. Also label each jar with the date. In Jar A place an assortment of twigs, dead leaves, and small stones obtained from a puddle or pond that has dried up; then gently add sterilized pond water until it reaches the marked level. Into Jar B pour sterilized pond water to the marked level. In Jar C place enough aquarium gravel to form a layer about 2 cm deep; then add unsterilized pond water to the marked level and a number of small organisms collected from a pond.

Record the macroscopic appearance of each jar's contents. Use a microscope to examine a sample drop from each jar. By means of sketches record any organisms you see.

Cover each jar with a glass plate. Each cover should be held up on one side by a matchstick or piece of cardboard, so that air can enter and leave the jars. Place the jars in a well-lighted location. Maintain the water level in all jars throughout the study by adding distilled water as needed.

Examine the jars macroscopically each day for the next three or four days. Watch for an appearance of cloudiness in the water and of scum on the surface. When cloudiness appears, again examine a drop of the water under the microscope, recording organisms by sketches. Stereomicroscopes or hand lenses will help you to examine small macroscopic

organisms. Throughout this investigation begin the record of each observation with the observation day (Day 0, Day 1, etc.) and the letter of the jar observed.

After the first few days examine the jars both macroscopically and microscopically each week for five or six weeks.

### STUDYING THE DATA

Arrange the data in chart form, listing the three jars on the vertical axis and the observation days on the horizontal axis.

• Which jar most closely resembles a permanent pond? (1)   • Which jar most closely resembles a temporary pond or puddle? (2)   • Can any of the jars be considered as a control? If so, which one? (3)   • On what day were organisms noted in Jar A? (4)   • Where did they probably come from? (5)   • How soon were organisms noted in Jar B? (6) • Where did they probably come from? (7)   • Did any organisms originally in Jar C disappear during the time of study? If so, what were they, and how can you account for their disappearance? (8)   • Did any organisms appear in Jars A and B and then disappear? If so, what were they, and how can you account for their disappearance? (9)

### CONCLUSIONS

• Did ecological succession occur? If so, in which jar was it most evident? (10)   • According to your data from this investigation, in which kind of natural freshwater community would succession be likely to occur most rapidly? (11)

### LAKES

The word "lake" usually implies a larger body of water than the word "pond," but there is much overlap in usage.

To the limnologist, a pond is a body of water so shallow that light penetrates to the bottom; a lake, on the other hand, has depths that remain always dark.

If a lake has no outlet, minerals washed in from the surrounding land accumulate. In arid regions this process is speeded up by the high rate of evaporation. The water becomes saturated with minerals, the most abundant usually being sodium chloride (NaCl), common table salt, as in the Great Salt Lake of Utah. The result is an environment unfavorable to almost all organisms. Some parts of the Great Salt Lake are beyond the influence of the freshwater streams that empty into it; in these parts only adult brine shrimp (*Artemia*), a few species of blue-green algae, and two species of brine flies can survive.

The eggs of brine shrimp, with directions for hatching, can be bought in most pet shops. Can you form and test some hypotheses concerning optimum conditions for the hatching of these organisms?

Most lakes have outlets and their waters do not accumulate minerals. The largest of all freshwater lakes is Lake Superior. It covers an area about the size of South Carolina but has a maximum depth of only 410 m. The two deepest lakes are Baikal (1750 m), in Siberia, and Tanganyika (1449 m), in Africa. Lake Superior is perhaps ten to twenty thousand years old, but both Baikal and Tanganyika were formed millions of years ago. Such wide variation in the size, depth, and age of lakes means that conditions for life in lake waters also vary greatly.

Lakes Baikal and Tanganyika illustrate an abiotic factor that is more important in lake ecosystems than in the shallow waters of ponds. Baikal has animals adapted to conditions in its deep water (at least down to 600 m), but no animals are found below 60 m in Tanganyika. How can this be explained?

The difference depends on the oxygen available in each lake. Oxygen dissolves very readily. Some oxygen in the water comes from photosynthesizing organisms near the surface, where light penetrates. Most of it comes from the air. Dissolved oxygen can move very slowly downward from the surface by a process called *diffusion;* but to penetrate very far, it must be mixed into the deeper waters. On the oceans, such mixing can be brought about by winds as they stir up large waves. But lake waves are rarely large enough to be effective mixers.

diffusion [dĭ fū′ zhən; Latin: *dis-*, apart, + *fundere, to pour*]: For a discussion of this process, see pages 387–388.

A different factor is important in carrying oxygen deep into Baikal. At 4°C, water is denser than at any other temperature. Therefore, when the temperature of the surface water falls to 4°C, the surface water sinks, forcing warmer water upward from below. Every autumn, as the surface of Baikal cools, there is a massive turnover of water. This same process occurs in all lakes and ponds where there is a wide difference in temperature between the seasons. In this way, the depths of such inland waters are supplied with oxygen. No such turnover takes place in Tanganyika, because the surface waters there never become much cooler than the waters beneath; oxygen is mixed only as far down as wave action stirs the water. Since animals require oxygen, they cannot live in the deeper parts of Lake Tanganyika.

Although animals are absent from the deeper waters of some lakes, anaerobic organisms are probably present on all lake bottoms. There organic matter that saprovores can use as food is plentiful; it continually drifts down from above as organisms in the upper waters die and their bodies sink.

Producer systems in lakes do not differ in general from those in ponds, except that the larger and deeper the lake, the more important the phytoplankton.

*Why is this so?*

### FLOWING-WATER ECOSYSTEMS

*Review the water cycle, Figure 1 · 15.*

Some of the water that falls on land runs directly into lakes, ponds, and streams, and some immediately evaporates. But much of it soaks into the ground, the proportion depending on the vegetation, the soil, and the slope of the land. Water that soaks into the earth reappears, usually in springs. From springs its course downward toward the sea may be short or long. Indeed, some springs are located at the very edge of the sea. But some springs in the Nile River system are more than 6400 km from the sea.

**Headwaters.** Most upland brooks receive their water directly from springs. Such waters are usually cool—though some hot springs do exist. Spring-fed brooks often flow down steep slopes. Tumbling through rapids and waterfalls, the water traps large numbers of air bubbles. From these oxygen can easily dissolve into the water. Since cool waters can hold relatively large quantities of gases in solution, brooks are usually well oxygenated.

*Why do such waters lack plankton?*

In the turbulent waters of brooks, plankton is absent. Producers are species that grow attached to stones or other objects: green algae, diatoms, and water mosses. Sometimes these organisms completely cover the stream bottom, providing both food and shelter for many kinds of insect larvae, which, in turn, are food for small fish.

The food supply of a brook ecosystem does not entirely consist of things that grow in the water itself. Land organisms—most notably, insects—are continually falling in and contributing to the diet of stream inhabitants. And dead organic matter is washed into streams with every rain. Anything not used immediately, however, is washed downward. Thus, in the headwaters of a stream system there is very little food for saprovores to work on.

U.S. Forest Service

**Figure 9 · 9**
Headwater stream (California). In addition to springs, where may such streams get their water?

**Middle reaches.** Farther downstream the water usually moves more slowly. Stream beds are wider, and the total volume of water is larger. Some sediments are deposited. Organic matter accumulates, providing food for saprovores. As the width of the stream increases, the amount of shading by trees along its banks decreases, and direct sunlight reaches most of the water surface.

Increased light increases the rate of photosynthesis. Thus biological productivity along the middle reaches is greater than in the headwaters. In slower waters some plankton organisms live, though many are swept downstream. Rooted seed plants similar to those in ponds grow in sediments of the stream bottom; they, too, may be washed away during floods.

Because of greater productivity, the middle reaches of a stream support a large number of consumers. On the bottom are mussels and snails, crayfish, and large numbers of different kinds of insect larvae. Dependent on these bottom dwellers are such higher-order consumers as catfish, turtles, bass, and garfish. And leeches parasitize these.

**Lower reaches.** As a river approaches the sea, it usually moves more and more slowly, dropping larger and

**Figure 9 · 10**

Where three major ecosystems meet: land, river, and ocean at the delta of the Mississippi.

erode [Latin: *ex*, out, off, + *rodere*, to gnaw]

levees [lĕv′ ĭz; Latin: *levare*, to raise]

penetration [Latin: *penitus*, inward]: passing into something

Many ancient riverside civilizations were agricultural. How did river ecosystems contribute to agriculture?

larger quantities of sediments. Thus, near its mouth a river often builds up land instead of eroding it. Banks along the lower reaches may actually become higher than the land behind them. During floods a river often breaks through these natural levees; in this way it may shift back and forth across its valley from one year to another. It is difficult to tell where the river ecosystem ends and terrestrial ecosystems begin.

In the lower reaches of a river, waters are usually muddy. This cuts down the penetration of sunlight and thus prevents growth of photosynthetic organisms in deeper parts of the channel. In the surface waters, however, plankton organisms are more numerous than farther upstream, though they are less abundant than in ponds. In the swampy lands along a river, many emergent and floating plants grow. Fruits, seeds, and other parts of these plants are swept into the river during floods, contributing to the food supply.

Consumers in the lower reaches are varied and numerous. Zooplankters are food for larger predators. Mollusks, crustaceans, and fish often grow large. In tropical rivers crocodiles are common. Many terrestrial birds and mammals obtain their food from river waters, just as many do from margins of ponds. And since ancient days man also has taken advantage of the abundant food in large rivers; many civilizations began along rivers.

### INLAND WATERS AND MAN

Man has had great effect on ecosystems of inland waters, just as he has had on land ecosystems. In both, his

activities have benefited some organisms and caused others
to disappear.

**Drainage.**   Marshes, ponds, and shallow lakes are basins where organic and mineral matter constantly accumulates. To channel such substances into his crops, man need
only remove the thin layer of water and plow the muck to
mix air into it. Crops then thrive. It is no wonder, therefore, that man has drained inland waters wherever possible.

With the invention of power machinery, man's ability
to drain marshes, ponds, and lakes increased enormously.
In the first three decades of this century, there was a
steady decrease in natural water areas in many parts of
the United States, especially in the grasslands of Minnesota
and the Dakotas. An unfortunate effect of this drainage
was a decrease in duck populations; the grassland ponds
and marshes had been the main breeding areas for many
species of ducks. But the drained areas have added considerably to the human food supply.

**Artificial ponds and lakes.**   If you stand on one of the
foothills of the Rockies in Colorado and look eastward, you
see the sun reflected on surfaces of dozens of ponds. But a
hundred years ago you would have seen nothing but
short-grass plain, spreading to the horizon.

Although drainage of standing waters continues, the
surface area of the inland waters of the United States has
actually increased during the last forty years. This has resulted from construction of dams, large and small, across
running waters.

Some dams are erected solely for providing a fall of
water to turn electric generators. Usually, especially in the
western states, they also are intended to store spring flood-
waters for irrigation in the summer. Still other purposes

Figure 9 · 11

Large reservoir, Lake Mead
(Nevada-Arizona). Even if
shore slopes are gentle,
such power and irrigation
reservoirs seldom have much
emergent vegetation. Can
you see why?

Josef Muench

John H. Gerard from National Audubon Society

Figure 9 · 12

Farm pond in a pasture. How does use by cattle affect the pond ecosystem?

Figure 9 · 13

Diagram of sewage pollution in a stream. Organisms are not drawn to scale, and distances are greatly decreased.

may be involved in large-scale dam construction. Whatever the purpose, the result is a lake—standing water where once there were land and stream. Such major changes in environment bring about major changes in biotic communities. A large dam may destroy fish (such as shad and salmon) that run up rivers to lay eggs in headwater streams, but it may greatly increase the habitat favorable for catfish.

Much of the new inland-water area is made up of small farm ponds, none of which cover more than a few thousand square meters. The number of farm ponds has par-

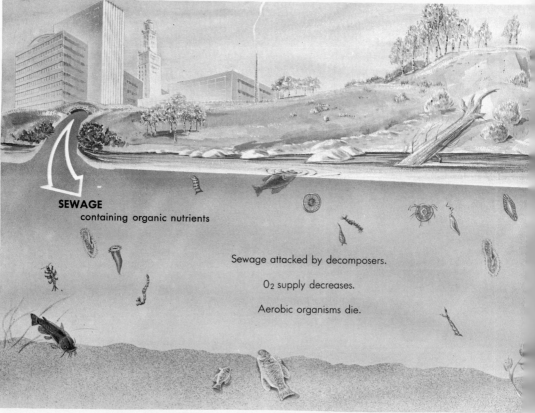

SEWAGE
containing organic nutrients

Sewage attacked by decomposers.

O₂ supply decreases.

Aerobic organisms die.

ticularly increased in regions where natural ponds are few. Some are dug merely to provide a supply of water in case of fire. But by and large, farm ponds are constructed with more thought to biological use than large reservoirs are. Often one purpose is to produce fish for food or sport — or both.

*How might a farmer increase the fish crop of his pond?*

**Pollution.** Man has straightened streams, dredged them deeper, and attempted to confine them with levees. His greatest influence on flowing-water ecosystems, however, has been through his use of them to wash away unwanted substances. Such substances are of many kinds; but most are harmful to living things in the waters and to living things on the banks, including man himself. Streams containing such harmful materials are said to be *polluted*.

One of the major pollutants is sewage. A small amount of sewage in a large stream may act as fertilizer, increasing the amount of life by providing materials for the growth of producer organisms. But if much sewage is emptied into a stream, most organisms will be unfavorably affected. In attacking the organic matter in sewage, saprovores use up

Sewage decreases.

O$_2$ supply increases.

Phytoplankton increases.

Aerobic consumers increase.

much of the oxygen in the stream. The resulting scarcity may favor anaerobic protists, but it is disastrous for all organisms that require oxygen.

Some pollutants are harmful to all organisms. From abandoned coal mines in northern Pennsylvania, acids have seeped into nearby streams in large quantities. These streams flow into the Susquehanna River—and now parts of the river are almost sterile. A few substances from industrial plants may be nearly as poisonous.

In recent years an entirely new kind of pollutant has been produced—one that is sure to become more abundant in the years ahead. This is the water that has been used to cool atomic reactors. Such water is very warm. When emptied into a stream, it produces abrupt temperature changes that are difficult for many aquatic organisms to tolerate. Further, such water may contain radioactive substances. Although such substances usually occur in small amounts, they can accumulate in the bodies of stream organisms, harming them and organisms that eat them.

## THE OCEANS

About 70 percent of the earth's surface is covered by the oceans. Further, if all the land were leveled off into the

Figure 9 · 14

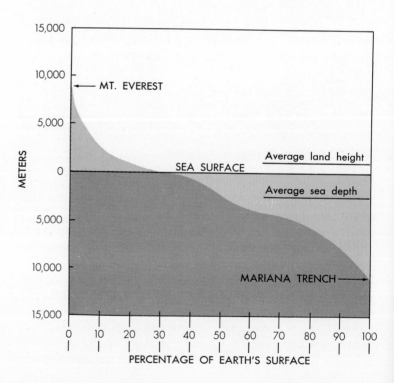

oceanic depths, leaving the earth with a smooth surface, a layer of water 2.5 km deep would cover the world. An observer from another planet might easily conclude that the oceans are the most important part of the earth. But we are land animals, and we find it difficult to adopt this view.

## THE OCEAN ENVIRONMENT

Knowledge of the oceans has grown rather slowly. Man has been moving about on the ocean surface for quite a while, and many peoples learned long ago to get a large part of their food from the sea. But until rather recently observations of the oceans were limited to the surface and the shore. Now, with new methods of exploration, man can penetrate the depths and live and work in capsules far beneath the surface. At last he is directly observing the ocean environment from within.

**Salinity.** Ocean environments differ in many ways from inland-water environments. Perhaps the principal difference lies in the chemical composition of the water itself. Seawater is about 3.5 percent minerals, or as *oceanographers* express it, about 35 parts per thousand. Most inland waters contain only minute amounts of dissolved minerals; the exceptions, such as Great Salt Lake, contain amounts of minerals much greater than in seawater.

The minerals dissolved in seawater are mostly substances called salts; therefore, the mineral content of seawater is referred to as *salinity*. Sodium chloride (table salt) is the most familiar salt. It is also the most common salt in the sea, accounting for over 75 percent of the dissolved minerals.

salinity [sə lĭn′ ə tĭ; Latin: *sal, salt*]

Salinities of surface waters vary somewhat above or below the average of 35 parts per thousand. There are also variations at different depths in the great ocean basins. At the surface, salinity is highest in the "horse latitudes," where evaporation is great and rainfall is low; salinity at the surface is lowest near the poles, where the seawater is diluted by fresh water from melting ice. The Red Sea, with very little inflow of fresh water and with high evaporation, has salinities of over 45 parts per thousand. The Baltic Sea, on the other hand, with a large inflow of fresh water and with rather low evaporation, has low salinities—less than 10 parts per thousand in many places.

horse latitudes: either of two belts of calms or light winds, situated at about 30° N. and 30° S. latitude

Formerly, geologists assumed that the waters of the oceans were once fresh and gradually became salty through the addition of minerals that washed in from the land. According to this reasoning, the present salinities in the sea could have been acquired in a few million years. But other evidence (mostly from rocks and the fossils they contain) in-

| ELEMENT | PARTS PER THOUSAND OF SEAWATER |
|---------|:-------------------------------:|
| Chlorine | 18.98 |
| Sodium | 10.56 |
| Magnesium | 1.27 |
| Sulfur | .88 |
| Calcium | .40 |
| Potassium | .38 |
| Bromine | .065 |
| Carbon | .028 |
| Strontium | .013 |
| Boron | .005 |
| Silicon | .003 |
| Fluorine | .001 |
| Nitrogen (compounds) | .0007 |
| Aluminum | .0005 |
| Rubidium | .0002 |
| Lithium | .0001 |
| Phosphorus | .0001 |
| Barium | .00005 |
| Iodine | .00005 |

**Figure 9 · 15**

Average mineral content of seawater. These elements occur as compounds; elemental nitrogen and oxygen dissolved from the air are not included.

The shells of most sea animals are mostly made of calcium carbonate. How does the existence of sea animals affect the supply of calcium ions in seawater?

dicates that the seas have had a rather high salinity for hundreds of millions of years. It seems, then, that the substances being washed into the sea every year have only a slight effect on the composition of seawater. The minerals in seawater, in other words, are not a mere accumulation of things washed in from the land. Rather, seawater represents a steady state: substances are continually added, but substances are continually removed. Seawater is the environment of marine organisms, but it is also the product of the activities of these organisms. The seas, like the atmosphere, would undoubtedly have a much different composition if life were absent.

**Other abiotic factors.** Climatic factors have much less importance in the oceans than on land. Surface temperatures do vary greatly—from slightly below 0°C in antarctic and arctic waters to 28°C in equatorial waters. Differences in surface temperatures influence the distribution of organisms living in surface waters or near shores. Reef-forming corals, for instance, will not grow in waters where the temperature falls below 20°C. At a depth of 200 m, however, the pole-to-equator temperature range is only 0° to 22°C, and at greater depths temperature differences disappear almost entirely.

The amount of light energy available to photosynthetic organisms is greatest at the surface and decreases rapidly with depth of water. The turbidity of the water affects the rate at which light decreases; in clear water light penetrates much deeper than in turbid water.

Ocean currents bring about the distribution of chemical compounds useful to organisms. Currents also affect water temperatures and salinities at any given place in the ocean. And currents, in turn, are affected by the world pattern of winds and by the rotation of the earth.

Salinity, temperature, light, current—on the basis of these and other factors oceanographers are able to recognize many marine ecosystems. It is possible to group these ecosystems in several ways. One way distinguishes three major oceanic regions: the open sea, the great depths, and the coastal waters.

turbidity [tûr bĭd' ə tĭ;  Latin: *turbare*, to disturb]: In disturbed waters sediments do not settle out; hence "turbidity" has come to mean cloudiness.

### THE OPEN SEA

The chief producers of the open sea are diatoms, other kinds of microscopic algae, and dinoflagellates. Upon this phytoplankton the entire life of this ecosystem depends. Upon it the zooplankton depends directly, and from it extend food chains of varying lengths—to tuna, sharks, whales, and oceanic birds, such as albatrosses.

Many efforts have been made to determine the density of plankton populations. Perhaps the most accurate results have come from the marine laboratory at Plymouth, England. The ocean water used in the investigations there

Douglas P. Wilson

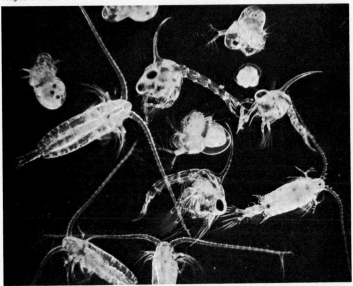

Figure 9 · 16

Marine zooplankters from the English Channel. Compare with Figure 9 · 3.

Figure 9 · 17

A plankton net being cast from the *Horizon,* research vessel of the Scripps Institution of Oceanography, California.

M. Woodbridge Williams

contained, at the very least, four and a half million phytoplankters in each liter of water! At present, oceanographers do not know enough to give accurate averages for the ocean as a whole. But the seas, like the land, vary greatly in productivity. The controlling factors in the sea, as in many places on land, may be the availability of a few important chemical elements, especially phosphorus and nitrogen, which are not abundant in marine waters. The teeming phytoplankton may use up these elements locally or seasonally, so that continuing growth depends on materials washing in from the land or welling up from the depths. Thus, for chemical reasons some areas, such as the Grand Banks of Newfoundland or the North Sea, are very productive; others, such as the Sargasso Sea, in the Atlantic, are extremely poor.

How does this relate to the location of great ocean fisheries?

The phytoplankton, of course, needs light, so its vertical distribution depends on how far light penetrates seawater. This depends on several factors, such as the angle at which the light strikes the water surface, the condition of the surface (whether smooth or broken by waves), and the transparency of the water itself. Within the water the longer wavelengths of light are absorbed most rapidly, which means that the reds and yellows disappear first, and the blues and violets penetrate farthest. Despite the deep penetration of blue light (550 m near Bermuda), phytoplankton is largely limited to the upper 70 m of water. All life below depends on organic materials that sink down from this surface zone.

transparency [Latin: *trans,* through, + *parere,* to appear]: Transparency and turbidity are inversely related: as one increases the other decreases.

## THE OCEAN DEPTHS

For a long time biologists thought that life could not exist in the dark and cold ocean depths because of the tremendous pressure of the water. The first clear evidence that this was a wrong assumption came in 1858, when one of the marine telegraph cables in the Mediterranean Sea broke and was hauled up for repair. It was encrusted with bottom-living animals, particularly sponges, some of which had grown at depths as great as 2000 m.

Further investigation revealed that water pressure in itself has no ill effect on organisms, provided they contain no spaces filled with air or other gases. The pressure is exerted equally on all sides and is the same inside and outside the organism. After all, we land organisms live under air pressure of 1000 g per cm², but we cannot feel it.

**Exploring the depths.** Though we do not normally notice air pressure, we have trouble with water pressure because we carry air into the water with us. Therefore, without using special apparatus, man can observe directly only the top 30 m of the ocean, and even this limit is reached only by people with special training and skill. After many attempts to devise apparatus that would enable divers to go deeper and stay down longer, success came in the nineteenth century, with the perfection of the diving helmet and air pump. In the twentieth century Jacques Cousteau's invention of the aqualung has allowed greater freedom of movement by eliminating the need for a hose connection to the surface. But none of these devices enables the diver to descend beyond a depth of 100 m.

Jacques Cousteau [zhăk kōos-tō']: 1910———. French oceanographer. The aqualung is a device for breathing under water.

In 1935 William Beebe and Otis Barton constructed their bathysphere for deep-sea observation. This was a heavy steel sphere with thick quartz windows, built to withstand the great pressures of the deep and equipped with compressed oxygen and chemicals to absorb excess carbon dioxide and moisture within. It was lowered into the sea with a cable. In the bathysphere Beebe was able to descend to about 1000 m in waters off Bermuda and report for the first time direct observations on living things at such depths in the sea.

William Beebe [bē' bǐ]: 1877–1962. American zoologist and naturalist. Otis Barton. 1901———. American engineer and deep-sea explorer

bathysphere [băth' ə sfïr'; Greek: bathos, depth, + sphere]

In 1958 Auguste Piccard designed the bathyscaphe, a vessel that can descend to great depths and come up under its own power. Electric motors make possible a limited amount of horizontal movement. The bathyscaphe combines a sphere similar to Beebe's bathysphere and—above this—a sort of "blimp"; bouyancy is achieved by filling the blimp with gasoline. Several tons of iron filings are used as ballast. On January 23, 1960, Jacques Piccard (son of Au-

Auguste Piccard [pē' kär']: 1884–1962. Belgian physicist

bathyscaphe [băth' ə skăf'; Greek: bathos, + scaphe, boat]

Figure 9 · 18
The bathyscaphe *Trieste*.

U.S. Navy

guste) and Lieutenant Don Walsh of the United States
Navy descended in the bathyscaphe *Trieste* to the bottom of
Mariana Trench, in the Pacific Ocean — 10,860 m below the
surface. In doing so, they reached the deepest place in the
oceans and the last unexplored geographic frontier.

U.S. Navy

Figure 9 · 19
Supplies arriving inside
*Sealab II*, a chamber in
which men lived beneath
the sea for forty-five days
in 1965. Men went out
through the hatch and at-
tached the block and tackle
to the supply container.

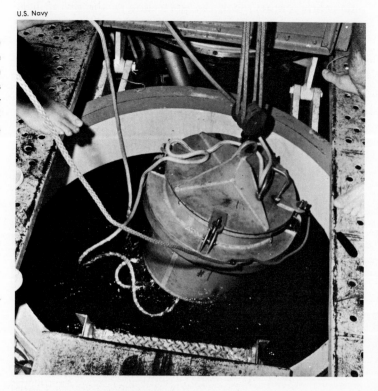

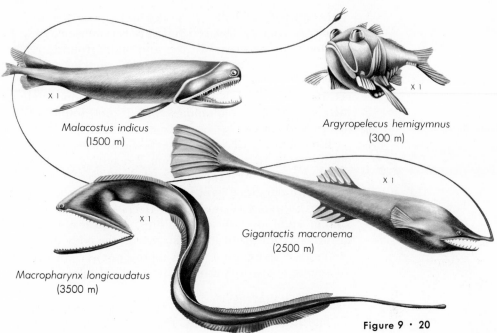

*Malacostus indicus*
(1500 m)

*Argyropelecus hemigymnus*
(300 m)

*Gigantactis macronema*
(2500 m)

*Macropharynx longicaudatus*
(3500 m)

**Figure 9 · 20**

Some fish of the ocean depths. Notice that they are small animals.

**Creatures of the depths.**    The ocean depths are a very special environment and require unusual adaptations if organisms are to survive and flourish there. The depths are cold and dark and quiet. There are no producers; all food must come from organic substances settling from the upper levels, so food is relatively scarce. And the adaptations that make possible life under the pressures of the deep also make ascent to upper levels fatal.

Fishes caught at great depths often appear (when brought to the surface) as though they had exploded. Why?

Diversity of organisms usually decreases as the depth increases. The number of individuals also decreases with depth, because life below the photosynthetic zone depends on food drifting down from above. And in general the greater the depth, the less the food supply.

Lamont Geological Observatory of Columbia Univ.

**Figure 9 · 21**

An acorn worm on the ocean bottom (South Pacific, depth about 4800 m).

bioluminescence [bī′ ō lōō′ mə-nĕs′ əns; Greek: *bios*, + *lumen*, light]

X 1/4

Figure 9 · 22

Squid.

Figure 9 · 23

Estuaries (Maryland). "Drowned" river valleys containing brackish waters form an ecosystem different from both marine and inland waters.

In the eternal night of the ocean depths, most animals are either black or dark red and have very sensitive eyes. In the unending darkness of caves and underground streams, however, most animals are white and blind. This difference is associated with *bioluminescence*—in the depths of the oceans, many animals have the ability to produce light in their bodies. But bioluminescence is not found in the blackness of caves.

Bioluminescence among deep-sea animals may serve one or more of several different functions: as a lure for prey, as an aid to escape, as a mark of recognition. The angler fish dangles a light in front of its mouth; apparently this lures unwary victims closer. Deep-sea shrimp and one kind of squid give off clouds of luminescent secretion when disturbed. Patterns of luminescence on the body may serve as marks of recognition in the depths, just as color patterns do among many organisms in the world of light.

### COASTAL WATERS

**The littoral zone.** With few exceptions, the ocean is relatively shallow near the continents. It is as though the continents were partially flooded, extending out a way under the surrounding waters. Such a submerged region is called the *continental shelf,* and it is generally defined as the ocean floor between the shore and a line where the average depth becomes greater than 200 m. The shelf tends to be widest at the mouths of large rivers and along areas of broad lowlands. It may be almost absent along mountainous coasts. Its average width is about 50 km.

Tom Hollyman from Photo Researchers

Burton McNeely

**Figure 9 · 24**
Life on a coral reef (Florida Keys). Corals, sponges, and the reef fishes are all conspicuous.

Many oceanographers call the waters on the continental shelf the *littoral zone* of the ocean. Here a considerable amount of light reaches the bottom. There is rarely enough light for vegetation at depths greater than 40 or 50 m, but in shallower waters a luxuriant growth of seaweeds is sometimes found. In middle and higher latitudes the most common and conspicuous ones are brown algae (Phaeophyta). Among these are the kelps, the giants among marine plants, which may reach a length of 35 m or more. There are no mosses or ferns in the sea, but about thirty species of seed plants have adapted to life in the marine environment.

littoral [lĭt′ ə rəl; Latin: *littus*, seashore, coast]

luxuriant   [lŭg zhoŏr′ ĭ ənt]: rich, abundant

In the littoral zone the nature of life on the bottom depends on physical characteristics—the presence of sand, rock, or mud, for example. Sandy bottoms generally occur where wave or current action washes away the finer particles. Plants are not usually abundant on such unstable bottoms. However, many kinds of animals burrow into the sand, especially crustaceans, mollusks, and annelid worms. There are also fishes, such as flounders, that partially or completely bury themselves in the sand. Mud bottoms have even larger numbers of burrowers, and most of the species are unlike those adapted to sand. Sea cucumbers, clams,

How might your knowledge of plants lead you to predict this fact?

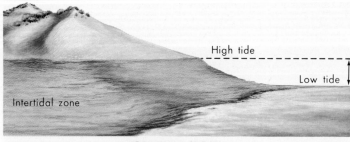

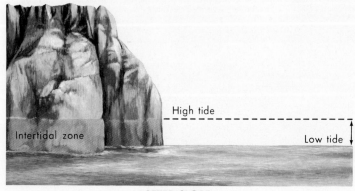

GRADUAL SLOPE

STEEP SLOPE

Figure 9 · 25

Even if vertical differences between high and low tide levels are alike, intertidal zones may differ greatly in extent.

and some crabs plow through the mud. On rocky bottoms currents are usually very strong, and many animals (barnacles and mussels, for example) attach themselves permanently to one place. Animals without shells hide in nooks and crannies among the rocks.

**The ocean edge.** Everywhere along the margins of the oceans we can see the effects of waves and tides. Tides vary greatly from place to place and, in a particular spot, from one time of month to another. In the Bay of Fundy in Nova Scotia, the maximum vertical change between high and low tides is 15.4 m. At the other extreme, the average tidal difference in the Mediterranean is only 35 cm. Wave action, too, varies greatly from day to day and place to place. Some coasts, such as parts of the American Pacific, are constantly pounded by heavy surf; others, especially in small, protected bays, may be no more exposed to wave action than are shores of small lakes.

Thus, along seacoasts there is an *intertidal zone*, where twice a day organisms are submerged and exposed. This is a difficult environment for life. Think of it: submerged in

Figure 9 · 26
Tide pool (California). On
rocky shores many aquatic
organisms live in pools left
above the waterline during
low tides.

William M. Graham from Photo Researchers

salt water; then, a few hours later, exposed to the air—to
bright, hot sun or freezing winds; and between times,
pounded by the advancing or retreating surf! On sandy
coasts life in this zone is limited to things that can burrow
in the sand or, like crabs, skitter over it. But on rocky
coasts life is surprisingly abundant. In cold waters brown
algae of various kinds are able to cling to the rocks, protected from the drying sun by a gelatinous coating. The
tangled algae then provide protection and support for
other algae, for protists, and for numerous animals. In
addition to these, barnacles, limpets, chitons, and snails
cling firmly to the rocks or the seaweeds, closing themselves
up tightly to survive the periods when they are exposed
to air.

Above the intertidal zone is the *spray zone*, where life of
the sea meets that of the land, and a few representatives
from each share common ground. Along beaches specialized land plants that resist the effects of salt spray reach out
to the farthest limit allowed by wave action. Shorebirds
forage in the debris left by the sea. Land crabs go down to

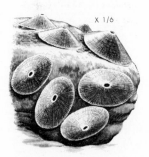

X 1/6

Figure 9 · 27
Limpets clinging to rocks
in the intertidal zone.

gelatinous [jĭ lăt′ ə nəs]: jelly-
like

debris    [də brē′,    dā′brē,
dĕb′rē]:  rubbish,  especially
that resulting from destruction

K. A. Wagner, Carolina Biological Supply Co.

**Figure 9 · 28**

High tide on a sandy beach (Florida). Here, by salt spray and beach erosion, the ocean gradually is pushing back the terrestrial ecosystem.

foray [fôr′ ā]: in warfare, a raid into enemy territory in search of plunder

the water to release their young, and sea turtles crawl out on the beach to bury their eggs. A few species of beetles inhabit beaches, and a few crustaceans hide in the debris. But for the most part, the spray zone is a "no man's land" into which only the daring make forays.

## INVESTIGATION 9.2

### EFFECTS OF SALINITY ON AQUATIC ORGANISMS

#### PURPOSE

This is an experimental investigation. Study the procedure and then set up an appropriate hypothesis before you begin work.

#### MATERIALS AND EQUIPMENT
(per pair of students)

Medicine dropper
Microscope slides
Cover slips
Living specimens of small aquatic organisms
Monocular microscope
Paper towels
Sodium chloride solutions (1%, 3%, and 5%)

#### PROCEDURE

Using a medicine dropper, place a drop of water containing the organism you are to study on a slide. Add a cover slip. Observe the organism for a few minutes to determine its normal appearance and actions. You may slow down the movement of some kinds of protists by adding to the water a few wisps of cotton or a bit of shredded paper towel. Record the name of the organism.

At one edge of the cover slip, place a drop of 1% salt solution. Draw the salt solution under the cover slip by holding a small piece of paper towel at the opposite edge of the slip. As the salt solution moves under the cover slip, observe carefully how the organism reacts. Notice changes in movements and changes in shape. Record the concentration (percentage) of the solution and the reactions observed. Continue observations until no new responses are observed. Replace the salt solution with water from the original culture in the same way you added the salt solution. • Are you making any assumption when doing this? If so, what?(1)   Record any observations that indicate recovery.

Repeat the procedure, using 3% salt solution. Repeat it with 5%.

## STUDYING THE DATA

Variability among individuals of a species in response to an environmental factor is common in biology. Therefore, all students who work with the same organism should discuss their results together. • Did all the individuals of the species react in the same way? If not, what differences were noted?(2) • Did the kind of reaction differ with different salt solutions? Try to explain any differences.(3) • If the organism failed to recover, how can you explain this?(4) • Which organism was most tolerant to change in salt concentration?(5) • Which organism was least tolerant?(6) • What kind of aquatic habitat do you think each of the organisms normally inhabits?(7)

## CONCLUSION

• Which of your data support the hypothesis you set up before beginning work?(8) • Do you have any data that tend to weaken your hypothesis? If so, which data?(9) • Taking all your data into account, restate your hypothesis in the form of a conclusion to the experiment.(10)

### FOR FURTHER INVESTIGATION

All the organisms in this exercise are small. Many larger animals (salmon, for example) regularly move from marine water into fresh water (or vice versa), apparently without harm; others cannot tolerate much change in salinity. You can devise means of testing the salinity tolerance of macroscopic aquatic animals such as crayfish, goldfish, guppies, or snails, using the principles employed in this exercise. If you use a marine species (for example, a clam worm) in your experiments, how should you modify your procedure? Caution: It is not necessary to kill the animals used in your experiments. Whenever they show signs of discomfort, return them to a less concentrated salinity.

Life in inland waters, while related to life on the surrounding land, has so many special characteristics that it is convenient to consider it separately. Inland-water ecosystems may be classified according to whether or not the water is flowing. In size, waters in basins range from puddles through ponds to lakes; flowing waters range from brooks to rivers. With few exceptions, inland waters are fresh waters, and, again with a few exceptions, they eventually flow down to the sea.

The chief producer organisms of the inland waters are microscopic algae and protists that float about in the water, the phytoplankton. Most of the first-order consumers are part of the floating, microscopic zooplankton. Communities in most inland waters have close relationships with the bordering land communities. However, the larger the body of water, the less important these relationships are.

In the seas the conditions of life—near the surface, at least—are affected by the climates of the earth. But oceanographers find that climate is less important in determining the limits of marine communities than are other factors. They make their basic division between the open, deep seas and the littoral waters on the continental shelves. In both of these, a distinction is made between the zone of swimming and floating organisms and the zone of bottom-dwelling organisms. Conditions of life change as we go toward great depths in the open sea; they also change as we move toward islands or continents, ending in the intertidal and spray zones of the shore.

## GUIDE QUESTIONS

1. What are the principal kinds of inland waters?
2. What is the function of the phytoplankton in pond communities?
3. What are some of the interrelationships between a pond community and the surrounding terrestrial community?
4. How do pond saprovores contribute to the maintenance of a pond community?
5. How do lakes become salty?
6. Why are living animals found deep in Lake Baikal but not in the depths of Lake Tanganyika?
7. How do producer populations in the headwaters of streams differ from the producers in ponds?
8. In which part of a river system are the interrelationships between land and water ecosystems closest?
9. In what ways has the proportion of inland-water area to land area been changed by man?
10. In what ways do streams become polluted?
11. What effects does salt water have on small organisms?
12. On what bases do oceanographers distinguish different kinds of marine ecosystems?
13. Why are some parts of the oceans more productive than others?
14. By what means have men explored the depths of the oceans?
15. What is bioluminescence?
16. How do communities on sandy bottoms differ from communities on rocky ones?

## PROBLEMS

1. Describe a pond in your area. In what ways does it resemble the pond discussed in the text? How does it differ?

2. How would a cloudy, windy day affect photosynthetic production by the phytoplankton in a pond?

3. A program designed to improve the fishing was introduced in a midwestern pond. First a fish poison was used to kill all the many small fish that were in the pond. Then the pond was restocked with game fish for recreational purposes. Instead of producing individuals of any worthwhile size, the new population tended to produce numerous but stunted individuals. How might you explain this result?

4. The concentration of hydrogen ions ($H^+$) and hydroxyl ions ($OH^-$) is as important in aquatic environments as in the soil. Where in North America can you find acid waters? Where can you find alkaline waters? What differences can you find among the living things in such waters?

5. Differences in the physical characteristics of water and air are important in understanding the contrast between aquatic

and terrestrial environments. You might consider such questions as these: (*a*) As the speed of a moving body increases, how does resistance change in air and in water? (*b*) What land organisms show the most streamlining? With what form of locomotion is this streamlining associated? (*c*) What water organisms show the most streamlining? With what niches in aquatic ecosystems in this streamlining associated? (*d*) Why do most plankton organisms have little or no streamlining? (*e*) How does locomotion by walking on the bottom of the ocean differ from locomotion by walking on land?

6. Estuaries, such as Chesapeake Bay and San Francisco Bay, represent a special kind of aquatic environment that has not been discussed in this text. Investigate the characteristics that distinguish estuarine environments from marine and inland-water environments and the resulting effects on aquatic life.

7. Though 80 to 90 percent of the world's photosynthesis occurs in the sea, man currently obtains most of his food from the land. To feed the human population properly, we will have to make much greater use of the sea. Investigate this human biological problem. Here are some questions to consider: (*a*) What nations at present make greatest use of marine food resources? (*b*) What kinds of marine organisms are eaten by man? (*c*) Man makes much use of terrestrial producers as food. Why is this difficult with aquatic producers? (*d*) How might man make greater use of aquatic producers as food? (*e*) Why does man's use of fish (second-, third-, or even higher-order aquatic consumers) represent an inefficient harvesting of the ocean's energy resources?

8. The distribution of biologically useful mineral compounds is not the same as the distribution of oceanic salinity. Find out where in the seas of the world the largest amounts of such minerals are and explain why they occur there. What effects do concentrations of such minerals have on the marine biota?

9. Though the seas are very large, pollution of marine waters by man can occur. Investigate the kinds of oceanic pollution and their effects on the marine biota.

## SUGGESTED READINGS

Amos, W. H. *The Life of the Seashore.* New York: McGraw-Hill Book Co., Inc., 1966. (A whole book devoted to the edge of the sea. Easy.)

————. "The Living Sand," *National Geographic Magazine,* June, 1965. Pp. 820–833.

Bates, M. *The Forest and the Sea.* New York: Random House, Inc., 1960. Chapters 4–6. (Excellent discussion of water environments and water life—particularly the environment of coral reefs. Fairly easy.)

Boolootian, R. A. *Biology of Coral Atolls.* (BSCS Pamphlet 10). Boston: D. C. Heath & Co., 1963. (This pamphlet describes the ecosystems in a special shallow-water marine environment of the tropics. Fairly easy.)

Carson, R. *The Sea Around Us.* New York: Simon and Schuster, Inc., 1958. (Beautifully written account of the oceans and their life. Fairly easy.)

Coker, R. E. *Streams, Lakes, Ponds.* Chapel Hill, N.C.: University of North Carolina Press, 1954. (The physical and chemical characteristics of water are discussed as background; then the living things in running and still waters are described. Somewhat advanced.)

DIETZ, R. S. "The Sea's Deep Scattering Layers," *Scientific American*, August, 1962. Pp. 44–50.

KENDEIGH, S. C. *Animal Ecology*. Englewood Cliffs, N.J.: Prentice-Hall, Inc., 1961. Chapters 5–7. (This reference is chiefly concerned with animals but has much background material on physical and chemical characteristics of both fresh and marine waters. Advanced.)

McELROY, W. D., and H. H. SELIGER. "Biological Luminescence," *Scientific American*, December, 1962. Pp. 76–87.

NIERING, W. A. *The Life of the Marsh*. New York: McGraw-Hill Book Co., Inc., 1966. (Neither entirely terrestrial nor entirely aquatic, marshes have been neglected in your textbook, but this book is a beautiful introduction to the marsh ecosystem.)

NIGRELLI, R. F. *Metabolites of the Sea*. (BSCS Pamphlet 7). Boston: D. C. Heath & Co., 1963. (This pamphlet considers the chemistry of organic substances that are found in seawater. Somewhat advanced.)

ODUM, E. P. In Collaboration with HOWARD T. ODUM. *Fundamentals of Ecology*. Philadelphia: W. B. Saunders Co., 1959. Chapters 9 and 10. (Well-organized summary of limnology and oceanography, with a large technical vocabulary. Very advanced.)

## Patterns
## of Life
## in the
## Past

### EVIDENCE OF THE PAST

In 1808 there were no public tours through the White House in Washington, as there are today. If there had been, housewives on tour would have been shocked to discover piles of old and dirty bones in one of the unfinished rooms. These were not leftovers from some great official dinner. Nor did the hoard of over three hundred bones belong to a favorite presidential dog. Indeed, some of the remains were gigantic—a leg bone large enough to use for a tent pole, for example. The truth of the matter was that Thomas Jefferson, the nation's science-minded President, had turned a part of the White House into a storage place for fossils.

hoard [hôrd]: a hidden supply of something

Jefferson was so intrigued by fossils that, at his own expense, he hired a crew of men to obtain specimens for him from famous Big Bone Lick in the hills of Kentucky. At about the same time, the first important natural-history museum in the United States grew up around the almost immovable mounted skeleton of a mastodon, which was eventually exhibited in a wing of Philadelphia's historic Independence Hall. But bones, shells, and other substances resembling living things or parts of living things had, for centuries before the first museums, been dug from the ground by wandering men—and always they excited interest and speculation.

intrigued [ĭn trēgd′]: deeply interested

X 1/76

Figure 10 · 1
Mastodon.

### WHAT IS A FOSSIL?

Being interested in fossils and knowing what fossils represent are two very different things. Some people once thought fossils were works of the devil. Others thought fossils were merely freakish accidents of natural geological

American Museum of Natural History

**Figure 10 · 2**

Excavation of a mastodon skeleton near New York in 1801.

remote [rǐ mōt´]: distant (here, in time)

petrified [pĕt´rə fīd´; Latin: petra, a stone, + facere, to make]

processes. Still others thought fossils were the result of the Great Flood (or perhaps many great floods). Some imaginative people even hoped that the fossil bones were skeletons of species still alive—that somewhere the animals might be thriving. Jefferson himself never seemed fully convinced that mastodons had disappeared completely from the surface of the earth. Although he didn't actually command the explorers Lewis and Clark to be on the lookout for them, he did quote an adventurer's secondhand tale that somewhere beyond the Missouri River there ranged gigantic living elephants. Lewis and Clark failed to find any.

Gradually, during the late eighteenth and early nineteenth centuries, scientists concluded that fossils are direct evidence of organisms that existed during remote past ages of the earth. Though often resembling in some ways the parts of present-day organisms, fossils represent in most cases species long extinct. This is the view held by most biologists today.

The majority of fossils represent the hard parts of organisms—wood, shell, bone. Sometimes fossils are these parts unaltered. Usually, however, they have been *petrified* —literally, turned to stone. In this process the original

Casts: brachiopods (New York). X 1

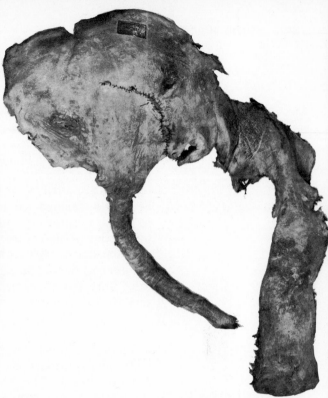

Soft parts: skin of a baby woolly mammoth found in permafrost (Alaska). X 1/8

Figure 10 · 3

Some kinds of fossils.

Carbon film: a primitive arthropod (British Columbia). X 1-1/4

Mold, or impression: starfish (New York). X 1

organic substances have been replaced, bit by bit, by minerals carried in soil water. The mineral substances may be chemically quite different from the substances they replace, but the form of the organisms—even the microscopic detail, in many cases—remains.

Fossils may also occur as thin films of carbon. The carbon, a component of all organic compounds, is all that remains after the living material has decomposed. Leaves of plants are often preserved in this manner. Or fossils may be molds—hollows left in the rock after the organic material has decayed. Or they may be casts, made of mud or some other sediment that filled the molds in the rocks and then hardened. Molds and casts preserve the shape but not the internal detail that petrified objects show. In a very few cases soft parts of organisms have been directly preserved—for example, flesh of woolly mammoths frozen in tundra permafrost.

*Any* indication of an organism's former presence is considered a fossil. Fossils may be footprints left by animals, burrows, nests of birds or insects, or even hardened dung of animals. The *paleontologist*, who is trying to unravel the fossil record, frequently finds himself confronted with strange and unfamiliar objects that are often difficult to interpret.

paleontologist  [pā lĭ an tŏl′ə-jĭst];  Greek:  *paleos*,  old,  + *onta*,  beings,  +  *logos*]

### THE GEOLOGICAL RECORD

Fossils are usually preserved in *sedimentary* rocks. Such rocks were once sediments—sand, mud, masses of shells. They were deposited at the bottoms of oceans, lakes, and ponds; in beds of rivers and streams; as dunes formed by the wind; or as great masses of unsorted materials dropped by glaciers. Sediments have been formed on the earth ever since water and wind and ice began to erode the landscape in one place and deposit the erosion products somewhere else.

strata  [strā′tə,  străt′ə;  Latin: *stratum*,  a  covering]:  singular, stratum

**The "book of the earth."**  The *strata* (layers) of sedimentary rocks are usually piled on each other like pages in a book, though at any one place on the earth's surface only a few pages may be found. As a whole, this "book of the earth" is now thought to represent about four billion years of time. But only a portion of the "book" particularly interests biologists—the part that records the history of living things.

**Difficulties with the record.**  Some things about this "book of the earth" are very upsetting. From the biological standpoint many of its "pages" are blank, containing no information about living things. This may be because no organisms existed at the time the rock strata were formed.

More often it is because organisms seldom die under conditions favorable for preservation. If you consider how few remains of present-day organisms you come across—perhaps one dead robin a year—you will begin to appreciate how lucky we are to have any knowledge at all of life in the past. Many extinct species, indeed, are known only from single specimens or mere fragments of specimens.

Another upsetting thing about this "book of the earth" is that many of its "pages" are missing. Conditions for the deposit of sediments were not always favorable whenever and wherever important biological events were occurring. Frequently the paleontologist must infer what biological events occurred by studying evidence from before and after a break in the record.

infer [ĭn fûr′; Latin: *in*, into, + *ferre*, to bear, carry]: to conclude by reasoning from (usually) few or uncertain data

The paleontologist's task is difficult at best, but another fault of the "book" makes his job even harder: the "pages" are often out of order, and of course they are not numbered. Although sedimentary strata were originally laid down one above another, with the youngest on top, they have been subjected to breaking, folding, shifting, and sliding during the earth's history. This has resulted in many rearrangements of their sequence. And sometimes fossils may be transferred from strata where they were deposited to strata of very different geological age.

**Geological time scale.**   With long experience and with evidence pieced together from many parts of the world, paleontologists have been able to put most of the known rock strata in sequence. Thus they can say that Devonian rock strata are older than Cretaceous or that Miocene rocks are younger than Eocene (Figure 10·4). But how much older or younger?

Devonian [dĭ vō′nĭ ən]
Cretaceous [krĭ tā′shəs]
Miocene [mī′ə sēn′]
Eocene [ē′ə sēn′]

Paleontologists have estimated the ages of rock strata and their accompanying fossils by various methods. In early attempts the total thickness of all the earth's sedimentary strata was estimated in meters. This was then divided by the estimated amount of time required for one meter of sediment to accumulate. Obviously this method was crude and inaccurate, because sediments do not accumulate at constant rates.

The most reliable method so far developed for rock dating depends upon the presence of *radioactive* chemical elements in the rocks. Physicists have observed that such elements change at a predictable rate, some of the atoms of the original element transforming into atoms of a different element. Careful laboratory studies have determined the *half-life*—the time in which half of any given amount of the original element is transformed—of each of these radioactive elements. With this knowledge at hand, it is possible

radioactive [rā′dĭ ō ăk′tĭv]: substances that give off radiations of energy such as X-rays (Figure 1·10)

| ERAS | PERIODS | EPOCHS | YEARS SINCE BEGINNING OF PERIOD OR EPOCH |
|---|---|---|---|
| Cenozoic | Quaternary | Recent | 10,000 |
| | | Pleistocene | 2,000,000 |
| | Tertiary | Pliocene | 10,000,000 |
| | | Miocene | 30,000,000 |
| | | Oligocene | 40,000,000 |
| | | Eocene | 60,000,000 |
| | | Paleocene | 75,000,000 |
| Mesozoic | Cretaceous | | 135,000,000 |
| | Jurassic | | 165,000,000 |
| | Triassic | | 205,000,000 |
| Paleozoic | Permian | | 230,000,000 |
| | Carboniferous | | 280,000,000 |
| | Devonian | | 325,000,000 |
| | Silurian | | 360,000,000 |
| | Ordovician | | 425,000,000 |
| | Cambrian | | 500,000,000 |
| Pre-Cambrian | | | 3,000,000,000+ |

Figure 10 · 4

The geological time scale.

Figure 10 · 5

The "book of the earth" is neat and orderly in the walls of the Grand Canyon (Arizona). These strata represent much of the Paleozoic era.

to determine the age of a rock that contains a radioactive element by calculating the ratio between the amount of the radioactive element and the amount of the element that has been formed from it.

For example, uranium breaks down through a series of steps and at a definite rate to form lead. In the same way, potassium breaks down to form argon and rubidium breaks down to form strontium. By selecting rocks from various

N. W. Carkhuff, U. S. Geological Survey

geological periods and then measuring the ratios between the elements in such pairs, it has been possible to approximate the ages of the rocks in years. The measurements are not perfect, but they have resulted in the establishment of a time scale that is probably more accurate than any previous ones.

**Importance of the record.** Despite all the shortcomings of the "book of the earth," biologists need this incomplete and often perplexing geological record of life in the past. It provides a basis for understanding the geographical distribution of life in the present. It shows that basic ecological processes and relationships have been active over long periods of time. And it is a major source of evidence about the great unifying theory of modern biology, evolution.

evolution: See pages 142–146.

## THE HISTORY OF LIFE

Man likes to look for the beginnings of things; biologists like to look for the beginning of their subject—the beginning of life. The fossil record gives no clues about the origin of life, for even the oldest fossils represent rather complex organisms. So biologists must resort to very indirect kinds of evidence and make many assumptions in thinking about the beginning of life. Thinking with such a background is referred to as *speculation*.

speculation:  [spĕk′yə lā′shən; Latin: *speculari*, to spy]

### ORIGIN OF LIFE

According to most geologists, the earth during its early history was very hot. Chemical activity must have been rapid, and atoms were therefore constantly forming and reforming into many kinds of molecules. Since organisms as we now know them are composed largely of combinations of carbon, hydrogen, oxygen, and nitrogen, we must assume that the environment in which life originated contained these elements. Our present atmosphere, containing water ($H_2O$), carbon dioxide ($CO_2$), elemental oxygen, and nitrogen, provides them all. Of these, oxygen, at least, could not have existed in the earliest ages of the earth because at the assumed high temperatures it would all have combined quickly with other elements.

**Some speculations.** According to one likely chemical assumption the primitive atmosphere included water vapor ($H_2O$), methane ($CH_4$) instead of $CO_2$, and ammonia ($NH_3$) instead of $N_2$. With the energy of heat and lightning, these compounds might have combined to form such substances as alcohols (for example, $C_2H_5OH$) or amino acids (the simplest of which is $C_2H_5O_2N$). Then, during millions

methane [mĕth′ān]

amino [ăm′ə nō′, ə mē′nō]

Alexander Ivanovich Oparin [ăl´ĭg zăn´dər ĭ vä´nŏ vĭch ō-pä´rĭn]: 1894——. Soviet biochemist

of years, an accumulation of such organic compounds within oceans, lakes, and pools might have produced a kind of "hot, thin soup," in which more complex organic molecules might have formed. Finally, these large, organic molecules might somehow have united to form a simple kind of reproducing "living thing." Such, at least, were the speculations of A. I. Oparin about forty years ago.

All this is very imaginative. But did not Louis Pasteur show a century ago that living things cannot come from nonliving materials? Could Pasteur have been mistaken? Not necessarily. He was concerned with conditions on the earth today, while these speculations assume an earth that had very different environmental conditions: the atmosphere was different; the temperature was different.

**Some experiments.**    There is no direct way to verify speculations on the origin of life. But a curious investigator might wonder what would happen if he exposed a simulated primitive atmosphere to an energy source. One did. In 1953 Stanley Miller was a student under Nobel laureate Harold C. Urey at the University of Chicago. He exposed a hot mixture of ammonia, methane, water, and hydrogen to an electric spark. When he later analyzed the substances in his apparatus, he found that some simple amino acids had indeed been produced!

Stanley Lloyd Miller: 1930——. American chemist

Harold C. Urey [ū´rĭ]: 1893——. American chemist. He won the Nobel prize in 1934.

Figure 10 · 6

Stanley Miller and the apparatus with which he made his investigation of Oparin's hypothesis.

Miller's experiment has received ample verification. Though difficult and quite dangerous, it has even been

UPI

repeated by some high school students. Other investigators have employed ultraviolet light and energy from a cyclotron instead of an electric spark and have obtained the same kind of results. Continuing research has been directed toward the synthesis of organic molecules more complex than amino acids. And some success has been achieved.

Do these experiments suggest a way in which life might have originated at some moment in the distant past? Perhaps. But it is a long way from amino acids to raspberries and rabbits—and to man.

## THE OLDEST FOSSILS

Even the most ingenious experiments will probably never make man's ideas about the origin of life better than speculations. But somewhere, somehow, at some time life on this earth *did* originate. So let us return to the factual evidence of fossils. How far back into time does the fossil record extend?

Fossils are fairly abundant in the sedimentary deposits of the last half-billion years. But in deposits older than the Cambrian period—that is, older than about 500,000,000 (0.5 billion) years—few traces of life are found. Recently, nevertheless, exploration of remote areas and the study of rock specimens by electron microscopy in the laboratory have revealed startling new evidence of the antiquity of life on our planet.

Late in the summer of 1965 a report was published announcing the discovery of fossils in rocks from southern Ontario that had been dated as 1,900,000,000 (1.9 billion) years old. These microscopic rod-shaped and spherical fossils clearly resemble modern bacteria. So rapid is the progress of modern science that even before some biologists read the report, the same authors published an account of bacteria-like organisms from a South African sediment dated at 3.1 billion years old! Naming the ancient organisms *Eobacterion isolatum*, the discoverers noted that

ingenious [ĭn jēn′yəs]: clever, original

Cambrian [kăm′brĭ ən]

antiquity [ăn tĭk′wə tĭ]: great age

*Eobacterion isolatum* [ē′ō băk- tĭr′ĭ ən ī′sō lā′tŭm]

Elso S. Barghoorn

**Figure 10 · 7**

**Electronmicrograph of *Eobacterion isolatum*.** ×66,000

"these organic remnants comprise the oldest known evidence of biological organization in the geologic record." By the time you read this paragraph, there may be finds from even earlier times.

Apparently the oldest known fossils were formed by bacteria, but other kinds of living organisms are represented in the pre-Cambrian geological record. Chemical compounds related to chlorophyll have been found in rocks dated at 1.1 billion years of age. This evidence suggests that photosynthetic organisms were early on the scene. Indeed, well-preserved fossils classified as green and blue-green algae have been collected in central Australia from pre-Cambrian limestones dated at 700,000,000 to 900,000,000 years old. In still more recent pre-Cambrian rocks are burrows of worms, skeletons of sponges, and shells of radiolarians. But the pre-Cambrian fossil record is everywhere scanty.

How can you explain the presence of consumers long before the presence of producers?

Dr. H. J. Hofmann and Edward Thorpe, Geological Survey of Canada
(neg. no. G.S.C. 200072-B)

Figure 10 · 8
In 1967 evidence for the ancient existence of organisms more complex than bacteria and algae was obtained. These 2-billion-year-old fossils from Canada are thought to represent casts or tubes made by wormlike organisms. x 1/2

## ECOSYSTEMS OF THE PAST

In pre-Cambrian rocks fossils are rare; in Cambrian rocks they are fairly frequent. And from this point in time up to the present, the paleontologist can view the life of the past with increasing confidence. Some speculation must remain, and careful interpretation of the evidence is always essential. But the evidence itself is more abundant in rocks from each succeeding age.

For a century after most biologists began to realize fossils were indications of ancient forms of living things, no clear meaning could be obtained from the accumulating collections. Then, in the middle of the nineteenth century, the theory of biological evolution linked in a great kinship group all the beings of the past and present. During the following century biologists were busy in an attempt to discover from the fossil evidence the lines of ancestry that link the organisms of the present to those of the past. This job is far from complete, but the broad outline of the history of organisms has been worked out. The results of this work have been presented in numerous readily available books, so the story is not repeated here.

In recent years many paleontologists have turned their attention to a study of the ecological relationships that existed among the organisms of past ages. Beginning with the fossils themselves, but also using geological evidence from the chemical and physical characteristics of the rocks in which the fossils occur, these *paleoecologists* have reconstructed both the biotic relationships of ancient communities and the abiotic environmental conditions —*paleoecosystems*. Let us take a look at some of these paleoecosystems.

See books by Matthews or Reed listed at the end of this chapter.

### THE BIOSPHERE IN CAMBRIAN TIME

If this textbook could have been written during the Cambrian period—let's say in 500,000,000 B.C.—the contents would have been very different. In Section Three this chapter, "Patterns of Life in the Past," would have been much shorter because there was much less past than there is now. "Patterns of Life on Land" would have been entirely missing because there was apparently no life on land at that time. But both "Patterns of Life in the Water" and "Patterns of Life in the Microscopic World" would have been very full chapters; the biosphere's inhabitants were living in oceans, lakes, and streams, and many of them were protists. Section Two, "Diversity among Living Things," might have made dull reading, because the majority of our familiar organisms, from palm trees to whales and from wheat stalks and mosquitoes to man himself, could not have been included. They had not yet arrived on the scene. On the other hand, the ecological concepts developed in Section One would still have had a place in our Cambrian book, because ecological relationships were much the same then as they are in the twentieth century A.D. Marine ecosystems were well developed in the Cambrian period. There were shallow-water and deep-water organisms, floating and swimming and bottom-dwelling kinds. Though their remains are not abundant, it seems probable that the chief producers were microscopic plankton species—just as is true today.

By the end of the Cambrian period, all the major animal phyla known today (except the chordates) were present. The largest and most conspicuous animals were arthropods. But today we would have some difficulty recognizing any of them; they were so different from modern arthropods that none of them could be placed in any of the modern arthropod classes. In fact, the organisms in all phyla were very different from those of today.

American Museum of Natural History

**Figure 10 · 9**
Fossil trilobites (New York).

trilobites [trī′lə bīts; Latin: *tri-*, three, + *lobus*, lobe]

Paleozoic [pā′lĭ ə zō′ĭk; Greek: *palaios*, ancient, + *zoion*, animal]

era [ir′ə]

Among the Cambrian arthropods, the ones that left the most abundant fossils were the trilobites, a class that disappeared from the fossil record at the end of the Paleozoic era. Most were small—2 to 6 cm in length—though a few were more than 50 cm long. Diversification was extensive; from Cambrian rocks alone more than a thousand species have been described. Most species had two large eyes.

But some had no eyes at all; these probably burrowed in the mud of the ocean bottom. Some were smooth; others had long, hollow spines over most of the body. Perhaps these spines were helpful in floating or in protecting the trilobites against predators. The many trilobite adaptations suggest that there were many ecological niches in the Cambrian seas.

### CARBONIFEROUS ECOSYSTEMS

**A seashore.** A group of students are out on an afternoon field trip. They are collecting organisms—tiny brachiopods with overlapping shells, bryozoans, a few horn corals. They find hundreds of plates and spines from sea urchins, and many of the small Life Saver-like discs which make up the stems of crinoids. Although the students cannot see them without microscopes, there are also multitudes of coiled foraminifera and innumerable tiny, branched spines from marine sponges.

Despite good collecting, the field trip is somewhat disappointing. No one has observed a fish or a sea gull. The breeze has the smell of pine rather than of salt. And the tide has gone far out; the closest ocean water is 1500 km away!

This particular marine ecosystem is located high in the Colorado Rockies—at a spot where the tide has been out for almost a quarter of a billion years. The students have been visiting a seashore of the Carboniferous period —ancient deposits, uplifted into a mountain ridge and now covered by a brushland and shadowed by pines and junipers. But the kinds of fossils the students have found leave no doubt that the ocean used to be here.

X 2

Figure 10 · 10
Horn coral.

Carboniferous [kär′bə nĭf′ər-əs; Latin: *carbo*, coal, + *ferre*, to bear]

Figure 10 · 11

Reconstruction of a marine scene from the Silurian period. How many of these organisms can you identify?

American Museum of Natural History

Water and swamp
Land

Figure 10 · 12

North America in the Carboniferous period.

Figure 10 · 13

Some trees of the coal-age forests: *Lepidodendron* and *Sigillaria* are lycopsids; *Cordaites* is a primitive gymnosperm; the seed ferns have no living species; *Calamites* is a sphenopsid.

**Coal-age forests.** By Carboniferous time life was no longer found only in the water. The first forest ecosystems fringed the shallow seas that covered much of the present North American continent. The trees in these forests were mostly relatives of the present-day horsetails, club mosses, and ferns. Some were gymnosperms—at least, strata of the late Carboniferous age contain some gymnosperm fossils. But the most familiar plants of today, the angiosperms, were entirely absent.

The climate in which these forests grew was probably warm and humid, with little or no seasonal change. Though some trees had branches, others bore their leaves at the top in single, large clumps, as palms do today. When older leaves fell, they left scars on the trunks in a characteristic pattern. But the leaves did not fall all at once; the forests were evergreen. Compared with tropical forests of today, the Carboniferous forests were shallow. The larger trees reached a height of about 30 m and had trunks 2 m in diameter. Beneath the trees was thick undergrowth made up mostly of ferns. Stream banks were lined with a dense growth of giant reedlike plants related to the horsetails of today. Thick tangles of moss probably covered the ground and green mats of algae probably grew in the water, but few of these soft and delicate plants have left traces in the fossil record.

Though fossils of the Carboniferous saprovores are rare, decay certainly occurred. But the accumulation of great beds of organic remains in which there is a large proportion of carbon indicates to the paleontologist that

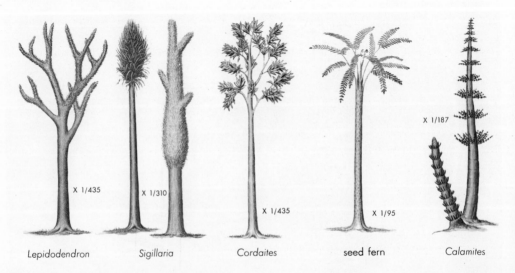

Lepidodendron     Sigillaria     Cordaites     seed fern     Calamites

X 1/435    X 1/310    X 1/435    X 1/95    X 1/187

decay was rather slow. These beds, hardened and compressed, we now call "coal." In coal itself remains are usually so altered we cannot see much detail; but in the beds of shale (mud turned to stone) that lie above and below the coal, we find many well-preserved fossils. From them we can form an excellent picture of the coal-age forests.

Insects were numerous. Predatory dragonflies that darted about in these forests were rather similar to modern kinds; one was the largest insect ever known, with a wingspread of almost 75 cm. Cockroaches were more abundant; except for differences in size — a few were nearly 10 cm long — some were almost identical to modern species. But most of the insects belonged to orders now extinct. And orders familiar today — mayflies, beetles, and mosquitoes — were not present.

*Why? What would have been the result if decay had been rapid?*

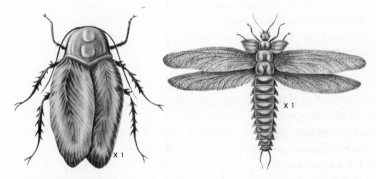

Figure 10 · 14
Carboniferous insects: a cockroach (*left*) and a possible ancestor of the dragonflies (*right*).

Land snails glided over the vegetation; they probably were important first-order consumers. Scorpions, centipedes, and spiders were higher-order consumers. The spiders (or perhaps we should call them spider-like animals) had no organs for producing silk, so they probably did not make webs.

The only large land animals were amphibians. Of these there were many kinds. Most somewhat resembled salamanders, though none were closely related to salamanders. Most had four legs, but they could not really stand; they waddled their way through the muck. Some kinds were snakelike, without legs. Still others had odd, triangular heads. These amphibians were probably all higher-order consumers. Many of them must have preyed on fishes in the streams and ponds rather than on terrestrial animals.

## A TRIASSIC ECOSYSTEM

In the Connecticut Valley of New England are rocks that contain large, three-toed footprints. When these were

**Figure 10 · 15**

Fossil footprints in the Connecticut Valley.

Hugh Spencer

Triassic [trī ăs′ĭk]

luster: shining with reflected light

discovered, many people—including most scientists—believed that they had been made by giant birds. But because these footprints are associated in many places with skeletons of reptiles, and because fossils of birds are unknown in the valley, it is now clear that the footprints were made by some of the early dinosaurs. Numerous other fossils help us build up a clear picture of an ecosystem that occupied the Connecticut Valley late in the Triassic period—about 175,000,000 years ago.

**The scene.** To geologists the characteristics of the rocks indicate that a slow, winding stream flowed through a valley. The stream carried materials from the highlands, which lay on both sides, to a broad, flat plain, where it deposited them. The rocks show cracks similar to those found today in drying mud; these cracks are filled with material that once was sand or dust. Moreover, the deposits show the luster seen on rocks and dried clay that have been exposed to the polishing of desert winds. There are occasional impressions of large raindrops, suggesting that the region had sudden hard showers such as are common in arid regions today.

**The vegetation.** Narrow bands of coal-like rocks seem to indicate that small ponds were present in this arid region. Almost all the fossil plants are from such rocks. There are remains of ferns and horsetails that probably grew around the ponds and water holes. Fossils of the large lycopsid and sphenopsid trees that had been abundant in the coal age are lacking, but there are fossils of gymnosperms such as cycads, conifers, and ginkgos. Though some fossil logs are 50 cm in diameter, it is unlikely that trees grew in the region. Probably they were uprooted and swept down from the

Margaret Matthew Colbert

Figure 10 · 16
Reconstruction of a stream-
side scene from the Triassic
period. How many of the
organisms can you identify?

uplands when the river was in flood. There was probably a scanty vegetation of small horsetails between the ponds.

**The animals.** The ponds were inhabited by aquatic insects and several kinds of fishes. Fossils of lungfishes and lobe-finned fishes, which could obtain oxygen from the air, have been found. But there were also predatory garlike fishes, which represent a line of fish development closer to most of the modern kinds. Like their modern descendants, these were not able to breathe air; because these fish had to live in water at all times, there must have been at least some permanent ponds. Numerous tracks of worms are found in rocks that were once mud along edges of pools.

Reptiles were abundant. Along the pond edges lived large crocodile-like reptiles, but they were only distantly related to the modern crocodiles. Paleontologists believe they were fish-eaters, because many fish bones have been found within their skeletons. Scurrying among the horse-tails between the ponds were lizard-like reptiles. The structure of their leg bones suggests they were fast-moving, and their small, sharp teeth indicate an insect diet. Several species of slender dinosaurs about 2.5 m high roamed the mud flats and left the tracks that first called attention to this paleoecosystem. All the dinosaurs were active and agile carnivores, preying upon smaller reptiles.

## AN EOCENE ECOSYSTEM

In the region now called the Geisel Valley of central Germany there was—about fifty million years ago—an

Geisel [gīʹsəl]

Yale Peabody Museum

X 1/14

ecosystem that can be visualized almost as clearly as if it existed today. An unusual combination of conditions brought about the fossilization of large numbers of organisms that seldom are formed into fossils. Organic materials that usually decay quickly and leave no trace were preserved in great detail.

**The fossils.** Trees of this ancient ecosystem are clearly represented by fossils of stems, leaves, seeds, even pollen. Among the most common kinds are sequoia, cypress, magnolia, rubber, palm, fig, cinnamon, and mango. There are fossils of various lianas. Fossil mosses are common, and many fossils of algae—plants that usually do not preserve well—are found. Among the remains of fungi are some that resemble the living genus *Penicillium*.

Snails are represented by fossils of both land and freshwater species. There are remnants of a number of crayfish. The most common insect remains are those of beetles, but fossil mayflies and stone flies are also present. Scales from the wings of butterflies are among the earliest known fossil evidence of these insects. And the fossilized larva of a fly was discovered in the nostrils of a fossilized mammal—evidence of a kind of parasitism still functioning today.

Thousands of fish skeletons have been found. They represent many modern families, such as those to which the bass, salmon, and pike belong. Scattered among the fish are remains of frogs and toads in all stages of development from tadpoles to adults. A study of chemical substances in the preserved frog skin has made it possible to conclude that the frogs were green in color. Evidence of color is extremely rare in organisms of the past. Painters of prehistoric scenes usually have to depend upon comparison of fossils with living organisms—and upon imagination.

The Geisel Valley beds include fossils of many reptiles. Primitive boa constrictors have been found—some of them so small that they appear to have just hatched. There were long-tailed, agile, tree-climbing lizards; there were terrestrial lizards; and there were burrowing lizards, some almost legless. Turtle skeletons are found lined up side by side in shallow depressions; perhaps death overtook the turtles while they were dormant. Most Geisel Valley turtles were members of a genus found today in the forests and streams of southeastern Asia and tropical America. The Geisel crocodiles had stubby snouts and limbs well adapted to swimming. Many of their eggs have been discovered, some with the embryo still visible inside.

X 1/24

**Figure 10 · 19**
**Modern hornbill.**

Bird remains are rare. There are bones—some quite fragmentary—of herons and cranes, of an owl-like bird, and of a hornbill, a member of a family that now exists only in the tropics of Africa, Asia, and Australia.

Among the fossil mammals in the Geisel Valley is an opossum, though marsupials today are restricted to Australia and America. Not only the skeletons of bats but even fragments of wing membranes, muscles, cartilage, and hair are preserved. Among the rodents are species related to the kangaroo rats of American deserts. All the primate fossils come from relatively small species—animals about 5 cm in length, excluding their long tails. These included several lemurs and tarsiers; today lemurs are restricted to Madagascar, while tarsiers are found only in the East Indies and the Philippines.

X 1/32

**Figure 10 · 20**
**A creodont.**

Representing the hoofed mammals are fossils of animals that resembled tapirs and fossils of mammals that were ancestral to horses. The carnivores known from this deposit are all very primitive kinds, the most important being the creodonts. These animals belonged to two families: one, a group of relatively large predators that were strong enough to kill even the biggest hoofed mammals of that time; the other, a group of small, weasel-like forest dwellers that probably preyed on rodents.

creodonts [krē′ə dŏnts′; Greek: *kreas*, flesh, + *odous*, tooth]

Finally, in the Geisel Valley deposits we even have evidence of protists. So perfect is the preservation here that traces of bacteria can be clearly identified in the eye cavities of fish skulls, in fossil frog skin, and in fossil insect muscle. Usually we have to assume the presence of these pathogens in ancient ecosystems; in this one we have evidence.

What additional evidence would you need to show that these protists were indeed pathogens?

**Visualizing the ecosystem.** From the evidence represented by these fossils and from geological study of the layers of rocks, paleontologists can describe the ecosystem of the Geisel Valley during the middle Eocene.

A river floodplain was dotted with numerous ponds and water holes. Along the river and around the ponds grew a thick forest, and on the surrounding hills was a grassland. The animal remains crowded around the ancient ponds and water holes indicate a lack of water elsewhere, so evidently there was a dry season. The turtles that apparently died while dormant were probably estivating rather than hibernating. This judgment is supported by the fact that some trees in the ecosystem (cinnamon, mango, palm) are species known to be intolerant of cold weather. Indeed, the whole assemblage of organisms was much like that of present tropical regions where wet and dry seasons alternate.

We can picture one of the ponds with its surrounding forest in more detail. The trees are tied together by lianas; the shaded ground is covered with mosses; the waters of the pond teem with algae. Turtles share the pond with crocodiles, fish, and frogs. Insects that spent their early life in the pond hover above it. Herons watch for fish in the shallows. Lizards chase insects on the ground and in the trees. There they meet with the fruit-eating tarsiers and lemurs. Boas rest along low-lying branches, waiting for small animals to pass. The weasel-like carnivores stalk herbivorous rodents, and the larger carnivores lie in wait for tapirs and bulky forest horses. And at dusk the bats and owl-like birds set out to feed.

Mesozoic [měs´ə zō´ĭk]

Altogether, this scene is much more familiar to our eyes than the ecosystems of the Paleozoic and Mesozoic. But it still is not modern. Most of the groups of animals and plants are familiar, but the species are not. And the assemblage of living things seems odd, too; some of the kinds of organisms living together here in the Eocene will be widely separated in the twentieth century. Sequoias grow side by side with rubber trees. Opossums inhabit the forest with hornbills. And what is a tropical forest doing in Germany? As is so frequently the case in science, the more we know, the more questions we raise.

## THE WORK OF THE PALEONTOLOGIST

Collecting facts is the first job in any science. Fossils are the facts of paleontology, so fossil collecting is a basic task for a paleontologist. Uncovering mastodon tusks at Big Bone Lick, chipping fossil ferns from a cliff in Greenland, stumbling upon a nest of fossil dinosaur eggs in Mon-

American Museum of Natural History

Figure 10 · 21
Fossil dinosaur eggs. In some cases the bones of the unhatched young have been found within the shells.  × 1/2

golia—such activities give paleontology a certain air of adventure. But an exciting and important discovery may come only after months or even years of searching. Fossil digging often turns out to be a long, hot, dusty, and painstaking occupation, with the paleontologist lying on the ground and brushing dirt away from a delicate bone with a toothbrush.

### STUDYING THE EVIDENCE

"A collection of facts is no more a science than a heap of bricks is a house," said Henri Poincaré. A collection of fossils may be nothing more than a hobby. But to the paleontologist a carefully prepared collection is only the beginning of his work. From careful study of all the varied remains of organisms—often mere fragments—he attempts to reconstruct the appearance of living things of past ages, to describe the ecosystems of which they were a part, and to understand the ways in which they changed during the long centuries of geological time.

Jules Henri Poincaré [zhyl än-rē′ pwăn kȧ rē′]: 1854–1912. French mathematician

You know scientific results must be verifiable. One of the principal ways that results can be made verifiable is to express data in numbers—as measurements. Therefore, one of a paleontologist's tasks when he returns from the field is to make measurements of his specimens. From comparisons of such measurements some preliminary conclusions may be drawn.

## INVESTIGATION 10.1

## PALEONTOLOGICAL COMPARISON

### PURPOSE

This investigation illustrates one of the methods used by paleontologists for determining relationships within a group of organisms.

Figure 10 · 22
*Hyracotherium.*

X 1/24

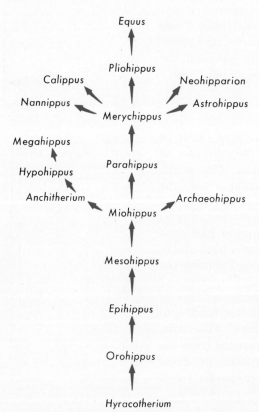

Figure 10 · 23

### BACKGROUND INFORMATION

The earliest animals that are considered as belonging to the horse family, Equidae, are members of the early Eocene genus *Hyracotherium*. In rocks of the late Eocene and of succeeding epochs of the Cenozoic, fossil remains of the family Equidae are abundant. Paleontologists have classified the animals represented by these fossils into about twenty genera. Since fossil material is abundant, paleontologists have a great many structural characteristics to consider when working out relationships within the horse family. By combining many kinds of evidence, they have arrived at some agreement about the relationships among seventeen of these genera, as shown in Figure 10 · 23.

In this investigation only one structural characteristic will be studied. In horses the grinding teeth are in the back of the mouth, separated from the front teeth by a toothless space. On each side of each jaw the grinding teeth (cheek teeth) consist of three premolars and three molars (Figure 10·24). The structural characteristic you are to study is the distance spanned by the cheek teeth.

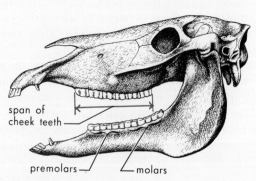

Figure 10 · 24

## MATERIALS

(per student)

Graph paper, 1 sheet

## PROCEDURE

The span of the cheek teeth has been measured in many fossil specimens of horses. Data are presented in Figure 10·25. When plotted on a graph, these data suggest certain relationships. Construct the graph by plotting the span of the cheek teeth on the vertical axis and geological time on the horizontal axis. Figure 10·26 shows the most convenient kind of grid; it should be made as large as possible so that the plotted points will not be crowded. As each point is plotted on the graph, place beside it the number (shown in Figure 10·25) of the genus it represents.

Connect the points representing the genera *Hyracotherium, Orohippus, Epihippus, Mesohippus,* and *Miohippus.* • What seems to have been the trend of evolution in the span of cheek teeth in the Equidae during Eocene and Oligocene times? (1) • Is it possible to continue a

| GENERA OF EQUIDAE | TIME OF EXISTENCE | SPAN OF CHEEK TEETH (in cm) |
|---|---|---|
| 1. *Hyracotherium* | Early Eocene | 4.3 |
| 2. *Orohippus* | Middle Eocene | 4.3 |
| 3. *Epihippus* | Late Eocene | 4.7 |
| 4. *Mesohippus* | Early Oligocene | 7.2 |
| | Middle Oligocene | 7.3 |
| 5. *Miohippus* | Late Oligocene | 8.4 |
| | Early Miocene | 8.3 |
| 6. *Parahippus* | Early Miocene | 10.0 |
| 7. *Anchitherium* | Early Miocene | 11.3 |
| 8. *Archaeohippus* | Middle Miocene | 6.5 |
| 9. *Merychippus* | Middle Miocene | 10.2 |
| | Late Miocene | 12.5 |
| 10. *Hypohippus* | Late Miocene | 14.2 |
| 11. *Megahippus* | Early Pliocene | 21.5 |
| 12. *Pliohippus* | Early Pliocene | 15.5 |
| | Middle Pliocene | 15.6 |
| 13. *Nannippus* | Early Pliocene | 11.0 |
| | Late Pliocene | 10.7 |
| 14. *Calippus* | Early Pliocene | 9.3 |
| 15. *Neohipparion* | Middle Pliocene | 13.1 |
| 16. *Astrohippus* | Middle Pliocene | 11.8 |
| | Late Pliocene | 11.8 |
| 17. *Equus* | Late Pliocene | 18.8 |
| | Pleistocene | 17.6 |

**Figure 10 · 25**

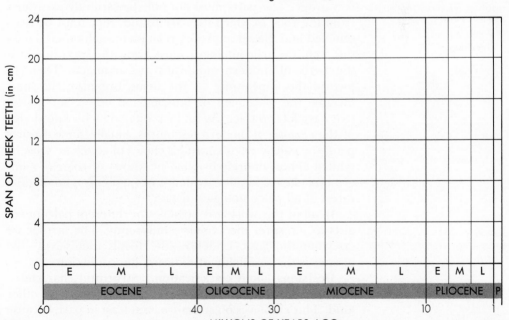

**Figure 10 · 26**

single line farther to the right on the grid? (2)   • Without drawing such a line, describe the trend of evolution in cheek-teeth span during the Miocene, Pliocene, and Pleistocene. (3)

Now you can find out whether the data on the span of the cheek teeth fit other relationships among the equid genera—relationships worked out by paleontologists from evidence provided by other structural characteristics. To do this, draw lines between dots on your grid to correspond to the arrows on Figure 10 · 23. For example: Draw a line from the dot for *Miohippus* to that for *Anchitherium*, continuing through that for *Hypohippus* to that for *Megahippus*. Draw another line from the dot for *Miohippus* to that for *Archaeohippus*. Draw a third line from *Miohippus* to *Parahippus*, etc.

## CONCLUSIONS

If data on a single characteristic conflict with relationships worked out from other characteristics, the data will produce a set of crossing lines when graphed.   • Do the data on the span of the cheek teeth support the relationships shown in Figure 10 · 23, or do they conflict with those relationships? (4)

• What was the approximate average change in the span of the cheek teeth per million years from *Hyracotherium* to *Miohippus?* (5)   • What was the average change per million years from *Miohippus* to *Megahippus?* (6)   • From *Miohippus* to *Equus?* (7)   • From these results what generalization can you make about the rate of evolution within the Equidae? (8)

• What evidence do you have that the direction of an evolutionary change can be reversed? (9)

## INTERPRETING THE EVIDENCE

**Restoring organisms.**   Even when all the hard parts of an organism are preserved, they are seldom found in perfect order. The parts must not only be carefully excavated from the rock in which they are found; they must be reassembled and placed in proper relation to each other. To do this well, the paleontologist must know the ways in which the parts of modern organisms are arranged. Then, to picture the appearance of the living organism, he must imagine the placement of muscles and other "soft parts" that have left no trace. Again he is guided by his knowledge of the *anatomy* of modern organisms. Finally, an artist may paint the paleoecosystem. In his choice of colors he must be guided almost entirely by what he knows of color in modern ecosystems, because evidence of pigments is among the rarest of all paleontological data.

excavate [ĕks'kə vāt'; Latin: ex, out of, + cavus, a hollow]: to dig out

anatomy [ə năt'ə mĭ; Greek: ana, on, up, + temnein, to cut]: structure of an organism

In all of this work it is possible for different paleontologists to interpret the evidence differently. The farther we go from the basic evidence—the fossils themselves—the greater is the possibility of differing interpretations.

**Decisions about classification.**   Structural characteristics are more often used by taxonomists than any other kind. This emphasis on structure is, at least in part, because

no other characteristics are usually found in fossils. And a kinship classification depends heavily upon knowledge of the ancestors—represented by fossils—of organisms now living. A look at Appendix II shows, however, that even many of the structural characteristics used in defining taxonomic groups are not likely to be preserved in fossils.

Consider the problem posed by a fossil from the Carboniferous period (Figure 10 · 28). The general form of the skeleton suggests either an amphibian or a reptile. A basic difference between reptiles and amphibians is the structure of their eggs. Amphibian eggs have no covering to protect them from drying out; therefore, they must be laid either in water or in very damp places. A reptile egg, on the other hand, has a shell; even more important, as the embryo within the egg develops, it becomes surrounded by a membrane, the *amnion*. The amnion holds a small amount of fluid in which the embryo develops. Any animal that develops from an amniote egg cannot be classified as an amphibian.

Unfortunately, no remains of eggs from the Carboniferous have been found; all we have is an assortment of fossils representing bones. The paleontologist must reason from the evidence of the skeleton, and the argument goes like this: The amniote egg is associated today with certain

Figure 10 · 27

Excavating a dinosaur (Montana). What information do you think the paleontologist should record in the field?

amnion [ăm'nĭ ən]

Figure 10 · 28

Skeleton (*left*) and a restoration based on it (*right*). How can a paleontologist decide whether this is an amphibian or a reptile?

X 1/22

kinds of skeletal structure. The amphibian pattern of reproduction is associated with quite different kinds of skeletal structure Therefore, when skeletal remains show parts that are like those of the skeletons of present-day reptiles, the paleontologist assumes that the animals represented by the fossil skeletons also had amniote eggs—that they were reptiles. Clearly, skeletons that combine amphibian and reptilian characteristics—and some are known—involve some risky reasoning.

### SOME PALEONTOLOGICAL CONCEPTS

In the foregoing examples of paleontological work, we can see a principle of paleontological interpretation. It has been stated thus: "The present is the key to the past." This means that unless we have evidence to the contrary, we interpret the past on the basis of our knowledge of the present. This applies to the structure of organisms, their functioning, their environment—indeed, it applies to the whole history of ecosystems on this planet.

### CHANGE AND STABILITY

No one can examine a large collection of fossils, especially if they are arranged in chronological order, without being impressed by change. Changes have occurred in single species of organisms, in large groups of species, in environmental conditions. Whole ecosystems have changed: where once there was oceanic life in Colorado there is now mountain forest. Such ecosystem changes are further examples of ecological succession. But instead of successions involving a few centuries or millennia, these successions involve millions of years.

**Extinction.** It has been estimated that at least 130,000 species of animals are known only from their fossil remains. The horn corals of the Colorado ocean ecosystem were apparently plentiful in seas for tens of millions of years. But no fossils of horn corals are known in rocks younger than the Paleozoic. Perhaps no large group of vertebrates has left so many fossils as have the dinosaurs. But no fossils of dinosaurs have been found in rocks younger than the Mesozoic. Many other large groups of organisms have likewise disappeared from the earth.

What caused such extinctions? We do not know. The problem has been a subject for speculation among paleontologists for a long time. Unfortunately, paleontological hypotheses are not often testable by experimentation. They must await the discovery of new evidence in the rocks. Perhaps we shall never learn what, for example, brought about the extinction of the dinosaurs. But as long as there

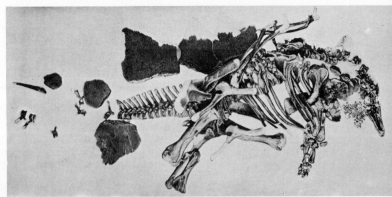

United States National Museum

*Stegosaurus*, a late Mesozoic reptile. Remains laid out as they were found.

Figure 10 · 29

Bones of another specimen, mounted in a museum.  X 1/50

Smithsonian Institution

Yale Peabody Museum
An  artist's  reconstruction.

Smithsonian Institution
Another artist's reconstruction.

are rocks that have not been opened by the paleontologist's pick, there is hope that we shall someday know.

When a species becomes extinct—as happened with the dinosaurs and horn corals—it will never appear on the earth again. This idea is related to a concept termed "Time's Arrow" by biologist Harold Blum. Evolution moves in only one direction—forward in time. It took many distinct biological steps over millions of years to produce, let's say, *Brontosaurus*. The same evolutionary steps will never occur in the same sequence again. Thus no *Brontosaurus*, none of the extinct dinosaurs, indeed none of the thousands of known species of extinct organisms, will ever live again.

*Brontosaurus* [brŏn'tə sôr'əs]

Figure 10 · 30
*Brontosaurus.*

**Ancestral forms.**   Though many species have become extinct, others seem to have merely changed through generation after generation until they are no longer recognizable as the same species. You might suspect that the most advanced forms in one geological period would give rise to the more advanced forms in the next. But the fossil record does not support this view. For example, reptiles did not become more and more advanced during the Mesozoic and finally, at the end of this geological period, give rise to mammals (which are considered more advanced than reptiles). On the contrary, the ancestors that had given rise to the varied reptilian groups were apparently also the ancestors of the mammals (Figure 10 · 31). Thus, the ancestors of mammals were early and primitive reptiles, not recent and advanced reptiles.

**Stability.**   While the fossil record shows abundant evidence of change, it also provides evidence of great stability. Sea urchins much like those of the Paleozoic ocean are common along twentieth-century ocean shores. Indeed, the whole ocean ecosystem of Colorado was not very different from some present-day marine ecosystems—though not, to be sure, in Colorado. Ferns and horsetails are found

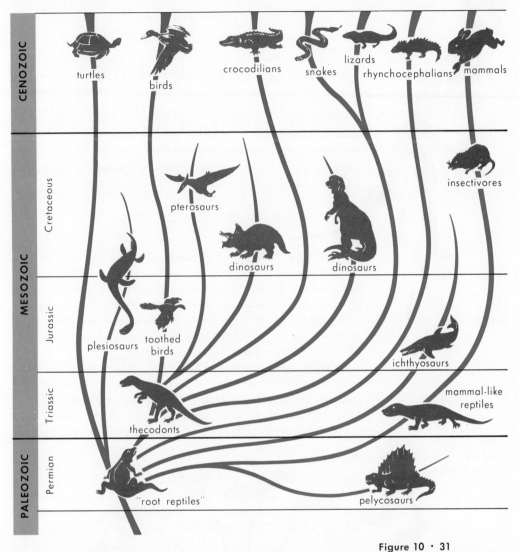

CENOZOIC

turtles    birds    crocodilians    snakes    lizards    rhynchocephalians    mammals

insectivores

Cretaceous

pterosaurs

dinosaurs    dinosaurs

MESOZOIC

Jurassic

plesiosaurs    toothed birds

ichthyosaurs

Triassic

thecodonts

mammal-like reptiles

PALEOZOIC

Permian

"root reptiles"    pelycosaurs

**Figure 10 · 31**

Relationships among reptiles, birds, and mammals, according to the existing fossil evidence.

today in Connecticut, though they are of different species from those in the Triassic ecosystem. And turtles and frogs—slightly different kinds—survive from the Eocene in Germany.

What happens to organisms and ecosystems through time depends in large measure upon the kinds of changes a particular environment undergoes and upon the adaptability of the associated organisms. Since environmental conditions tend to change less in aquatic than in terrestrial ecosystems, it is not surprising that many of the kinds of organisms that existed in ancient seas are still found in modern seas.

Can you think of any reasons for this?

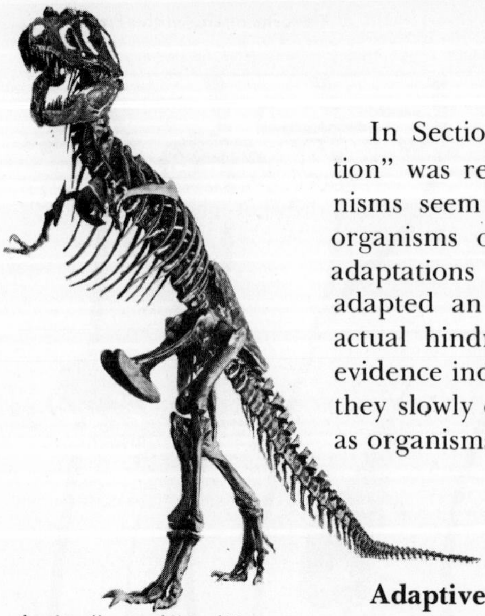

# ADAPTATION

In Section Two the concept called "structural adaptation" was repeatedly mentioned: many structures of organisms seem to be fitted to the ecological niches that the organisms occupy. It is possible to think of structural adaptations as static—unchanging. But a structure that adapted an organism to one environment might be an actual hindrance in a different environment. The fossil evidence indicates that structural adaptations are not static; they slowly change as environmental conditions change or as organisms disperse into new environments.

American Museum of Natural History
**Figure 10 · 32**

*Tyrannosaurus* [tĭ răn'ō sôr'əs].
x 1/40

**Adaptive radiation.** Again and again during the history of life on Earth, the descendants of a small group of organisms that were originally adapted to a narrow range of ecological conditions dispersed into a great variety of ecosystems. As they did so—their fossil remains indicate—many features of their structure changed in ways that adapted them to their new ecosystems.

This process, known as *adaptive radiation*, is well demonstrated by the dinosaurs. The ancestors of dinosaurs are thought to have been small, slender reptiles that had long tails, ran on their hind legs, and consumed insects with their sharp teeth. From these ancestors developed animals

**Figure 10 · 33**

Adaptive radiation in the class of mammals.

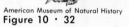

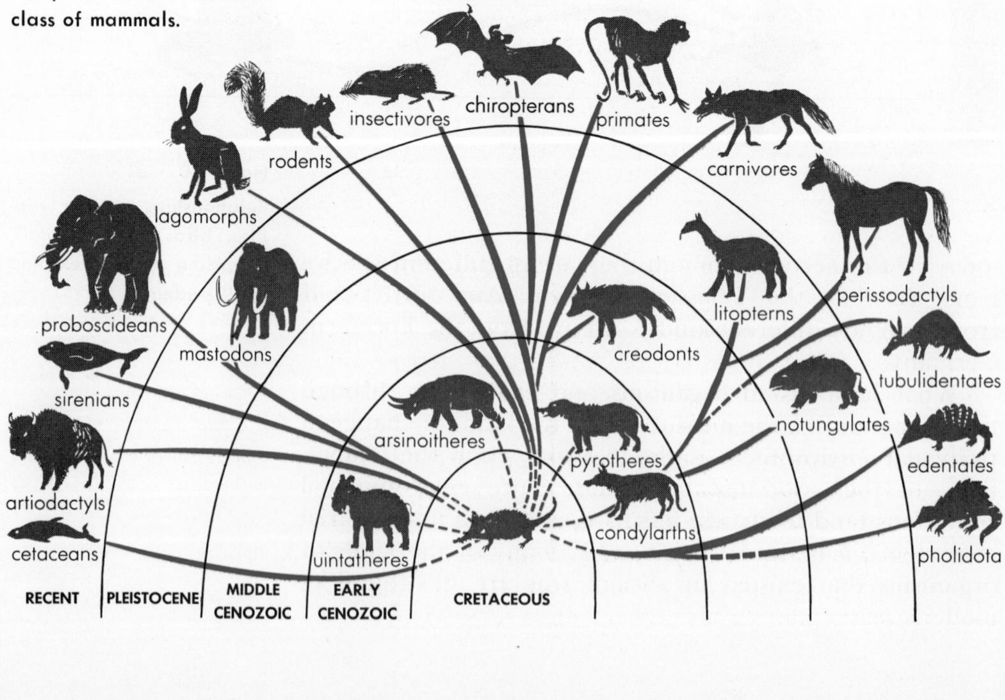

insectivores · chiropterans · primates
rodents · carnivores
lagomorphs · perissodactyls
proboscideans · mastodons · litopterns · creodonts · tubulidentates
sirenians · notungulates · edentates
arsinoitheres · pyrotheres
artiodactyls · condylarths · pholidota
cetaceans · uintatheres

| RECENT | PLEISTOCENE | MIDDLE CENOZOIC | EARLY CENOZOIC | CRETACEOUS |

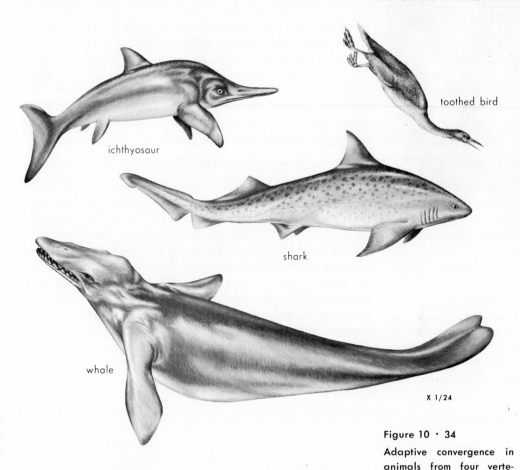

toothed bird

ichthyosaur

shark

whale

X 1/24

Figure 10 · 34
Adaptive convergence in animals from four vertebrate classes.

with great structural diversity. There were huge, four-legged, swamp-dwelling, first-order consumers. There were two-legged, second-order consumers, ranging from small insect-eaters, which were much like their ancestors, to the ten-ton *Tyrannosaurus*. And there were toothless dinosaurs that may have fed on fruit; duck-billed, swimming dinosaurs; dinosaurs with parrot-like beaks; dinosaurs with horned heads; and plated and armored dinosaurs. The bony fishes, probably originating in small freshwater streams, similarly show a history of adaptive radiation. And among plants the angiosperms, with their many kinds of leaves, flowers, and so on, have adaptively radiated into a great variety of terrestrial niches.

**Adaptive convergence.** On the other hand, the fossil record also shows examples of *adaptive convergence*. In such cases, descendants of quite different ancestors have developed similar forms as they adapted to similar ways of life. In many animal groups, species that burrow have appendages that are shorter than those of their ancestors—or,

Figure 10 · 35

Modern African euphorbia.

discontinuous [dĭs′kən tĭn′yoo-əs]: separated, not connected

Figure 10 · 36

Past and present distribution of the camel family. What is the evidence for the past distribution?

● Probable point of origin

▨ Past distribution

▨ Present distribution

sometimes, no appendages at all. Perhaps the best example is the long, narrow form that enables an animal to swim swiftly through the water as an aquatic predator (Figure 10 · 34). And adaptive convergence is also known among plants. In arid parts of the Old World, many plants of the euphorbia family have so adapted to their environment that they closely resemble the plants of the cactus family growing in New World deserts.

### LIGHT ON THE PRESENT FROM THE PAST

In discussing the distribution of organisms in Chapter 8 (page 287), we presented two hypotheses to explain some puzzling cases. On the whole, fossil evidence favors the second: that each species originated in one place and then spread into other places. But some taxonomic groups of organisms undoubtedly once were more widespread than they are today. The evidence is especially good for *discontinuous distributions* — geographic distributions in which taxonomically related organisms are found today in widely separated regions and are absent from intervening regions.

An example of this in Chapter 8 was furnished by the tapirs. During the Eocene, tapirs were present in the Geisel

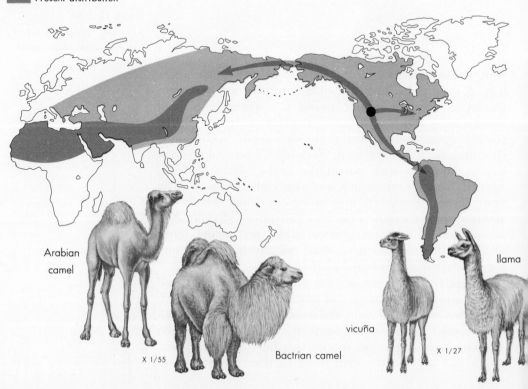

Arabian camel

Bactrian camel

vicuña

llama

X 1/55

X 1/27

Valley of Germany. Germany is about midway between tropical America and Malaysia, the present-day homes of tapirs. Fossils from other places show that tapirs once existed in many parts of the regions that separate the geographic ranges of living tapirs.

In the marsupial mammals we see another case of discontinuous distribution that the Geisel Valley fossils help us to explain. And sequoia trees are found today only in the western United States and in China; during the Eocene they were present in the Geisel Valley. Of course, no one paleoecosystem provides evidence on all distributional problems; Figures 10 · 36 and 10 · 37 show examples of discontinuous distribution to which the Geisel Valley contributes no evidence.

Recall now the basic principle presented on page 364, "The present is the key to the past." In the study of discontinuous distribution, we can see that sometimes the reverse is true: the past sheds light upon the present. The paleontologist must travel far and wide over the earth to seek his evidence; to interpret that evidence, he must allow his mind to move freely back and forth between present and past.

Figure 10 · 37

Past and present distribution of tulip trees, genus *Liriodendron*. How can biologists determine the part of the world where the genus originated?

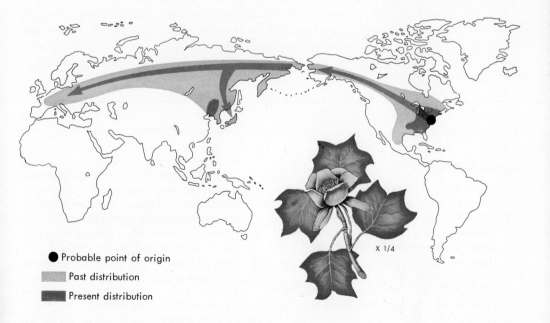

● Probable point of origin

Past distribution

Present distribution

X 1/4

Direct evidence for the existence of life in the past lies in fossils preserved in rocks of the earth. This evidence, gathered from many places, has been arranged in a sequence of geological time. Using various methods, paleontologists have estimated the ages of rocks and fossils—and hence the approximate length of divisions in the geological time scale.

There is no fossil evidence for the earliest life on the earth. Speculation about the origin of life must, therefore, be based on indirect evidence. It seems probable that life of some kind has existed on the earth for at least three billion years, but fossils older than five hundred million years are rare. In the Cambrian, the earliest period from which fossils are abundant, there was already a great diversity of organisms. The closer we come to the present, the more abundant fossils become, and, therefore, the more detailed our knowledge of organisms.

Fossil evidence shows that throughout the history of life, organisms have lived in communities. Producers, consumers, and saprovores are found together almost as far back as the fossil record goes. But a complete picture of any ecosystem in the past is seldom possible. Fossils are formed accidentally, and organisms without hard parts are unlikely to be fossilized. Therefore, the paleontologist usually has only scattered and fragmentary evidence. He must use great care in interpreting such evidence.

The basic principle in paleontological interpretation is to use knowledge of the present to picture the past except as fossil evidence indicates otherwise. By careful interpretation combined with careful field and laboratory work, paleontologists have been able to trace ancestral lines of development among many organisms; to recognize extinction, stability, adaptive radiation, and adaptive convergence as concepts in the history of life; and to interpret problems in the present distribution of organisms.

## GUIDE QUESTIONS

1. From what evidence do paleontologists obtain their ideas of life in past ages?
2. How was the paleontological evidence formed?
3. What are sedimentary rocks? Why are they the most important kind of rocks for paleontologists?
4. What difficulties do paleontologists encounter in reading the "book of the earth"?
5. How can the age of a sedimentary rock be determined?
6. Pasteur showed that spontaneous generation does not occur. How, then, is it possible to speculate about the origin of life from nonliving materials?
7. What experimental evidence supports the *possibility* of such an occurrence?
8. How far back in time do the oldest fossils now known date? What present-day organisms most resemble the organisms represented by these fossils?
9. In what kind of environment did all the organisms known from Cambrian fossils live?

10. Compare a forest of Carboniferous time with a forest of today.

11. What class of land vertebrates apparently originated between Carboniferous and Triassic times?

12. What class of land vertebrates apparently originated between Triassic and Eocene times?

13. How is each statement about the Geisel Valley ecosystem supported by the fossil evidence?

14. What does your study of the paleontological evidence in the family Equidae indicate about size change in this family?

15. You are shown paintings by two different artists of an organism known only from fossils. Why may the two paintings differ?

16. By what reasoning would a paleontologist decide whether a particular fossil represented a reptile or an amphibian?

17. By what basic principle is the interpretation of paleontological evidence guided?

18. Extinction of a species is usually considered to be final and permanent. How is this related to the concept of "Time's Arrow"?

19. What are adaptive radiation and adaptive convergence?

20. How can fossils help to explain the discontinuous distribution in present-day organisms?

## PROBLEMS

1. The broad view of the history of life has been developed through study of fossils from all parts of the world. In any one region, such as a state, deposits representing only a few of the geological time divisions are likely to be found. Obtain a geological map of your state. From it construct a geological time scale, indicating the time divisions that are represented in your state and those that are not. You may be able to collect some fossils yourself.

2. In Greenland and in Antarctica, beds of coal occur. These were formed from abundant plant remains; today the regions are covered with ice caps. How can you account for this evidence of great photosynthetic activity at high latitudes such as these?

3. Investigate the origin of the names given to the geological time intervals listed in Figure 10·4.

4. In eastern Colorado and western Nebraska are extensive deposits of fossils in rocks of Oligocene age. Known as the White River deposits, these rocks were formed from silts in which there were streaks of gravel. The fossils represent, among others, the following organisms: grasses, reeds, hickories, and hackberries; freshwater clams, several kinds of freshwater fish, frogs, snakes related to the boas, and several species of large land tortoises; among mammals, saber-toothed cats and species closely related to the modern dogs, members of the camel family, four species of horses, and several species of rhinos. Some of the rhinos were much like those of the present day; others had long, slender legs much like those of horses; still others, much like the hippos of today, had heavy bodies with short legs and large feet. Using the evidence given here, describe the ecosystem represented by the White River deposits. Does your interpretation agree with those of other students? How do you support your interpretation in places where it differs from theirs? What additional evidence would give further support to your interpretation?

5. By means of research and the kind of reasoning used in this chapter, try to reconstruct ecosystems represented in the fossil remains found in the La Brea tar pits of Los Angeles and in the Florissant region of Colorado. You will need to find out what geological times these deposits represent, the conditions under which the fossils were formed, and the kinds of fossils present.

6. Using the evidence presented in this chapter, devise your own interpretation of the Geisel Valley ecosystem. This is worth doing, of course, only if you can find new interpretations. But remember that interpretations must be consistent with evidence.

7. Fossil skeletons of ichthyosaurs have been discovered with fossil skeletons of

small ichthyosaurs inside them. What possible interpretations of this situation can you devise? What additional evidence would you look for to support one interpretation or another?

8. Investigate the hypotheses that have been advanced to explain the extinction of the dinosaurs. If one seems more reasonable than others, explain why you think so.

9. Land organisms do not become fossils as often as water organisms do. Fossilized land organisms usually show evidence of having drowned or of having been washed into bodies of water from the land. Why are these statements usually true? What exceptions can you find? Finally, what generalizations can you make about the physical conditions that favor fossilization?

10. Suppose that every individual organism of the past had been fossilized. Why would the fossil record still be incomplete today? Suppose that all organisms that ever lived had been carbonized—as in coal and in the fossils of many leaves and some fish—and suppose that all bones and shells had been preserved unchanged. What effect would this have on the biogeochemical cycles described in Chapter 1?

11. Two groups of hoofed mammals, the litopterns and the notungulates, inhabited South America for a long time. During this time there was no land connection between South and North America. Soon after the Panama land bridge was reestablished in the Pliocene, these animals became extinct. How can you account for this?

12. The fossil record of the rhinoceroses is nearly as good as that of the horses, but it has not been described in easily obtained publications. If you have the necessary library resources and the ability to tackle technical literature, you can work out the rhinoceros story on your own. Begin with Osborn, Henry F., "The Extinct Rhinoceroses," *Memoirs of the American Museum of Natural History*, Vol. 1, pp. 75–164, 1903; and Wood, Horace E., "Trends of Rhinoceros Evolution," *Transactions of the New York Academy of Sciences*, 2nd Series, Vol. 3, pp. 83–96, 1941.

## SUGGESTED READINGS

AUFFENBERG, W. *Present Problems About the Past.* (BSCS Pamphlet 6). Boston: D. C. Heath & Co., 1963. (Contains a good description of a Miocene ecosystem. Fairly easy.)

COLBERT, E. H. *Dinosaurs: Their Discovery and Their World.* New York: E. P. Dutton & Co., Inc., 1961. (A nontechnical account of the best-known group of extinct animals. Fairly easy.)

DOUMANI, G., and W. LONG. "Ancient Life of the Antarctic," *Scientific American*, September, 1962. Pp. 168–176+.

ERICSON, D. B., and G. WOLLIN. "Micropaleontology," *Scientific American*, July, 1962. Pp. 96–104+.

GLAESSNER, M. F. "Pre-Cambrian Animals," *Scientific American*, March, 1961. Pp. 72–78.

MATTHEWS, W. H. *Fossils: An Introduction to Prehistoric Life.* New York: Barnes and Noble, Inc., 1962. (A full but simple outline of paleontology. Includes information on fossil collecting. Easy.)

NEWELL, N. D. "Crises in the History of Life," *Scientific American*, February, 1963. Pp. 76–92.

REED, W. M. *The Earth for Sam,* ed. PAUL F. BRANDWEIN. Rev. ed. New York: Harcourt, Brace and Co., 1960. (For gaining an understanding of the full sweep of the fossil record with a minimum of effort.)

SCHAEFFER, B., and M. MANGUS. "Fossil Lakes from the Eocene," *Natural History,* April, 1965. Pp. 10–21.

SIMPSON, G. G. *Life of the Past.* New Haven, Conn.: Yale University Press, 1953. (More advanced than Reed, but not a textbook. For students who want more than just a description of strange organisms.)

YOUNG, R. S., and C. PONNAMPERUMA. *Early Evolution of Life.* (BSCS Pamphlet 11). Boston: D. C. Heath & Co., 1964. (The title is somewhat misleading. Deals with the origin of life. Requires some background in biochemistry.)

**WITHIN THE INDIVIDUAL ORGANISM**

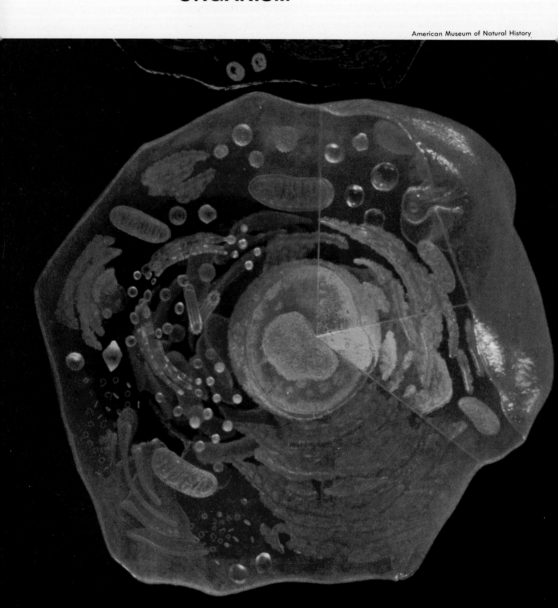

Thus far individual organisms have been the basic biological units of our study. Individuals vary greatly in size: A redwood tree may extend 100 m from root to tip, and a blue whale may weigh 150 metric tons; a single bacterium, on the other hand, may be only 0.4 $\mu$ across and weigh a small fraction of a milligram. But regardless of their size, we have treated all of these as equal units—as individuals interacting with other individuals and with the abiotic environment.

We have viewed living things somewhat as a traffic engineer looks at automobiles. He is concerned with the way they move about, with what happens when they collide, and with how they may be managed. He is not concerned with the way their motors are constructed, with the principles involved in their braking systems, or even with their source of energy. The mechanic, on the other hand, is concerned with the structure of the automobile—with gears, pistons, and valves—and with the way the energy of gasoline is transformed into motion of turning wheels. He is not concerned with traffic patterns. The traffic engineer assumes that the automobile runs; the mechanic must know how it runs. One looks at automobiles from the outside; the other, from the inside.

The time has now come to change our point of view in biology—to shift from the outside view to the inside view. What activities within the organism produce the activities we have seen from the outside? To understand these internal activities of an organism, we must examine its parts. Is there any basic internal unit from which the parts are constructed? And internal activities imply internal energy. We have seen how energy goes from organism to organism in the biosphere, but what happens to this energy within the individual organism?

These are some of the questions we shall consider in the following chapters.

# The Cell

## SOME HISTORY

If we examine a fairly large organism — yourself, perhaps — we can easily identify a number of parts. Externally there are eyes, arms, and hair; inwardly are teeth and tongue; and after a bit of dissection (imaginary, of course!) we find the heart, liver, stomach, and other organs. Proceeding in this way, we find smaller and smaller parts. In the case of the human body, investigation of structure through dissection — the study of human anatomy — had almost reached the limits of macroscopic vision by the sixteenth century. When, in 1543, Andreas Vesalius published his great work, *De Humani Corporis Fabrica* ("Concerning the Structure of the Human Body"), many persons no doubt considered the subject finished.

## DISCOVERY OF CELLS

Today Vesalius' work appears to have begun, rather than ended, the scientific study of human structure, because in the next century the microscope was developed.

In that turbulent seventeenth century Leeuwenhoek was not the only curious observer, though none had lenses as fine as his. Some fifteen years before Leeuwenhoek's first letter to the Royal Society, an Italian, Marcello Malpighi, had seen small, thin-walled blood vessels, later named capillaries. Then in 1665 Robert Hooke, a secretary of the Royal Society, found interesting microscopic structures in cork (the bark of a Mediterranean oak) and in stems of various plants. In cork he observed neat rows of thick-walled compartments that reminded him of honeycomb. Because of this, he called the compartments "cells."

dissection [dĭ sĕk′shən; Latin: *dis-*, apart, + *secare*, to cut]

Andreas Vesalius [və sā′lĭ əs]: 1514 – 1564. Flemish anatomist

Marcello Malpighi [mäl pē′gĭ]: 1628 – 1694. Italian anatomist

capillaries [Latin: *capillus*, hair]

Robert Hooke: 1635 – 1703. English physicist, mathematician

compartments [Latin: *com-*, with, + *partiri*, to divide]

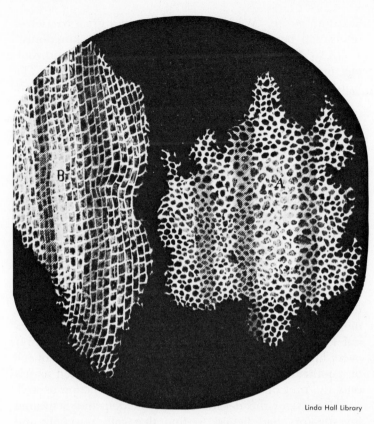

Figure 11 · 1
Hooke's drawings of cork
(*Micrographia*, 1665).

Linda Hall Library

The story of Hooke's cells closely parallels the story of Leeuwenhoek's "little animals." During the following century and a half many men saw both cells and "little animals," but no one fully understood their significance.

Hooke himself found that in many living materials (the cork, of course, was dead) the cells were filled with a liquid substance. Gradually attention shifted to this liquid. In 1809 the Frenchman Jean Baptiste de Lamarck wrote: "Every living body is essentially a mass of cellular tissue in which more or less complex fluids move more or less rapidly."

Jean de Lamarck [zhäN də lə-märk´]: 1744–1829. French naturalist

Lamarck was a bold originator of generalizations, but he was not good at seeking out facts to support them. His statement did not receive support until 1824, when Henri Dutrochet wrote that "the cell is truly the fundamental part of the living organism." Because the boundaries of plant cells are easier to see than those of animal cells, this idea was at first more acceptable to botanists than to zoologists. But by 1839 the generalization was fully developed with respect to both animals and plants. Two Germans, Matthias Schleiden, a botanist, and Theodor Schwann, a zoologist, did much to convince their co-workers of its usefulness. As

Henri Dutrochet [äN rē´doo´trə-shě´]: 1776–1847. French physiologist

Matthias Schleiden [shlī´ dən]: 1804–1881

Theodor    Schwann    [shvän]: 1810–1882

Schwann wrote, "We have thrown down a great barrier of separation between the animal and vegetable kingdoms."

In so doing they began the joining of botany and zoology into the unified science of all life—into biology. The word itself had already been originated in its French form by Lamarck in 1802.

### THE CELL THEORY

Thus "cell," which once referred to an empty space, came to mean a unit of living matter. Leeuwenhoek's "little animals" were interpreted as the least possible degree of cellular organization—that is, single cells. All other organisms could then be regarded as aggregations (groupings) of cells—very highly organized and differentiated aggregations, to be sure, but nevertheless reducible to cell units.

The cell theory did not lead immediately to a great new era of research. Despite the microscope's usefulness, detailed studies of cells had to await another technological development—dyes that could make cellular structures more clearly visible. This came with a great spurt in chemical knowledge in the 1850's and 1860's. Soon thereafter every life process was being associated with one type of cell or another. The cell quickly came to be regarded as not only the unit of structure but the unit of function as well.

Already, in the decade after Schleiden and Schwann, investigators had begun to find that cells normally and

aggregations [Latin: *ad*, to, + *gregare*, to herd]

differentiate [dĭf′ə rĕn′shē āt; Latin: *dis*-, apart, + *ferre*, to carry]: become distinct or different

Such dyes came to be called stains by microscopists. What stains have you used?

R. D. Allen and S. R. Taub

### Figure 11 · 2

*Paramecium.* The complex structure of this protist has led some biologists to regard it not as a single cell but as an organism that has lost cellular structure. X 450

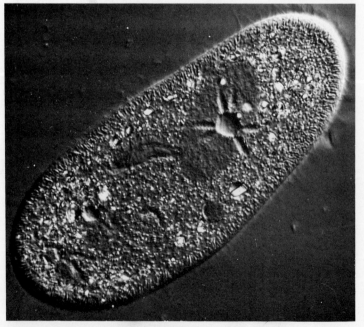

regularly come into being through the division of parent cells. Soon the ideas were established that since the beginning of life there has been no break in the descent of living cells from other cells of the past and that all of heredity and all of evolution must be embodied in cells.

Today the cell theory may be summarized as three main ideas: (1) The cell is the unit of structure of living organisms. (2) The cell is the unit of function in living organisms. (3) All cells come from preexisting cells.

*Why is this generalization called a theory?*

## CELL STRUCTURE

Differences among cells are great—in size, shape, and internal structure. When you study Figure 11 · 3, do not assume that all the structures shown are to be found in all cells or that all structures known to occur in cells are included. The diagram is intended only to assist you in remembering some of the principal structures of cells. Therefore, some structures that you may encounter in more advanced studies have been omitted. And it would be impossible to find any cell that, in every way, looks like the diagram.

Nearly every cell contains at least one *nucleus* (plural, "nuclei"). Under the microscope the nuclei of living cells are usually difficult to see, but they are readily visible when stained with various kinds of dyes. Compared with the rest

*nucleus [noō′klĭ ŭs; Latin: nux, nut]*

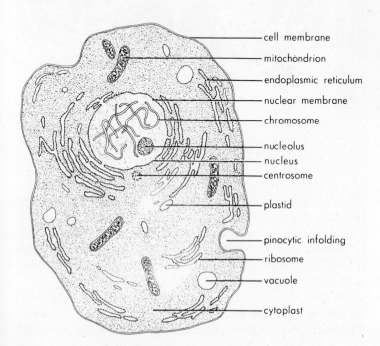

cell membrane
mitochondrion
endoplasmic reticulum
nuclear membrane
chromosome
nucleolus
nucleus
centrosome
plastid
pinocytic infolding
ribosome
vacuole
cytoplast

**Figure 11 · 3**

**Cell structures. This is a *diagram*; it does not picture any particular kind of cell.**

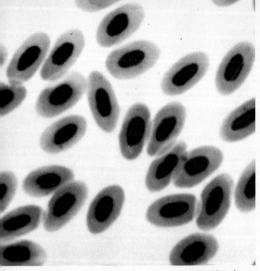

Victor Larsen

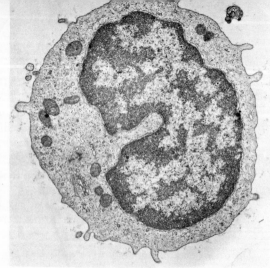

Mercy Institute of Biomedical Research

**A. Red blood cells of a bird.** X 1200

**B. Human white blood cell.** X 10,400

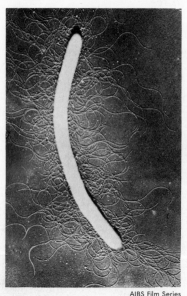

AIBS Film Series

**C. A bacterium.** X 6000

Winton Patnode from Photo Researchers

**D. A desmid, a green alga.** X 785

**Figure 11 · 4**

**Diversity among cells.**

nucleoli [nōō klē′ə lī′]

of the cell, nuclear substances react differently to stains or take up different amounts of them. This causes a contrast between the nucleus and the surrounding parts of the cell. Unfortunately, most stains kill the cell; but a development in microscopy of the last thirty years—the phase-contrast microscope—allows nuclei to be seen in unstained living cells.

Within the nucleus are one or more small bodies that usually stain even more deeply than the nucleus itself. These are the *nucleoli* (singular, "nucleolus"). In almost all animal cells, in most protist cells, but in rather few plant cells a small structure, the *centrosome,* is found just outside (or in a few cases, just inside) the nuclear membrane. Nucleoli and centrosomes will be discussed later in relation to cell division.

centrosome [Greek: *kentron,* center, + *soma,* body]

The body of the cell outside the nuclear membrane is known as the *cytoplast.* The cytoplast surrounds the nucleus, although the position of the nucleus varies in different kinds of cells—sometimes it is near the center, sometimes far to one side. With the staining methods most commonly used, the cytoplast as a whole absorbs less stain than the nucleus, so it appears lighter.

cytoplast [sī'tə plăst; Greek: *kytos* + *plassein,* to form, mold]

Within the cytoplast are various kinds of small structures (*organelles*) that can be made visible with special staining methods. Even without stains it is easy to see the *plastids,* for most of them are naturally colored by pigments. Plastids are found in cells of plants and some protists. Among the variety of plastids, *chloroplasts,* containing green pigments (chlorophylls), are of major concern to us, because they are involved in photosynthesis.

organelles [ôr'gə nĕlz']: "little organs"

chloroplasts [Greek: *chloros,* green, + *plassein*]

Under a light microscope *mitochondria* (singular, "mitochondrion") appear only as very tiny, rod-shaped bodies that may either be scattered throughout the cytoplast or concentrated in certain places. But under an electron microscope each mitochondrion shows up as a somewhat sausage-shaped body containing parallel infolded layers of membranes (Figure 11 · 5).

mitochondrion [mī'tə kŏn'dri-ən; Greek: *mitos,* thread, + *chondros,* cartilage]

**Figure 11 · 5**

**Mitochondria in a cell from a mouse kidney.**    X 53,000

John H. Luft

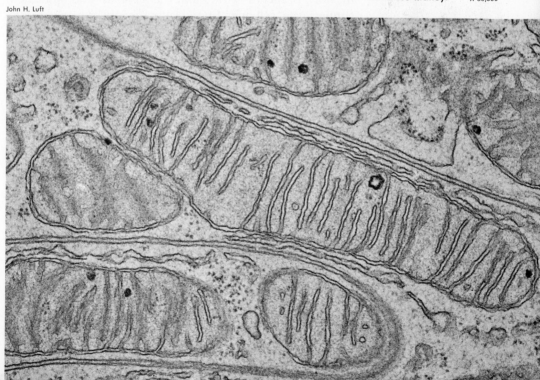

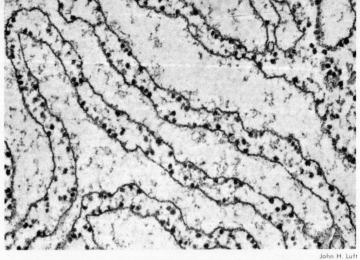

**Figure 11 · 6**

Detail of the endoplasmic reticulum. Note the layered structure.    x 160,000

**Figure 11 · 7**

Part of the cell membrane in a mouse cell.    x 61,000

John H. Luft

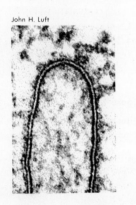

endoplasmic reticulum [ĕn'də-plăz'mĭk rĭ tĭk'yə ləm; Greek: *endon*, within, + *plassein*, and Latin: *retum*, a net]

ribosomes [rī'bə sōmz']

vacuoles [văk'yoŏ ōlz'; Latin: *vacuus*, empty]

The boundary between the cell and its environment is the *cell membrane*. Under a light microscope the membrane appears merely as the outer surface of the cytoplast, but under an electron microscope it clearly has a two-layered structure (Figure 11 · 6). Chemical investigations show that the cell membrane is composed of protein and fatlike substances. Possibly it is made up of two protein layers with a layer of fatlike substance between, which would account for the double appearance of the membrane. The membrane that surrounds the nucleus has a similar structure.

The electron microscope reveals within the cytoplast a membranous network called the *endoplasmic reticulum*. This network branches throughout the cytoplast and appears to connect the cell membrane with the nuclear membrane. Adhering to the endoplasmic reticulum are organelles called *ribosomes*. Other ribosomes are found floating within the cytoplast.

The substance of the cytoplast is a complex and constantly changing mixture of a great variety of organic, and some inorganic, substances in water. Some of these substances clump together to form granular bodies that are sometimes visible under high magnification of a light microscope. Both animal and plant cells contain droplets of liquid (sometimes containing solid particles) that are called *vacuoles*. Vacuoles, usually small and few in the cells of animals and protists, are frequently large and numerous in plant cells.

In addition to cell membranes, the cells of plants and some protists are surrounded by nonliving cell walls. Cell walls are not replacements for cell membranes, but in a living cell the two structures are pressed so closely together that they are frequently difficult to distinguish from one another.

## INVESTIGATION 11.1

### DIVERSITY IN CELL STRUCTURE

#### PURPOSE

This is an observational exercise in which you will compare the structures of several different kinds of living cells — as far as these structures can be seen with a light microscope.

#### MATERIALS AND EQUIPMENT
(for each student or pair of students)

Onion, cut into pieces about 1 cm²

Forceps (fine-pointed)

Microscope slide

Scalpel

Medicine droppers, 3

Cover slips

Monocular microscope

Iodine — potassium-iodide solution (I₂KI)

Paper towels

Elodea leaves

Toothpicks (sterile)

Physiological saline solution

Methylene blue solution

Dissecting needles, 2

Frog blood

Frog skin

#### PROCEDURE

You will be provided with small pieces of onion. On the inner, concave, side the skin (epidermis) may be readily peeled off with forceps. Place a small piece of epidermis (*much* smaller than a cover slip) on a slide, avoiding overlapping or wrinkling. Add one or two drops of water and a cover slip.

Examine the onion epidermis under the low power of the microscope. Look for cell boundaries. Draw a *small section* of the field of view to show how the cells are arranged.

Place a drop of iodine — potassium-iodide stain along one edge of the cover slip. Pull it under the cover slip, using the technique given in Investigation 1.4.

Record any changes that occur as the stain spreads across the onion epidermis. Then switch to high power and draw a single cell, including as much detail as you can see. Label all the parts you can identify. Even with the high power of your microscope, you will be able to see only a few of the parts known to occur in cells.

(*Note*: Be sure to clean slides thoroughly with water and paper towels before placing another kind of material on them.)

With forceps remove a young leaf from near the tip of an elodea plant. Place it on a clean slide and add a drop of water and a cover slip. Observe the leaf under low power. • By slowly turning the fine adjustment back and forth, determine the number of cell layers in the leaf. (1)   Switch to high power. Select an average cell and focus on it carefully.   • Is there any evidence that the cell is living? If so, what is the evidence? (2)   Make a drawing of the cell, including as much detail as you can see. Label all the parts that you can identify.

Using the blunt end of a sterile toothpick, scrape the inside surface of your cheek. Do not dig a hole in your cheek; you should obtain a barely visible mass of material. Rub this material on a *clean* slide. Add a drop of physiological saline solution and stir thoroughly with the toothpick. Examine under low power. By carefully using the fine adjustment, try to observe the three-dimensional shape of the cells. • Would you describe them as spherical, disk-shaped, or neither? (3)   Add a drop or two of methylene blue and a cover slip. Find several cells well separated from the others. Draw one or two of them, including as much detail as you can see. Label all the parts that you can identify.

Place a drop of diluted frog blood on a clean slide. Add a drop of methylene blue and a cover slip. Most of the cells to be seen are red blood cells. Find an area where the cells are neither too crowded nor too scarce and center it in the field of view. Switch to high power. Draw one or two cells and label all the parts that you can identify.

Place scrapings from a frog's skin on a clean slide. Add a drop of physiological saline, one or two drops of methylene blue, and a cover slip. Locate cells with low power and then switch to high power. Draw one or two cells and label all the parts that you can identify.

### SUMMARY

Draw a table like that at the right, allowing a column for each kind of cell structure observed.

Review your sketches and notes. For each kind of cell examined, place an $X$ beneath the name of each cell structure observed.  • Does the lack of an $X$ indicate that the structure was not present in the cells observed? Why or why not? (4)

• On the basis of your observations, which kind of cell (plant or animal) seems to have more angular, less rounded shapes? (5)  • Which has more clearly defined    boundaries? (6)  • What    cell structure may be involved in these characteristics? (7)

| SOURCE OF CELL | CELL WALL | CYTOPLAST | NUCLEUS |
|---|---|---|---|
| Onion epidermis | | | |
| Elodea leaf | | | |

### SOME CELL PHYSIOLOGY

We might study the parts of a clock and still not understand how the clock runs. But it is certain that we could never understand how a clock runs without studying its parts. Investigation of a mechanism's structure is chiefly aimed at learning how it operates. We have been studying some of the visible parts of cells—the structure of cells. Now we can try to understand how a cell runs—how it operates, how it functions. This study of biological function—of biological activity—is called *physiology*.

physiology [fĭz'ĭ ŏl'ə jĭ; Greek: *physis*, nature, + *logikos*]

### METABOLISM

The activities of organisms require energy changes. Since cells are the basic functional units of organisms, it follows that these energy changes must take place within cells. For example, you can move your arm because muscle cells can change chemical energy into the mechanical energy that shortens muscles. In one way or another all activities or functions of organisms basically involve energy changes and chemical reactions. The resulting very large number of continuing chemical reactions in cells are collectively known as *metabolism.*

metabolism    [mə tăb'ə lĭz'əm; Greek: *metaballein,* to change]

In obtaining energy for its activities a cell constantly uses up energy-rich molecules, converting them into energy-poor molecules that are useless for metabolism. But one of the cell's most striking characteristics is its always shifting but, on the average, constant composition—its steady state. Maintaining this steady state, while the stock of useful energy-rich substances is always being reduced and the burden of energy-poor substances is always being added to, obviously demands that substances continually enter and leave a cell.

## TRANSPORT IN CELLS

A cell, then, is an open system. Yet there is a definite boundary—the cell membrane—between a cell and its environment. While the cell membrane acts as a barrier between the living substance and the environment, it must also allow various substances to pass through it. Furthermore, there are internal membranes—the nuclear and mitochondrial ones, for example—through which substances must pass. And of course substances must move from one part of the cell to another. All this adds up to a complex physiological problem: How do substances move into cells, out of cells, and within cells?

**Diffusion.**    The biologist must constantly use concepts developed by physicists and chemists. At this point we need to use the physicists' molecular theory of matter. This theory states that all matter is made up of tiny particles, *molecules,* which are in continuous motion. (Originally the particles were all called molecules—hence the name of the theory; now some may go by other names, such as ion, but we shall continue to use "molecule" for all of them.) The higher the temperature, the faster the molecules move. In solids each molecule's motion is restricted to vibration. In liquids, gases, and dissolved solids the molecules also vibrate, but in addition they move easily from one place to another. These movements appear to be helter-skelter in direction —one molecule bumps into another, and both go off in new directions. This may be described as *random* movement.

molecules [Latin: *moles,* a mass]

vibration [Latin: *vibrare,* to shake]

Do you know any of the evidence on which the molecular theory is based?

If you place a colored, soluble solid in a test tube of water, you observe that over a period of days the color gradually spreads throughout the water. According to the

**Figure 11 · 8**

Diagram of stages in diffusion. In *D* the particles continue to move; but because each moves randomly, they remain evenly distributed in the available space.

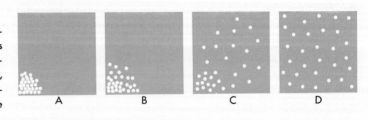

A          B          C          D

diffusion [dĭf yū'zhən; Latin: *dis-*, apart, + *fundere*, to pour]

molecular theory, as the colored substance dissolves, its molecules begin to move in a random manner. This random movement gradually carries them from a place where they are more abundant per unit volume (that is, where their concentration is greater) to places where they are less abundant per unit volume (that is, where their concentration is less). This process is called *diffusion*. Diffusion continues until the molecules of the colored substance are evenly distributed throughout the water in the test tube.

At the same time that the molecules of colored substance are diffusing, the water molecules are also diffusing. Originally there was a *low concentration of water molecules* where the concentration of the colored substance was high and a *high concentration of water molecules* where the concentration of the colored substance was low. The molecular theory, of course, applies to the water molecules as well as to the molecules dissolved in the water.

After the solution is completely uniform, collisions and rebounds continue. But for every molecule that moves from right to left there is another that moves from left to right. Thus the movement is continuous among the molecules without a net change in their distribution—and therefore there is no more diffusion.

Now of course all this movement of molecules implies energy. Where does this energy come from? The energy used in diffusion is the heat of the solution itself. Within cells the energy for diffusion is the cell's heat. Because this heat energy is unavailable for other work by the cell, diffusion does not "cost" the cell any energy.

## INVESTIGATION 11.2

### DIFFUSION THROUGH A MEMBRANE

#### PURPOSE

In this investigation you will explore the diffusions of substances that are separated from one another by a membrane.

## MATERIALS AND EQUIPMENT
### (for each team)

Cellulose tubing, 20-cm lengths, 2

Soluble-starch solution, 15 ml

Rubber bands, 2

Glucose solution, 15 ml

Iodine solution

Beakers, 600 or 1000 ml, 2

Glass-marking crayon

Tes-tape or piece of Clinitest tablet
    in test tube

## PROCEDURE

Open the cellulose tubing by moistening and then rubbing it between the thumb and forefinger. Tie a tight knot about 1 cm from one end of each piece of tubing.

Into one tube pour soluble-starch solution to within about 5 cm of the top. Pinch the top of the tube together tightly and rinse the tube under running water to remove any starch from the outside. Fasten the top of the tube tightly with a rubber band and place the tube in a beaker of water (Figure 11 · 9). Mark the beaker A. Add enough iodine solution to give the water a distinct yellowish color.

iodine solution

cellulose tubing
containing
starch solution

water in beaker

**Figure 11 · 9**

Into the second tube pour glucose solution to within about 5 cm from the top and repeat the procedure given in the previous paragraph—but do not add iodine solution to the water in the beaker. Mark this beaker B.

Allow the tubes to stand about twenty minutes. Then dip a piece of Tes-tape into the water in Beaker B (or pour a small quantity of the water into a test tube containing a fragment of a Clinitest tablet). Record the color. Observe the tube in Beaker A. Record any color change you see in either the tube or the water in the beaker.

Let Setup B stand overnight. The next day record any change observed.

### STUDYING THE DATA

• On the basis of the chemical test for starch, what must have happened to the iodine molecules in Setup A? (1)   • On the basis of the chemical test for glucose, what must have happened to the glucose molecules in Setup B? (2)   • From the evidence obtained by allowing Setup B to stand overnight, what other substance must have passed through the membrane? (3)   • Which material did not pass through a membrane? How do you know? (4)

### CONCLUSIONS

Physicists can show that the molecules of any one substance are all about the same size but that the molecules of different substances are different in size. Measurements show that iodine molecules and water molecules are very small, glucose molecules are considerably larger, and starch molecules (synthesized from many glucose molecules—page 413) are very large.   • On this basis suggest a hypothesis to account for the observations made in this exercise. (5)   • In this hypothesis what assumption must you make about the structure of the membrane? (6)

**The cell membrane.**   The contents of cells are largely solutions or suspensions of materials in water; all active (that is, not dormant) living cells exist in a water environment. Cells of the human body are no exception. Every one of our living cells (cells of the outer skin are dead) is coated with moisture. Therefore, an active living cell is a mixture of things in water, separated by its cell membrane from another mixture of things in water, its environment. The cell membrane is the boundary that separates this unit of living materials from the rest of the universe. Within the cell membrane occur all the activities that, taken together, make up what we mean by "life." (Actually, the membrane is living too, so the word "within" must be thought of as including the membrane itself.) Through the cell membrane, then, must pass everything that the cell obtains from the environment, and through it must pass also everything that the cell returns to the environment.

**Diffusion through membranes.**   A paper bag will hold potatoes, but it will not hold water very long. A plastic bag will hold water, but oxygen will pass through the plastic fast enough to keep a goldfish alive in the water (but not fast enough to keep *you* alive—you need more oxygen than a goldfish does). The paper bag is *permeable* to water but not to potatoes; the plastic bag is permeable to oxygen but not to water. A membrane that is permeable to some substances and not to others is said to be *differentially* permeable.

permeable [pûr′mǐ ə bəl; Latin: *per*, through, + *meare*, to glide, flow]

differentially [dǐf ə rěn′shǐ ə lǐ]

Among molecules that diffuse easily through cell membranes are those of water, carbon dioxide, and oxygen. Many ions of inorganic substances also diffuse easily. But the molecules of many compounds that are dissolved or suspended inside the cell are too large to pass through the cell membrane by diffusion.

The *direction* in which any given kind of molecule or ion diffuses is determined, as we have discussed above, by its concentration. If the concentration is greater outside the cell, the direction of diffusion is into the cell. The direction is outward if the concentration is higher within the cell.

Differential permeability is of special importance when we consider the water-diffusion relationships of a cell. Let us assume that Compound X, whose molecules are too large to diffuse through the cell membrane, is found in a relatively high concentration within a cell but does not occur in the fluid outside the cell.

First, *imagine* that the cell has no membrane. The tendency for the solution to become uniform results in the diffusion of the molecules of X from the area of their higher concentration to the area of their lower concentration (Figure 11 · 8). Also (and this is very important) water molecules diffuse from the area of their higher concentration (which is where the concentration of X is lower) to the area of their lower concentration (which is where the concentration of X is higher). This, of course, is the situation that was described earlier (pages 387–388).

Now consider the *real* situation. The high and low concentrations of X are separated by the differentially permeable cell membrane. Obviously only *one* of the two movements of molecules can occur—the movement of water molecules through the cell membrane into the cell (Figure 11 · 10). Therefore water accumulates inside the cell. This creates pressure on the membrane from the inside. The pressure may even be sufficient to burst the membrane.

*Why must the concentration of water molecules be lower where the concentration of other molecules is higher, and vice versa?*

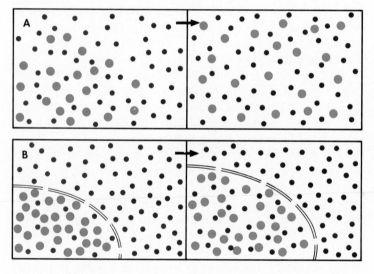

**Figure 11 · 10**

Diagram of diffusion without a differentially permeable membrane (A) and with such a membrane (B). Black dots represent water molecules; blue dots represent molecules of a substance dissolved in water.

A paramecium lives in a freshwater environment. Within a paramecium there is a much higher concentration of molecules that cannot diffuse through its cell membrane than there is outside. Just as in Figure 11 · 10, water diffuses from the environment into the paramecium because the concentration of the *water* is higher outside the paramecium than it is inside. In the paramecium, however, the excess water is continuously accumulated in a vacuole and periodically expelled to the exterior. The paramecium must constantly "pump" water out or it will be flooded. This, of course, is work—it costs energy.

As you saw in Investigation 11.2, substances other than water diffuse through cell membranes. Some relatively large molecules of kinds that are soluble in fat or oil can diffuse through quite freely. This is probably because

*Review your data from Investigation 9.2. Can you now give a fuller explanation of your results?*

they easily enter into solution in the fatty part of the cell membrane.

All of this sounds as though cell membranes and non-living membranes function alike. To some extent this is true. But unlike nonliving membranes, cell membranes have constantly changing permeabilities. Substances that pass readily through a living membrane at one time may not pass through at other times. Such changes in permeability are frequently observed by biologists, but they are difficult to explain.

**Active transport.** Not all movements of substances through cell membranes can be explained by diffusion. For example, in most cells the concentration of potassium ions is many times greater inside the cell than it is outside. It can be demonstrated that potassium ions readily pass through cell membranes by diffusion. Then how is it possible for a cell to retain a high concentration of potassium ions when there is a low concentration in the environment? Why is it that these ions do not leave the cell by diffusion?

In fact, there *is* a constant diffusion of potassium ions from the cell. Careful investigation has shown, however, that the cell has a mechanism that moves potassium ions from the environmental fluid into the cell at a rate at least as great as the rate at which they are lost by diffusion. This inward movement of potassium can be called an "uphill" movement, because it is opposite to the natural direction taken by the diffusion of the ions. Cell physiologists use the term "ion pumps" for mechanisms that move ions "uphill" from a region of low concentration to one of high concentration. Of course these are not mechanical devices, but their action requires the expenditure of energy — work — just as it is necessary to use energy to operate a water pump or an air pump.

In addition to ions, many other things are now known to be moved from lower to higher concentrations. And this occurs not only through external cell membranes but also through the membranes of mitochondria and nuclei. Any such movement is called *active transport*.

**Pinocytosis.** Materials that pass through cell membranes by diffusion and active transport are in the form of relatively small molecules and ions. However, very large molecules, even large aggregations of molecules, and volumes of liquid can also pass through cell membranes. Just how the cell accomplishes this is not thoroughly understood, but electronmicrography has been very helpful in picturing the process. At present it seems that a mass of solid or liquid matter lying adjacent to the cell is surrounded by extensions of the membrane. When the mass is

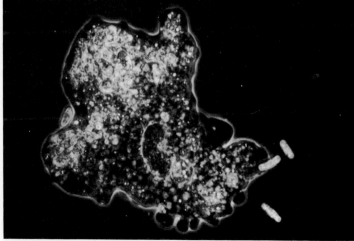

Harry Wessenberg

**Figure 11 · 11**

An ameba feeds by a process somewhat similar to pinocytosis. Here a solid particle is being surrounded by a pseudopod.   × 300

completely enclosed, it may move off as a vacuole into the cytoplast. Although separate terms have been applied to such intake of solid and liquid substances, here we refer to both by the single term *pinocytosis*.

Many cells form large molecules that are then passed through their cell membranes into the environment. Often this transfer involves the accumulation of the molecules in granules that are surrounded by membranes similar in appearance to cell membranes. The granules then move to the cell surface so that the membrane of a granule comes in contact with the cell membrane. The fused membranes rupture, permitting the granule to escape. If we consider the granule as approximately equivalent to a vacuole, this process is somewhat similar to pinocytosis except that it moves material in the opposite direction through the cell membrane. In any case, like pinocytosis it requires expenditure of energy by the cell.

pinocytosis   [pĭ nō sī tō′sĭs; Greek: *pinein*, to drink, + *kytos*]

**Cyclosis.** In most cells diffusion probably accounts for the distribution of substances within the cytoplast. In many kinds of cells, however, substances are carried about by the motion of the matter making up the cytoplast. Especially in plants and protists it is possible to observe this "streaming," called *cyclosis*, with the high power of an ordinary laboratory microscope. Although the exact way in which cyclosis occurs is not known, it is clear that it requires the expenditure of energy, just as active transport and pinocytosis do.

cyclosis [sĭ klō′səs]

## CELL DUPLICATION

The third major idea in the cell theory is that all cells are produced by preexisting cells. Why and when does one cell become two? Biologists are not at all sure. Indirectly such cell duplication is probably related to the maximum size that a *given kind* of cell can manage to maintain. Among cells of different kinds there is an enormous variation in size. For example, the yolk of an ostrich egg (a single cell) is about 300,000 times larger than a rickettsial cell. But for a given kind of cell there may be a maximum limit to the size it can maintain. If so, then for the cell to continue growing, it must divide, even though attainment of a certain size is not the direct cause of division.

attainment [ə tān′mənt; Latin: *ad*, to, + *tangere*, to touch]: here, reaching

Whatever the cause, cells *do* divide; and when one cell has divided into two, cell reproduction has taken place. Usually the nucleus and cytoplast divide almost simultaneously, but sometimes they behave differently. The nucleus may divide, but not the cytoplast; such division, if repeated, will give rise to a structure like the hypha of *Rhizopus* (Figure 11 · 12). Or the nucleus may divide, with division of the cytoplast occurring at some later time, as in spore formation by ascomycetes.

simultaneously [sī′məl tā′nē əs-lī; Latin: *simul*, together with]: refers to two things happening at the same time

Is the structure of *Rhizopus* an exception to the cell theory?

### MITOSIS

Division of the nuclear substances seems to be a very important part of cellular reproduction. Mature human red blood cells, which have no nuclei, never divide; instead, they survive a short time (about 110 days) and then disintegrate. On the other hand, the cells of blue-green algae divide even though they have no definitely organized nuclei. However, special staining methods have shown that the same substances that characterize nuclei in other organisms occur in blue-green algae.

disintegrate    [dĭs ĭnt′ə grāt′; Latin: *dis-*, apart, + *integer*, whole]

In the great majority of cells there *is* a definite nucleus, and nuclear division is observable as a clear sequence of events. So much attention has been concentrated on this sequence that the name for it, *mitosis*, is sometimes incorrectly applied to the whole process of cell division.

mitosis [mī tō′sĭs; Greek: *mitos*, a thread]

Mitosis is a remarkably uniform process. There are, however, some slight differences between the ways it occurs in most plant cells and in most animal cells. We shall describe and illustrate mitosis of animal cells and then, in the laboratory, investigate mitosis in plant cells.

Mitosis is a *continuous* process. Therefore, it can be illustrated adequately only in motion pictures. In studying the illustrations in this book and your microscope slides, use your imagination to fill in between the "still pictures."

X 1250

**Figure 11 · 12**

**Hypha of black bread mold (*Rhizopus*).**

### CELL DIVISION IN ANIMALS

The first observable event in animal mitosis is the division of the centrosome. The two portions of the centro-

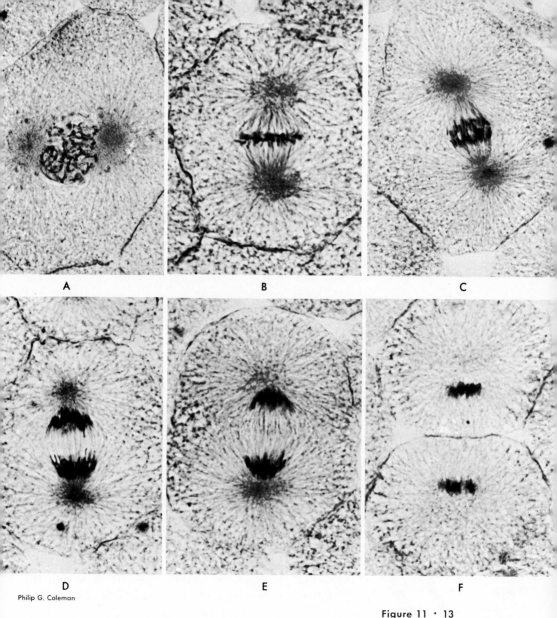

A  B  C

D  E  F

Philip G. Coleman

Figure 11 · 13

Six photographs of mitosis
in the cells of an embryonic
whitefish. In A the process is
just beginning, and in F it
is nearly completed; but
the times between photo-
graphs are not equal. How
many cell parts can you
identify?    X 1000

some separate and begin to move around the nucleus.
(Refer to Figure 11 · 13 as you read on.) Fiber-like structures develop around them, radiating from each half centrosome like the spokes of a wheel. As the two portions of
the centrosome continue to move away from each other,
the fibers between them lengthen, forming a structure
called a *spindle*. While these events are occurring, the nucleolus diminishes in size and disappears. The nuclear
membrane disintegrates and also disappears.

At the time that the parts of the centrosome are
moving, the nuclear material increases in stainability. This

chromosomes    [krō′mə sōmz′;
Greek: *chroma*, color, + *soma*,
body]

kinetochore    [kĭ′nĕ′tə kōr;
Greek: *kinetos*, moving, + *chor-
os*, a place]

equidistant [ē′kwə dĭs′tənt; Latin: *aequus*, equal, + *distare*, to
stand apart]

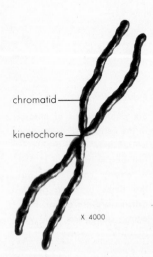

chromatid ———

kinetochore ———

X 4000

**Figure 11 · 14**

A chromosome before sep-
aration of chromatids.

enables an observer to see a set of threadlike parts, called
*chromosomes*, in the nucleus. Close examination shows that
each chromosome is double from the time it can first be
seen. Each strand of a chromosome is called a *chromatid*. The
chromatids are attached to each other at a single point, the
*kinetochore* (a synonym is "centromere"). Gradually the
chromosomes become shorter, thicker, and more distinct.
Under high magnification it becomes clear that this is due
to coiling, just as a long, thin wire can be coiled into a
shorter and thicker spring.

By the time the spindle is complete—that is, when the
centrosome halves are 180° apart on the circumference of
the nucleus—the chromosomes are fully coiled. If we call
the positions of the centrosome halves the "poles" of the
spindle, then we can imagine a plane across the center of
the spindle and equidistant from the poles. This we call the
*equatorial plate.* (Because of high magnification the cells in
the photographs appear two-dimensional, so the equatorial
plate seems to be a line rather than a plane.) The chromosomes move toward the equatorial plate, and their kinetochores become attached to spindle fibers. The kinetochore
of each chromosome now divides, so the paired chromatids
separate from one another; however, each kinetochore
remains attached to a fiber of the spindle.

The chromatids from each chromosome move apart.
Once separated from its former partner, each chromatid of
a pair is referred to as a chromosome. One member of each
pair moves away from the equatorial plate and toward one
pole of the spindle; the second moves toward the other pole.
Each kinetochore leads the way as though pulled by a
shortening of the spindle fibers; the rest of the new chromosome trails along.

Now the fibers of the spindle begin to fade and the
chromosomes start to uncoil. At each pole a new nuclear
membrane forms around the group of chromosomes, leaving the centrosome outside. A nucleolus appears within
each new nuclear membrane. At some time before the next
nuclear division occurs, the chromosomes become double
(with two chromatids) again; but this cannot be seen. The
formation of new nuclei ends mitosis.

Usually division of the cytoplast begins as new chromosomes approach the poles. A furrow forms around the cytoplast in the equatorial plate and deepens until the original
cell is cut in two. Because they cluster near the equatorial
plate, the mitochondria in the cytoplast are distributed
more or less equally between the two new cells. The division
of the cytoplast, unlike that of the nucleus, is not always
equal, but its completion ends cell division.

## SIGNIFICANCE OF MITOSIS

Nuclei were discovered and named by Robert Brown, who in 1831 reported seeing small bodies within plant cells he had studied. How little he understood the importance of his discovery is shown by the fact that he merely mentioned it in a footnote. Because the unstained nucleus is difficult to see with ordinary microscopes, practically nothing was learned about it until stains came into use. Thus, the behavior of the nucleus during mitosis was first described less than a hundred years ago. But even before the discovery of mitosis biologists had begun to ask questions to which mitosis is clearly related: Why does each "daughter cell" have the characteristics of the "parent cell"? What determines the characteristics of a cell? How are activities of a cell controlled?

The elaborate sequence of events in mitosis appears to be a device to ensure exact, equal division of the nuclear substance—which suggests that this substance is very important. Research during the past eight decades has amply supported this idea. Abundant evidence shows that complex nuclear substances regulate the activities of a cell and that the characteristics of a cell, both structural and functional, are expressions of these activities. Thus, maintaining characteristics from one cell generation to the next depends upon the duplication and separation of the chromosomes in the parent cell, with full, identical sets being transmitted to all daughter cells. Apparently each bit of chromosome material is duplicated before the chromosomes become visible in mitosis. Thus the chromatids in a pair are exact duplicates throughout their length. Then the events of mitosis provide that one chromatid of each pair ends up in each new cell.

Robert Brown: 1773–1858. Scottish botanist

elaborate [ĭ lăb'ə rĭt; Latin: ex, out, + laborare, to work]

## INVESTIGATION 11.3

## MITOSIS AND CELL DIVISION IN PLANT CELLS

### PURPOSE

In this investigation you will learn how to prepare plant cells for microscopic observation of mitosis and cell division. You will then compare your observations with illustrations of mitosis and cell division in animal cells.

### BACKGROUND INFORMATION

If an onion is placed with its base in water and kept in the dark for several days, slender white roots will sprout from it and grow into the water. This growth occurs partly by multiplication of cells. Therefore, if the end of a root is

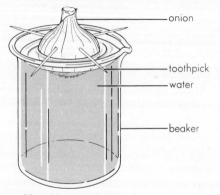

**Figure 11 · 15**
Setup for growing onion-root tips.

cut off, mounted in water, and examined under the microscope, you might expect to see cell division and mitosis. But in fact very few of the steps in these processes can be observed. There are simply too many cells closely packed together to permit much to be seen. However, root tips *can* be quickly and simply prepared so that individual cells—or parts of them—are clearly observable.

In an alternative procedure, a root is stained and then gradually saturated with a supporting substance such as paraffin. It is cut into a series of very thin slices with a microtome, and the slices are mounted on slides. The mounting medium is one that hardens and thus makes a permanent preparation.

### MATERIALS AND EQUIPMENT

Solution of one part concentrated
   hydrochloric acid and one part
   95% alcohol solution
Watch glasses, Syracuse, 2
Forceps, fine-pointed
Onion roots, in 70% alcohol
Carnoy's fluid (with chloroform)
Microscope slide
Scalpel or razor blade
Aceto-orcein solution
Cover slip
Cleansing tissue
Monocular microscope
Prepared slide, long sections of onion-root tip

### PROCEDURE

Pour hydrochloric acid—95% alcohol solution into a Syracuse watch glass to a depth of about 3 mm. Using forceps, pick up a root that has been fixed in 70% alcohol, *grasping it by the cut end* and not by the pointed end. (Caution: In all later operations handle the root by the cut end only.) Transfer the root to the watch glass. Allow it to remain in the solution for five minutes. This treatment breaks down the cementing material that holds the cells together. Shortly before the five minutes is up, pour Carnoy's fluid (with chloroform) into a second watch glass, again to a depth of 3 mm. Using forceps, transfer the root to this second watch glass and allow it to remain there for three minutes. This treatment hardens the material which has been softened by the acid treatment and reduces damage to the cells in subsequent procedures. Again using forceps, transfer the root to the center of a clean slide. Using a scalpel or razor blade, cut off the tip (the last 2 mm or less of the root) and discard the rest. Immediately add one or two drops of aceto-orcein solution. Cut the tip into small pieces and allow these to remain in the solution for five minutes. This solution stains certain cell structures, including nuclei and chromosomes. Do not let the preparation dry up; if it appears to be doing so, add another drop of solution. Next place a clean cover slip over the pieces of root tip and tap lightly on the cover slip with the point of a pencil held vertically. This will separate the cells and spread them out under the cover slip. Now, fold a cleansing tissue several times so that it is the same shape but slightly larger than the slide. Then make a final fold in the tissue, bringing its ends together. Place the tissue on the table and insert the part of the slide where the cover slip is located into the final fold, making a "sandwich," with

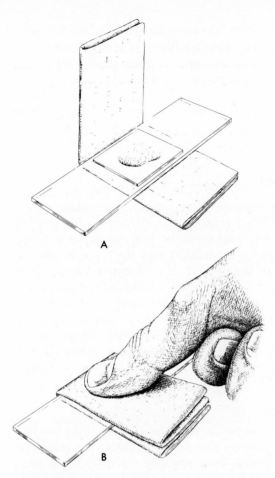

**A**

**B**

Figure 11 · 16
Making a "squash" preparation.

several layers of tissue under the slide and several on top of the cover slip. With the "sandwich" resting flat on the table, press down vertically with your thumb on the upper layer of cleansing tissue. Be careful to apply pressure without twisting so that the cover slip is not moved laterally in relation to the slide. This will further spread the cells and flatten them. Finally, carefully remove the slide from the cleansing tissue. You have now made a "squash" preparation.

#### OBSERVATIONS

Examine the slide under low power of the microscope. Move the slide so that you scan the entire area under the cover slip. Look for cells in which the nucleus appears to be made up of distinct threadlike parts. Such cells were undergoing mitosis at the time they were killed. Locate an area where cells in various stage of mitosis are numerous. Switch to high power and examine this area carefully. If necessary, adjust the diaphragm of your microscope to increase the clarity of the image. Draw at least five entire cells, each in a different stage of mitosis. Then number your drawings in the order in which you think the stages occur during mitosis. Use the illustrations of animal-cell mitosis on page 395 as a guide.

Now examine a prepared slide containing longitudinal sections of onion-root tip. Study each section first under low power and then under high power. • In what region of the root tip are most of the cells that are undergoing mitosis? (1) • How does the shape of cells undergoing mitosis compare with that of cells located in other parts of the sections? (2) Study a number of cells in different stages of mitosis plus several which do not appear to be dividing. • Are any structures visible in these cells on the prepared slide that you could not see in the "squash" preparation? If so, draw one or more cells showing these structures. (3) Refer to the illustrations of dividing animal cells on page 395. • What differences, if any, can you find in the ways mitosis and cell division occur in animal cells and in plant cells? (4)

#### FOR FURTHER INVESTIGATION

1. If you were attempting to determine the number of chromosomes present in cells of a bean root, would it be better to use "squash" preparations or sections of the root?

2. Suppose you suspected that frequency of mitosis in onion roots varied

with the time of day. How would you go about getting data to confirm or refute your suspicion?

3. Do all the events in mitosis take about the same time, or do some of them occur faster than others? How would you proceed experimentally to obtain information to answer this question?

## DIFFERENTIATION

unicellular [ū′nə sĕl′yə lər; Latin: *unus*, one, + *cella*]

After cell division one of two things may follow: either the daughter cells separate or the daughter cells remain together. In the first case there are two unicellular individuals—cell duplication is identical with the reproduction of the individual. In the second case repeated cell divisions result in groups of connected cells. If the cells in the group remain approximately alike, the group is a colony. But if the cells come to differ from each other in various ways, the group becomes a multicellular individual. Because cells usually increase in size between divisions, repeated cell divisions usually result in the growth of a colony or multicellular individual.

multicellular [mŭl′tĭ-; Latin: *multus*, many, + *cella*]

### A PUZZLE

paradox [Greek: *para*, beyond, + *doxa*, opinion]: an apparently contradictory statement

Buried in the last paragraph is a paradox. If the mechanism of mitosis ensures that both daughter cells will have the *same characteristics*, then how can any of the cells in a group derived from the same parent cell come to *differ* from the others? But differ they do, as you know from observing blood and skin cells of the frog; both of these descended from a single cell! Indeed, every multicellular organism—an oak tree, a cow, a man—develops from a single cell; yet the adult contains cells of a great many kinds.

What is known about this process of *differentiation*? In the past seventy years a multitude of ingenious experiments have provided biologists with information about the mechanisms. It is clear that the cell's final differentiation involves (1) selective use of information stored in the chromosomes, (2) ways in which adjacent cells affect each other in the developing organism, and (3) factors in the environment. Yet the fundamental question—How does differentiation occur?—remains unanswered.

### RESULTS OF DIFFERENTIATION

Differentiation is an orderly process. Cells do not become endlessly different; they become different in limited and predictable ways. Further, they become different in

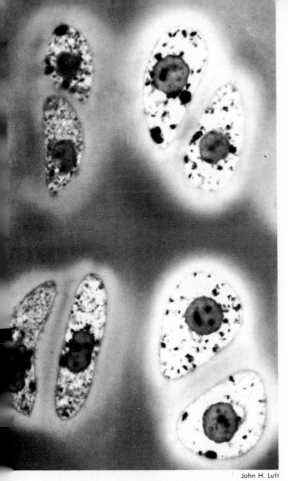

John H. Luft

A. Cartilage from a frog. X 1350

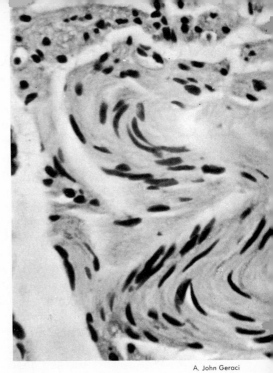

A. John Geraci

B. Spinal cord. X 100

Figure 11 · 17

Diversity among tissues.

D. Wood. X 35

Harold V. Green

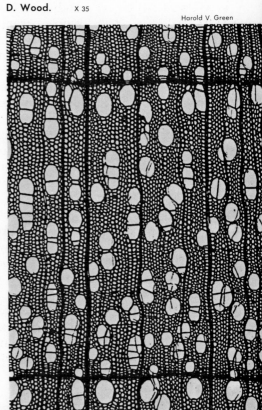

C. Pith from a grape stem. X 60

Martin H. Zimmerman

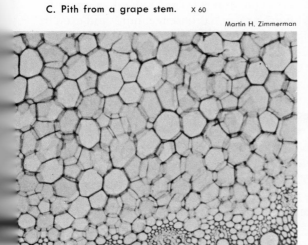

groups rather than individually. Microscopic examination of a multicellular organism therefore may reveal the same basic structural characteristics in each member of a particular group of cells. In another group all cells may be similar among themselves but differ from those in the first group. Groups in which all cells have similar structural and functional characteristics are called *tissues*.

A tissue might be considered a population of similar cells, just as a species is a population of similar individuals. In both cases one population is surrounded by other populations—in the first case, by other kinds of cells; in the second, by other kinds of individuals. In both cases a population has many close and necessary relations with adjacent populations. And just as we can artificially remove a portion of a population of individual organisms—a mouse colony, for example—from its ecosystem and keep it in a laboratory, we can also remove a population of similar cells—muscle tissue, perhaps—and cultivate it in a test tube. In such laboratory situations many valuable things can be learned about tissues and the structure and functioning of the whole organism. But under natural conditions neither a mouse colony nor a muscle tissue lives alone.

What things would you have to do in order to maintain a tissue culture of, say, muscle?

Some multicellular organisms, such as sponges and some algae, seem to have no organization other than that of tissues. But most have different tissues grouped into body parts that perform one or more functions for the whole organism. Such a body part—a leaf or a heart, for example—is called an *organ*. Organs, like tissues, can be removed from the organism and tended artificially, but this is not done as often as with tissues.

Finally, organs may be considered as parts of groups that perform some large function—circulation, for instance. Such a group of organs is called an *organ system*. In the plant kingdom this term has little meaning, and even in the animal kingdom an organ system is a less definite thing than an organ or a tissue.

## AGING

No cell lives forever. It either divides to form new cells or dies. Many years ago August Weismann suggested that unicellular organisms are potentially immortal—that is, unless they die because of unfavorable environmental effects (lack of food, accumulation of poisonous wastes, being eaten by other organisms, etc.), they produce endless numbers of cell generations. This appears to be a valid generalization. But, of course, to be really certain it would be necessary to maintain such organisms for very long

August Weismann [vīs'män]: 1834–1914. German biologist

valid [Latin: *valere*, to be strong]: well supported by observations

periods of time in environments containing no unfavorable factors.

Weismann further suggested that in multicellular animals only reproductive cells — those that give rise to new individuals — are potentially immortal. They are passed essentially without change from one generation to the next. In differentiating, the other cells, the "body cells," lose the ability to give rise to new individuals; so when the organism in which they occur dies, they die without descendants. One difficulty with this idea arose when zoologists found that during the early part of an animal's development they could not always clearly trace the origin of the reproductive cells. However, in the main, Weismann's generalization is probably valid.

Like so many generalizations in biology, this one raises further questions. Why do body cells age and die? Do aging and death in body cells, as in microorganisms, result from harmful environmental effects? Or do they result from internal changes that are caused by differentiation?

Perhaps there is no simple answer that holds for all kinds of cells. It seems clear that in many vertebrates the cells of the outer layer of skin and of the lining of the intestine die as a result of unfavorable environmental conditions. On the other hand an internal cause — lack of nuclei — has been suggested as the cause of the early death of red blood cells of mammals. But the red blood cells of birds, which *do* contain nuclei, also have a short life-span.

Some evidence exists that hereditary changes occur early in the differentiation of some kinds of cells. Some of these changes may be harmful to the metabolic processes. In recent years some biologists have come to believe that the accumulation of such harmful changes may "slow down" a cell and result in what we call aging. But why do not such changes also occur and accumulate in reproductive cells and in unicellular organisms?

Many kinds of cells that are grown in tissue cultures in the laboratory, where they are maintained in an excellent environment, survive and go through cell division almost indefinitely. This suggests that aging, failure to divide, and death may be caused by the cellular environment within the body. But differentiation of cells is itself, at least in part, dependent on that internal environment. In many respects, therefore, tissue-culture cells may not be "normally" differentiated, so we cannot have complete confidence in such evidence.

Like the problem of differentiation, the problems of aging and death of cells are complex. Perhaps we shall understand more when we are able to think about the

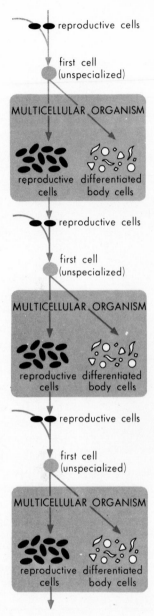

**Figure 11 · 18**

Weismann's concept of the continuity of cells in successive generations of multicellular organisms.

entire life history of a cell as a continuous process rather than about division, differentiation, aging, and death as separate processes.

---

The concept covered by the word "cell" has changed greatly since cells were discovered. Today the cell is regarded as the unit of structure, of function, and of reproduction in living things. Even in its present state, however, the cell theory cannot be perfectly applied to all organisms.

Cells differ greatly in size, shape, and kinds of parts. In general, the cell consists of a nucleus and a cytoplast which can be distinguished by differences in reaction to stains. Within the cytoplast are organelles that carry on special cell functions. Separating the cell from its environment is a membrane; through it must pass, inward, all the materials the cell uses and, outward, all the materials the cell discards. Diffusion, active transport, and pinocytosis account for much of this inflow and outflow and also for the passage of substances through membranes within the cell. Diffusion and cyclosis move substances within the cytoplast itself. The energy used for various cell activities comes from chemical reactions within the cell. The sum of these chemical reactions is metabolism.

In one-celled organisms, duplication of cells results in new individuals. In multicellular organisms, cell duplication results in increasing the number of cells within the individual. Mitosis, the series of nuclear changes that occurs during cell duplication, is remarkably similar in all cells. Mitosis provides each new cell with a set of chromosomes that is a duplicate of the set in the parent cell.

Although cells tend to produce daughter cells like themselves, the daughter cells differentiate during the development of multicellular organisms. In multicellular organisms, groups of cells that are similar in structure and function are called tissues. Different tissues may be organized into organs. Finally, in studying the larger animals, it is convenient to consider organs that together perform some major function as parts of an organ system.

---

## GUIDE QUESTIONS

1. How has the meaning of the word "cell" changed since Hooke's time?
2. What is the cell theory? Why do you think it is called a "theory"?
3. How are staining techniques useful in the study of cells?
4. Contrast cells of plants, animals, and protists, using the principal cell structures as the basis for distinguishing them. Is the distinction clear-cut?
5. What is meant by the metabolism of a cell?
6. What are the *facts* of diffusion? How does the molecular theory explain the facts?

7. Molecules of different sizes can pass back and forth through a cell's membrane, yet the substance of the cell remains easily distinguishable from the substance of its environment. Explain.

8. If water molecules are less concentrated outside a cell membrane than they are within the membrane, what will be the direction of water diffusion?

9. What observations by cell physiologists support the theory of active transport?

10. How do particles that pass through cell membranes by pinocytosis differ from particles moved by diffusion and active transport?

11. Which of the processes by which substances move into and out of cells require the use of a cell's energy?

12. The terms "mitosis" and "cell division" are not synonymous. Explain.

13. In your own words describe the principal events that occur during mitosis.

14. What seems to be the biological meaning of mitosis?

15. How does cell differentiation seem to contradict this meaning?

16. Distinguish between cells, tissues, organs, and systems.

17. When cells differentiate, which of their abilities often declines?

18. Why do cells age?

**PROBLEMS**

1. During the late nineteenth century most knowledge of detailed cell structure was gained by studying stained dead cells. Some biologists objected to many conclusions drawn from such observation, arguing that the processes of killing, staining, and mounting cells on slides might cause cell structure to appear very different from cell structure in life. What kinds of evidence are now available to meet at least some of these objections?

2. Examine various kinds of cells from multicellular organisms, either under the microscope or by means of photomicrographs in books. Discuss the relationships between the structural forms of the cells and their functions.

3. Working in a police laboratory, you are given a tiny sample of material and asked to identify it as either plant or animal matter. How could you decide which it is?

4. On the basis of your understanding of the diffusion of water, describe what would happen to (a) a marine jellyfish placed in a freshwater stream, and (b) a frog placed in ocean water. Some fish (for example, shad and striped bass) annually swim from the ocean into freshwater rivers and back. How are they able to do this?

5. In this chapter mitosis in cells that have a single, well-defined nucleus was described. Investigate what is known about the behavior of nuclear material (chromatin) during division in (a) a "cell" that has more than one nucleus—*Paramecium,* for example, and (b) a "cell" that lacks a nucleus—a blue-green alga.

6. Much of the money available for cancer research goes into studies of cell differentiation. Why?

7. In what ways are cells of multicellular organisms held together?

8. The living substance of cells is often called "protoplasm." Many biologists object to the use of the term. Find out why.

9. Much of the modern understanding of cell structure has resulted from invention of new optical instruments. What kinds of information have been provided by means of electron microscopes? By means of phase-contrast microscopes?

## SUGGESTED READINGS

(See also books by Asimov, by Mercer, and by Loewy and Siekevitz listed at the end of Chapter 12.)

GREEN, D. E. "The Mitochondrion," *Scientific American,* January, 1964. Pp. 63–66+.

HOLTER, H. "How Things Get into Cells," *Scientific American,* September, 1961. Pp. 167–174+.

MAZIA, D. *Cell Division.* (BSCS Pamphlet 14.) Boston: D. C. Heath and Co., 1964. (Emphasis on the details of mitosis and the problems that cell biologists are exploring.)

ROBERTSON, J. D. "The Membrane of the Living Cell," *Scientific American,* April, 1962. Pp. 64–72.

SIMPSON, G. G., and W. S. BECK. *Life: An Introduction to Biology.* 2nd ed. New York: Harcourt, Brace & World, Inc., 1965. Chapter 3. (Fine illustrations and clear writing make this one of the best accounts of cells written for college freshmen.)

SOLOMON, A. K. "Pumps in the Living Cell," *Scientific American,* August, 1962. Pp. 100–108.

SPRATT, N. T. *Introduction to Cell Differentiation.* New York: Reinhold Publishing Corp., 1964. (A clear discussion of present-day understanding based on experimental investigation. Requires some knowledge of genetics.)

SWANSON, C. P. *The Cell.* 2nd ed. Englewood Cliffs, N.J.: Prentice-Hall, Inc., 1964. (An excellent summary of modern cell studies. Fairly advanced.)

# Bioenergetics

## LIFE, ENERGY, AND CELLS

Two hundred seeds of a sequoia tree would not even fill a tablespoon. Planted in a favorable environment, each seed may develop into a towering organism such as the "General Sherman" tree, which is almost 90 m high and has a circumference of more than 33 m. Where does the energy to build the tons of organic compounds in leaf, stem, and root come from?

You walk along the shore of a pond: frogs leap from the bank; ducks dabble in the shallows; swallows fly through the air. What is the source of the energy for all this muscular activity?

From the very beginning, this course has repeatedly emphasized that life always involves energy. Sections One and Three examined the general scheme of energy flow through the biosphere in some detail. As yet, however, we have not investigated the chemical means by which living things perform the various kinds of energy changes involved in this scheme. We are now in a position to do so.

According to the cell theory a cell is the functional unit in any organism. In Chapter 11 we began to discuss cellular function—cellular physiology; now we continue the discussion, centering our attention upon the biochemistry of energy transformations—*bioenergetics*.

If a cell has a pigment that can trap radiant energy, it stores the energy in chemical form (food) by the process of photosynthesis. If a cell does not have such pigment—or if it has the pigment but lacks a supply of radiant energy—it must obtain energy from food. In any case, energy to carry on moment-to-moment cell processes comes from food,

bioenergetics [bī′ō ĕn′ər jĕd′-ĭks; Greek: *bios*, life, + en, in, + *ergon*, work]

whether the food be made within the cell or taken in from the environment.

A pine tree is a producer organism. But many cells in its roots, its trunk, its branches—all those cells that do not contain chlorophyll—function like the cells in a consumer. Even its green cells, when they are not supplied with light, depend upon energy-containing carbon compounds to sustain life until they are again exposed to sunlight. The release of energy from food occurs in all cells at all times—as long as they are alive. It is appropriate, therefore, to begin the consideration of bioenergetics with the energy-releasing processes of cells.

## INVESTIGATION 12.1

### BIOENERGETICS: AN INTRODUCTORY VIEW

#### PURPOSE

In this investigation you will measure the effects of some biochemical reactions.

#### MATERIALS AND EQUIPMENT
(for each team)

Pea seeds, 80
Beakers, 50 ml, 2
Volumeter
Graduated cylinder, 100 ml, 1
Glass beads, a volume of about 100 cc
Paper towels
Glass rod
Nonabsorbent cotton
Spatula, porcelain
Ascarite, about 3 cc
Medicine dropper
Water colored with eosin
   (for special team)
Pea seeds, a volume of about 400 cc
Beakers, 400 ml, 2
Vacuum bottles, 2
Nonabsorbent cotton
1-hole rubber stoppers to fit vacuum bottles, 2
Thermometers (−10 to +110°C), 2
Glycerin

#### PROCEDURE

**Day 1.** Place 40 small pea seeds in a small beaker and add water until the seeds are well covered. Place another 40 pea seeds in a second beaker without water. Set the beakers aside for twenty-four hours. • Considering your experience in Investigation 1.2, what effect should soaking have on dormant embryos within seeds? (1)

Assemble a volumeter as illustrated in Figure 12·1. Before continuing this investigation, you must understand how

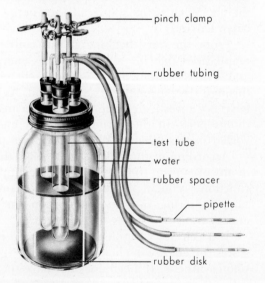

Figure 12 · 1
Volumeter.

pinch clamp

rubber tubing

test tube

water

rubber spacer

pipette

rubber disk

this apparatus works. The teacher will demonstrate its use.

A special team in each class will place two additional lots of peas (each having a volume of about 200 cc) in beakers, adding water to cover the seeds in one beaker and leaving the second without water. Set the beakers aside for twenty-four hours.

**Day 2.** Remove the stoppers from the volumeter tubes. Measure 50 ml of water into a 100-ml graduated cylinder. Add the 40 soaked seeds to the cylinder and record the level of the water in the cylinder. Remove the soaked seeds and put them in one of the volumeter tubes. Again measure 50 ml of water into the cylinder. Add the 40 dry seeds. Then add glass beads until the water reaches the level recorded for the soaked seeds. Remove the seeds and glass beads. Dry them on a paper towel and place them in a second tube of the volumeter. Again measure 50 ml of water into the cylinder. Add glass beads until the water reaches the level recorded for the soaked seeds. Remove the beads and dry them. Then put them in the third volumeter tube. • What is the role of this third tube in the experimental design? (2) • What is the purpose of the glass beads? (3)

Using a glass rod, loosely pack cotton to a depth of 1 cm over the material in each tube. With a porcelain spatula, add about 1 cc of Ascarite to the top of the cotton in each tube. *Caution: Ascarite burns. Be very careful not to get it on your skin or your clothes.* Replace the stoppers. Place the tubes in the volumeter. Arrange the volumeter pipettes so they are level on the table.

Using a dropper, place a drop of colored water in the end of each pipette. In each of the two pipettes attached to the tubes containing peas, adjust the drop to a position near the outer end. In the third pipette, adjust the drop to a position near the middle. To make each

adjustment, open the clamp at the top of the tube to which the pipette is attached and, using a medicine dropper, draw or push air through the system.

Leave the apparatus set up for five minutes. During this pause assign three team members to read the three pipettes; assign a fourth student to time the readings. Record the position of each marked drop at time zero. Then record the position of each drop at two-minute intervals for a total of twenty minutes.

Meanwhile the special team should proceed as follows: Mark two vacuum bottles *A* and *B*. Place a layer of moist cotton in the bottom of Bottle A. Then add the 200 cc of seeds that have been soaked for twenty-four hours. Lubricate a thermometer with glycerin and insert it through a one-hole stopper that fits the vacuum bottle. Position the stopper in the vacuum bottle so the bulb of the thermometer is among the peas but the mercury is visible above the stopper. Into the bottom of Bottle B place a layer of dry cotton and add the dry seeds. Fit Bottle B with a thermometer as you did Bottle A. Wait five minutes; then record the temperature in each bottle. Set both bottles in a place designated by the teacher.

**Day 3.** Record the temperature in each vacuum bottle.

### STUDYING THE DATA

For each tube of the volumeter, subtract the reading at time zero from each of the subsequent readings. • What does a positive number in these derived data indicate about the volume of air in the tube-pipette system? (4) • What does a negative number indicate? (5) Graph all the derived data on one grid, using lines of different colors to represent the three tubes. • Which line represents changes in a tube not associated with living things? (6) Compare the other two lines with this. • Which one of these other two most resembles it? (7)  • State a hypothesis to account for any difference you found between the data from the tube containing the dry peas and the data from the tube containing the soaked peas. (8)   At the beginning of the investigation, each tube-pipette system contained air, a mixture of gases.  • If you found changes in the position of the marked drops, which of these gases do you think changed in amount? (9)   Ascarite is a substance that absorbs carbon dioxide.  • Why do you think it was included in each tube-pipette system? (10)

## CONCLUSIONS

• What evidence does this investigation provide that physiological activity involves chemical changes? (11)   • What evidence does it provide that physiological activity involves energy change? (12)

### FOR FURTHER INVESTIGATION

You can use the volumeter to investigate these problems: (a) How do advancing stages of seed germination affect the rate of the biochemical process measured by the apparatus? (b) Do small animals produce results in the volumeter like those obtained with seeds?

## ENERGY-RELEASING PROCESSES

Energy to carry on cell processes comes from foods. The ways in which energy is released from foods are remarkably similar among the most diverse kinds of cells. But the details are extremely complex, so biochemists still have many unsolved problems to investigate.

### SOME BASIC POINTS

Foods are carbon compounds that contain hydrogen, oxygen, and often other elements as well. Chemically, foods are somewhat like the fuels burned in stoves and furnaces. Indeed, furnace fuels such as wood, coal, and oil are carbon compounds derived from dead cells. They serve as fuels because they contain chemical energy. During the chemical reactions of burning, which reduce them to simpler compounds, this energy is released in the forms of heat and light.

Chemical energy in foods is likewise released by chemical reactions. But in cells the chemical reactions are quite different from those in stoves. And only a relatively small amount of the energy appears as heat and light.

**Energy units.**   Energy is customarily measured in units called *calories*. A calorie is defined by physicists as the amount of heat energy required to raise the temperature of 1 g of water 1°C. Thus, by definition, a calorie is a unit of heat. But since all forms of energy are interchangeable, the calorie can be used as a unit of measure for energy

calories [Latin: *calor*, heat]

of all kinds. Biologists generally use the "big" Calorie —capitalized—which is equal to one thousand "small" calories.

In some books the Calorie is abbreviated Kcal. Can you explain this abbreviation?

**Catalysis and enzymes.** In stoves, release of energy from fuels occurs only at high temperatures. But temperature in living cells is never high enough for such energy-releasing chemical reactions. So how can they occur? By *catalysis*.

catalysis [kə tăl′ə sĭs; Greek: *kata*, down, + *lyein*, to loosen]

Chemists discovered long ago that small quantities of certain substances can greatly speed some chemical reactions without being used up in the reactions. For instance, a small quantity of finely powdered platinum will cause some gases that normally do not react together to react with explosive rapidity; yet the quantity of platinum does not change. Platinum catalyzes the reaction. In cells, also, catalysts accelerate chemical reactions. Cell catalysts, however, are different from such catalysts as powdered platinum; they are organic compounds made by living cells. Because they differ so widely from inorganic catalysts, they have a special name—*enzymes*.

enzymes [ĕn′zīmz; Greek: *en*, in, + *zyme*, a material to raise bread dough]

According to the evidence that biochemists have at present, each enzyme in a living cell catalyzes just *one* chemical reaction; that is, enzymes are *specific* in their actions. Though many chemical reactions *could* take place among the hundreds of compounds in a living cell, only those reactions *do* occur for which there are appropriate enzymes. Moreover, these reactions are orderly. Their timing depends in part on the location of the enzymes in the cell. One reaction, catalyzed by a certain enzyme, occurs at one place; then the products of this reaction pass on to another place, where another enzyme catalyzes a second reaction. Thus the chemical changes in a cell are controlled as to location and sequence as well as to kind.

**INVESTIGATION 12.2**

### A STUDY OF BIOCHEMICAL REACTIONS

#### BACKGROUND INFORMATION

Hydrogen peroxide ($H_2O_2$) is a highly active chemical, often used for bleaching; it is usually sold as a 3% solution in water. Within cells, hydrogen peroxide is thought to be formed continually as a by-product of biochemical processes. Because it is *toxic*, or poisonous, it would soon kill the cell if it were not removed or broken down immediately.

## MATERIALS AND EQUIPMENT
(for each team)

Test tubes, 13 × 100 mm, 9

Glass-marking crayon

Test-tube rack

Graduated cylinder, 10 ml, 1

Fresh 3% hydrogen peroxide solution,
about 100 ml

Scalpel

Manganese dioxide powder

Forceps

Fresh liver, 3 pieces about 6 mm in
diameter

Fine sand

Mortar and pestle

Bunsen burner

Ring stand

Beaker

Fresh potato

## PROCEDURE

Arrange the test tubes in the rack and number them *1* to *9*. Measure 2 ml of water into Tube 1. Mark each of the other tubes at the 2-ml level. Measuring by these marks, pour 2 ml of hydrogen peroxide solution into Tubes 2 to 9. After each of the following steps, record your observations. Compare observations on different tubes whenever you think it appropriate.

Into Tube 1 sprinkle a small amount (about as much as you can get on a scalpel blade) of manganese dioxide powder. Repeat for Tube 2.

Using forceps, select a small piece of fresh liver and drop it into Tube 3.

Into Tube 4 sprinkle sand in an amount equal to that of the manganese dioxide used in Tubes 1 and 2.

Place in a mortar a piece of fresh liver (about the size of that used in Tube 3). Add a little fine sand and grind the liver. Transfer the resulting mixture to Tube 5.

Place a third piece of liver in boiling water for a few minutes. Drop the boiled liver into Tube 6.

Place an amount of manganese dioxide equal to that used in Tube 1 in a test tube with about 2 ml of water. Place the test tube in boiling water for a few minutes. Then pour the tube's contents into Tube 7.

Using the scalpel, cut two cubes of fresh potato, each the size of the liver used in Tube 3. Place one potato cube in Tube 8.

Wash the mortar thoroughly. Grind the other potato cube with sand. Place the potato-sand mixture that results in Tube 9.

## DISCUSSION AND CONCLUSIONS

• What was the purpose of Tube 1? (1)

• Do you have any evidence that manganese dioxide catalyzes the breakdown of hydrogen peroxide instead of reacting with it? (2)   • What additional steps in the procedure would be needed to confirm this? (3)   Definite experimental evidence exists to show that manganese dioxide is indeed a catalyst in this reaction. Consider the formula of hydrogen peroxide and the kind of reaction you observed in Tube 2.   • What are the most likely products of the breakdown of hydrogen peroxide? (4)   • How might you confirm your answer? (5)

• How do you explain the difference in activity between the whole piece of liver and ground liver? (6)   • Why is Tube 4 necessary for this explanation? (7)   • How do you explain the difference in activity between fresh and boiled liver? (8)   Suppose that someone comparing Tubes 2 and 3 concluded that liver contained manganese dioxide.   • What evidence do you have either for or against this conclusion? (9)   • If you cannot support the conclusion, explain the reaction in Tube 3. (10)

• What additional information do the results from Tubes 8 and 9 provide? (11)

## CELLULAR RESPIRATION

The energy-releasing process in cells can be given several names. "Burn," the name used in making comparisons, is misleading, because it implies high temperatures. Sometimes the more general chemical term "oxidation" is used. But among biologists it is customary to speak of the main kind of energy-releasing process as *cellular respiration.* Breathing—the ordinary meaning of the term "respiration"—is related to cellular respiration but is not directly a part of it.

oxidation [ŏk′sə dā′shən]: here, a chemical process involving combination with oxygen

In the burning of fuels, energy is released as light and heat. In cellular respiration, however, the chemical energy in foods is transformed into motion (on a large scale, as in muscle, or on a small scale, as in the movement of molecules or ions by active transport). Or it energizes reactions that form new chemical compounds. Or, to a very small extent, it may be transformed into light (as in fireflies). And some heat is also released, but this is lost energy as far as cell processes are concerned.

Although lost for cell processes, how may this heat be of temporary advantage to a "warm-blooded" animal?

**Glucose.** One of the principal carbon compounds broken down when energy is released in cells is *glucose.* Many other multicarbon compounds in cells can be converted to glucose, so it is by way of glucose that energy release can best be explained. A glucose molecule contains a series of six linked carbon atoms with oxygen and hydrogen atoms attached. Its formula is $C_6H_{12}O_6$. Biochemists also write it as shown in Figure 12·2A. This diagram is known as a *structural formula;* such a formula is useful because the same numbers and kinds of atoms can be arranged in many patterns, each pattern having its own

glucose [gloo′kŏs; Greek: *glykys,* sweet]

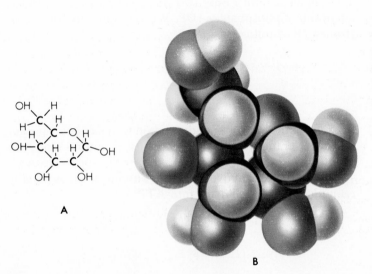

A

B

**Figure 12 · 2**

**Glucose. (A)** Structural formula. **(B)** Model. Here atoms are shown as spheres, each kind in a separate diagrammatic color. Try to find in the model the atoms shown by symbols in the formula.

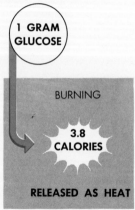

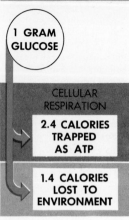

Figure 12 · 3

Does the amount of energy obtained from a food depend upon the way it is released?

adenosine triphosphate [ă dē′-nə sĭn trī fŏs′făt]

identical: exactly the same

characteristics and thus representing a distinct chemical compound. Of course, atoms in a molecule seldom occur in the flat shape of a formula on paper. To show the three-dimensional shapes of molecules, chemists use models, as in Figure 12 · 2B.

**Energy in small packets.** Heat energy released by the burning of gasoline can be channeled to move the piston of an engine and the wheels of a car. But the use of energy by a cell is not simple and immediate; it does not occur in great bursts followed by long periods of idleness, as in a gasoline engine. It is gradual and continuous.

If you had a hundred-dollar bill, you might find it difficult to use in making day-to-day purchases—a hamburger, a pack of notebook paper, a comb. It would be much easier to use if exchanged for a hundred one-dollar bills. So, too, with energy in the cell. The bigger bursts of energy from glucose are put into "small change." This "small change" is the chemical energy in what are called "energy-transfer compounds." The most important is a complex substance known as *adenosine triphosphate*, usually abbreviated ATP.

Each molecule of this substance includes a main section which we shall symbolize as $A$. Attached to this section are three identical groups of atoms called *phosphate* groups. We will symbolize each phosphate group as ℗. ATP may thus be written $A-℗\sim℗\sim℗$. Each wavy line indicates the attachment of a phosphate group whose removal is accompanied by the release—or transfer—of a small amount of energy.

No matter where energy is required in the cell, ATP or some other energy-transfer compound is the usual source. Each ATP molecule releases a bit of energy whenever the terminal phosphate group breaks off, leaving $A-℗\sim℗$. This molecule, with only two phosphate groups, is called adenosine *di*phosphate—ADP. We can show its formation from ATP as follows:

$$A-℗\sim℗\sim℗ \rightarrow A-℗\sim℗ + ℗$$
$$\downarrow$$
$$\text{energy}$$

You cannot keep spending money from your pocket without eventually facing the necessity of putting money in again. Likewise, the cell cannot continually "spend" its ATP and carry on the above reaction without also continually rebuilding some ADP back into ATP:

$$\text{energy}$$
$$\downarrow$$
$$℗ + A-℗\sim℗ \rightarrow A-℗\sim℗\sim℗$$

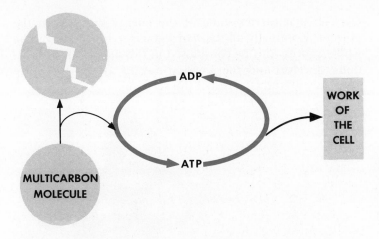

Figure 12 · 4

The ATP-ADP cycle in relation to molecular energy of foods on the one hand and work energy of cell activity on the other.

Thus there is a continual ADP-ATP cycle.

**From glucose to carbon dioxide and water.** Now let us look a little further into cellular respiration, through which energy is made available for ATP formation. A step-by-step breakdown of glucose molecules occurs. In the course of this breakdown hydrogen is removed from the fragments of the glucose molecule. Each hydrogen atom becomes a hydrogen ion and a *high-energy* electron—an

Figure 12 · 5

A diagram of cellular respiration.

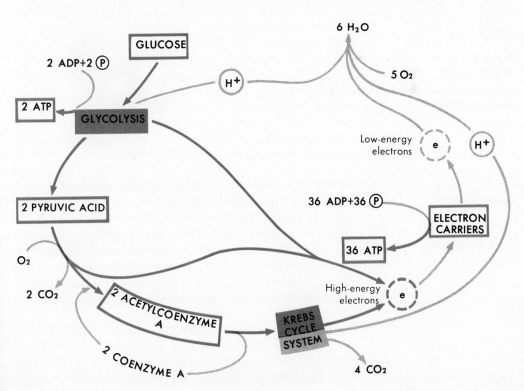

electron that carries some of the energy that was in the glucose. Eventually all the hydrogen is stripped away. The whole process can be considered in two major sets of reactions: *glycolysis* and the *Krebs-cycle system*. (Refer to Figure 12 · 5 as you study the rest of this section.)

glycolysis [glī kăl′ə səs]

Named for Hans Krebs, 1900——, British (German-born) biochemist

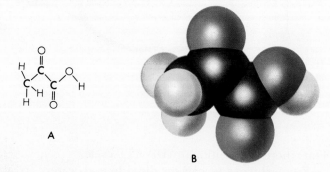

**Figure 12 · 6**

**Pyruvic acid. (A) Structural formula. (B) Model.**

A

B

Glycolysis consists of a series of reactions, each catalyzed by its own specific enzyme. As a result of these reactions energy is released, and each six-carbon molecule of glucose is changed to two molecules of a three-carbon compound, pyruvic acid. Each of the two pyruvic acid molecules, by

pyruvic [pī rū′vĭk]

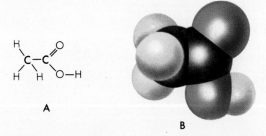

**Figure 12 · 7**

**Acetic acid. (A) Structural formula. (B) Model.**

A

B

removal of a molecule of carbon dioxide, is converted to a molecule of a two-carbon compound, *acetic acid*, releasing still more energy. But the acetic acid molecules never really exist by themselves; rather, they are immediately attached to a molecule of *coenzyme A*, forming *acetyl coenzyme A*. Coenzyme A is formed from one of the B vitamins. If this vitamin is lacking in the diet of an animal, coenzyme A cannot be formed and the process of cellular respiration is blocked.

acetic [ə sĕt′ĭk]

acetyl coenzyme A [ə sĕt′əl kō ĕn′zīm′ā′]

After the formation of acetyl coenzyme A, the second part of cellular respiration—the Krebs cycle—begins. The first step is the transfer of acetic acid from acetyl coenzyme A to a molecule of a four-carbon compound, *oxaloacetic acid*.

oxaloacetic [ăk′sə lō′ə sĕt′ĭk]

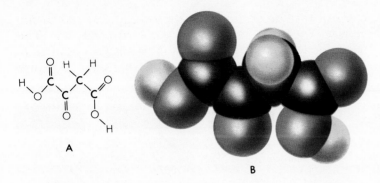

Figure 12 · 8

Oxaloacetic acid. (A) Structural formula. (B) Model.

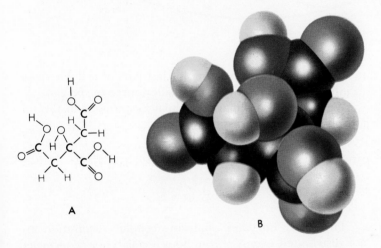

Figure 12 · 9

Citric acid. (A) Structural formula. (B) Model.

This forms a six-carbon compound, *citric acid*. Then, through a series of reactions (each reaction catalyzed by its own enzyme), hydrogen, high-energy electrons, and two carbon atoms (each forming a molecule of $CO_2$) are removed from the citric acid molecule. Left over is a molecule of the four-carbon oxaloacetic acid. This molecule is now available to start the Krebs cycle again by receiving acetic acid from another acetyl coenzyme A.

Each glucose molecule yields *two* molecules of acetyl coenzyme A, and two molecules of carbon dioxide are formed from each one of acetyl coenzyme A. Therefore, the Krebs-cycle system produces *four* $CO_2$ molecules from the breakdown of one glucose molecule.

The high-energy electrons resulting from glycolysis and the Krebs cycle are passed to a series of substances we may call "electron carriers." In going from one carrier to another, the electrons give up energy, which is used to form ATP molecules. Depleted of much of their energy, the electrons are finally united with hydrogen ions and oxygen

citric [si′trĭk]

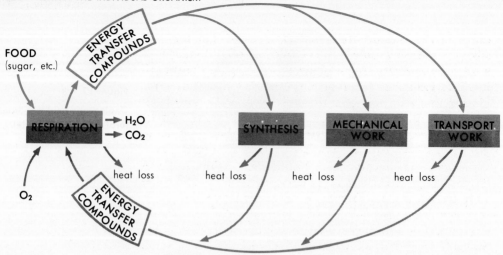

**Figure 12 · 10**

The relationship of respiration to cell activities. Into what form does all food energy eventually go?

to form water. It is only for this last part of cellular respiration that a cell requires an outside source of oxygen.

We can now summarize cellular respiration in the following chemical expression:

$$C_6H_{12}O_6 + 6\,O_2 \xrightarrow{\text{enzymes}} 6\,CO_2 + 6\,H_2O$$
$$\downarrow$$
$$\text{energy to ATP}$$

The many enzymes catalyzing cellular respiration are not distributed evenly throughout a cell. Those concerned with the reactions of glycolysis are in the cytoplast. Those concerned with the Krebs-cycle and electron-carrier systems are in the mitochondria. Since most of the energy is released in the mitochondria, they are sometimes called the "powerhouses" of a cell.

### OTHER PATHWAYS OF ENERGY RELEASE

What happens if a cell does not have a supply of oxygen to complete the process of cellular respiration? In our own bodies, for example, muscular exercise may require that energy be supplied faster than it can be released by cellular respiration. The necessary oxygen cannot travel from lungs through blood vessels through cell membranes into muscle cells fast enough. And during hard exercise we cannot even breathe fast enough to meet the demand for oxygen. Do the muscle cells die?

No. Under such circumstances glucose is partially broken down by *fermentation*. This is a general term for anaerobic pathways of energy release. Various anaerobic pathways differ in the end products that are formed, but they are alike in releasing only a small fraction of the energy in a glucose molecule. Some biochemists estimate that in cellular respiration as much as 60 percent of the energy in a glucose molecule may be transferred to ATP. (Figure 12 · 3 shows that cellular respiration traps in ATP about 2.4 calories of the 3.8 calories in a gram of glucose—that is, $2.4 \div 3.8 = .6 = 60\%$.) If you now contrast Figure 12·11 with Figure 12·5, you will see that fermentation produces only two ATP molecules per glucose molecule, as compared with thirty-eight produced by cellular respiration. So in fermentation only about $2/38 \times 60\%$, or 3.2%, of glucose energy is released. Thus fermentation is somewhat like a faulty furnace that allows unburned coal to pass through with the ashes.

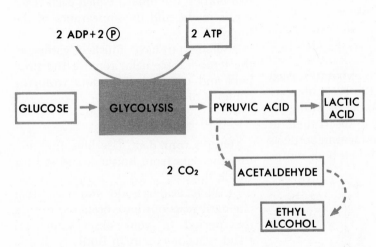

Figure 12 · 11

Fermentation. In mammalian muscle cells anaerobic energy release leads to lactic acid. Another pathway leads to ethyl alcohol.

The cells of man and other animals can release energy by fermentation for a time. But eventually they must have oxygen to continue into the more efficient cellular respiration. However, some organisms—for example, *Clostridium tetani*, the bacterium of lockjaw—exist entirely by inefficient fermentation. Others, such as yeasts, can exist very well anaerobically, but if oxygen is available they change to the more efficient method, aerobic respiration.

Would you expect *Clostridium* cells to have mitochondria? Why or why not?

Some of the waste products of fermentation in other organisms are very useful to man. For example, under anaerobic conditions yeasts convert pyruvic acid to ethyl alcohol ($C_2H_5OH$), a waste product. The lactic acid formed by some bacteria curdles milk during cheese-making. And the distinctive flavors of many cheeses are the result of substances left over from the energy-releasing processes of still other microorganisms.

## INVESTIGATION 12.3

### FERMENTATION

#### MATERIALS AND EQUIPMENT
(for each team)

Vacuum bottles, 2

Stoppers, 2-hole, to fit bottles, 2

Glass tubing, about 8 cm long, 2

Thermometers, 2

Glycerin

Rubber tubing, lengths of about 35 cm, 2

Beakers, 250 ml, 2

Limewater, 300 ml

Molasses, 25% solution in water, 400 ml

Glass-marking crayons

Dry yeast, about 1/4 package

Drinking straw

#### PROCEDURE

Assemble two sets of apparatus, each as shown in Figure 12·12. Lubricate glass tubing and thermometers with glycerin before attempting to insert them in the stoppers. Label one vacuum bottle as *A* and the other as *B*. When both setups

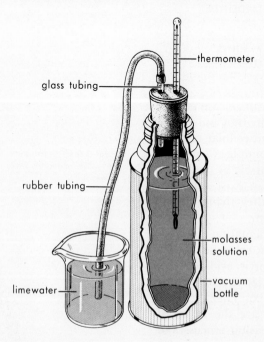

thermometer

glass tubing

rubber tubing

molasses solution

vacuum bottle

limewater

Figure 12 · 12

are complete, remove the stopper from Bottle A and add 1/4 package of dry yeast. Mix the yeast with the molasses solution by gently swirling the bottle. Then replace the stopper.

Wait five minutes. While you are waiting, blow your breath through a drinking straw into a sample of lime-water. Record the result. At the end of five minutes, record the temperature in each bottle and the time. As frequently as possible during the next forty-eight hours, record the temperatures in the two bottles, the time at which each reading is made, and the appearance of the limewater.

When you have finished gathering the temperature data, remove the stoppers and compare the odors from the contents of both bottles.

#### STUDYING THE DATA

Graph your data. Use blue for plotting the data from Bottle A and red for Bottle B.

• What evidence do you have that chemical reactions have occurred during the period of your observation? (1) • Did reactions occur in Bottle A, Bottle B, or both? If both, was any difference evident in the amount of reaction? (2) • Are conditions within the bottles aerobic or anaerobic? Explain your answer. (3) • What evidence do you have that a gas is produced in the bottles? (4) • Was it produced in both bottles? If not, in which one was it produced? (5) • In what way does the gas resemble the gas in exhaled breath? (6) • Did the contents of the bottles smell alike at the end of the experiment? If not, how did they differ? (7)

#### CONCLUSIONS

• What variable in the setup accounts for any differences you may have observed between results in Bottle A and Bottle B? (8) • In what ways did fermentation seem to resemble respiration (as observed in Investigation 12.1)? (9) • In what ways did fermentation seem to differ from respiration? (10)

### FOR FURTHER INVESTIGATION

1. If you can obtain some unpasteurized milk, you can use the above apparatus to investigate another kind of fermentation. Compare it with the kind shown in Investigation 12.3.

2. The amount of gas produced by yeasts can be used as a measure of fermentation. Devise an apparatus to measure the gas and investigate the effects of environmental variables on fermentation (for example food, temperature, light).

## SYNTHESES

The release of chemical energy from compounds in the cell involves the breaking down of large molecules into smaller ones. You might suppose, therefore, that the building up of large molecules from smaller ones would require energy—and this is actually the case. Any such process is a *synthesis* (plural, "syntheses"). The energy for *photo*synthesis comes from the sun. In other biological syntheses, the energy to build up large molecules comes from the breakdown of other molecules in the ways discussed above.

You probably know something about three groups of chemical compounds called carbohydrates, fats, and proteins. These are ordinarily thought of as foods. They also make up much of the substance of cells. A hungry lion can make use of the fat and protein and carbohydrate of your cells as food, and you can do the same with the cells of a bean. In addition to these compounds (and the ever-present water), it has been discovered within the past forty years that another group makes up a considerable portion—sometimes a very large portion—of cells. These compounds are called *nucleic acids.*

nucleic [noō klē′ĭk]

Thus, in studying the chemistry of synthesis in the cell, we are studying the way in which cell substances are produced—and since growth usually involves an increase in the numbers of cells, in a long-range view we are studying how we grow.

### CARBOHYDRATES

Carbohydrates contain only the elements carbon, hydrogen, and oxygen, with the ratio of hydrogen atoms to oxygen atoms usually 2 to 1, as in water. Sugars, starches, and cellulose are familiar carbohydrates.

The structural formula of glucose is shown in Figure 12·2. It is one of the *simple sugars*—which means that it is a sugar containing 3 to 7 carbon atoms. The glucose molecule can be changed in many ways, and the synthesis of many cell substances may be thought of as beginning with glucose.

sucrose [sōō′krōs]

The most familiar of all sugars is sucrose, or "table sugar." The formula of sucrose is $C_{12}H_{22}O_{11}$. This looks much like the result of adding together two glucose molecules ($C_6H_{12}O_6$), except that two hydrogen atoms and one oxygen atom are missing. The chemistry of the matter is rather more complicated than this suggests. In the first place, the atoms in a molecule of a simple 6-carbon sugar called *fructose* are rearranged, forming a molecule of glucose. Then the newly made glucose molecule is combined with a molecule of fructose to form a molecule of sucrose. In the process, two hydrogen atoms and an oxygen atom are split off. Enzymes and a small amount of energy from ATP are needed to bring about this synthesis. The process can be summarized as follows:

fructose [frŭk′tōs]

$$C_6H_{12}O_6 + C_6H_{12}O_6 \xrightarrow[\text{enzymes}]{\overset{\text{energy from ATP}}{\downarrow}} C_{12}H_{22}O_{11} + H_2O$$

(glucose)  (fructose)                    (sucrose)

dehydration [Latin: de, from, + Greek: hydor, water]

Such a synthesis is termed a *dehydration synthesis* because water is produced during the reaction.

disaccharide [dī săk′ə rīd′; Greek: dis, twice, + sakcharon, sugar]

Sucrose is called a *di*saccharide, because it is built with *two* simple-sugar units. Maltose and lactose are two other disaccharides we shall encounter later in a discussion of digestion. Also by dehydration synthesis we can obtain *tri*saccharides, made from three simple sugars, and *poly*saccharides, made from many simple sugars. In these syntheses, one water molecule is split off for each sugar-to-sugar link. Starch and cellulose are familiar polysaccharides.

poly- [Greek: polys, much, many]

## FATS

Like carbohydrates, fats are composed of carbon, hydrogen, and oxygen atoms only, but in fats the ratio of hydrogen to oxygen atoms is always *greater* than 2 to 1. Weight for weight, fats contain more chemical energy than do carbohydrates. A gram of fat contains about 9 Calories of chemical energy; a gram of carbohydrate contains only about 4 Calories. The word "oil" is used for fats that are in the liquid state at room temperatures (about 20°C).

In motile organisms food is usually stored as fat rather than as carbohydrate. Can you suggest an explanation?

Fats are built up from *glycerol* and *fatty acids.* Glycerol (glycerin) is perhaps best known as an ingredient of candies and cough medicine. Glycerol is a 3-carbon molecule which can be formed from glucose. The simplest fatty acid is

glycerol [glĭs′ə rŏl′]

What use have you recently made of glycerin in your laboratory work?

acetic acid (Figure 12 · 7); it is the acid in vinegar. Other fatty acids are built up from acetic acid, so they usually have even numbers of carbon atoms. The ones most commonly used in building fats have from 14 to 18 carbon atoms. Because the −COOH group of atoms is characteristic of the molecular structure of the organic acids, we can symbolize any fatty acid as $R-COOH$; here $R$ stands for the rest of the molecule.

The −COOH group of a fatty acid can react with the −OH groups of glycerol in the manner shown in Figure 12 · 13. Note that three molecules of fatty acid react with one molecule of glycerol. The three acid molecules may all be the same kind of fatty acid, or they may be different kinds. As in the synthesis of carbohydrates, water molecules are split off in the process; it is a dehydration synthesis. And both energy and specific enzymes are required for the reaction.

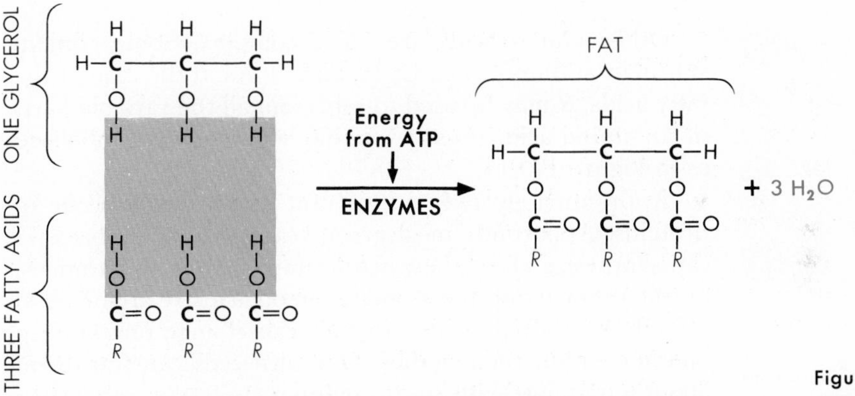

Figure 12 · 13
Formation of a fat.

Fats are only one group within a broader chemical grouping, *lipids*. All lipids are formed from organic acids, but not necessarily in combination with glycerol. Many organisms produce various nonfat lipids. The plant wax carnauba, which is used as a floor and automobile polish, is an example.

lipids [lĭ′pĭdz, lī′pĭdz; Greek: *lipos*, fat]

carnauba [kär nou′bə]

### PROTEINS

Molecules of fat are large, and those of polysaccharides larger still; but generally much larger and more complex than these are protein molecules. Ordinarily, protein molecules contain thousands of atoms—sometimes tens of thousands. Proteins occur in bewildering variety. Undoubtedly every species of organism has characteristic proteins shared by no others, and it is even possible that every individual organism has proteins found in no other individual.

The basic building units of protein molecules are *amino acids*. Amino acids always contain at least four kinds of atoms. These are the three kinds of atoms that glucose contains: carbon, hydrogen, and oxygen—plus a fourth kind, nitrogen.

**Figure 12 · 14**

The simplest amino acid, glycine. (A) Structural formula. (B) Model.

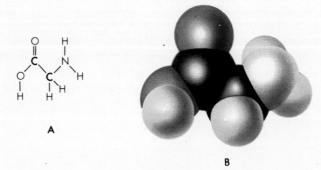

A

B

AMINO PART    ACID PART

**Figure 12 · 15**

Basic structure of an amino acid. In the glycine molecule what is the R?

tripeptide [trī pĕp'tĭd]

Other amino acids are more complex. Some contain sulfur in addition to C, O, H, and N. As in the case of the fatty acids, *R* may be used to represent all the variable parts of an amino acid; thus *any* amino acid may be symbolized as in Figure 12 · 15.

Approximately twenty different amino acids occur in proteins. Apparently most green plants and some bacteria can synthesize all of these from simple materials. Animals, on the other hand, must obtain amino acids ready-made in their food, though many animals can change one kind to another within their bodies. Our own cells can transform about ten amino acids in this manner.

Once the necessary amino acids are made or obtained, the synthesis of proteins is a matter of linking the amino acids together. When a bond between amino acids is made, a water molecule is split off (another case of dehydration synthesis) and energy from ATP is used. This can be illustrated in the combining of three amino-acid units (Figure 12 · 16). The resulting molecule is called a *tripeptide*. A longer chain would be a *polypeptide*. The name "protein" is used when the chain, coiled up like a spring, becomes about a hundred units long.

The number of ways in which more than twenty different amino-acid units can be combined into hundred- or thousand-unit structures is almost beyond imagination. Thus, the number of possible kinds of protein is practically without limit.

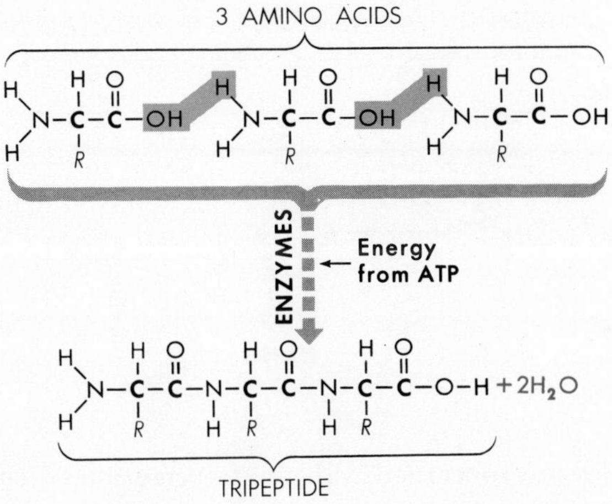

3 AMINO ACIDS

ENZYMES

Energy from ATP

TRIPEPTIDE

Figure 12 · 16

Formation of a tripeptide.

## NUCLEIC ACIDS

In the 1920's it became clear that much of the dark-staining material in the nucleus of a cell is composed of a class of substances called nucleic acids. At times nucleic acids may make up more than 50 percent of a cell's dry weight. Therefore, in discussing the synthesis of cell substances, it is necessary to consider nucleic acids along with carbohydrates, lipids, and proteins.

There are two different series of nucleic acids: *ribose* nucleic acids (RNA) and *deoxyribose* nucleic acids (DNA). The RNA series is built from units which contain ribose, a 5-carbon sugar; the DNA series is built from units containing deoxyribose, another 5-carbon sugar that differs from ribose in having one less atom of oxygen. In the units from which nucleic acids are synthesized, ribose or deoxyribose is attached, at one point, to a phosphate group ($-PO_4$) and, at another, to one of five different kinds of carbon-nitrogen structures called *bases:*

ribose [rī′bōs]

deoxy- [dē ŏk′sə-]

| base ——— | 5-carbon sugar | ——— phosphate |

Such a molecule is called a *nucleotide.* In addition to being the units from which nucleic acids are built, nucleotides have other functions in biochemistry. Figure 12 · 17, for example, shows how a nucleotide, adenosine monophosphate (AMP) is chemically related to ATP and ADP.

nucleotide [noō′klĭ ə tĭd]

The ribose nucleic acids (RNA) are found throughout cells. They participate in the synthesis of proteins. In most cells deoxyribose nucleic acids (DNA) occur mainly in the nuclei; but in cells of blue-green algae, which have no organized nucleus, they are distributed throughout. DNA

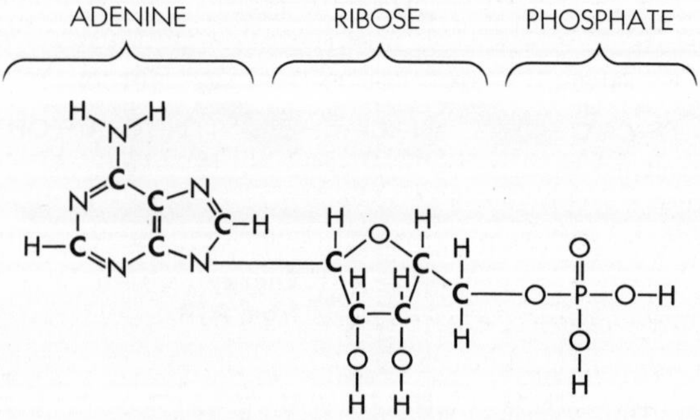

ADENINE          RIBOSE          PHOSPHATE

Figure 12 · 17

Structural formula of a nucleotide, adenosine monophosphate. Addition of a phosphate group would make this ADP; addition of two phosphate groups would make it ATP. Adenine is one of the bases.

molecules are concerned with the transmission of characteristics from one generation to the next—that is, with heredity.

## PHOTOSYNTHESIS

All living cells release energy; all living cells put energy into synthesizing new cell molecules. For this reason we discussed these processes first in considering bioenergetics. But in the long run all living cells (except a few bacteria) are dependent upon solar energy. And only certain specialized cells of plants and of a few protists can trap this solar energy. Thus photosynthesis, though last to be discussed here, is the first bioenergetic process when we view the biosphere as a whole.

Joseph Priestley: 1733–1804. English clergyman, chemist

In 1772 Joseph Priestley placed a shoot of a mint plant in a container of water and inverted a glass jar over it so that air could not enter. Much to his surprise, the shoot remained alive for several months. In another experiment he noted that a burning candle was quickly extinguished when covered with a jar. But then Priestley placed a shoot of mint under the jar, and in a few days the candle, when lighted, burned again for a short time. And the "restored" air was, as he phrased it, "not at all inconvenient to a mouse which I put into it." But other investigators were unsuccessful when they attempted to repeat Priestley's experiments. As a matter of fact, he himself failed when he tried again, six years later.

Jan Ingen-Housz [yän ing'ən-hous]: 1730–1799. Dutch physician and naturalist

The reason for this failure became clear in 1779, when Jan Ingen-Housz showed that plants act in the manner described by Priestley only when they are exposed to sunlight. He found, moreover, that only the green tissues take part in this process. Soon it became apparent that these results could be traced to the release of oxygen by plants. Then in 1782 Jean Senebier discovered that illuminated

Jean Senebier [zhǎn sə ně-byě']: 1742–1809. Swiss naturalist

plants absorb carbon dioxide. And in 1804 Nicolas de Saussure showed that the increase in plant weight after exposure to sunlight is greater than the weight of the carbon dioxide taken in. He concluded that growth in plants results from the intake of both carbon dioxide and water.

Nicolas de Saussure [dē sō'- soōr']: 1767–1845. Swiss chemist and naturalist

By 1845 Julius Robert Mayer was able to recognize that the essential steps in photosynthesis are the absorption of energy in the form of light and the transformation of this light energy into chemical energy, which is then stored in compounds manufactured by the plant. Thus, more than a century ago scientists in western Europe had already worked out the basic scheme of photosynthesis.

Julius Robert Mayer [mī'ar]: 1814–1878. German physicist

## MACHINERY OF PHOTOSYNTHESIS

It is characteristic of scientists to be unsatisfied. The Mayer scheme for photosynthesis was clear, but there were many questions that could be asked about it. If you are developing some scientific understanding, you should be able to list several. One certainly would be: Does photosynthesis occur everywhere in a cell or only at certain places?

Botanists long observed that oxygen is produced in photosynthesizing cells only in the vicinity of chloroplasts. To demonstrate clearly that photosynthesis occurs only in chloroplasts, it is necessary to remove chloroplasts from the rest of the cell. Removal of chloroplasts was accomplished in the 1930's, but at first biologists could not secure convincing evidence of photosynthesis in these isolated chloroplasts. However, in 1954 Daniel Arnon, of the University of California, and his co-workers were able to demonstrate that chloroplasts, separated from all other parts of the cell, can carry on the entire process of photosynthesis: carbon dioxide and water were combined by the illuminated chloroplasts, and both oxygen and carbohydrates were formed.

Daniel Arnon: 1910——. American (Polish-born) plant physiologist

**Chloroplasts.**    For a long time little was known about the internal structure of chloroplasts. During the past

Hugh Spencer

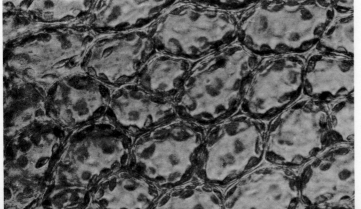

Figure 12 · 18
Chloroplasts in cells of a moss.

grana [grăn'ə; Latin: grains]

twenty-five years, however, improved microscopic techniques have made it possible to show that many chloroplasts contain small, disk-shaped bodies called *grana* (singular, "granum"). If very thin slices of chloroplasts are examined under an electron microscope, each granum is found to be made up of a number of flat plates. Each plate is composed of layers of chlorophyll, protein, and lipid molecules.

There is considerable diversity in the details of this structure. For example, in members of the grass family, some of the plates extend out into the colorless material in which the grana are embedded, forming continuous connecting layers between grana. And in the blue-green algae, which lack chloroplasts, the platelike structures form a network or a series of parallel layers within the cell substance.

Why are enzymes located in the protein layer?

The layered structure of the grana allows maximum exposure of chlorophyll molecules to light. It also brings chlorophyll in contact with the protein layers, in which the enzymes required for photosynthesis are located.

**Figure 12 · 19**

**Electronmicrograph of a single tobacco chloroplast.**

x 20,000

T. E. Weier

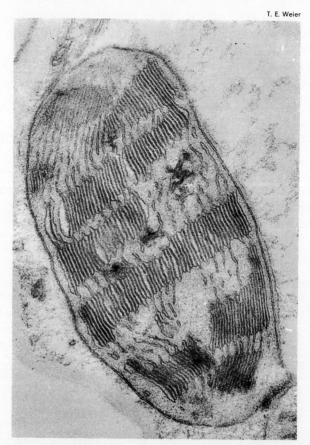

**Chlorophylls.**    Four different kinds of chlorophyll are now known, identified as *a, b, c,* and *d.* Chlorophyll *a* is believed to be present in all photosynthetic plants. In green algae, bryophytes, and tracheophytes, there is also some chlorophyll *b.* In the diatoms and brown algae, chlorophyll *c* occurs instead of *b;* in the red algae, chlorophyll *d* is present instead of *b.*

Chlorophyll molecules are quite complex; the formula for chlorophyll *a,* for example, is $C_{55}H_{72}O_5N_4Mg$. Although the structural formulas of the chlorophyll molecules are well known, little is yet understood about how organisms produce them. It is known, however, that they are produced inside chloroplasts — except, of course, in the case of the blue-green algae, which have no chloroplasts — and that usually very few are formed in the absence of light.

INVESTIGATION 12.4

## SEPARATION OF LEAF PIGMENTS

### INTRODUCTION

How does the biochemist know that the green color of leaves is the result of a mixture of several kinds of pigments? Obviously he cannot know unless he has some method of separating the pigments from the leaves and from each other. Separating the multitude of cell substances from each other is an important step in any biochemical study. Many methods are used to accomplish this. Substances that are soluble in water (sugars, for example) are easily separated from substances that are insoluble in water (fats, for example). But many substances found in organisms are so much alike that the usual methods of separation employed by chemists fail.

In the late nineteenth century the principle of chromatography was dis-covered by a Russian chemist. At first this method was used (as its name implies — Greek: *chroma,* color, + *graphein,* to write) only to separate substances that have color — pigments. By the 1930's, however, chromatography was being used for the separation of colorless substances. And to the original technique — separation on paper — had been added techniques for separation on other materials.

Much of the spectacular progress that has occurred in biochemistry during the past forty years resulted from the application of chromatography to problems that had previously been impossible to investigate.

You will use the simplest kind of chromatography to separate some of the pigments in leaves.

## MATERIALS AND EQUIPMENT
(for each team)

Paper clip
Test tube, 18 × 150 mm, 1
Test tube, 25 × 200 mm, 1
Cork (to fit the larger test tube)
Filter or chromatography paper, several strips
Scissors
Glass-marking pencil
Developing solution (8% acetone, 92%
   petroleum ether)
Test-tube rack
Spinach leaves
Fine sand
Acetone
Mortar and pestle
Cheesecloth
Cleansing tissue
Funnel, long-stem
Funnel support
Pencils, 2
Pipette, with a very fine tip

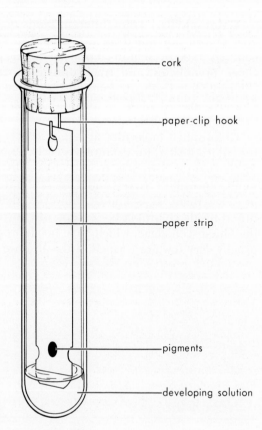

cork

paper-clip hook

paper strip

pigments

developing solution

Figure 12 · 20

## PROCEDURE

Assemble the apparatus shown in Figure 12 · 20, but do not add the solution yet. Handle the paper with great care. Even the slightest amount of oil from your fingers will seriously affect the results. When you have the length of the paper properly adjusted, mark on the larger test tube the level of the lower end of the notch. Remove the paper strip from the hook. Then pour developing solution into the test tube to a depth about 5 mm below the mark that you made. Place the cork, with the hook attached (*but without the strip of filter paper*), in the test tube. Place the tube in an upright position in a rack.

Place two or three spinach leaves, a little fine sand, and about 5 ml of acetone in a mortar, and grind thoroughly. Place a layer of cheesecloth in a funnel, and add a layer of cleansing tissue. Pour the acetone (which now contains extracted pigments) into the funnel, and collect the filtrate in the smaller test tube. • What is the color of the filtrate? (1) • Is there any evidence that more than one pigment is dissolved in the acetone? (2)

Support the strip of paper across two pencils so that the portion between the notches does not touch the table. Using a fine-pointed pipette, place a drop of the pigment extract on the paper. Allow it to dry. Add another drop in the same place, and allow it to dry. Repeat until at least four drops have been placed on the paper—one on top of another. When the final drop has dried, remove the cork from the large test tube and hang the strip on the hook. Insert the cork, with the paper strip attached, in the test tube. Be sure that the pigment spot does not touch the surface of the developing solution. If necessary, adjust the length of the hook to avoid this. Be sure the cork is tight. Watch the developing solution rise. When its upper edge almost reaches the hook, remove the cork from the tube and hold it until the paper has dried.

## STUDYING THE DATA

Examine the *chromatogram*. • How many bands of color can you see? (3) • How many bands might be made up of chlorophylls? (4)   • What other colors can you see in the chromatogram? (5) • Why were you unable to see these colors in the leaf? (6) • Do you think that all the leaf pigments were soluble in the acetone? Why or why not? (7) • Suggest a hypothesis to explain the change of color that often occurs when a leaf dies. (8)

Now consider the process by which the pigments were separated. • From what point did all the pigments start as the developing solution began to rise? (9) • When did all the pigments start to move, and when did they all stop? (10) • In what characteristic, then, must the pigments have differed? (11)

## FOR FURTHER INVESTIGATION

1. Why were the pigments studied in this investigation extracted with acetone? Why was water not used? What liquids besides acetone can be used to extract these pigments from the leaf?

2. Are there any leaf pigments that are not extracted by acetone? If so, what are the pigments, and how can they be extracted?

3. What effect does the kind of developer have on the success of chromatography? Try 100% acetone, 100% petroleum ether, 100% alcohol, and different mixtures of any two or all of these three. Does the nature of the pigments you are trying to separate affect the success of chromatography? Using some of the developers listed above, try separating other pigments, such as those in the inks of ball-point pens.

## BIOCHEMISTRY OF PHOTOSYNTHESIS

During the nineteenth century and the early part of the twentieth, many measurements were made of the amounts of $CO_2$ and $H_2O$ taken in by illuminated, chlorophyll-bearing cells and of the amounts of oxygen and energy-rich carbon compounds formed there. Although we now know that a large number of different energy-rich compounds are formed during photosynthesis, the kinds identified and measured at that time were simple sugars (such as glucose) or the insoluble starch synthesized from them. The results of these investigations can be summarized in the following equation:

$$6\ CO_2 + 6\ H_2O \xrightarrow[\text{enzymes}]{\text{light energy}} C_6H_{12}O_6 + 6\ O_2$$

If this equation were written with the arrows pointing in the opposite directions, you would recognize it as the one

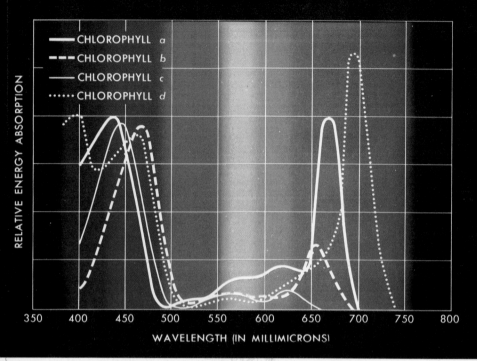

RELATIVE ENERGY ABSORPTION

——— CHLOROPHYLL *a*
- - - CHLOROPHYLL *b*
——— CHLOROPHYLL *c*
······ CHLOROPHYLL *d*

WAVELENGTH (IN MILLIMICRONS)

350    400    450    500    550    600    650    700    750    800

**Figure 12 · 21**

Patterns of energy absorption of the chlorophylls. The background shows the appearance of the wavelengths to our eyes. What wavelengths (colors) do chlorophylls absorb least?

given for cellular respiration. Of course, such equations indicate merely the beginning and the end of a process. It is now known that many of the intermediate steps are not the same in photosynthesis and respiration.

Long before the end of the nineteenth century, many chemists and biologists attempted—without success—to identify some of the intermediate substances that must be produced before glucose is formed. Events occur so rapidly in photosynthesis that identification of the substances involved seemed impossible. By 1905, however, experimental evidence had revealed that photosynthesis takes place in two distinct sets of reactions. One set, called the "light reactions," occurs only while a chlorophyll-bearing cell is exposed to light. This is immediately followed by a set of "dark reactions," for which light is not required.

**The source of oxygen.** Basic to further understanding of photosynthesis was another problem: Where did the oxygen come from? For many years $CO_2$ was considered the most likely source. But the problem could not be solved until a way was found to distinguish between oxygen derived from $H_2O$ and oxygen derived from $CO_2$.

An atom of ordinary oxygen is 16 times heavier than a hydrogen atom. But there is an *isotope* of oxygen—another form of the oxygen atom—with an atomic weight 18 times

derived: received or obtained from

isotope [ī'sə tōp'; Greek: *isos,* equal, + *topos,* place]

that of hydrogen. This isotope, $O^{18}$, can be distinguished from $O^{16}$ with an instrument called the mass spectrometer. In 1941 Samuel Ruben and Martin Kamen, working at the University of California, exposed plants to carbon dioxide that contained $O^{18}$. The mass spectrometer showed that all the oxygen given off by the photosynthesizing plant was $O^{16}$. Ruben and Kamen exposed other plants to ordinary $CO_2$ but supplied them with water containing $O^{18}$. With the mass spectrometer the oxygen given off by these plants was identified as $O^{18}$. Clearly, the oxygen came only from the water, not from the carbon dioxide.

During the past twenty years much more has been learned about the biochemistry of photosynthesis. Let us now look at the present state of knowledge.

**The "light reactions."**   In the first phase of photosynthesis, light energy absorbed by the chlorophyll is transformed into chemical energy and temporarily stored in two compounds. One of these, ATP, has already been discussed. The second is *reduced nicotinamide adenine dinucleotide phosphate,* abbreviated $NADPH_2$.

Experimental evidence now available indicates that ATP is formed in two different ways within chloroplasts. In the first, a cyclic set of reactions (Figure 12 · 22), light energy is

spectrometer  [spĕk trŏm′ə tər]

Samuel Ruben: 1913 – 1943. American chemist

Martin Kamen: 1913——. American (Canadian-born) biochemist

nicotinamide adenine [nĭk′ə- tēn′ə mĭd′ ăd′ən ēn′]

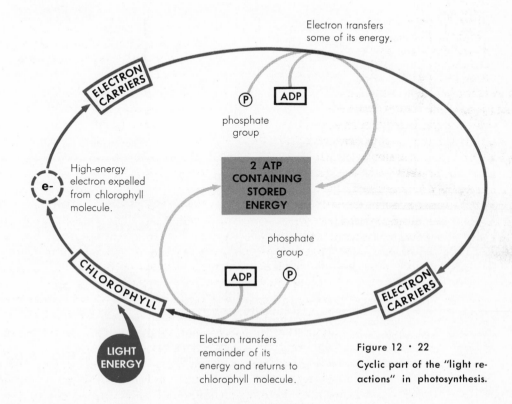

Electron transfers some of its energy.

ELECTRON CARRIERS

ADP

phosphate group

High-energy electron expelled from chlorophyll molecule.

e-

2 ATP CONTAINING STORED ENERGY

phosphate group

ADP

ELECTRON CARRIERS

CHLOROPHYLL

LIGHT ENERGY

Electron transfers remainder of its energy and returns to chlorophyll molecule.

Figure 12 · 22

Cyclic part of the "light reactions" in photosynthesis.

absorbed by a molecule of chlorophyll, causing an electron to be expelled from the molecule. This high-energy electron is passed along a series of electron carriers. As the electron moves along this series, its energy is transferred to enzyme systems that catalyze the change of ADP to ATP. Before the electron returns to a chlorophyll molecule, two or more molecules of ATP have been formed.

In the second way, a noncyclic set of reactions (Figure 12·23), both ATP and NADPH$_2$ are formed. Water is involved in this set of reactions; it supplies the hydrogen that combines with NADP (*oxidized nicotinamide adenine dinucleotide phosphate*) to form NADPH$_2$ again.

Light absorbed by some as yet unidentified pigment molecule causes a high-energy electron to be expelled. The pigment is probably either chlorophyll *b* or one of the yellow pigments present in chloroplasts. Biochemists now think that as the electron leaves the pigment molecule, it is replaced by an electron from a hydroxyl ion (OH⁻) obtained from the ionization of water. The high-energy elec-

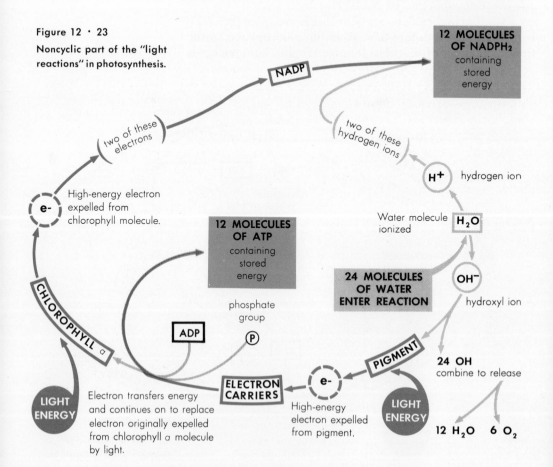

Figure 12 · 23

Noncyclic part of the "light reactions" in photosynthesis.

tron from the pigment is picked up by electron carriers. Light is absorbed at the same time by a chlorophyll *a* molecule, and a second high-energy electron is expelled. Electron carriers then transfer the first high-energy electron to this chlorophyll molecule. But as the electron moves to the chlorophyll molecule, its energy goes into the formation of an ATP molecule from ADP. Notice that in this chain of reactions, light energy is absorbed at one point by the pigment molecule and at a second point by the chlorophyll *a* molecule. Two high-energy electrons, expelled from chlorophyll molecules, and two hydrogen ions ($H^+$), from ionized water, join a molecule of NADP; thus an energy-rich molecule of $NADPH_2$ is formed. The light energy absorbed by the chlorophyll molecules has now been transferred to the $NADPH_2$. For every 24 molecules of water entering this noncyclic set of reactions, 12 molecules of ATP and 12 molecules of $NADPH_2$ are formed.

One important detail remains to be considered. When each of the $OH^-$ ions derived from the water loses an electron, it becomes an OH *radical*—a chemical term for a group of atoms that is neither an independent molecule nor an ion. Twenty-four of these radicals combine to form 12 molecules of water and 6 molecules of oxygen—the oxygen that is given off by photosynthesizing organisms.

**The "dark reactions."**    The basic result of this phase of photosynthesis is the formation of multicarbon molecules

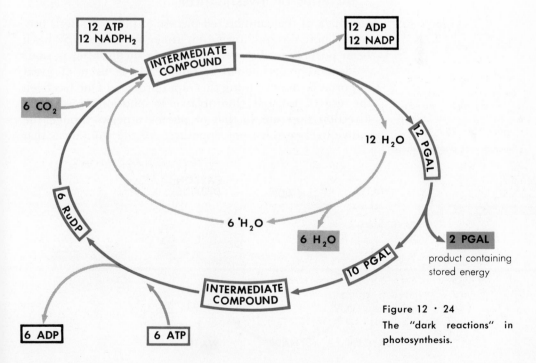

Figure 12 · 24
The "dark reactions" in photosynthesis.

Melvin Calvin: 1911———. American biochemist

ribulose diphosphate [rĭ′byə-lōs dī fŏs′fāt]

phosphoglyceraldehyde [fŏs′-fə glǐ′sər ăl′də hīd′]

containing chemical energy that can be used later by the cell. Through many years of ingenious investigations, Melvin Calvin and his colleagues at the University of California in Berkeley have worked out many of the details of the more than twenty reactions involved. For these investigations Calvin was awarded a Nobel prize in 1961.

The carbon source in the "dark reactions" is carbon dioxide. In a series of steps, carbon dioxide is combined with the complex molecule *ribulose diphosphate* (RuDP); this eventually results in a 3-carbon molecule, *phosphoglyceraldehyde* (PGAL). For every 6 molecules of $CO_2$ taken up by the cell, 12 molecules of PGAL are formed. But 10 of these are cycled back into the series of reactions that produce RuDP; only 2 molecules of PGAL are left to form carbohydrates—for example, glucose—and eventually all the other multicarbon compounds in cells.

To accomplish all this, a supply of energy must be available. It comes from the compounds formed during the light phase—ATP and $NADPH_2$. As the energy is released from ATP, ADP is formed. This ADP is then available for conversion into ATP during the "light reaction." Likewise, as energy is released from $NADPH_2$, NADP is formed. And this is also available for conversion into $NADPH_2$ during the "light reaction." Thus, ATP and $NADPH_2$ act as carriers of energy.

### METHODS OF INVESTIGATION

Much of the complicated picture of photosynthesis presented here was unknown even fifteen years ago. How has it been possible to discover so much in such a brief period?

Several experimental techniques have been of great importance in permitting this rapid progress. One has been the use of isolated chloroplasts. Respiration moves in a direction opposite to that of photosynthesis—though the individual steps are not opposites. All the substances that

Figure 12 · 25

Summary of photosynthesis.

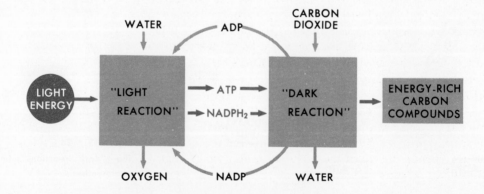

Ian E. Bush, "Automation of Steroid Analysis," *Science*, Vol. 154, pp. 77–83, Oct. 7, 1966

**Figure 12 · 26**
As the biochemist attacks more complex problems, he develops more complex tools. The apparatus shown increases the speed with which chromatographic records can be obtained.

are involved in respiration are present in a cell with all the substances involved in photosynthesis. Even when all these substances are separated and identified, how can the biochemist decide which are respiration substances, which are photosynthesis substances, and which are, perhaps, part of both processes? In chloroplasts only the substances of photosynthesis occur. Thus, the study of isolated chloroplasts has greatly simplified the tracing of the steps in the photosynthetic process by removing from the picture the steps by which multicarbon compounds are broken down.

You read how isotopes of oxygen were used in solving one of the problems involved in photosynthesis. You saw how chromatography can be used to separate a mixture of substances. A combination of methods involving isotopes and chromatography has been especially useful in the study of the "dark reactions" of photosynthesis. In one procedure carbon dioxide that contains carbon-14 ($C^{14}$), a radioactive isotope of carbon, is supplied to single-celled algae. Shortly afterward, the algae are killed and the substances in them removed. These substances are then separated by chromatography, and the ones that have taken up $C^{14}$ can be detected by a device sensitive to radioactivity (a Geiger counter, for example). By killing some of the algae every few fractions of a second, the investigator can determine the order in which the substances containing $C^{14}$ are formed. From this information, diagrams such as Figure 12 · 24 can be constructed.

Geiger counter [gī'gər]: This device transforms the energy of certain radiations into sounds or light flashes that man can detect.

## INVESTIGATION 12.5

### PHOTOSYNTHETIC RATE

#### PURPOSE

You will study the effect of light intensity on the rate of photosynthesis in a living plant. • After reading the procedure state a hypothesis for the experiment. (1)

#### BACKGROUND INFORMATION

The rate of oxygen production can be used as an indication of the rate at which a plant is carrying on photosynthesis. Because oxygen is only slowly soluble in water, visible bubbles of oxygen may be formed by a photosynthesizing aquatic plant; these can be easily observed. If the bubbles are of uniform size, the number of bubbles formed per time unit indicates photosynthetic rate, provided all other factors affecting rate are held constant.

#### MATERIALS AND EQUIPMENT
(for each team)

Sprig of elodea
Glass rod
String
Graduated cylinder, 250 ml
Sodium bicarbonate solution (0.25% in pond
 or aquarium water), 250 ml
Battery jar or small aquarium
Thermometer
Ring stand with clamp
Lamp with reflector and 150-watt bulb
Razor blade
Forceps
Watch with second hand

#### PROCEDURE

Prepare the setup shown in Figure 12·27, as follows: With string fasten a healthy sprig of elodea to one end of a glass rod. Place this in a 250-ml graduated cylinder so the tip of the sprig is located at the bottom of the cylinder.

Add sufficient 0.25% bicarbonate solution to the cylinder to cover the cut end of the sprig to a depth of 5 cm. Place this whole setup in a battery jar or small aquarium filled with water at room temperature. Using a ring stand and clamp, suspend a thermometer with the bulb located near the cylinder. Place a lamp with a 150-watt bulb 10 cm from the elodea sprig.

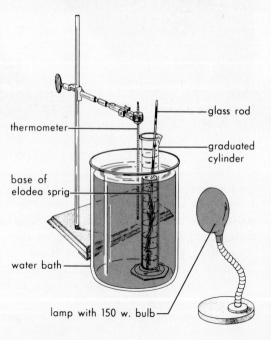

thermometer

glass rod

graduated cylinder

base of elodea sprig

water bath

lamp with 150 w. bulb

Figure 12 · 27

Turn on the lamp and observe the base of the sprig. If all goes well, after several minutes small bubbles will appear and rise through the bicarbonate solution at regular intervals. If no bubbles appear, lift the rod out of the cylinder so that a short section of the sprig base can be cut off with a sharp razor blade. Immediately return it to the cylinder. If large bubbles that become detached only after an extended time are formed, gently crush the base of the sprig with a pair of forceps.

When the rate of bubble formation has become fairly uniform, count the number of bubbles formed during each of five one-minute intervals, allowing a minute or two between counts. Record the average number of counts per minute. Increase the distance of the lamp from the sprig to 20 cm. Observe, count, and average the data as before. Increase the lamp distance to 40 cm and make a final determination of average rate of bubble formation per minute. At frequent intervals throughout the experiment, check the temperature of the water in the battery jar. If the temperature rises more than 2°C, add sufficient cold water or ice cubes to reduce it to the original temperature.

## DISCUSSION

Graph the data, showing the distance between lamp and sprig on the horizontal axis and the average number of bubbles per minute on the vertical axis. • What is the general direction of the slope of the line? (2) • How is the change in distance of lamp from plant related to the change in light intensity received by the plant? (3) • What, then, is the relationship between light intensity and photosynthetic rate as indicated by your data? (4)

• What other environmental factors may affect photosynthetic rate? (5) • In the design of this experiment, which of these factors are controlled? How? (6) • Are any factors uncontrolled? If so, how might you change the design to control them? (7)

### FOR FURTHER INVESTIGATION

1. Plan and carry out an experiment in which light intensity is held constant and some other factor affecting photosynthetic rate is varied.

2. In terms of exchange of gases, what process in living organisms is the opposite of photosynthesis? How does this process affect any attempt to measure photosynthetic rate with a high degree of accuracy? Using measurements of gaseous exchange as a basis, plan and carry out an experiment designed to eliminate errors introduced by this process.

All energy for the activities of living things comes from multicarbon compounds that either directly or indirectly come from photosynthesis.

Several biochemical pathways are involved in the release and transfer of energy in cells. Reactions along these pathways go on continuously in all cells. Two series of reactions are of particular importance: glycolysis, which breaks down glucose to pyruvic acid; and the Krebs cycle, which oxidizes acetic acid (coming from breakdown of carbohydrates, fats, or proteins) to carbon dioxide and water. Other, less efficient pathways end with other products.

All these pathways result in the transfer of energy to energy-transfer compounds, the most common being ATP. The breakdown of ATP to ADP releases energy in small amounts. Such energy may be used for synthesis of large molecules (such as fat or protein) from smaller molecules, for contraction of muscles, for beating of cilia, for active transport of ions or molecules, or for any other activity performed by the cell.

Eventually, after many reactions all the chemical energy that becomes available to organisms through photosynthesis becomes heat and is lost to the biosphere.

## GUIDE QUESTIONS

1. Why is the study of energy in living things—bioenergetics—of basic importance to an understanding of biology?
2. What experimental evidence do we have for the idea that living things lose energy to their environments?
3. How are many chemical reactions brought about in living things at relatively low temperatures?
4. How can chemical energy in a substance be measured?
5. How is cellular respiration different from burning?
6. What part does ATP play in the use of energy by cells?
7. What are the main steps in the breakdown of a glucose molecule to carbon dioxide and water?
8. What chemical processes occur in mitochondria?
9. In what ways does fermentation differ from cellular respiration?
10. Where does a cell obtain energy for syntheses?
11. From what chemical units are polysaccharides synthesized?
12. How do fats differ from other lipids?
13. From what chemical units are polypeptides synthesized?
14. How does a protein differ from a polypeptide?
15. How is ATP related chemically to the nucleic acids?
16. List the conditions necessary for photosynthesis.
17. Describe the structure of a chloroplast. How is its structure related to its function?
18. How can the acetone-soluble pigments in leaves be separated? How many chlorophylls usually occur in leaves?
19. In what general ways are photosynthesis and cellular respiration similar? How do they differ?
20. What seems to be the effect of light energy on chlorophyll molecules?
21. How do water molecules enter into the light phase of photosynthesis?
22. How does the light phase of photosynthesis prepare for the dark phase?
23. How have isotopes of chemical elements played a part in the investigation of photosynthesis?

## PROBLEMS

1. In Simpson and Beck (Chapter 2) or another reference find out how biochemists picture the way in which enzymes act in metabolic reactions. Then use this model to explain enzyme specificity.

2. A certain chemical substance is known to increase the activity of an enzyme called nitrate reductase. This enzyme reduces nitrate ions to nitrite ions, which are then used in the synthesis of amino acids. What practical use might be made of this information?

3. Calculate the surface area and volume of ten spheres having diameters of 1 mm, 2 mm, 3 mm, and so on to 10 mm. Plot the two sets of results on the same grid, allowing the vertical axis to represent both $mm^2$ and $mm^3$. Keeping in mind the requirements of all living cells for energy and materials from which energy is released, comment on the meaning of your graph. How might cells grow large while avoiding the biological consequences of large size?

4. As you are running in a track meet, your rate of breathing increases. When the

race is over, your breathing rate continues to be high for a considerable period. Explain this, using your knowledge of cellular physiology.

5. Proteins in the cells of a wheat plant differ from the proteins in your cells. How can the differences be explained? What must happen when you use wheat as a nutrient for the formation of your protein?

6. Experiments with photosynthesizing tracheophytes have shown that when they are grown in an atmosphere without oxygen they take up carbon dioxide at $1\frac{1}{2}$ times the rate in natural atmosphere, which is about 20% oxygen. (a) What does this information indicate about the relationship between photosynthesis and cellular respiration? (b) How might this relationship affect the composition of the earth's atmosphere? (c) How does this information affect Oparin's speculations (Chapter 10)?

7. Many botanists believe that the concentration of carbon dioxide in the air was much greater during the Carboniferous period, when most of the large coal deposits were being formed, than it is

at present. What might be the basis for their belief? Is there any reason to suppose that the concentration of carbon dioxide in the air has increased during the last 150 years?

8. Some biochemists have argued that the formation of carbon compounds from carbon dioxide should not be considered a part of photosynthesis. How might this viewpoint be defended?

9. According to the theory of the origin of life discussed in Chapter 10, energy for the first living things must have come from chemical compounds formed by the heat and electrical energy in the earth's atmosphere at that time. Later some organisms apparently began to use energy from sunlight to build up foods. How might this have happened?

10. Gather whatever information you can find about conditions on the surface of Mars and Venus. Then, using your knowledge of cell metabolism, comment on the possibility of life existing on these planets. What life-supporting equipment would probably be desirable for astronauts planning trips to these planets?

## SUGGESTED READINGS

ALLFREY, V. G., and A. E. MIRSKY. "How Cells Make Molecules," *Scientific American,* September, 1961. Pp. 74–82.

ARNON, D. I. "The Role of Light in Photosynthesis," *Scientific American,* November, 1960. Pp. 104–109.

ASIMOV, ISAAC. *Life and Energy.* Garden City, N.Y.: Doubleday & Co., Inc., 1962. (Biochemistry and biophysics are well covered in this book written for the nonscientist. Easier than Lehninger or McElroy.)

BAKER, J. J. W., and G. E. ALLEN. *Matter, Energy, and Life.* Palo Alto, Calif.: Addison-Wesley Publishing Co., Inc., 1965. (A very useful introduction to the chemical and physical aspects of living systems. No previous knowledge of physics or chemistry is assumed.)

BASSHAM, J. A. "The Path of Carbon in Photosynthesis," *Scientific American,* June, 1962. Pp. 88–100.

LEHNINGER, A. L. *Bioenergetics.* New York: W. A. Benjamin, Inc., 1965. (An extremely well-written account of most aspects of bioenergetics at a somewhat advanced level.)

———. "How Cells Transform Energy," *Scientific American,* September, 1961. Pp. 62–73.

Loewy, A., and P. Siekevitz. *Cell Structure and Function.* New York: Holt, Rinehart & Winston, Inc., 1963.

McElroy, W. D. *Cellular Physiology and Biochemistry.* 2nd ed. Englewood Cliffs, N. J.: Prentice-Hall, Inc., 1964. (Contains excellent diagrams of biochemical processes and many structural formulas. Advanced.)

Mercer, E. H. *Cells: Their Structure and Function.* New York: Doubleday & Co., Inc., 1962. (An inexpensive book that emphasizes present theories in biochemistry. Recommended for the student's personal biology library.)

Rabinowitch, E. I. and Govindjee. "The Role of Chlorophyll in Photosynthesis," *Scientific American,* July, 1965. Pp. 74–83.

Simpson, G. G., and W. S. Beck. *Life: An Introduction to Biology.* 2nd ed. New York: Harcourt, Brace & World, Inc., 1965. Chapters 2 and 4. (Fine illustration and clear writing make this one of the best accounts of cell physiology written for the level of college freshmen.)

Stegner, R. *Plant Pigments.* Chicago: Rand McNally & Co., 1967. (Considers leaf pigments and other plant pigments also. Contains suggested laboratory work. Fairly easy.)

Stein, W. H., and S. Moore. "Chemical Structure of Proteins," *Scientific American,* February, 1961. Pp. 81–86.

# The Functioning
# Plant

## PLANTS AS ORGANISMS

As producers, green plants are of primary importance
to other organisms in the web of life. But plants carry on
many activities other than photosynthesis—they use nutrients, grow, reproduce, and so forth. Chapter 12 discussed photosynthesis; here you will consider some of the
other processes that go on in plants.

## VASCULAR PLANTS

An estimated 80 percent of the photosynthetic activity
on Earth occurs in the seas—and as we saw in Chapter 9,
mostly in single-celled plants and protists. But we are land
animals and thus far have made only small use of the sea's
productivity. By and large our food is obtained, directly or
indirectly, from land plants.

Moreover, land plants are the plants with which we are
most familiar, the plants with which we most like to surround ourselves—even in hot, dry houses and dim, stuffy
hotel lobbies. It seems reasonable, therefore, to use the
tracheophytes—the group to which almost all familiar land
plants belong—as the chief examples in continuing this
discussion of plant physiology.

### LEAVES

The first tracheophytes, in the Paleozoic era, probably
had chlorophyll in most of the cells that were exposed to
light. But very early in the history of land plants, flat, green
structures appeared that were exposed more or less per-
pendicularly to the sun's rays. These organs—leaves—were

well developed on plants long before the end of the Paleozoic era, and they are characteristic of almost all tracheophytes today.

Do you know of any tracheophytes that lack leaves?

In general, botanists consider leaves as organs of photosynthesis. To call a leaf an "organ" may seem somewhat strange. In the human body, organs are usually one of a kind or, as in the case of eyes and lungs, two; on the other hand, a large land plant may have thousands of leaves. However, according to the discussion in Chapter 12, a leaf is an organ—a structure composed of a number of tissues and performing some general function in the life of an organism.

Figure 13 · 1

Variation in leaves taken from a single white poplar tree.

X 1/2

**External view.** Variability in appearance is one of the most characteristic features of leaves. Examine the leaves on any one plant. No two leaves are exactly alike. Shapes and sizes vary according to the age of the plant, amount of light received, and other factors. Yet for any particular species of plant, leaf shape is usually distinctive and constant enough to be used as a basis for identification.

petiole [pĕt′ĭ ōl′; Latin: petiolus, little leg, stalk]

A leaf may or may not have a *petiole* (stalk) connecting the *blade* (broader part) to the plant stem. In the needle leaves of many conifers there is neither blade nor petiole. In most leaves the blade is in one piece, but in some leaves the blade is divided into separate parts. Or leaves may be so highly modified that they no longer function in photosynthesis—*spines* of cactus, for example. Whatever the form, however, there is no doubt that the primary function of most leaves is photosynthesis.

See Figure 5 · 10.

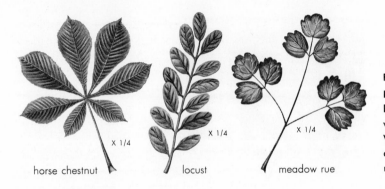

horse chestnut          locust          meadow rue

**Figure 13 · 2**
In these three *compound* leaves each blade is divided into separate parts. What other plants with compound leaves can you name?

**Inside leaves.**   Figure 13 · 10 shows in three dimensions the cellular structure of a photosynthesizing leaf—from a geranium, a raspberry, or a poplar, perhaps. Because only a small section can be seen with a microscope at any one time, this kind of drawing must be constructed by the artist from the study of a great many different microscopic views.

Several different tissues can be distinguished in the figure. With your knowledge of photosynthesis, you can set up a number of hypotheses about the functions of these tissues, basing this action on a generalization used since Chapter 4: that structure and function go together. As cells in a multicellular organism differentiate in structure, they usually acquire special functions in the life of the organism—they become *specialized.*

Photosynthesis requires chlorophyll, and chlorophyll usually occurs in chloroplasts. Since the *mesophyll* cells contain chloroplasts, you can confidently hypothesize that the mesophyll is the specialized tissue in which photosynthesis occurs. And you might suspect that more photosynthetic activity takes place in the closely packed upper layers of mesophyll, since the upper leaf surface usually gets the most light. (The upper *epidermal* tissue covers the leaf but allows light to pass through.)

mesophyll [mĕs'ə fĭl; Greek: *mesos,* middle, + *phyllon,* a leaf]

Both of the raw materials of photosynthesis—$H_2O$ and $CO_2$—are present in air. But the amount of water vapor varies a great deal, and water molecules are not as abundant in air as in the cytoplast of leaf cells. Thus, according to the principle of diffusion, leaves should lose $H_2O$ to the air. The amount of $CO_2$ in the air does not normally vary much, but it does vary within chlorophyll-bearing cells. $CO_2$, therefore, might either be given off or taken in by them. An exchange of gases between inner leaf cells and the air is further suggested by the air spaces between the cells of the lower mesophyll. Indeed, Figure 13 · 10 does show that numerous slitlike pores, *stomates,* lead from the

epidermal [Greek: *epi-,* upon, + *derma,* the skin]

stomates [Greek: *stoma,* mouth]

upper epidermis

mesophyll

lower epidermis
stomate
guard cell

A

X 75

upper epidermis

mesophyll

lower epidermis
stomate
guard cell

B

**Figure 13 · 3**

Leaves vary internally as well as externally. Sections through two leaves from one privet plant: (A) A leaf that was exposed to full sun. (B) A leaf that was shaded most of the day. How many structural differences can you see?

outside of the leaf through the leaf's epidermis and into the air spaces of the mesophyll. Therefore, you might hypothesize that gas exchange occurs through these pores.

If water is lost through these stomates, how does it enter the leaf? In the figure we see tubular structures labeled *veins*. As these evidently are structures through which liquids can flow, you might hypothesize that water comes to the leaf from other parts of the plant by way of these veins.

Through years of experimentation, mostly during the nineteenth century, plant physiologists have confirmed these hypotheses. Now we shall go a little beyond the hypotheses and discuss matters that are not quite so obvious.

**Loss of water from leaves.** Air contains less water than cells do. As air moves among mesophyll cells, water must diffuse into the air—the plant loses water. And the

**Figure 13 · 4**

Lower leaf epidermis from three kinds of plants. Which cells contain chlorophyll?

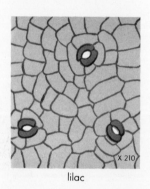

lilac

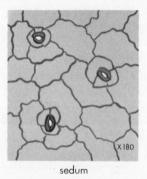

sedum

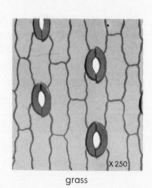

grass

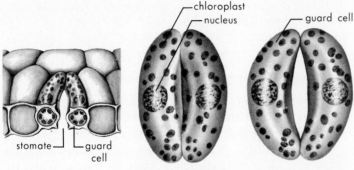

Figure 13 · 5
Stomate action. *Left*: A section through an open stomate. *Right*: The changes in guard-cell shape that regulate the stomate.

drier the air, the more rapidly the water is lost. Each stomate that lets air in and out of the mesophyll is surrounded by a pair of specialized cells, *guard cells*. The inner walls of the guard cells are thickened. Thus, when their water content increases, the cells bend outward and this opens the stomate, as shown in Figure 13 · 5. When the water content decreases, the stomate is closed (closed in a relative sense—never tightly closed). We might hypothesize that this is a mechanism for opening stomates when the air is moist and closing them when the air is dry.

But this hypothesis is not confirmed by observation. In most land plants the stomates are open during daylight hours, when the water content of the air is usually relatively low, and closed at night, when the water content is usually higher. Moreover, experiments have shown, changes in the shape of guard cells are related not to the water content of the air, but to the amount of carbon dioxide dissolved in the cell substance. Therefore, the action of guard cells seems to be associated more with the supply of $CO_2$ than with the control of water loss. However, this still does not explain another observation of plant physiologists: that stomates of potato plants are closed for only about three hours after sundown. Botanists still have much to learn about stomates.

What metabolic processes in guard cells affect their supply of $CO_2$?

Regardless of the action of guard cells, land plants lose much water through the stomates of their leaves. But they also lose some water directly through their epidermal cells—not only through the leaf epidermis but through the surface of the whole plant. This loss is reduced, but never completely stopped, by the *cuticle*, which covers the outer surface of epidermal cells. Cuticle is composed mostly of a waxy material—a lipid. It is very thin in some cases, as on lettuce leaves, and quite thick in others, as on pine leaves.

cuticle [kū′tə kəl; Latin: *cutis*, skin]

All loss of water vapor from plants, both through the stomates and through the epidermal surface, is called *transpiration*. Plant physiologists have made many measure-

transpiration [Latin: *trans*, across, + *spirare*, to breathe]

ments of transpiration rates. Black raspberries lose water through their leaves at the rate of 3.8 ml per cm² of leaf surface per day. Put in a different way: Mature apple trees (Grimes Golden variety) lose water at the rate of 15 liters per tree per hour. And in still another way: A single corn plant has been found to transpire 200 kg of water during a growing season. Such data clearly indicate the large amounts of water that land plants require.

What variables in the environment might have effects on such measurements?

Much of the rigidity of leaves results from pressure of cytoplasts against cell walls. When water is lost from the cytoplasts, pressure against the walls decreases. When this internal pressure decreases, a leaf loses its rigidity; we say it wilts. Because water is continually being lost from leaf cells, rigidity of leaves can be maintained only by continual replacement of water. This is one function of veins in leaves; they bring water from other parts of the plant body.

## INVESTIGATION 13.1

### TRANSPIRATION

#### PURPOSE

You will investigate experimentally the effect of one environmental factor on transpiration from a leafy shoot.  • Read the procedure and then state a hypothesis appropriate to the design of the experiment. (1)

#### MATERIALS AND EQUIPMENT
  (for each team)

Erlenmeyer flask, 500 ml
Two-hole stopper (to fit flask)
Glass tubing, bent to a right angle
Rubber tubing, about 20 cm long
Large battery jar or bowl
Leafy potted plant (all teams but one)
Solid glass rod (one team only)
Scalpel
Water at room temperature
Collodion or warm paraffin
Pipette, 1 ml
Cork (with hole to fit pipette)
Burette clamp
Ring stand
Watch
Plastic bag

String
Graph paper, 1 sheet per student
Pencils, 3 colors

#### PROCEDURE

Set up the apparatus shown in Figure 13·6, as follows: Into one hole of a two-hole stopper insert a length of glass tubing bent to a right angle. Attach a length of rubber tubing to the glass tubing. Immerse the pot in a large container of water so the base of the plant is covered to a height of 5 cm. Cut through the stem at a point well under the water surface. Keeping the cut end of the shoot under water, insert it in the second hole of the stopper. (One team should use a piece of solid glass rod instead of a leafy shoot.) The stem must fit snugly in the hole. Fill a flask to the brim with water at room temperature. Quickly insert the stopper, with the shoot (or glass rod) and the tubing, into the flask. (Caution: Remove books and papers from the table; inserting the stopper may cause some overflow.) It is necessary to have

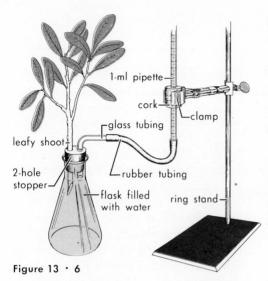

leafy shoot

1-ml pipette

cork

glass tubing

clamp

2-hole stopper

rubber tubing

flask filled with water

ring stand

**Figure 13 · 6**

the flask full in order to force water upward into the tubing. Seal the apparatus — especially where the stem and stopper are joined — with either collodion or paraffin.

Insert a pipette through a cork. Fill the pipette with water. Hold your index finger over the top of the pipette and insert the lower end into the rubber tubing that is connected to the flask. Seal the connections with collodion or paraffin. Clamp the cork containing the pipette to a stand for support.

As soon as the apparatus is assembled, note the position of the water level in the pipette. Record its position and the time at which the reading was taken. Two minutes later again note the position of the water column, and record. Continue to take readings at two-minute intervals until you have five readings.

As soon as the fifth reading has been taken, begin to fan the air near the leafy shoot. Members of the team should take

turns fanning. At two-minute intervals record the position of the water column in the pipette until five more readings have been made.

As soon as the fifth reading (tenth since the beginning) has been made, cover the leafy shoot loosely with a plastic bag. Gather the mouth of the bag together and tie it shut around the base of the stem. At two-minute intervals record the position of the water column in the pipette until five more readings have been made.

**STUDYING THE DATA**

• Where may water have been lost from the apparatus? (2)  • Compare the results from the experimental setups with the results from the control setup. What do you think happened to the water in the experimental setups? (3)  • Do the results obtained from the use of the plastic bags provide any confirmation of this? If so, how? (4)  • How can you determine the amount of water lost from the apparatus? (5)

Express your data in graphic form. Plot time along the horizontal axis and the pipette readings along the vertical axis. Connect the plotted points, using a different color for each of the three segments that represent the three conditions of the leafy shoot.

• What is the variable in this set of data? (6)  • How do you account for any changes in the slope of your graph line? (7)

**CONCLUSIONS**

• Do your data confirm the hypothesis? If so, how? (8)

## INVESTIGATION 13.2

### STOMATA AND PHOTOSYNTHESIS

#### PURPOSE

In Part A of this investigation you will observe the appearance and abundance of stomates and the behavior of their guard cells. In Part B, you will experiment to find a relationship between stomates and photosynthesis.

#### MATERIALS AND EQUIPMENT
#### (for each team)

*For Part A*

Fresh leaves (several kinds)

Microscope

Slides

Cover slips

Forceps

Razor blades

Droppers

*For Part B*

Potted plants, 2

Scissors

Beakers, 400 ml, 3

Forceps

Hot plate

Beaker, 1000 ml

Alcohol

Petri dishes, 4

Iodine solution

Test tubes, 4

Petroleum jelly

Paper towel

Absorbent cotton

Benzine

#### PROCEDURE: PART A

Tear a leaf at an angle while holding the lower surface upward. The tearing action should peel off portions of the lower epidermis, which will appear as a narrow, colorless zone extending beyond the green part of the leaf. Immediately place a small piece of the epidermis in a drop of water on a slide. Do not allow the fragment to dry out. Add a cover slip.

Using the low-power objective of your microscope, locate some stomates. Then switch to the high-power objective. Make a sketch to show the shape of a stomate, its guard cells, and a few adjacent epidermal cells.

Count the number of stomates in ten high-power fields of the microscope and average. Remember that in Investigation 1.3 you calculated the diameter of the high-power field. Use this figure now to calculate the area. Then find the average number of stomates per mm² on the leaf surface.

In the same manner, count the stomates on the upper epidermis of the same leaf. Examine as many other kinds of leaves as possible and compare the number of stomates per mm² for the upper and lower surfaces of each kind of leaf.

#### STUDYING THE DATA

• Did you find exactly the same number of stomates per square millimeter in different areas of a piece of leaf epidermis? (1)  • If you wished to compare the number of stomates per mm² for two species of plants, what steps should you take to assure a reliable comparison? (2) • What variations in the extent to which the stomates are open can you observe? Can you explain this variation? (3)

#### PROCEDURE: PART B

If carbon dioxide enters, the leaf through the stomates, then plugging up the stomata should prevent photosynthesis. The following experiment will test this hypothesis.

Select two healthy plants of the same species. Place one where it will receive no light and the other where it will be exposed to sunlight. After three days remove a leaf from each plant, identifying the illuminated one by placing a small notch in its margin. Immediately drop the leaves into a beaker of boiling water. When they are limp, transfer them to a beaker half full of alcohol. Place this beaker in an electrically heated water bath. *Never heat alcohol over an open flame or permit its vapor to come into contact with an open flame.*

Heated alcohol slowly extracts chlorophyll from leaves; it also makes them brittle, because most of their water is removed. After about ten minutes take the leaves out of the alcohol and drop them into a beaker of water at room temperature. After a minute or so, the leaves will become quite soft. Spread each leaf out in a petri dish and cover it with iodine solution.

Allow the iodine solution to act on the leaves for several minutes. Then remove both leaves from the iodine solution, rinse them in water, and spread them out in petri dishes of water placed on a white piece of paper. Record the color of each leaf.

Select four similar leaves on the plant that has been kept in the dark. Do not remove them from the plant. Thoroughly coat the upper surface of one of these leaves with petroleum jelly. Cut one notch in its margin. Coat a second leaf on its lower surface and cut two notches in its margin. Coat a third leaf on both upper and lower surfaces and cut three notches in its margin. Do not coat the fourth leaf, but cut four notches in its margin. A layer of petroleum jelly,

though transparent, is a highly effective barrier across which many gases cannot pass.   • In what ways would you suspect that coating a leaf with petroleum jelly would alter the normal pattern of exchange of gases between it and the air? (4)   Place the plant where it will be exposed to sunlight.

After three days, remove all four leaves, place them on paper towels, and remove the petroleum jelly by gently rubbing the leaves with absorbent cotton saturated with a solvent such as benzine. Use the iodine test on each leaf, following the procedure used before. Devise a scheme for comparing the color reactions of the four leaves, and record your observations.

### STUDYING THE DATA

• In the design of this experiment, what was the purpose of the first set of iodine tests? (5)   • If you use this test as an indication of photosynthetic activity, what assumption are you making? (6)

• In the design of this experiment, what is the purpose of the leaf marked with four notches? (7)

• In which of the leaves did photosynthetic activity appear to have been greatest? (8)   • In which of the leaves did photosynthetic activity appear to have been least? (9)

### CONCLUSIONS

• What do your data suggest concerning the distribution of stomates in leaves of your species of plant? (10)
• What assumption must you make in drawing this conclusion? (11)

### ROOTS

Water is lost by terrestrial tracheophytes principally through their leaves. Except for epiphytes terrestrial plants obtain their water from the soil through their roots. With

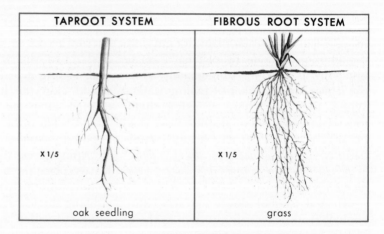

| TAPROOT SYSTEM | FIBROUS ROOT SYSTEM |
|---|---|
| X 1/5 | X 1/5 |
| oak seedling | grass |

Figure 13 · 7
Kinds of root systems.

To what ecological conditions do you think each of these kinds of root systems is adapted?

Hugh Spencer

Figure 13 · 8
A radish seedling. What part of the plant was first to emerge from the seed coat?   x 9

the water they absorb mineral nutrients. Roots have three additional functions: anchorage, storage of food, and the transportation of absorbed water and dissolved minerals. This last function will be discussed later in connection with stems.

**Anchorage.**   Anyone who has pulled weeds in a garden or removed dandelions from a lawn is well aware that the roots of a plant anchor it firmly in the soil. In some species the lower end of the uprooted plant is a tough network of roots. This is a *fibrous* root system, and it is characteristic of corn, beans, and clover, for example. In other species the plant is anchored by a long, tapering root with only a few small branches. This is a *taproot* system, found in dandelions and young oak trees.

Much of a root system remains in the soil when a plant is pulled up. If a stream of water is used to gently wash away the soil, the smaller branch roots remain undamaged and the root system can be seen more completely. When carefully exposed in this way, the root system of a rye plant less than 60 cm in height was estimated to have a total length of about 480 km and a total surface area of more than 600 m². No wonder most land plants are so firmly anchored in the soil!

**Absorption.**   If radish seeds are allowed to germinate in a moist petri dish, the structure of the young root can be seen without the hindrance of soil and entirely undamaged. The tip of such a young root is pointed and bare. Just back of the tip is a region that appears (in a macroscopic view) to be covered with a fuzzy white growth. Observed over a period of several days, this fuzzy band seems to move in the direction of growth as the root lengthens.

The fuzzy region owes its appearance to the presence of numerous *root hairs*. Each root hair is an extended part of

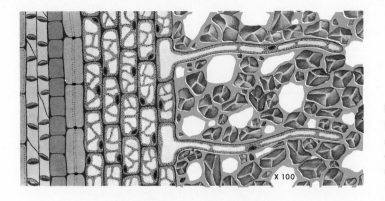

Figure 13 · 9

Root hairs penetrating into soil. On the left are conducting tissues of the root; soil is shown as in Figure 7 · 12.

an epidermal cell that has a thin cell wall. The central part of a root-hair cell is occupied by a large vacuole; this is filled with water in which sugars, salts, and a variety of other compounds are dissolved. Root hairs penetrate the spaces between soil particles and are in contact with soil water. It is principally through these specialized cells that the water required by a plant is obtained.

The substances dissolved in soil water are seldom as concentrated as the substances dissolved in the cytoplast and vacuole of the root hair. Dissolved substances usually pass freely through cell walls; but because cell membranes are differentially permeable, many substances inside root-hair cells cannot pass out through the membranes. Such conditions make possible an inward diffusion of water.

You may want to review pages 390–392.

Thus, we can explain the entry into land plants of the two materials required for photosynthesis: carbon dioxide enters chiefly through leaf cells by way of stomates; water enters chiefly through the root hairs.

But a plant requires substances in addition to $CO_2$ and $H_2O$ — mineral nutrients. It requires nitrogen and phosphorus to synthesize proteins and nucleic acids. It requires magnesium to synthesize chlorophyll molecules. A rather long list of additional elements is needed by plants of one kind or another. All of these elements are obtained from soil water in the chemical form of dissolved compounds. Roots take in nitrogen, for example, in the form of ammonium ions or nitrate ions. Because the mineral nutrients are continually used by the synthetic metabolic activities of a plant, they are usually less concentrated inside root-hair cells than in the surrounding water. Usually, therefore, they pass into root hairs by diffusion.

Frequently, however, mineral substances needed by a plant are *less* concentrated in soil water than in the root-hair cells. Under these circumstances, diffusion would carry

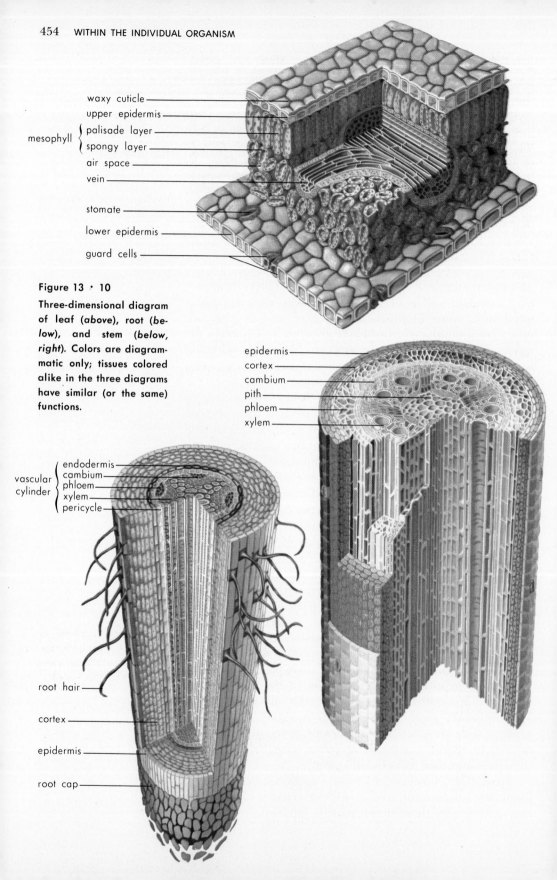

waxy cuticle
upper epidermis
mesophyll { palisade layer
spongy layer
air space
vein
stomate
lower epidermis
guard cells

epidermis
cortex
cambium
pith
phloem
xylem

vascular cylinder { endodermis
cambium
phloem
xylem
pericycle

root hair

cortex

epidermis

root cap

**Figure 13 · 10**

Three-dimensional diagram of leaf (*above*), root (*below*), and stem (*below, right*). Colors are diagrammatic only; tissues colored alike in the three diagrams have similar (or the same) functions.

the substances *from* the cells *into* soil water. Nevertheless, experiments have shown that plants can absorb substances that exist only in low concentrations in soil water. Hans Burström of Sweden grew some barley seedlings in a solution containing 20 parts of a potassium compound per million parts of solution (0.002%). Then he cut off the tops of the plants and collected the sap that welled up out of them. The sap was found to contain 32 parts of the potassium compound per million.

Hans  Burström  [Byr'ström]: 1906——

Further experiments have confirmed the conclusion that root hairs and other plant cells can move substances in solution in a direction opposite to that of diffusion. If diffusion alone accounted for such movement, ions would be most concentrated in the soil water, less concentrated in the root hairs, and progressively less concentrated the farther a cell is from the root hairs. But in certain tissues in roots, minerals accumulate at even higher concentrations than in root hairs themselves. Further, when cells are moving dissolved substances in a direction opposite to that of diffusion, cell respiration speeds up. Clearly, absorption of mineral nutrients involves active transport as well as diffusion.

Why is a speeding of cell respiration an indication of active transport?

Root hairs are the usual points of entry for water and mineral nutrients. On their inner sides these special epidermal cells are in contact with other root cells (Figure 13 · 9). Absorbed substances move deeper into the root by diffusion or active transport from one layer of cells to another. Eventually they reach the conducting tissues, through which they move upward to the stem and leaves.

**Storage.** The *cortex* (Figure 13 · 10) of a young root may be sloughed off as the root grows older, or it may form part of the bark around the root. Sometimes the plant stores food in the cortex and sometimes in modified cells of the

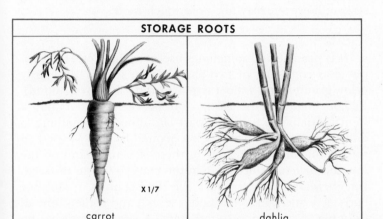

**STORAGE ROOTS**

X 1/7

carrot

dahlia

Figure 13 · 11

When large quantities of food are stored, both taproots (*left*) and fibrous roots (*right*) may be thickened.

**Figure 13 · 12**

In some plants, roots sprout from stems, grow downward, and penetrate into the soil. This banyan tree grows near the state capitol of Hawaii.

conducting tissues. The food is usually stored as insoluble starch, but sometimes as sugars.

Both taproot and fibrous-root systems may have parts where food storage is concentrated. In polar regions, the middle latitudes, and those tropical biomes with dry seasons, perennial plants always store a considerable amount of food in roots. Plants that live through only one growing season, however, may not store much food.

What plant stores so much sugar in its root that we use it as a sugar source?

### STEMS

It is possible and sometimes useful to think of a tracheophyte as consisting of two parts: a root system (ordinarily below ground) and a shoot system (ordinarily above ground).

For botanists the distinction between a root and a stem — usually the principal part of a shoot — has nothing to do with position above or below ground level; it is based on the arrangement of tissues in these structures and on the way the structures originate in the embryo within the seed. But the easiest way to make the distinction is to look for buds. A white potato has buds ("eyes") and is therefore an example of an underground stem. A sweet potato has no

Lynwood M. Chace

**Figure 13 · 13**
**An opening hickory bud.**

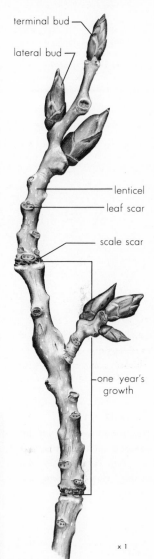

terminal bud

lateral bud

lenticel

leaf scar

scale scar

one year's
growth

x 1

**Figure 13 · 14**
**A dormant woody twig.**

terminal [Latin: *terminare*, to
end, limit]

lateral [Latin: *lateris*, a side]

lenticels [lĕn'tə sĕlz']

buds; it is a root. Most stems, however, grow above ground, supporting leaves and reproductive organs in light and air.

**Macroscopic structure.** Stems differ greatly in structure. The only way to appreciate their diversity is to examine a number of stems. It is convenient to use a portion of a woody twig from a deciduous plant as a starting point in discussing stem structure.

Such a twig, when the leaves have fallen, usually bears conspicuous *buds*. A bud is a miniature shoot, consisting of a short length of stem, tiny leaves, and (sometimes) flowers. Growth from a *terminal* bud lengthens the twig; growth from a *lateral* bud starts a new branch. A bud may or may not be covered with protective *scales* (modified leaves); when growth is resumed in the spring, the scales leave scars on the twig. For a few years, old scale scars may remain visible, and from their positions growth in different years can be compared. The places where the petioles of fallen leaves were attached to the twig are also marked by scars. *Lenticels* are simply openings in the bark through which atmospheric gases diffuse into and out of the living cells.

Older woody stems—tree trunks, for example—are best

In ebony wood there are no growth rings. In what biome do you think ebony grows?

viewed in cross section. A rather thick bark is characteristic of both older stems and older roots. The bark surrounds the wood. Wood usually shows annual growth rings. Wood *rays* extend radially from the center outward toward the bark; these are routes along which liquids move laterally.

Only the tissues of the inner bark and the outer part of the wood are alive; the rest of the wood and bark is composed of dead cell walls such as Hooke saw in cork. Most of the plant liquids (sap) move up and down stems through dead cells—upward through wood, downward through bark. Wood through which sap moves upward is called *sapwood.* The central wood loses its conducting function; it is then called heartwood. It may serve to support the upper parts of a tree, but this is not always important—many trees stand erect and live for years after the heartwood has rotted away.

**Microscopic structure.**   Figure 13 · 10 shows in three dimensions the microscopic structure of a young stem. This is a stem from a dicotyledonous plant. By examining several stems through a microscope, you will find—as with roots and leaves—that there are many variations.

*Pith* is a tissue characteristic of young stems; it may be large or small; in older plants of many species it does not

**Figure 13 · 15**
Heartwood was not yet developed when this tree was cut. Pith is visible in the center. How old was the tree?   × 1

Ross E. Hutchins

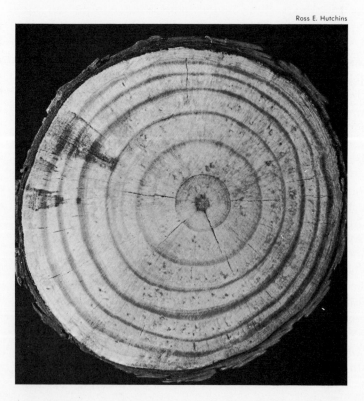

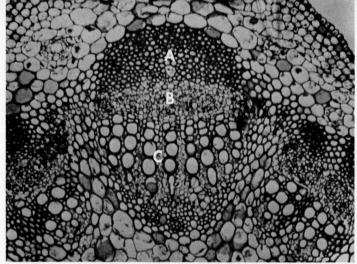

Hugh Spencer

**Figure 13 · 16**
Fibrovascular bundles in a cross section of a sunflower stem. In each bundle the dark outer tissue is fiber (A); next within is phloem (B); and inside that, xylem (C). ×110

persist as an organized tissue. The *cambium* tissue consists of cells that divide and form new tissues of other kinds. It separates the bark from the rest of the stem. Because *xylem* cells are continually being formed along the inner margin of the cambium, most of the stem eventually consists of xylem tissue; this is the wood of an old stem. *Phloem* tissue is continually being formed along the outer margin of the cambium; it makes up much of the inner bark of an old stem. Among the xylem and phloem cells are the vascular tissues mentioned in Chapter 5. Mixed in with the vascular tissues are *fiber* cells, forming a tissue that strengthens the stem. Sometimes fibers and vascular tissues occur in bundles. These *fibrovascular bundles* scattered in pith tissue can be seen macroscopically in corn stems.

Within xylem are found *tracheids* and *vessels*. Tracheids develop from elongated, single cells that develop thick walls and then die. Pits occur at many points in the walls of these dead cells. In most cases these pits are so closely paired on adjacent cells that only a thin layer of cell wall separates two adjoining tracheids. At these points, water and dissolved materials can easily pass from one tracheid into another.

Vessels are made up of elongated, thick-walled cells joined end to end. When a vessel cell is fully formed, a hole develops in the wall at each end of the cell; then, as in the tracheids, the living substance dies and disappears. Thus tiny, elongated pipes are formed, extending through the stem. Because water and salts can pass from one end of a vessel to the other without having to pass through pits, vessels would seem to be more efficient for transporting sap than tracheids. However, some of the tallest trees are gymnosperms that possess no vessels.

Long lines of phloem cells make up structures called *sieve tubes*. As the cells of a sieve tube develop, small holes

cambium [kăm′bĭ əm]

xylem [zī′lĕm; Greek: *xylon*, wood]

phloem [flō′ĕm; Greek: *phloos*, bark of a tree]

The fibers of some plant stems are commercially valuable. What are some examples?

tracheids [trā′kĭ ĭdz; Greek: *tracheia*, windpipe]

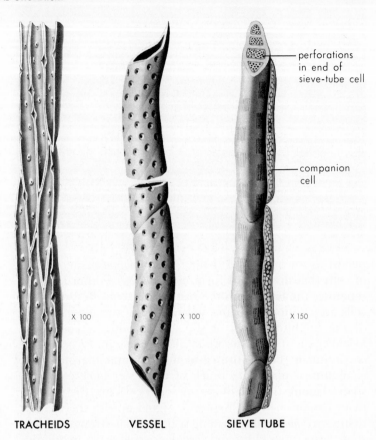

perforations
in end of
sieve-tube cell

companion
cell

X 100                    X 100                    X 150

Figure 13 · 17
Cells from conducting tis-
sues of tracheophytes.     **TRACHEIDS**        **VESSEL**        **SIEVE TUBE**

form in their end walls. Through these holes the cytoplast of one cell connects with the cytoplast of adjacent cells, making a continuous cell-to-cell system. As a sieve tube matures, the nuclei in the cells disintegrate. But the sieve tube continues to function as long as the cytoplasts remain alive. Located beside each sieve-tube cell are one or two smaller *companion cells.* These *do* have nuclei and are believed to regulate the activity of the adjacent sieve-tube cells.

**Conduction.** Through the two series of vascular tissues — xylem and phloem — moves sap, a complex mixture of minerals, foods, and other materials in solution. Unlike the blood in your vascular system, the sap in a plant is not moved by the pumping action of a heart. How, then, do liquids move in a plant?

To date, all the observations of botanists do not add up to an entirely satisfactory answer. Many experiments show that water from the root rises through xylem — from root xylem to stem xylem to xylem in the veins of leaves. Even in the tallest trees, water moves against the force of gravity

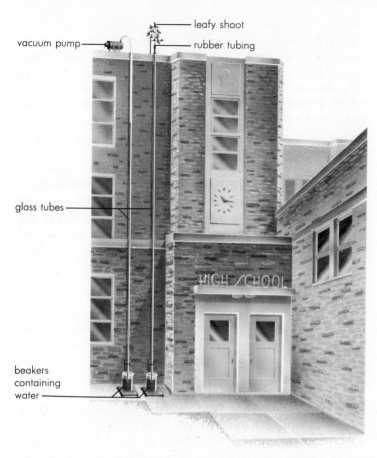

vacuum pump

leafy shoot

rubber tubing

glass tubes

beakers
containing
water

Figure 13 · 18

An experiment on rise of
liquids in stems.

from the roots to the topmost leaves. Let us consider this
upward movement.

Suppose you have a bottle of ginger ale. You place a
straw in the liquid, apply your lips to its upper end, and
suck. Immediately you are rewarded: the liquid rises to
your mouth through the straw. Now let us look at a similar
but less familiar situation. A beaker of water is placed on
the ground next to a school building. You climb up to the
third floor, 13 m above the ground, and, using a long piece
of glass tubing, you attempt to draw the water up from the
beaker. Try as you may, you never succeed. Being stub-
born, you borrow a vacuum pump from the physics lab,
connect it to the tubing, and turn the pump on. This is also
unsuccessful. If the school is near sea level, the water will
rise about 10.3 m above the beaker, but no farther. In
Denver, Colorado, at an altitude of 1609 m, the water in
the tube can be raised only to a height of about 8.4 m. But
in many trees water rises to a much greater height.

Now a new experiment—one involving a living plant.

How might these results be
explained?

Suppose we hold a leafy shoot under water and cut off the top 20 cm with a sharp knife. We insert this cut tip into a short piece of rubber tubing. We then connect the other end of the tubing to a 14-mm length of slender (less than 0.5 mm internal diameter) glass tubing that is filled with water. We make certain that there are no leaks in the system. Now we place the lower end of the glass tube in a beaker of boiled water containing a dye so that it can be easily seen. (Boiling removes dissolved air that could form bubbles in the tube.) The entire setup makes a continuous, water-filled system extending from the mesophyll cells in the leaves down through the xylem tissue of the stem into the rubber tubing and the long glass tube, ending in the container on the ground. Gradually the dyed water from the container begins to rise—first 3 m, then 6, 9, and finally to the tip of the shoot—more than 14 m (that is, 3.7 m above the limit reached with a vacuum pump). How is this possible?

Knowing an important property of water is basic to understanding the movement in this system. Under certain conditions a column of water has remarkable *tensile strength* (resistance to breaking when pulled lengthwise). Here are the conditions: (1) the water must be contained in tubes of very small diameter; (2) the walls of the tubes must be made of a material to which water molecules will adhere; (3) the water must not contain gas bubbles that break the column of water. Under these conditions, as water molecules are lost by evaporation from the upper end of the column (the leaves), their *cohesion* (attraction for adjoining water molecules) results in a pull, which is transmitted throughout the length of the system. This causes more water to move up into the tube from below. In this way, water can be moved upward in columns many times higher than 10.3 m. The water column is pulled up just as a wire would be pulled, rather than being pushed up by atmospheric pressure, as it is in a vacuum-pump system.

In 1915 these physical facts were used by H. H. Dixon to develop the "transpiration-tension" theory for explaining the rise of liquids in plant stems. According to this theory, in a living tree the system of vessels in the xylem corresponds to the slender glass tubing, and soil water in contact with root surfaces corresponds to the dyed water in the container. Sugars produced by photosynthesis are contained within the mesophyll cells. As water evaporates from the mesophyll tissue and passes out through the stomates (transpiration), the concentration of dissolved materials increases. Water molecules then pass into these mesophyll cells from the xylem vessels and tracheids by

tensile [tĕn′sĭl; Latin: *tendere,* to stretch]

adhere [ăd hĭr′; Latin: *ad,* + *haerere,* to stick]

cohesion [kō hē′zhən; Latin: *com-,* together, + *haerere*]

Henry H. Dixon: 1869–1953. British botanist

diffusion. As they move into the mesophyll, cohesion between these water molecules and water molecules in the xylem tissues develops a force that pulls more liquid up the stem.

However, some experimental results do not fit this theory. If the shoot of a well-watered grapevine is cut off and a vertical glass tube is sealed to the rooted stump, sap will rise in the tube. In this situation one condition assumed in the transpiration-tension theory is not present — there is no transpiration. Here it seems that the rise of the sap must come about through a push from below rather than a pull from above. This push has been called *root pressure*. Measurements of the force of root pressure have indicated that water could be pushed to a height of 90 m under some conditions.

In spite of these measurements, plant physiologists think root pressure is not an important factor in the rise of liquids in plants. For one thing, not all plants develop root pressure when their shoots are cut — and some that do not are tall trees. Secondly, in plants that do develop root pressure, the pressure is lowest in the summer, when the plants are moving the most liquid. Moreover, root pressure is simply a name for an observed fact; it is not an explanation. As yet no botanist has fully explained where the force of root pressure comes from. So Dixon's theory still remains the most reasonable *single* explanation for the rise of liquids in plant stems.

Now consider the phloem. Liquids moving through phloem contain much dissolved food, in contrast to the inorganic nutrients that are usually the principal contents of xylem liquids. In general, movement in the phloem is from the leaves, where foods are produced by photosynthesis, downward through stems to roots, where much of the food is stored. But this is not always so; occasionally, movement in the phloem is reversed.

Under what circumstances would the xylem liquids contain a large amount of dissolved food?

We might think the downward movement in the phloem is easily explained — gravity alone might be the cause. But the sieve cells of the phloem are not mere empty tubes; they contain living cytoplasts, through which the moving liquids must pass. Of course, substances can diffuse through cytoplasts, but the rate at which the food-rich liquids move through the phloem is known to be thousands of times faster than diffusion could account for. And in many cases the direction of movement is from lesser concentration to greater concentration — opposite to that of diffusion. Some kind of active transport must be involved.

**Other stem functions.** Conduction of liquids is the principal function of stems. But in many plants, stems

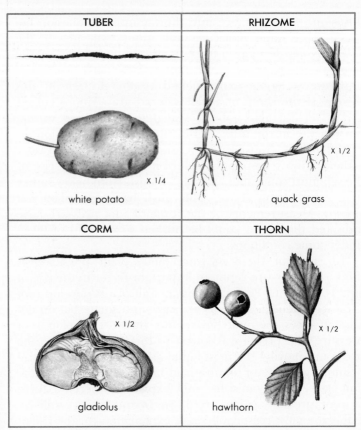

| TUBER | RHIZOME |
|---|---|
| white potato X 1/4 | quack grass X 1/2 |
| CORM | THORN |
| gladiolus X 1/2 | hawthorn X 1/2 |

Figure 13 · 19

Structural adaptations of stems. Tubers, corms, and rhizomes are underground stems. What do you think is the principal function of each kind of stem?

Robert J. Rodin

Figure 13 · 20

Storage stem of a South African plant. In this environment what do you think might be the chief substance stored?

perform other functions also. Some stems may carry on photosynthesis. In most herbaceous plants photosynthesis occurs in chlorophyll-bearing cells just beneath the epidermis of stems. Even in woody plants young twigs frequently contain photosynthetic tissues. And some plants have no leaves; in these all photosynthesis occurs in stems.

In most modern plants, however, the functions of stems in food production are supplying water by conduction and supporting leaves where they may be exposed to sunlight. In forests, sturdy trunks hold leaves of trees far above the surface of the ground; plants with weaker stems are left in the shade below, where they must adapt to the reduced light that filters down—or perish. Some plants are almost stemless. The leaves of dandelions, for example, spread out on the surface of the ground, appearing to grow directly from the top of the root. Some such "stemless" plants are shade-tolerant; others (such as dandelions) grow mostly in places where few taller neighboring plants cut off solar radiation.

In many plants stems serve as storage organs. Sugar-cane plants store sucrose in their stems. Great quantities of water as well as food are stored in cactus stems. When the storage function of stems is highly developed, other functions may be less evident or absent. The best-known examples of food storage occur in underground stems that have no other important function.

In addition to white potatoes, what examples can you name?

### GROWTH

You may be still growing, but you know that a time will come when you will cease to grow — at least in height. Mammals, birds, and arthropods have definite limits to growth, but most other animals and all multicellular plants continue to grow throughout their lives — usually at a gradually slowing rate. Nevertheless, there is a fundamental difference between growth in animals and growth in multicellular plants.

**Meristems.** Growth in multicellular organisms occurs primarily by means of the addition of new cells, followed by enlargement of these cells. In animals these new cells are added in all directions. As you grow, your proportions change; but most of the time growth occurs throughout your body. This is so because most kinds of animal cells retain the ability to reproduce — even though they differentiate in other respects.

In vascular plants, cells that have differentiated — into xylem, phloem, and mesophyll, for example — generally lose the ability to divide. Each cell of such tissues is formed from another kind of tissue, an undifferentiated tissue that continues mitosis and cell division as long as the plant lives. This tissue, no matter where it occurs in the plant, is called a *meristem.*

In root tips meristematic tissue is located just behind a *root cap* (Figure 13 · 10). This meristem forms root-cap cells on the side toward the tip. These cells do not accumulate because they are constantly worn away as the root pushes through the soil. To the rear, this meristem forms cells that differentiate into root tissues, each with a specialized function. Only these become a permanent part of the root.

The tips of stems also contain meristems. As a stem lengthens, the tissue at its tip remains meristematic. Small masses of meristem are also left behind, and from them branches and leaves develop. Each branch has a meristem at its tip. In most leaves, however, all the cells differentiate into xylem, phloem, mesophyll, etc. This differentiation takes place at an early stage in leaf formation. For example, in deciduous woody plants, leaves for the following year are fully formed within a bud before the end of the growing season. The cells, though, are quite small. In spring,

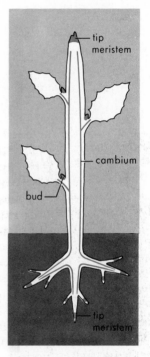

**Figure 13 · 21**

Location of principal meristems — a diagram.

meristem [měr′ ə stěm′; Greek: *meristos,* divided]: Note that there is no relation to the word "stem."

Refer to Figure 13 · 13.

Figure 13 · 22
Tip of an elodea shoot.

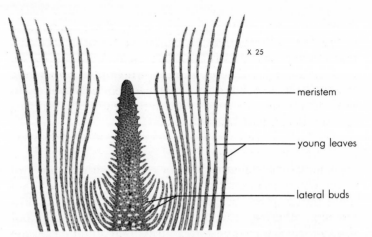

X 25

meristem

young leaves

lateral buds

X 1/10

Figure 13 · 23
Bark and cambium were removed from a strip around the trunk of this tree a year before the top was cut off. Can you explain this result?

phototropism [fō tŏt′rə pĭz′əm; Greek: *photos*, a light, + *tropos*, turning]

Figure 13 · 24
What are the principal changes that a year has made in these stems?

leaves expand by the enlargement of these small cells, without the addition of new cells. Leaves of grasses and some other plants are an exception: in them a meristem remains at the base of the leaf, and the leaf can increase in length even after most of the blade has been cut off by a grazing animal or a lawn mower.

Not all the cells left behind along a lengthening root or stem branch off or differentiate. Except in monocots, the layer of meristem called the cambium remains along the length of each stem and root. From cambium new xylem and phloem are formed, increasing the stems and roots in diameter. Cambium remains as a boundary between the central core of wood (xylem) and the outer layer of bark (phloem). Bark can usually be peeled from a tree trunk rather easily because the walls of the cambium cells are thin and easily broken.

**Chemical control of growth.** For a long time it has been known that most green plants grow toward light—a response often called *phototropism*. This is easily observed in plants growing on windowsills, where almost all the light comes from one side. Nearly ninety years ago, Charles

X 3

four-year-old stem          five-year-old stem

Darwin and his son, Francis, investigated the mechanism of this response. From previous studies the Darwins knew that several zones can be distinguished in a developing plant stem. At the tip is the meristem; just behind it is a zone of elongation, in which the newly formed cells enlarge lengthwise; behind this is a zone in which the cells become xylem, phloem, fibers, and other tissues.

Charles Darwin: 1809–1882. English naturalist

The Darwins observed that the bending toward the light occurs not at the very tip, but in the zone of elongation, a few millimeters behind it. They experimented with very young seedlings of grasses and oats, which have a covering called the *coleoptile* over the first leaves. When they placed a tiny metal cap over the tips of the coleoptiles, the zones of elongation no longer bent. Somehow, light shining on the tip affected the cells in the zone of elongation below it. The Darwins concluded that "when seedlings are freely exposed to a lateral light some influence is transmitted from the upper to the lower part, causing the latter to bend."

coleoptile [kŏ'lĭ ŏp'til; Greek: *koleos,* sheath, + *ptilon,* feather]

What was this "influence"? In later years this investigation was pursued by others. In 1910 Boysen-Jensen performed an experiment based on the hypothesis that the "influence" carried from the tip to the cells in the region of elongation was a chemical substance. He placed oat seedlings in a container that provided light from only one side. He cut off the coleoptile tips of some and left others intact. The intact seedlings bent toward the light source; the tipless seedlings grew straight upward. Then he used

Peter Boysen-Jensen: 1883–1959. Danish botanist

intact [ĭn tăkt'; Latin: *in-,* not, + *tangere,* to touch]: here, whole

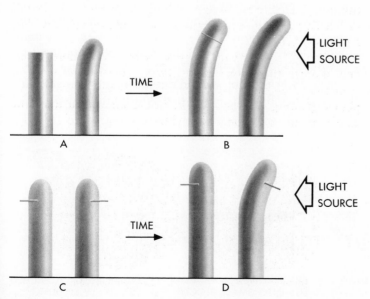

LIGHT SOURCE

TIME

A          B

LIGHT SOURCE

TIME

C          D

**Figure 13 · 25**

Boysen-Jensen's two experiments. A and B show the first experiment; C and D show the second.

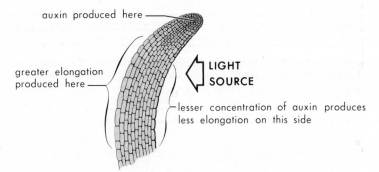

auxin produced here ———

greater elongation
produced here ———

LIGHT
SOURCE

——lesser concentration of auxin produces
less elongation on this side

**Figure 13 · 26**
How differential elonga-
tion of cells on opposite
sides of a shoot produces
bending.

gelatin to fasten the tips to the stumps of the tipless coleoptiles. These seedlings now began to bend toward the light
in the same way as the controls (intact plants). Something
had evidently passed from the tip through the nonliving
gelatin to the stumps—most probably a chemical substance.

How did the supposed chemical substance cause the
bending toward the light? A year later, in an attempt to
obtain information on this question, Boysen-Jensen inserted
thin pieces of mica partway through oat coleoptiles and
just behind the tips. In designing this experiment, he assumed that the chemical substance from the tip of the plant
could not pass through the mica as it evidently had done
through the gelatin. When the seedlings were placed so
that the mica was on the side toward the light source, the
seedlings bent toward it. When they were placed so that the
mica was away from the light source, they did not bend.
From these results Boysen-Jensen concluded that some
substance produced by cells in the coleoptile tip moved
down the side of the coleoptile opposite to the light and
increased elongation of cells on that side. Greater lengthening of cells on the "dark" side made the plant bend toward the light (Figure 13 · 26).

In 1928 Frits Went worked out techniques for collecting
the substance Boysen-Jensen had shown must exist. Tips of

Frits Went: 1903———. American (Dutch-born) botanist

**Figure 13 · 27**
Went's method of mea-
suring auxin production.

leaves pulled
out to support
agar block ———

LAYER OF AGAR WITH
SEEDLING TIPS

TIPS REMOVED AND AGAR
CUT INTO SMALL BLOCKS

AGAR BLOCK ATTACHED
TO TIP OF SEEDLING

oat coleoptiles were cut off and placed on thin layers of agar (similar to the agar in the plates you used in Investigation 6.3, but without nutrients). Later the agar was cut into blocks. The tips were then removed from the agar and discarded. Each small agar block was placed on the edge of a seedling from which the tip had been removed. Without exposure to light the seedling bent—and always away from the side on which the piece of agar was placed. Evidently the substance in the tip had diffused into the agar, and then from the agar it had diffused into the coleoptile. Further, Went found he could measure the amount of the substance by measuring the angle of bending that an agar piece produced in a seedling.

Because the substance produced in the seedling tip stimulated increased elongation, it has been referred to as a growth substance and named *auxin*, but its exact chemical nature has not yet been determined. However, many known chemical substances have the same effect on the growth of plants. One of these, indoleacetic acid, is effective in extremely small amounts. For example, 0.0000005 milligrams applied to one side of an oat seedling will bring about a clearly visible bending. Indoleacetic acid has been found to be present in plants; it is very possible that it is a natural auxin.

auxin [ŏk'sĭn; Greek: *auxein*, to increase, grow]

indoleacetic [ĭn'dəl ə sēt'ĭk]

### Figure 13 · 28

The top row of holly cuttings was treated with beta-indolebutyric acid; the bottom row was not treated. How might this substance related to growth be used commercially?

U.S. Dept. of Agriculture, Beltsville, Md.

Many man-made chemical substances have effects similar to those of indoleacetic acid. One, called "2,4-D," stimulates growth when used in small quantities; but large quantities of it can kill many kinds of plants. Since 2,4-D at the concentrations usually used does not affect members of the grass family, it is used to control other plants in lawns and in grainfields.

Further evidence that there is still much to learn about the chemical control of growth in plants is shown by the case of the "silly seedlings." A number of years ago, Japanese rice farmers noticed that some individual rice plants sometimes grow gigantically tall and then droop, fall over, and die. Japanese botanists found that these *bakanae* ("silly seedlings") are infected with a fungus. They studied the effects of the *bakanae* disease and discovered that certain substances formed by the fungus — *gibberellins* — bring about the strange growth of the *bakanae*. When treated with gibberellins, many kinds of plants grow to double or triple their normal height; but many species are only slightly affected by such treatment. And it is now known that some tracheophytes as well as fungi produce gibberellins. The study of gibberellins and their effects is a very active field of botanical research.

*bakanae* [bä kä nä ĕ]

gibberellins    [jĭb′ər ĕl′ĭnz; named after the fungi in which they were first found, the genus *Gibberella*]

## INVESTIGATION 13.3

## RATE OF GROWTH: LEAVES

### INTRODUCTION

Within a seed, a plant embryo exists; in most cases much of the embryo consists of a bud. On pages 465–466 it was pointed out that the multiplication of leaf cells takes place chiefly while the leaf is still in a bud. And the expansion of the leaf from the bud is largely a result of the enlargement of cells. A simple and convenient study of growth can be made by beginning with the leaves in this embryonic bud.

### MATERIALS AND EQUIPMENT
(for each team)

Bean seeds, 18
Beaker, 250 ml
Fungicide solution
Scalpel
Hand lens
Metric ruler
Seed flat or box
Sand or vermiculite
Graph paper, 1 sheet per student

## PROCEDURE

Select 18 bean seeds of approximately the same size. Place in a beaker. Add fungicide solution to the seeds until the volume of the solution is approximately twice that of the seeds. Allow the seeds to remain in the fungicide twenty minutes. Then pour off the solution and rinse the seeds thoroughly with water. Fill the beaker with water and leave the seeds in it overnight.

After twenty-four hours take 3 seeds from the beaker. Using a scalpel, cut carefully through the seed coat of each of the 3 beans. Remove the seed coats and open the beans. Using a hand lens, find the embryo plant that lies between the two large cotyledons in each seed. Measure the length of the embryo leaves in each seed. In your data book, record the measurements and calculate the average length.

Plant the remaining 15 seeds about 1.5 cm deep and 5 cm apart in sand or vermiculite. After planting, water thoroughly; provide abundant light and a relatively constant temperature; keep the "soil" damp but not flooded.

On Days 3, 6, 10, 13, 17, and 20 after planting, measure the length of the first two leaves of 3 plants to the nearest millimeter. On Day 3 (and possibly on Day 6 also) you may find it necessary to dig up 3 germinated seeds, since the plants may not have grown above the surface. If this is necessary, discard these seeds after you have made your measurements. After the plants appear above the "soil," measure the leaves on the same 3 plants each measurement day. Make the measurement along the center vein (midrib) of each leaf, from the apex to the base; do not include the length of the petiole. Average the measurements each day.

## STUDYING THE DATA

Plot the data (time on the horizontal axis, average length of leaves on the vertical axis) on a graph. The rate of growth is indicated by the slope of the graph line. • Does the slope change? If so, describe the change. (1)  • When did the most rapid growth occur? (2)  • Are there fluctuations? If so, try to explain them. (3)  Compare this graph with the ones you drew in Investigations 2.1, 2.2, and 2.3. • Which does this one most resemble? (4)  • In which part of the graphs—beginning, middle, or end—is there most resemblance? (5)

## SUMMARY

• From your study of the graphs, what general statements can you make that apply to all of them? (6)

## FOR FURTHER INVESTIGATION

1. Obtaining data on growth of individual plants through maturity usually requires a considerable amount of time. Figure 13·29 shows data on the growth of a bamboo—a plant that grows quite

| AGE (in weeks) | AVERAGE HEIGHT (in meters) |
|---|---|
| 1 | 0.7 |
| 2 | 1.5 |
| 3 | 2.5 |
| 4 | 4.0 |
| 5 | 6.2 |
| 6 | 8.3 |
| 7 | 10.2 |
| 8 | 12.0 |
| 9 | 13.2 |
| 10 | 13.8 |
| 11 | 14.1 |
| 12 | 14.2 |

Figure 13 · 29

rapidly. Draw a graph from these data. Compare it with the graph of leaf growth.

2. Is the shape of a growth-rate graph influenced by the kind of measurement recorded? Weight rather than a linear measurement has frequently been used in growth studies. The data in Figure 13 · 30 were obtained from a field of corn. Every two weeks after the seedlings appeared above ground, several plants were pulled and weighed. The weights were averaged and recorded. Graph these data, and compare the graph with other growth-rate graphs.

| AGE (in weeks) | AVERAGE WEIGHT (in grams) |
|---|---|
| 2 | 21 |
| 4 | 28 |
| 6 | 58 |
| 8 | 76 |
| 10 | 170 |
| 12 | 422 |
| 14 | 706 |
| 16 | 853 |
| 18 | 924 |
| 20 | 966 |

Figure 13 · 30

## NONVASCULAR PLANTS

The great majority of multicellular plants are tracheophytes; but bryophytes, most fungi, and many of the algae are also multicellular. Their structures differ from those of tracheophytes, but they carry on the same basic functions: absorption of nutrients, transportation of dissolved substances, storage of food, growth, and so forth.

Many bryophytes appear to have roots, stems, and leaves. Microscopically, however, none of these parts resemble the roots, stems, and leaves of tracheophytes. In particular, they lack vascular tissues—xylem and phloem. Because botanists use the terms "root," "stem," and "leaf" to indicate vascular organs, these words should not be used in naming the parts of liverworts or mosses.

More important than the naming of the structures, however, is the effect that the lack of vascular tissues has on the physiology of the plants. A few bryophytes live in water; but most are land plants, getting their water from the soil. Because they lack vascular tissues, the upward transportation of soil water in them is, apparently, not efficient enough to allow growth to heights above 40 cm—at least, this is the maximum height among bryophytes. Even such heights are reached only in environments with a high humidity, where transpiration must be very slow. On the other hand, many mosses are able to go into a dormant

Nathan W. Cohen (Both Photos)

A                                    B

Figure 13 · 31
(A) A clump of dry moss. (B) The same clump two minutes after water was added at its base. What has happened to the moss plants?
x 2

state when the water supply is low. Such species survive in some very dry places, as in deserts and small crevices in rocks, where they actively grow only during a few days after each rain.

Fungi, too, have no conducting tissues. But the lack of chlorophyll is a much more distinctive characteristic in the physiology of fungi. Fungi, like animals and many protists, are consumers. They must obtain their energy from food, multicarbon compounds that they secure from the environment. Unlike animals, however, they seldom require such molecules as amino acids from the environment. Like other plants, if supplied with multicarbon compounds and with mineral nutrients, they can usually synthesize all the organic substances they require. During their metabolic activities, many fungi produce substances that are rare or unknown among other organisms—the complex acids of lichen fungi, for example. In recent years biochemists have become very interested in the special physiology of fungi.

Multicellular algae also lack vascular systems; but because they live in water, this is no hindrance to their growth. Indeed, some of the brown algae reach a length of 45 m, far longer than most middle-latitude deciduous trees are high. Such seaweeds, however, are seldom more than a few centimeters thick, so none of their cells are far from the environmental water and the mineral nutrients it contains.

All algae carry on photosynthesis. Many contain chlorophylls $c$ and $d$ instead of the chlorophyll $b$ characteristic of tracheophytes and bryophytes. Apparently this does not cause any great difference in the biochemistry of photosynthesis. However, most groups of algae have a physiological characteristic that is useful in classification—the kind of food they store (see Appendix II). Although most plants store food principally as starch, some of the algae store it in the form of other polysaccharides or even oils.

The conspicuous land plants are multicellular, with differentiated tissues and organs. Most of these are tracheophytes; therefore, this chapter has been devoted largely to the structure and physiology of these plants. The structure of leaves is adapted to their principal function of photosynthesis. The structure of roots is adapted to their principal function of absorption. The structure of stems is adapted to their principal function of conduction. In general, the structure of tracheophytes is adapted to life in land environments.

Growth in multicellular plants results from the production of new cells and their subsequent enlargement. The production of new cells occurs only in specialized tissues—a characteristic that helps to distinguish multicellular plants from animals. Studies of responses of plants to environmental factors—such as light—have led to the discovery that plant growth is regulated by chemical means.

Finally, some aspects of the physiology of nonvascular plants have been compared and contrasted to the physiology of vascular plants and of animals.

## GUIDE QUESTIONS

1. On what basis can we call a leaf a plant organ?
2. What characteristics of leaf structure (internal and external) seem to be related to leaf function in photosynthesis?
3. What is transpiration?
4. How does wilting of leaves occur?
5. What are the principal functions of roots?
6. Through what root structures does a plant absorb most of its water and nutrients?
7. What evidence indicates that absorption of substances from the soil involves more than simple diffusion?
8. How do stems differ from roots?
9. What are the principal differences between xylem and phloem tissues?
10. Explain the transpiration-tension theory of conduction in your own words.
11. In what ways is the idea of root pressure unsatisfactory as a general explanation for the rise of liquids in stems?
12. How does conduction occur through phloem tissue?
13. Summarize the functions that plant stems perform.
14. What is the function of meristems?
15. How did Boysen-Jensen demonstrate that tissue at the tip of a shoot produces a substance causing elongation of stem cells?

16. How did Went measure this substance?
17. In what ways do gibberellins resemble auxin?
18. Mosses never grow very tall. What seems to be the principal reason for this?
19. Metabolically fungi resemble both animals and other plants. How?

## PROBLEMS

1. The leaves of water lilies (tracheophytes) float. The plants are rooted in mud at the bottom of ponds. How might the cellular structure of their roots, stems, and leaves differ from cellular arrangement in the roots, stems, and leaves of terrestrial tracheophytes?

2. A few species of tracheophytes do not carry on photosynthesis. In what ways might you expect their roots, stems, and leaves to differ from those of photosynthetic tracheophytes?

3. In Chapter 5 it was pointed out that most roots are not exposed to light and contain no chlorophyll. How is the gas exchange between root and environment different from the gas exchange between leaf (in sunlight) and environment?

4. During the growing season farmers spend considerable time cultivating their crops—loosening the soil between plants. What advantages does this have for the crop plants? Investigate the practice called "dry farming." How is it related to the physiology of plants?

5. Ten years ago a farmer built a fence 1.5 m high and attached one end of it to a tree that was 7 m high. Now the tree has grown to a height of 14 m. How far above the ground is the attached end of the fence? Explain your answer.

6. The following questions concern lateral growth in woody stems: (a) How is an annual ring formed in the wood of a tree? (b) Within a given biome, how would the annual ring formed in a wet year differ from one formed in a dry year? (c) Sometimes two rings are formed in one year. How might this happen? (d) What is the science of *dendrochronology* and how is it used? (e) What happens to phloem tissue as the trunk of a tree increases in diameter? (f) Would you expect to find annual rings in the bark of a tree?

7. A plant is placed in an atmosphere containing abundant carbon dioxide, but no growth occurs. What are some possible explanations for this?

8. In a middle-latitude biome a pine and an apple tree are growing side by side. Compare the requirements of these two trees for water throughout the year.

## SUGGESTED READINGS

DOYLE, W. T. *Nonvascular Plants: Form and Function.* Belmont, Calif.: Wadsworth Publishing Co., Inc., 1964. (Emphasizes use of nonvascular plants in biological research.)

FOGG, G. E. *The Growth of Plants.* Baltimore: Penguin Books, Inc., 1963. (Though growth is the focus of attention, all phases of plant physiology are discussed in this book. Somewhat advanced.)

GALSTON, A. W. *The Life of the Green Plant.* 2nd ed. Englewood Cliffs, N.J.: Prentice-Hall, Inc., 1964. (A brief account of the physiology of plants —chiefly tracheophytes—but one covering all aspects of the subject. Fairly advanced.)

GREULACH, V. A., and J. E. ADAMS. 2nd ed. *Plants: An Introduction to Modern Botany.* New York: John Wiley & Sons, Inc., 1967. (Modern, college-level treatment of plant physiology, with clear, carefully selected illustrations.)

VAN OVERBEEK, J. *The Lore of Living Plants.* New York: McGraw-Hill Book Co., Inc., 1964. (An excellent discussion of plant physiology. Contains suggestions for student investigations. Fairly easy.)

WENT, F. W., and EDITORS OF LIFE. *The Plants.* New York: Time, Inc., Book Division, 1963.

WILSON, C. L., and W. E. LOOMIS. *Botany.* 4th ed. New York: Holt, Rinehart & Winston, Inc., 1967. Chapters 5–9 and 11. (An excellent college-level discussion of structure and functions of tracheophytes.)

ZIMMERMANN, M. H. "How Sap Moves in Trees," *Scientific American*, March, 1963. Pp. 132–138+.

# The Functioning Animal

## INVESTIGATION 14.1

### ANIMAL STRUCTURE AND FUNCTION

#### INTRODUCTION

What functions are performed by both men and grasshoppers, by both men and earthworms, by both men and jellyfish? Your first reaction may be that these species have very little in common. But they are all animals, and gradually you will think of functions that all animals must perform if they are to survive.

No one species can fully illustrate animal structure and function: man, grasshopper, earthworm, jellyfish—we might learn much from any of these. But for a long time frogs have been favorite laboratory animals. And frogs have some advantages: they are of a convenient size, they are easily obtained, they are easily kept in the laboratory, and they are comparatively inexpensive. Still more important, they are vertebrates—enough like ourselves to throw some light on our own structure and function, yet sufficiently unlike us to provide some important contrasts.

#### MATERIALS AND EQUIPMENT
(for each team)

*For Procedure A*
Live frog
Gauze bandage, 60 cm
Aquariums, at least 60 cm long and
    containing water to a depth of
    at least 10 cm, 2 for the whole class
*For Procedure B*
Pithed frog
Dissecting pan
Pins, 10
Forceps, 2
Scissors
Scalpel
Watch with a second hand
Pipette
Sodium chloride crystals
Petri dish
Distilled water
Microscope slide
Sugar solution
Medicine dropper
Monocular microscope

Paper towels
Saline solution (0.7% sodium chloride)
Plastic bag
Glass-marking crayon
Rubber band
Refrigerator

*For Procedure C*
Dead frog (from Procedure B)
Dissecting pan
Pins, 10
Forceps
Hand lens
Scissors

## PROCEDURE A: THE LIVE FROG

Moisten the top of the table where the frog will be placed. To aid you in handling the animal, a piece of gauze bandage has been tied to one of its legs. Tie the other end to a table leg or to any other fixed object. Sit quietly by the table and allow time for the frog to become accustomed to its surroundings. By avoiding sudden motions, you will increase your opportunities for making accurate observations.

Compare the general structure of the frog's body with that of your own. Think of your body as consisting of a head, neck, trunk, and four appendages. • Are any of these lacking in the frog? If so, which? (1)   Consider a cat, cow, or lizard. • What major division of the body is present in these and many other vertebrates but is lacking in the structure of both frog and man? (2)   Compare the body structure to the left and to the right of the frog's backbone. • What kind of symmetry does the frog's body have? Your body? (3)

Locate the eyes. • In what ways do the frog's eyes differ from yours? (4) The ears are located behind and below the eyes. The eardrum is stretched across the ear opening. • How do your ears differ from those of the frog? (5) • In what ways does the skin of the frog differ from yours? (6)

In the human body each of the upper appendages consists of a series of parts called the upper arm, the forearm, the wrist, the hand, and the fingers; each of the lower appendages consists of the thigh, shank, ankle, foot, and toes. • Are any of these parts lacking in the appendages of the frog? If so, which? (7) • In what ways do the *terminal* parts (those that are farthest from the trunk) of the frog's appendages differ from those of man? (8)

Using the eraser end of a pencil, gently prod the frog until it jumps. • What is the function of each pair of appendages in the jumping process? (9) You can leap somewhat as the frog does, but the frog cannot stand erect as you do. • By examining the structure of the frog's legs and trunk, give evidence to support the preceding statement. (10)

You must observe very carefully to see the frog breathe. First locate the nostrils. (Ducts lead from the nostrils to the posterior part of the mouth cavity.) Then, without touching the frog, watch the floor of the mouth (upper throat). When it is lowered, the mouth cavity enlarges. • From where can air come to fill the enlarged mouth cavity? (11)   Observe the motion of the nostrils. • How does this motion relate to the motion of the floor of the mouth? (12) • As the floor of the mouth is raised, where can the air in the mouth cavity go? (13) • When you breathe, where does the principal motion occur? (14) • Can you breathe with your mouth open? Can the frog? (15)

Remove the gauze bandage from the frog's leg. Place the frog in the water at one end of a large aquarium. Observe the motions used to swim. • How are the toes used in swimming? (16) • What structure is associated with the toes in swimming? (17) • Are these structures present on the fingers? (18)   Try to get the frog to float. • What is the position of the eyes, ears, and nostrils with respect to the surface of the water? (19) • Hold the frog under water for two minutes. Do you observe any breathing movements? Try to explain. (20) • While the frog is under water, do you see any eye structure that is lacking in man? If so, describe it. (21)   Return the live frog to the container designated by your teacher.

## PROCEDURE B: DISSECTION OF PITHED FROG

Each team will be provided with a frog in which the brain and spinal cord have been destroyed—a *pithed* frog. Such an animal can have no sense of feeling. However, its tissues remain active for a number of hours, making possible the direct observation of several kinds of functions.

Place the frog on the dissecting pan, ventral side up. Fasten the frog to the wax in the pan by inserting pins through the ends of the appendages and into the wax. The skin of the frog is attached quite loosely to the muscles. With forceps, hold the skin free from the muscles of the ventral body wall; use scissors to make a small crosswise cut through the skin at the midline of the abdomen (Figure 14 · 1A). Insert one tip of the scissors into this opening, and cut anteriorly along the midline of the body to the region of the throat. Then cut posteriorly along the midline to the region of the anus (Figure 14 · 1B). Next cut laterally from the ends of the longitudinal incision (Figure 14 · 1C). There are now two flaps of skin that can be opened to the side. To open them fully and pin them down (Figure 14 · 1D), you must separate the skin from the body wall in a few places; a sharp scalpel is the best instrument for this job.

Now open the muscular body wall, following the procedure used in opening the skin. The organs of the body cavity lie just inside the body wall; therefore, be sure to lift the body wall from the organs beneath and to insert only the tip of the scissors when cutting. As you cut anteriorly, you will run into the breastbone; be very careful to avoid cutting the organs that lie beneath it. In opening the body wall laterally, you may remove about 8 mm of the breastbone. Some effort will be required to open the body wall at the anterior end.

Observe the beating of the heart. • How many times does it contract per minute? (22) Carefully slit the thin, transparent membrane that surrounds the heart.   • Do the contractions travel from the anterior toward the posterior part of the heart? Vice versa? In neither direction? (23)

Open the mouth and locate the *glottis,* a slitlike opening in the floor of the mouth. (Do not confuse it with the larger opening into the esophagus.) Insert the end of a pipette into the glottis, and blow gently on the other end of the pipette. If you have located the glottis, the lungs will become inflated.   • Describe their appearance. (24)

Female specimens may contain so many eggs that organs in the posterior part of the body are difficult to see. If this is true of your specimen, use forceps to remove the eggs. Carefully pick the eggs out a few at a time without disturbing other organs. Attached to the egg masses are white, coiled tubes. These are the *oviducts,* through which the eggs pass when they are laid. Remove these also.

Sprinkle a few crystals of sodium chloride along the surface of the intestine. Observe for at least two minutes. • Describe any movements of the intestine. (25)   Using the scissors, snip across the small intestine about 1.5 cm from the stomach and the same distance from the large intestine. Free the small intestine from the *mesentery* (the membrane that holds it in place) and drop it

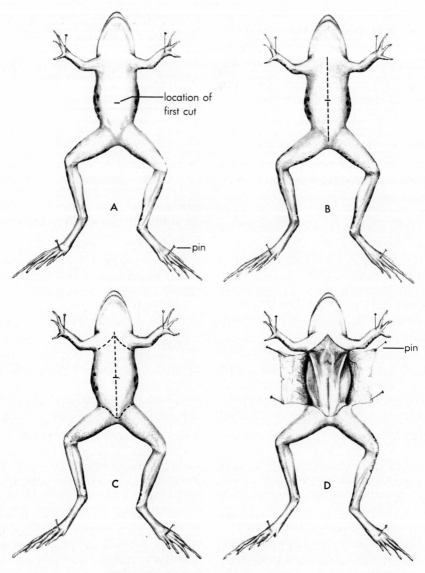

location of first cut

A

pin

B

C

D

pin

Figure 14 · 1

Steps in opening the body cavity of a frog.

into a petri dish containing distilled water. • Describe any reaction. (26) Now
cut off a piece about 5 mm long. Slit the
piece open and spread it out, inner side
up, on a slide. Add a drop or two of
warm sugar solution and observe (without a cover slip) under low power of a
monocular microscope. Note the small
projections on the inner wall of the intestine. • Describe their activity. (27)

Remove the pins from the frog. Close
the body wall and the skin over the body
cavity. Wrap the frog in a paper towel
that has been dipped in saline solution.
Mark a plastic bag with your team symbol. Place the frog in the bag, fasten the
bag with a rubber band, and store in a
refrigerator.

## PROCEDURE C: DISSECTION OF DEAD FROG

Remove the frog from the plastic bag and paper towel. Pin it to the dissecting pan, as in Procedure B.

Just posterior to the heart is the reddish-brown liver. • How many sections does it have? (28)   On the frog's right side the liver covers the *gall bladder.* Using forceps, raise the liver and find the gall bladder.   • What color is it? (29)

On the left side the liver partially covers the stomach. The diameter of the stomach depends upon the amount of food it contains.   • Toward which side does the stomach curve from anterior to posterior end? (30)   At its posterior end the stomach leads into the small intestine; where these two portions of the alimentary canal join, a narrow constriction, the *pyloric valve,* is visible. Between the inner edge of the curved stomach and the first loop of the intestine is the *pancreas.* After you have located the pyloric valve and the pancreas, remove the stomach. Using scissors, slit the stomach along its outer curvature and spread it open.   • Observe the inner surface with a hand lens. Describe it. (31)

You have already removed most of the small intestine and, if your specimen is a female, the eggs and the oviducts. Now push the mesentery and remaining organs aside and look for the kidneys, which are attached to the back. They are reddish-brown in color.   • Describe their shape. (32)   If your frog is a male, you will find a *testis,* a yellowish, bean-shaped organ, attached to each kidney. Attached to the anterior end of each kidney you may find a cluster of yellowish, finger-like structures, the *fat bodies;* they vary in size, depending upon the season of the year. Compare the fat bodies in your frog with those in frogs dissected by other teams.   • Are the fat bodies usually larger in males or in females? (33)

• Using a hand lens, locate the thin tube that leads from the posterior end of each kidney. To what does it lead? (34)

Dispose of your frog as directed by the teacher.

### SUMMARY

• On the basis of this investigation and your understanding of your own body, write a brief comparison of the structures and functions of frog and man. (35)

### FOR FURTHER INVESTIGATION

1. Divide a group of live frogs into two sets, each containing the same number of individuals. Weigh and mark each frog. Leave one set overnight in a container with a small amount of water; then weigh again. Leave the other set overnight in a container without water; then weigh again. Compare the data from the two sets of frogs. Suggest an explanation.

2. Remove the entire skin of one of the dead frogs used in Investigation 14.1 and study the muscular system. Some of the muscles of frog and man are compared on page 459 of Moment's *General Zoology* (Boston: Houghton Mifflin Company, 1967).

3. Prepare one of the frogs as a skeleton. First, remove as much flesh as possible, using scalpel and forceps. This is a rather difficult task because many of the bones are small and delicate; be careful not to cut through the small ones in the appendages and the thin ones in the head. Second, gently simmer the roughed-out skeleton for about thirty minutes in a little water to which some soap powder has been added. Third, gently scrape the remaining flesh from the bones, using a scalpel and a stiff-bristled toothbrush. Finally, using thin wire, assemble the bones in their natural relationship to each other and attach them to a piece of stiff cardboard.

## ACQUIRING ENERGY AND MATERIALS

Animals live almost everywhere: in water, in soil, under logs, in trees, and within other organisms. And accompanying this diversity of environments is an astonishing structural diversity. However, there is one striking similarity among all animals—they spend a great deal of time either eating or hunting for food. Our primitive ancestors, too, spent most of their time seeking and consuming food. Today you don't spend much time hunting, but consider how much of your parents' time is spent in earning money to pay the food bill. The reason for this dominant animal activity has been with us since Chapter 1: Eating is the means by which animals acquire both energy and materials for the repair of tissues and for growth.

In the general sense, "food" is the word for things that animals eat, but in this book we have used it in a special sense—to indicate materials from which organisms can release usable energy. Materials that can be used in any manner—for repair, for growth, for regulation of body processes, as well as for energy release—are nutrients. Thus all foods are nutrients, but not all nutrients are foods.

As they eat, animals obtain, in addition to foods in the narrow sense, minerals (such as iron and calcium compounds), vitamins (used in regulating various body functions), and water. And for the release of energy, all animals must also obtain oxygen, which is usually not classified as a nutrient. Acquiring energy and materials, then, is a matter of taking in things from the environment.

nutrition [nōō trĭsh'ən;  Latin: *nutrire*, to suckle, nourish]

## NUTRITION

The processes by which animals obtain, distribute, and use nutrients are known collectively as *nutrition*. Nutrition can be considered under three heads: (1) ingestion (taking food into a digestive cavity); (2) digestion (the breakdown of large food molecules to small molecules that can pass through cell membranes); and (3) absorption.

ingestion [ĭn jĕs'chən;  Latin: *in*, in, + *gerere*, to carry]

**Ingestion.**   A microscopic particle of food might be overlooked by many animals, but to a sponge it is a meal. Sponges have no special organs for food-getting. Indeed, they have no organs at all; their bodies are merely collections of cells. One kind of sponge cell has a flagellum similar to that of *Euglena*. The beating of such flagella keeps a current of water moving through the sponge. When a food particle comes by, one of the cells may engulf it and draw it into a vacuole, just as an ameba does. This process of taking food into some cavity of the body (*ingestion*) is a characteristic of animals that distinguishes them from plants.

See Figure 11 · 11.

But you will find some exceptions noted in Appendix II.

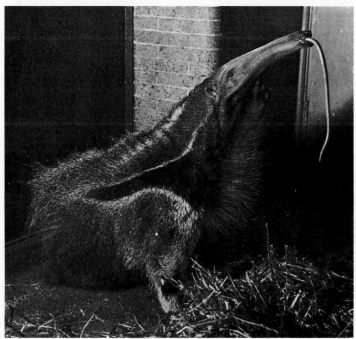

New York Zoological Society

New York Zoological Society

**Figure 14 · 2**
The long, sticky tongue of an anteater is an organ of ingestion. How do you think it is used?

Many other aquatic animals ingest food that is brought to them by water currents. Some, however, actively pursue food. And for land animals, mere waiting seldom provides a sufficient supply. In any case, an animal must have some means of seizing a food object. If the food consists of active, living organisms, they have to be caught. One way in which predators do this is by poisoning the prey. For example, the tentacles of coelenterates are equipped with stinging capsules. Each capsule contains a long, spirally coiled, hollow thread with barbs near its base. When some food organism brushes one of the tentacles in passing, the thread is shot out with such force that it pierces the body of the victim, injecting it with a paralyzing poison. The stunned or dead animal is then drawn into the "mouth" by the tentacles.

paralyzing: causing to lose the power of movement

When a leech finds a victim, it attaches itself by means of a posterior sucker. Then an anterior sucker is applied, a wound is inflicted with a three-toothed jaw, and the blood of the victim is taken in as food. The victim may not suffer serious injury. A leech may remain attached to the same food source for a long time, or it may drop off until another meal is needed.

inflicted [Latin: *in*, on, + *fligere*, to strike]

In Figure 4 · 26 diversity of mouthparts among insects was illustrated. Among vertebrates, jaws, beaks, and teeth are structures that aid ingestion. The lower jaw of a snake can be completely disengaged from the upper jaw, and the

disengaged: taken apart

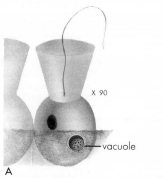

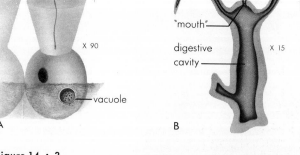

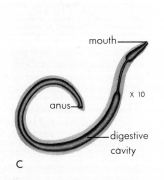

**Figure 14 · 3**

Kinds of digestive cavities: (A) *Intracellular* (vacuole) —in a cell of a sponge. (B) *Extracellular* with one opening (sac)—in a hydra. (C) Extracellular with two openings (alimentary canal)—in a roundworm.

intracellular and intercellular: Compare these terms with *intra*specific and *inter*specific, page 88.

digestion [dĭ jĕs'chən; Latin: *dis-*, apart, + *gerere*]

gizzard [gĭz'ərd]

two can be moved independently so that food is forced into the throat. This adaptation permits snakes to swallow prey much larger than their mouth openings.

Ingested food enters some sort of cavity within an animal's body—a *digestive cavity*. Digestive cavities are of three main kinds, as shown in Figure 14 ·3: a temporary, completely enclosed food vacuole; a sac; and a tubular alimentary canal.

**Digestion.** In Chapter 11 we discussed the entry of materials into cells; by and large, only relatively small molecules can pass readily through cell membranes. But most foods that animals ingest are neither small molecules nor even very tiny particles. Even the microscopic particles taken in by sponges are much too large to pass through cell membranes. But until a food is actually within a cell, until it has passed into a cell through a cell membrane, it cannot be of use to that cell. In almost all cases, then, foods taken in by animals must be broken down into small molecules. The processes by which this breakdown is accomplished are known collectively as *digestion*.

Although most foods must be changed chemically during the course of digestion, chemical reactions proceed very slowly unless food is first reduced to relatively small pieces or particles. This breakdown of large pieces of food into smaller particles is the *physical phase* of digestion. Most mammals have teeth that cut or grind the food. But in many other animals the physical phase of digestion is accomplished by muscular movements of the digestive cavity. The gizzard of a bird, for example, is a specialized part of the stomach that grinds food into small particles; in some species its effectiveness is increased by bits of sand and small pebbles that the bird swallows while eating. Although the physical phase of digestion is important in most species, in many it is unimportant. For example, a python may swallow a whole young pig and then lie quietly for as long as

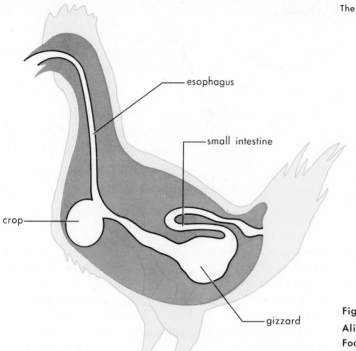

esophagus

small intestine

crop

gizzard

Figure 14 · 4
Alimentary canal of a bird.
Food is swallowed without
being chewed and is stored
temporarily in the crop.

a week while chemical digestion proceeds without a physical phase.

The *chemical phase* of digestion is simply the reverse of the synthetic processes described in Chapter 12. The bonds connecting units in large molecules are broken by *hydration cleavage*—the reverse of dehydration synthesis.

In sponges and to a varying degree in coelenterates and flatworms, chemical digestion is intracellular—that is, it takes place "inside" a cell. But because a cell forms a food vacuole by surrounding a food particle with a section of cell membrane, a vacuole really is an enclosed bit of an organism's environment. Enzymes that catalyze the reactions of the chemical phase of digestion are secreted into the food vacuole. As chemical digestion proceeds, the resulting small molecules pass from the vacuole into the cytoplast. Only then is food truly inside the cell.

In most animals, however, digestion is largely or exclusively extracellular—enzymes are secreted *from* cells *into* a digestive cavity. Thus a digestive cavity is really only an extension of the environment of the animal—part of the environment more or less surrounded by the body of the organism. A hamburger in your stomach is still part of your environment and is not really part of your body. Only when digestion has reduced it to small molecules that can

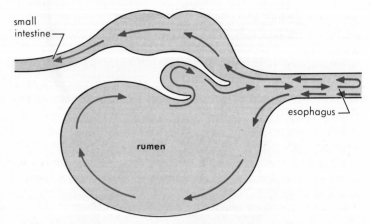

**Figure 14 · 5**

The complex stomach of a cow. Food is swallowed as quickly as it is ingested, stored in the rumen, and later brought back into the mouth for chewing. Bacteria in the other parts of the stomach carry on cellulose digestion, for which a cow has no enzymes. What ecological relationship exists between cow and bacteria?

pass through cell membranes does it actually become part of you.

The chemical phase of digestion is basically similar in all animals. However, there is great variation in the form and complexity of digestive systems in which it occurs. In the digestive sac of coelenterates, some of the cells lining the cavity are specialized as enzyme-secreting cells, and some have flagella that move the foods through the cavity; but there is no grouping of cells with a common structure and function into tissues. In the simple digestive tube of a roundworm, digestive enzymes are produced entirely by cells in the lining of the tube, but in most animals with digestive tubes there are specialized digestive glands. Many herbivorous vertebrates (cows, rabbits, horses, geese) have special digestive chambers that contain great numbers of cellulose-digesting microorganisms. Vertebrates have no cellulose-digesting enzymes but can use compounds produced by these microorganisms.

**Absorption.** The rate at which small molecules resulting from digestion can leave the digestive tube to pass into the cells of an animal's body is dependent on the amount of internal surface available. The greater the amount of internal surface, the higher the rate of transfer of digested substances out of the digestive cavity. Folding is a common method by which the amount of internal surface is increased. In addition to folds, the lining of a part of the digestive tube of a mammal has many minute, finger-like processes known as *villi*. These villi increase the amount of internal surface as much as a hundred-fold.

Where did you observe such folding?

villi [vĭl′ī; Latin: tufts of hair]

**Digestion in man.** Thus far we have discussed the nature of the digestive process and have looked briefly at some digestive specializations among various animals. Now let us examine in some detail the digestive system of a complex animal. It is convenient to use man—ourselves—as an example.

Digestion begins in the mouth, where the teeth break large pieces of food into smaller pieces. *Saliva,* secreted by three pairs of *salivary glands,* flows into the mouth cavity, where it moistens the food and begins to change it chemically. However, food is usually not in the mouth long enough for much chemical digestion to occur there. The tongue keeps the food in position between the teeth during chewing and then pushes the chewed food to the back of the mouth cavity. There muscular contractions carry it into the *esophagus* and thence into the stomach.

saliva [səlī′və; salivary [săl′ə-vĕr′ē]

In the stomach muscular contractions knead the food, breaking it up and mixing it with *gastric juice,* secreted by *gastric glands* in the wall of the stomach. Gastric juice is mostly water; the contents of the stomach, therefore, soon acquire the consistency of a cream soup. Gastric juice contains hydrochloric acid and the enzyme *gastric proteinase.*

esophagus [ē sŏf′ə gəs; Greek: oisophagos, passage for food]

gastric [găs′trĭk; Greek: gaster, stomach]

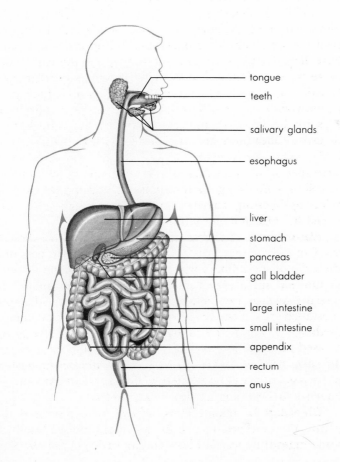

tongue

teeth

salivary glands

esophagus

liver

stomach

pancreas

gall bladder

large intestine

small intestine

appendix

rectum

anus

**Figure 14 · 6**

**Digestive system of man. The *appendix,* attached to the large intestine, is a sac that has no known function in man. The *rectum* (Latin: straight) is the posterior end of the large intestine.**

pyloric [pī lôr'ĭk; Greek: *pyloros*, gatekeeper]

chyme [kīm; Greek: *chymos*, juice]

Can you explain why vomit sometimes tastes sour and sometimes bitter?

Hydrochloric acid provides the acid conditions required for the action of this enzyme, which catalyzes the breaking of peptide bonds in some protein molecules, producing large fragments of protein molecules (polypeptides). Contraction of the *pyloric valve* (a circular layer of muscle in the wall of the digestive tube between the stomach and the small intestine) holds the food mass in the stomach up to four or five hours.

From time to time the pyloric valve relaxes, permitting some of the *chyme* (semi-digested food) to pass from the stomach into the small intestine. In the small intestine three more digestive juices are added to the chyme. These juices are alkaline and therefore neutralize the hydrochloric acid of the chyme. This is important because the enzymes that are active in the small intestine require an approximately neutral medium. The first of the juices is *bile*, which is secreted by the liver and stored in the gall bladder. Human bile contains no digestive enzymes. But bile is important because it neutralizes acid and contains substances that

**Figure 14 · 7 (right)**

Portion of a small intestine. You can see small villi on the surfaces of the folds of the inner side. x 3

A. John Geraci

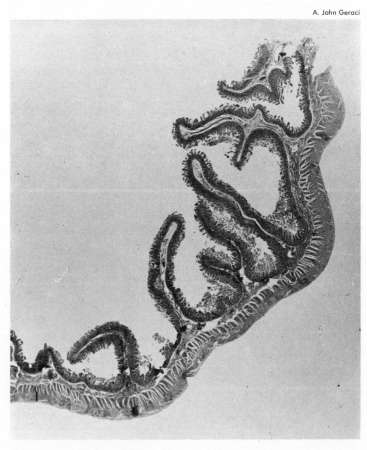

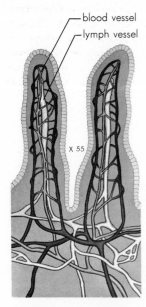

blood vessel
lymph vessel

X 55

**Figure 14 · 8 (above)**
Two villi.

cause large globules of fat to be broken up into fine droplets. This permits the chemical digestion of fats to take
place much more rapidly. *Pancreatic juice* contains several
enzymes that catalyze the digestion of carbohydrates, proteins, and fats. Additional enzymes are added to the small
intestine in the *intestinal juice.* Most chemical digestion occurs in the small intestine.

pancreatic [păn'krĭ ăt'ĭk]

Also in the small intestine, almost all absorption of
nutrients occurs. Through the surface of the villi, amino
acids, simple sugars, and other nutrients are absorbed by
diffusion or active transport into the blood. Some fat molecules are absorbed without being digested; they pass into
the lymph vessels of the villi. Most of the fatty acids and
glycerol recombine during absorption to form fat, which
then passes into the lymph vessels; very small amounts of
fatty acids are absorbed into both the lymph vessels and the
blood vessels.

lymph [lĭmf]

Normally digestion and absorption are completed in
four to seven hours, and substances left in the small intestine then pass into the large intestine. There much of the
water is absorbed. Undigested foods and indigestible substances, together with mucus, dead cells from the lining of
the digestive tube, and bacteria, make up the *feces*, which
leave the digestive tube through the *anus.*

feces [fē'sēz]
anus [ā'nəs]

| SECRETION | ENZYME | SUBSTANCES ACTED UPON | PRODUCT |
|---|---|---|---|
| saliva | amylase | starch | maltose |
| gastric juice | gastric proteinase | some protein | polypeptides |
| pancreatic juice | amylases | starch | maltose |
| | lipase | fats | *glycerol* and *fatty acids* |
| | pancreatic proteinases | protein | polypeptides and smaller fragments |
| | peptidases | polypeptides and smaller fragments | *amino acids* |
| intestinal juice | disaccharidases | sucrose, maltose, lactose | *simple sugars* |
| | peptidases | polypeptides | *amino acids* |

**Figure 14 · 9**
Summary of chemical digestion in mammals. Products
absorbed are shown in
italic type. In what connection were these substances
discussed in Chapter 12?

## INVESTIGATION 14.2

### THE ACTION OF A DIGESTIVE ENZYME

#### BACKGROUND INFORMATION

In Chapter 12 the discussion of enzymes centers on those involved in energy release and in syntheses. Now you will study an enzyme that acts in digestion. In Figure 14·9 check on the action of salivary amylase. Because this enzyme is secreted into the mouth cavity, it is easily available for study.

#### MATERIALS AND EQUIPMENT

*For Procedure A*

Unsweetened cracker

Test tubes, 4

Thermometer (−10°C to 110°C range)

Funnel and support

Filter paper, 2 sheets

Iodine—potassium-iodide solution

Benedict's or Fehling's solution

Test-tube holder

Bunsen burner

Paraffin

*For Procedure B*

Test tubes, 7

Paraffin

Glass rod

pH test paper

Beakers, 7

Starch solution

Ring stand

Bunsen burner

Test-tube holder

Benedict's or Fehling's solution

Thermometers (−10°C to 110°C range), 5

Ice

Hydrochloric acid solution, pH 6

Hydrochloric acid solution, pH 3

Sodium hydroxide solution, pH 8

Sodium hydroxide solution, pH 11

#### PROCEDURE A: ESTABLISHING THE NORMAL ACTION OF THE ENZYME

The teacher will first demonstrate the action of maltose on warm Benedict's (or Fehling's) solution.

Crush a piece of cracker (about 1 cm²) into a test tube. Add warm water (about 37°C) to a depth of about 5 cm. Shake and then pour into a funnel lined with filter paper. Collect part of the filtrate (the liquid that seeps through the filter paper) to a depth of about 1 cm in a second test tube. Collect another part to a depth of about 2 cm in a third test tube. Test the first portion of the filtrate for starch and the second portion for maltose. If the test for maltose is positive (that is, if it indicates the presence of maltose), try another brand of cracker.

Now one student should chew a piece of paraffin and spit the accumulated saliva into a test tube. When a few milliliters have been collected, test for maltose. If the test is positive, try another student.

A student who has saliva testing negative for maltose should then chew a piece of cracker (about 9 cm²) testing negative for maltose. After thorough chewing (two or three minutes), deposit the mass of cracker and saliva into a funnel lined with filter paper. Add about 5 ml of warm water (37°C) and collect about 3 ml of the filtrate in a test tube. Test the filtrate for maltose.   • Considering the procedure used, what conclusion can be drawn from a negative test? From a positive test? (1)

#### PROCEDURE B: VARYING THE CONDITIONS OF ENZYME ACTION

In Procedure A the enzyme action occurred in its normal situation in the mouth (*in vivo*—Latin: in a live [condition]). To test the action of the enzyme under other conditions, we must work *in vitro* (Latin: in glass—that is, in a test tube, beaker, etc.).

Using paraffin, collect saliva from the student who provided the saliva used in Procedure A. You will need seven test tubes, each containing saliva to a depth of about 2 cm. Using a wide-range pH test paper, determine the approximate pH of the collected saliva.

1. Add a few drops of starch solution to Tube 1. Shake. Place the test tube in a beaker containing water at 37°C and allow it to remain there ten minutes. Then remove and test for maltose.

2. Add a few drops of starch solution to Tube 2. Shake. Place the test tube in a beaker containing boiling water and allow it to remain there ten minutes. Then remove and test for maltose.

3. Add a few drops of starch solution to Tube 3. Shake. Place the test tube in a beaker containing crushed ice and allow it to remain there ten minutes. Then remove and test for maltose.

4. To Tube 4 add a volume of pH 6 hydrochloric acid solution equal to the volume of saliva. Mix by rolling the tube between the palms of the hands. Add a few drops of starch solution and again mix. Place the tube in a beaker containing water at 37°C and allow the tube to remain there ten minutes. Then remove and test for maltose.

5. To Tube 5 add an equal volume of pH 3 hydrochloric acid solution. Mix. Add a few drops of starch solution and again mix. Place the tube in a beaker containing water at 37°C and allow the tube to remain there ten minutes. Then remove and test for maltose.

6. To Tube 6 add an equal volume of pH 8 sodium hydroxide solution. Mix. Add a few drops of starch solution and again mix. Place the tube in a beaker containing water at 37°C and allow the tube to remain there ten minutes. Then remove and test for maltose.

7. To Tube 7 add an equal volume of pH 11 sodium hydroxide solution. Mix. Add a few drops of starch solution and again mix. Place the tube in a beaker containing water at 37°C and allow the tube to remain there ten minutes. Then remove and test for maltose.

### STUDYING THE DATA

If the work has been divided among teams, assemble the data on the chalkboard. • Under what conditions of temperature and pH does the enzyme act *in vivo?* (2) • Under which of the experimental temperature conditions did the enzyme act *in vitro?* (3) • Under which of the experimental pH conditions did the enzyme act *in vitro?* (4)

### CONCLUSIONS

• Use the data to work out a general statement concerning the effect of temperature variation on the action of the enzyme. (5) • Use the data to work out a general statement concerning the effect of pH variation on the action of the enzyme. (6) • Would you expect intracellular enzymes to be more sensitive or less sensitive to variations in temperature and pH than are extracellular enzymes? Why? (7)

### FOR FURTHER INVESTIGATION

In this investigation conditions were varied rather crudely. More refined techniques can be devised to test the effects of lesser differences in the conditions. Because the amount of color change in the test solutions is in proportion to the amount of maltose, you can make this a quantitative study by carefully controlling the amounts of starch and test solutions and the time allowed for reaction.

## OBTAINING OXYGEN

For short periods of time animals may release energy by anaerobic methods, but eventually they depend on cellular respiration. Therefore animals must live in environments where oxygen occurs, and they must be able to supply a sufficient amount of oxygen to their cells. Likewise, they must be able to rid themselves of carbon dioxide. The exchange of these gases is respiration in the original sense of the word.

In small animals—such as rotifers and many planktonic crustaceans—uptake of oxygen and release of carbon dioxide can occur entirely through the body surface. This is because the body surface is large compared with the volume of living material that requires oxygen and produces carbon dioxide. As size increases, the ratio of surface area to volume becomes smaller, though in very flat bodies or in very long, cylindrical ones, the change in ratio remains relatively slight. In general, then, larger animals do not have body surfaces large enough to allow a sufficient exchange of gases with their environments. Thus, all but very small or slim animals have organs that increase the surface area through which respiration may occur.

In aquatic animals such organs are usually feathery or platelike structures called *gills*. These may be waved through the water, or the water may pass over them as the animal moves; dissolved oxygen then diffuses in and carbon dioxide diffuses out through the membranes of the outermost gill cells. Gills are remarkably similar in a wide variety of water animals.

Any surface through which the respiratory gases can diffuse is also a surface through which water can diffuse. Therefore, animals that live on land may lose a great deal

**Figure 14 · 10**

Gills in three aquatic animals. The body of the marine annelid is enclosed in a mud tube; only the gills are exposed.

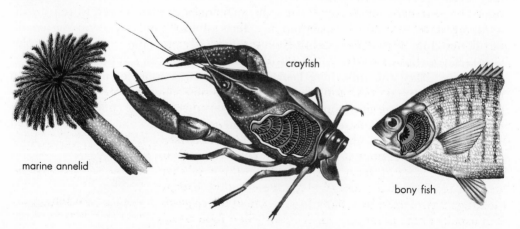

crayfish

marine annelid

bony fish

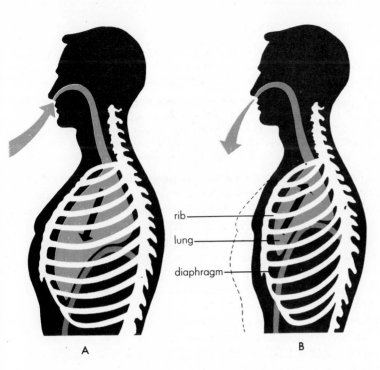

rib
lung
diaphragm

A                        B

Figure 14 · 11
Movements of breathing in man.

of water through their respiratory organs. For this reason, terrestrial animals that breathe through gills or through the body surface (slugs, earthworms, and salamanders, for example) must live in places where air is moist—that is, where evaporation is slow.

For terrestrial animals that live where the air is dry, an extensive surface is needed within the body where air can be kept moist. Two principal ways of meeting this requirement have evolved. In insects and some other arthropods, a complicated system of air tubes extends to all parts of the body, bringing oxygen directly to most cells. Movements of the body help move air through the tube system. In air-breathing vertebrates air passes into a pair of sacs so finely partitioned that they have a spongy appearance—lungs. Through the moist surface of the lungs respiratory gases diffuse.

Again we can take man as an example. Movement of the ribs and diaphragm enlarges the chest cavity, lowering the air pressure in the lungs so that external air moves inward. As the air is drawn in through the nostrils and passes through the nasal cavities, it is warmed and moistened. Into the *pharynx* pass both the stream of air from the nasal cavities and food from the mouth. The opening that leads to the lungs is protected by a flap of tissue called the *epiglottis*. It is usually open, admitting air; it closes when food passes

diaphragm [dī′ə frăm′; Greek: *dia-*, through, + *phragma*, fence]

Why is this method of breathing impossible for a frog?

pharynx [făr′ingks; Greek: the throat]

epiglottis [ĕp′ə glŏt′is; Greek: *epi*, upon, + *glotta*, the tongue]

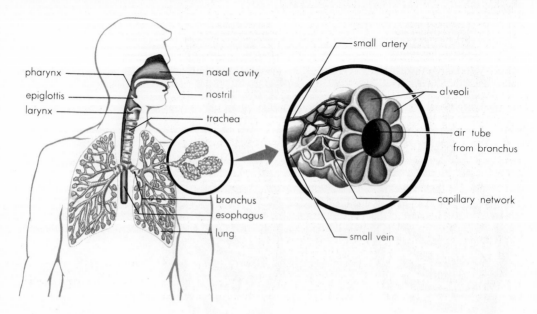

**Figure 14 · 12**

The breathing system of man.

trachea [trā′kĭ ə; Latin: *tracheia*, windpipe]

bronchi [brŏng′kī; Greek: *bronchos*, windpipe]

alveoli [ăl vē′ə lī′; Latin: small hollows, cavities]

by on the way to the esophagus (not always in time, as you may know from personal experience).

The *trachea*, the air passage that extends through the neck ventral to the esophagus, divides in the upper chest into two *bronchi*. Each bronchus leads to a lung, where it branches and rebranches, the smallest divisions ending in almost microscopic air sacs, *alveoli*. The enormous number of alveoli provide a very large area of moist surface. The walls of the alveoli are extremely thin and contain a dense network of tiny blood vessels. Respiratory gases diffuse into and out of the blood through the thin membranes.

## TRANSPORTING MATERIALS IN THE BODY

In a playful mood one day, a child placed a rubber band tightly around the tip of her cat's tail. Then her attention was turned to other activities, and the rubber band was forgotten. Several weeks later, when the cat's tail was grasped, off came the tip—the rubber band still around it. This incident clearly points up the importance of the circulation of blood. When blood does not reach cells, they are deprived of the food and oxygen it brings to them; also, they are unable to rid themselves of the poisoning wastes that blood takes from them. For such cells, the result is death.

deprived: kept from having

An early milestone in the development of biological science was the discovery of the circulation of the blood. This occurred in the early part of the seventeenth century—the century of Leeuwenhoek—through the research

Figure 14 · 13
William Harvey: 1578–1657.

of an English physician, William Harvey. As a physician, Harvey was interested in the physiology of man; but as a scientist, his curiosity pushed his investigations in many other directions, too. In his book, *On the Motion of the Heart and Blood,* he wrote:

> I have also observed, that almost all animals have truly a heart, not the larger creatures only, and those that have red blood but the smaller and seemingly bloodless ones also, such as slugs, snails, scallops, shrimps, crabs, crayfish, and many others; nay even in wasps, hornets and flies. I have with the aid of a magnifying glass, and at the upper part of what is called the tail, both seen the heart pulsating myself, and shown it to many others.

pulsating: moving rhythmically, beating

### SIMPLER TRANSPORT SYSTEMS

However, Harvey did not know that many animals have much simpler transport systems—lacking not only hearts but even a circulating fluid. The living substance of cells is in constant motion. In a single-celled organism, such movements are an adequate transportation system. They are also adequate in some multicellular organisms. In sponges and coelenterates, for example, almost all cells have some part of their surface exposed to the environment; each cell can obtain its own oxygen and get rid of its own wastes. Though not all cells in these animals take in food, no cell is very far from those that do; so diffusion and active transport are sufficient for the distribution of food materials.

Approximately the same situation occurs in free-living flatworms, but in them the distribution of digested foods is aided by a greatly branched digestive sac that extends to all parts of the body. In roundworms a fluid-filled body cavity surrounds the digestive tube. As the worm wriggles, the fluid is squeezed about from place to place, and in this crude way substances dissolved in it are eventually carried to and from the body cells.

## CIRCULATORY SYSTEMS

Usually, an animal that has a body fluid in which substances are transported also has a system of tubes through which the fluid flows. Muscular pumps (usually called hearts) propel the fluid (usually called blood), and the direction of flow is controlled by valves within the tubes. Regardless of detailed anatomical arrangements, the basic function performed by such a *circulatory system* is always the same: At a place where blood flows slowly, in contact with thin membranes, substances move in or out by diffusion or active transport. The blood then moves rather rapidly to another place where it again flows slowly, in contact with thin membranes, and substances again move in or out.

*It is also referred to as a vascular system. Why?*

**Invertebrate systems.**  In arthropods and most mollusks blood is pumped through tubes (blood vessels) that empty into body spaces. Through these spaces the blood moves about sluggishly, in close contact with the tissues. Eventually it gets back into another set of tubes, which carry it back to the pumping point. Such an incomplete vascular system is called an *open* circulatory system.

Annelids, on the other hand, have a *closed* circulatory system—blood is enclosed in vessels throughout its course. In an earthworm the system consists of five pairs of hearts and a complicated set of more and more finely branched vessels; these vessels eventually link up again and empty into a large dorsal vessel. This vessel returns the blood to the hearts. Valves along the walls of the vessel keep the blood flowing in one direction throughout the system.

*You can easily see the movement of blood in the dorsal vessel of an earthworm.*

**Vertebrate systems.**  In vertebrates circulation also occurs in a closed system. Vessels of this system are of four kinds. A single, very muscular *heart,* consisting of two or more chambers, keeps blood moving through the system. *Arteries* have rather thick, muscular walls and carry blood away from the heart. *Veins* have relatively thin walls that contain little muscle tissue; they carry blood toward the heart. *Capillaries* have very thin walls; they connect arteries with veins.

*arteries [Latin: arteria, windpipe or blood vessel. (Ancient anatomists could not determine whether vessels in dissected animals had contained air or blood.)]*

By ingenious experiments, William Harvey showed that blood leaves a vertebrate heart through arteries and

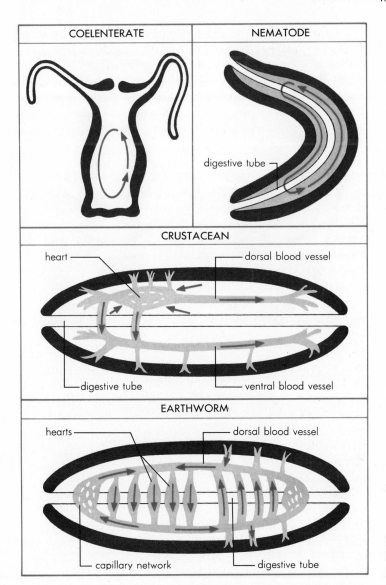

| COELENTERATE | NEMATODE |
|---|---|

digestive tube

CRUSTACEAN

heart — — dorsal blood vessel

— digestive tube — — ventral blood vessel

EARTHWORM

hearts — — dorsal blood vessel

— capillary network — — digestive tube

Figure 14 · 14
Diagrams of fluid transport in four invertebrate animals.

returns to the heart through veins. Therefore, by reasoning he concluded that blood circulates. But he did not know by observation how blood passes from arteries to veins. Harvey lived in the first part of the seventeenth century, before the use of the microscope became widespread. Later in the century Marcello Malpighi first observed capillaries and thus confirmed Harvey's reasoning.

In all mammals and birds the heart is a double pump. Its right and left sides are enclosed in the same wall, but each side has its own veins and arteries. In mammals the

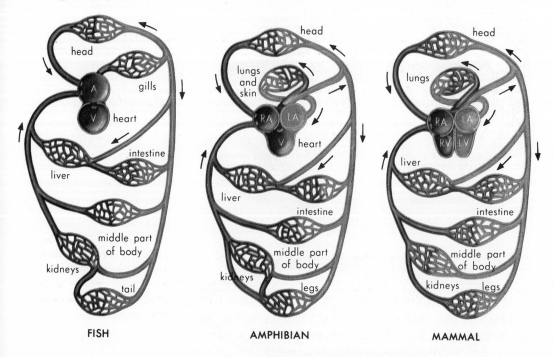

FISH          AMPHIBIAN          MAMMAL

**Figure 14 · 15**

Diagrams of circulation in three vertebrate classes. Red indicates oxygenated blood; blue, deoxygenated blood. A = atrium; V = ventricle.

atrium [ā'tri əm; Latin: the central court of an ancient Roman house]

ventricle [Latin: *ventriculus*, a little stomach]

right side receives blood from almost all parts of the body and sends it to the lungs. The left side receives blood from the lungs and sends it to all other parts of the body. Each of the pumps has two chambers. An *atrium* receives incoming blood. When the heart muscle relaxes, this blood passes into a *ventricle*. When the heart contracts, the walls of the ventricle give the blood a strong push that sends it out through an artery.

Arteries near the heart contain flaps of tissue that act as valves. When blood is being pushed by contraction of the ventricles, the flaps flatten out and blood flows away from the heart. When the ventricles relax between heartbeats, back pressure of the blood forces the flaps open, preventing the blood from flowing back toward the heart. Such valves are numerous in veins.

The millions of microscopic capillaries have walls only a single cell thick. Through these walls occurs the passage of substances to and from cells—the principal function of blood circulation. As blood flows slowly through the capillaries, substances move from the blood into the cells of the body tissues, and other substances move from the tissues into the blood.

**BLOOD**

In the simpler kinds of marine animals, there is little difference between the body fluids and seawater. But in

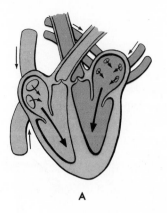
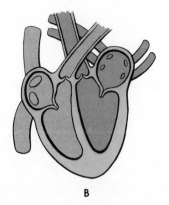
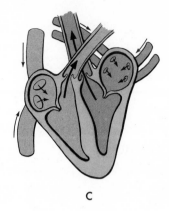

A                              B                              C

Figure 14 · 16
Three steps (A to C) in the
pumping action of a mam-
malian heart. Why does
the blood not flow back
into the atria when the ventricles contract?

land animals the body fluids are complex mixtures of substances in water, and the environment is a mixture of gases.
These two examples are extremes; there are many intermediate degrees of difference between the fluids within
animals and the substances in their environments. Such
differences are great in freshwater animals and sometimes
rather marked in complex marine animals. In general,
blood in organisms with circulatory systems is more or less
different from the fluids in the environment.

There is great variation in the blood of different animal
groups. Some bloods are red; others are greenish, brownish, or colorless. Some contain cells. But all bloods are
made up of water in which many substances are dissolved
or suspended.

**Plasma.**   When we watch human blood flow from a
small wound, it appears to be a uniform red liquid. But if
we examine a thin smear of it under the microscope, we see
many faintly reddish cells; other cells show up when the
smear is stained. By means of a centrifuge, these cells
can be concentrated and a clear yellowish liquid—*plasma*
—obtained.

About 91 percent of human plasma is water. The rest is
made up of substances dissolved or suspended in the water—about 8 percent proteins, and close to 0.9 percent
minerals, especially compounds of calcium, potassium,
sodium, and phosphorus. There are also small amounts of
amino acids, simple sugars, and wastes from metabolism.

Research during recent years has shown that there is
great complexity in blood proteins. Among them are the
antibodies that result from infection. But many blood
proteins are inherited. In general, the more closely related
animals are taxonomically, the more blood proteins they
have in common. But even individuals within the same

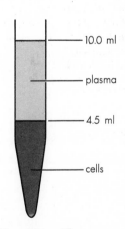

10.0 ml

plasma

4.5 ml

cells

Figure 14 · 17
Centrifuged human blood.
What percent of the sample
was plasma?

plasma [Greek: *plassein*, to
form]

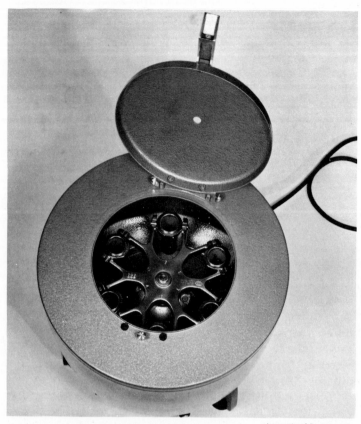

**Figure 14 · 18**

A centrifuge. Liquids that contain tiny solid particles (as does blood) are placed in the tubes. Rapid whirling separates the particles from the liquid, as shown in Figure 14 · 17.

International Equipment Co.

corpuscles [kôr′pəs əlz; Latin: *corpusculum*, little body]

platelets [plāt′lĭts; Greek: *platys*, broad, flat]

hemoglobin [hē′mə glō′bĭn]

anemia [ə nē′mĭ ə; Greek: *an-*, without, + *haima*, blood]

Why is the activity of an anemic individual reduced?

species have some protein differences; it may even be that the blood of each individual has its own unique proteins.

**Blood cells.**  Whole blood contains *red cells* (red corpuscles) and *white cells* (white corpuscles). Usually considered with them are *platelets*, which are fragments of cells. The oxygen-carrying ability and color of blood are primarily due to an iron-containing pigment in the red cells, *hemoglobin*. When oxygen is abundant around a red cell (as it is, for example, in the lung capillaries), it combines with the hemoglobin in the cell, forming *oxyhemoglobin* (bright red in color). When oxygen is scarce around a red cell (as it is likely to be in active muscle tissue, for example), the oxygen is released, leaving hemoglobin (a duller red). In the condition called *anemia* there is either an abnormally low number of red cells or a low hemoglobin content.

Human red cells live 110−120 days; then they are removed from circulation and destroyed in the liver and spleen. The liver salvages iron ions from these cells, and cells in the bone marrow use these ions in making new red cells.

| ELEMENT | DIAMETER (in microns) | NUMBER (per cu. mm) | MAIN FUNCTION |
|---|---|---|---|
|  ⬤ red corpuscles | 7-8 | 4,500,000-5,500,000 | oxygen transport |
|  ⬤ white corpuscles | 9-12 | 7,000-10,000 | defense against microorganisms |
| ⬤ platelets | 2-4 | 300,000 (much variation) | blood-clotting |

Figure 14 · 19

A comparison of some characteristics of blood "elements," a term used by those who wish to emphasize that platelets are only fragments of cells.

White cells have no hemoglobin and are therefore colorless. Unlike red cells, they do not merely float along in the plasma; a white cell can move about very much like an ameba, even slipping through the thin walls of capillaries and wandering about among the cells of muscle and other tissues. There are several varieties of white cells, which differ in size, reaction to stains, and function. Primarily, however, white cells serve to destroy invading particles, such as pathogenic organisms. They do this by engulfing and digesting the particles much as an ameba does. Some white cells also seem to aid in the repair of wounds.

Platelets are colorless, usually spherical, and without nuclei. Their life-span is estimated to be four days.

**Clotting.** Normally when a vertebrate animal suffers a small wound, the blood at the surface of the wound clots. But if blood is gently drawn into a paraffin-lined vessel, it will not clot. Neither exposure to air nor slowing of the flow is the cause of clotting. The process of clotting illustrates the complexity that research sometimes reveals behind apparently simple biological processes.

Clotting begins with the platelets. Whenever they are exposed to a rough surface—almost any surface other than the smooth lining of the blood vessels—they tend to stick to it and then to break up. As they do so, they release a substance called *thromboplastin*. The thromboplastin acts as an enzyme to bring about a change in *prothrombin*, a protein in the plasma. This reaction, which will not occur unless calcium is present (as it always is in normal blood), converts prothrombin to *thrombin*. Thrombin then acts as an enzyme to convert *fibrinogen*, a blood protein, into *fibrin*, an insoluble substance that forms threads within the plasma. Blood cells are trapped in a network of fibrin threads, thus building up a clot.

thromboplastin [thräm′bō′plăs′-tən; Greek: *thrombos*, a clot, lump, + *plassein*]

prothrombin    [prō thrŏm′bĭn; Greek: *pro*, before, + *thrombos*]

fibrinogen [fī brĭn′ə jən; Latin: *fibra*, fiber, + *genitus*, born]

## LYMPH

Some plasma readily passes through the capillary walls, though little of its protein content does so, and white blood cells may also escape from the closed vascular system. But red cells never pass through the walls of the blood vessels. Thus the fluid that bathes cells, though much like blood, is nearly colorless and is lower in protein content.

Some of this fluid may ooze back into the blood capillaries; the remainder of it collects in another set of vessels, where it is called *lymph*. These vessels join each other, forming larger vessels. Contractions of the muscles that surround the lymph vessels move the lymph along. In the walls of the small intestine, lymph vessels absorb fats; and many of the metabolic wastes of cells pass into the tissue fluid. Thus lymph has a higher fat content and a higher waste content than does blood.

Eventually all lymph vessels join, forming a duct that carries the lymph to the region of the left shoulder; there the lymph is emptied into a vein. Thus the fluids that leave the blood at the capillaries are brought back into the blood again.

Enlargements occur at several points in the lymphatic system. In these enlargements, or *lymph nodes*, the vessels divide into tiny twisted passages; as a result, the lymph flows slowly through the nodes. Here pathogenic organisms and other foreign materials that may have entered the body are attacked by white blood cells. During an infection the lymph nodes may contain so many white blood cells that they become greatly swollen. You may have felt them in your armpits or in your neck during a severe cold.

## INVESTIGATION 14.3

### A HEART AT WORK

#### PURPOSE

You will study the effects of varying environmental temperature on the heartbeat of a small animal. • After studying the procedure, state an appropriate hypothesis. (1)

#### BACKGROUND INFORMATION

Crustaceans of the genus *Daphnia* are abundant in small bodies of fresh water. Individuals are just about large enough to be seen with the naked eye in good light. But when magnified even 20 times, many of the internal organs—including the heart—can be seen through the body wall. Become familiar with the appearance of the animal before you begin the Procedure. Look carefully for the beating heart. Do not confuse its motion with that of the legs, which also beat rhythmically. Some internal organs other than the heart move also.

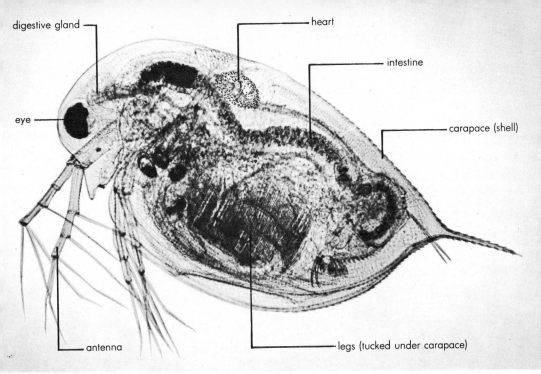

digestive gland

heart

intestine

eye

carapace (shell)

antenna

legs (tucked under carapace)

Thorne Films, Inc.

**Figure 14 · 20**

*Daphnia.*    x 125

## MATERIALS AND EQUIPMENT
### (for each team)

*Daphnia*, in a small beaker of aquarium
   water, 6 to 8
Thermometer (−10° to 110°C range)
Medicine dropper
Microscope slide with depression
Stereomicroscope
Watch with second hand
Beaker large enough to hold *Daphnia*
   beaker
Crushed ice
Hot water
Graph paper, 1 sheet per student

## PROCEDURE

Check the temperature of the water
in which the *Daphnia* are living. It should
be at room temperature before the
experiment begins. With a medicine
dropper, transfer one *Daphnia* to the
depression in the slide. Soak up excess
water with a piece of paper towel. By
keeping the amount of water at a minimum, you increase the likelihood that

the animal will lie on its side, in which
position heart action can best be seen.

One member of the team keeps time
with a watch, while another observes the
specimen through the stereomicroscope
and counts the heartbeats. It may be
difficult to count as rapidly as the heart
pulsates. If so, try tapping with a pencil
on a piece of paper and then counting
the dots. When the observer is ready, the
timer says "Go!" At the end of fifteen
seconds, he says "Stop!" Multiply the
count by 4 to obtain the number of
heartbeats per minute. Make at least
three timed counts, allowing each member of the team to take a turn as an observer or timer. Return the *Daphnia* to
the beaker.

Place the beaker of *Daphnia* in a
larger beaker containing water and
crushed ice. Stir the water in the *Daphnia*
beaker gently with the thermometer.
When the water temperature reaches the
point assigned to your team by the
teacher, quickly transfer a *Daphnia* to the

slide and make at least three counts as speedily as possible.

As soon as the *Daphnia* is removed from the beaker, members of the team who are not timing or counting should remove the *Daphnia* beaker from the large beaker, pour out the ice water, and replace it with hot water (50° to 70°C).

Place the *Daphnia* beaker in the larger beaker again. Stir the water in the *Daphnia* beaker gently with the thermometer. By the time the water temperature reaches the second point assigned to your team, counting at the lower temperature should be finished. Quickly transfer a *Daphnia* from the warm water to the slide and make at least three counts as speedily as possible.

### STUDYING THE DATA

Consider the data obtained from *Daphnia* at room temperature. • Why were several counts taken by each team? (2) • What factors might account for the variability in these data? (3) Assemble on the chalkboard the room-temperature data from all teams. • Compare the variability in the data from all teams with the variability in the data from your own team. How can you account for any differences? (4) • Calculate the average rate of heartbeat from the assembled class data. (5) • Which is likely to be more reliable—the average obtained by your team or the average obtained by the entire class? Explain. (6)

Assemble the data on heartbeat at different temperatures. If two or more teams obtained data at the same temperature, calculate a general average for that temperature. Graph the data, placing rate of heartbeat on the vertical axis and temperature on the horizontal axis.

### CONCLUSIONS

• On the basis of your graph, make a general statement concerning the effects of variation in environmental temperature on the rate of heartbeat in *Daphnia*. (7) • Does your graph support your hypothesis? Explain. (8) • Would you expect similar effects of temperature on heartbeat of a frog? Of a dog? Explain. (9)

### FOR FURTHER INVESTIGATION

1. Young pond snails have thin shells through which the heart can be seen, just as in *Daphnia*. Make a study of snail heartbeat for comparison with that of *Daphnia*. Try to account for any differences you observe.

2. The easily observed heart of *Daphnia* can lead to some understanding of the way in which drugs affect heartbeat rate. Investigate the effects of alcohol (about 5%), of a tranquilizer (such as chlorpromazine), and of a stimulant (such as dexedrine sulfate) on *Daphnia* heartbeat.

### REMOVING MATERIALS FROM THE BODY

Large sea turtles shed tears when they go ashore to lay their eggs. These are neither tears of joy nor tears of sorrow. They have nothing to do with egg-laying and are shed at other times also, but they are most likely to be observed by man when the turtles are ashore. This shedding of tears is merely a way in which salts acquired from seawater are kept from accumulating in the body of the animal. All organisms must constantly release materials into the environment, just as they must constantly take materials in from the environment.

### EXCRETION, SECRETION, AND ELIMINATION

The process by which waste materials are removed from cells is called *excretion*. If the substance that passes out of the cell is one that is in some way useful to the organism, then the process is called *secretion*. Because carbon dioxide is a metabolic waste formed in every living animal cell, it is an excretion from each cell. Gastric juice, which passes through the membranes of cells that line the stomach, is a secretion because substances in it are useful in digesting food. In these two examples the distinction between excretion and secretion is clear, but sometimes the distinction is difficult to make.

excretion [ĭk skrē'shən; Latin: ex, out of, + cernere, to sift]

secretion [sĭ krē'shən; Latin: se-, aside, + cernere]

Both secretion and excretion involve the passage of substances through cell membranes. They may occur by diffusion. Frequently, however, a substance is more abundant in the environment outside a cell than it is within. Then energy is required to "pump" the substance out of the cell by the process of active transport.

Once a substance has passed out through the cell membrane of an organism, it has been excreted or secreted. But—especially in multicellular organisms—it may not be entirely out of the body of the organism. For example, tears are secreted (or excreted—this is one of the cases where it is difficult to decide) from cells above the eye into ducts that empty onto the surface of the eyeball. Tears in the tear ducts are no longer in cells, but they are still within the body, at least in the usual sense. The process by which substances are forced out of body cavities—either small ones, such as tear ducts, or large ones, such as the digestive tube—is called *elimination*.

elimination [Latin: ex, out of, + limen, threshold]

To clarify the usage of the three terms "excretion," "secretion," and "elimination," consider bile. Bile contains substances useful in digestion; it is thus a secretion from cells of the liver. Some of the bile substances, however, have no usefulness—substances derived from the destruction of old red blood cells, for example. These are wastes, so bile is also an excretion. Finally, bile becomes a part of the substances that are eliminated from the digestive tube through the anus.

### KINDS OF EXCRETION

Now consider a little more carefully what we mean by "wastes." Some products of metabolism are, in one way or

toxic [Greek: *toxikon*, a poison]

another, toxic to living substance. One example is the ammonia that is formed in the breakdown of proteins. Some substances, however, are toxic only if large amounts accumulate in the cells—for example, sodium chloride, which is always present in cells. But this salt is always being taken in by diffusion from the environment. Only by continuous excretion can the normal proportion of sodium chloride be maintained in the cells. Even water, which forms such a large proportion of any cell, must be kept in balance between income and outgo. In general, then, any substance can be called a waste if an organism has too much of it.

Can you show how this definition of "waste" involves circular reasoning?

In small aquatic animals wastes may simply diffuse out through cell membranes, in the way that respiratory gases are exchanged with the environment. Sponges and coelenterates—though not always small—also excrete wastes directly through the body surfaces, since all their cells are close to the water environment. Most animals, however, have special devices for ridding the body of wastes.

**Water.** By the process of cellular respiration, water is constantly being produced by animal cells. What happens to this water depends on the kind of environment in which the animal lives. Consider a jellyfish living in the ocean. Its cells contain a complex mixture of substances in water. Outside the cell membranes is another complex mixture in water—the salty sea. If the concentrations of water molecules in the two mixtures differ, water molecules move from one to the other by diffusion. But in jellyfish—and a great many other marine invertebrates—the concentrations inside and outside are normally almost equal. As fast as metabolic water is produced, it diffuses into the environment.

Now consider a planarian living in a freshwater stream. There are very few dissolved substances in fresh water; the concentration of water molecules is high. But in a planarian's cells the percentage of dissolved substances is high, which means that the water concentration is relatively low. Therefore, water is always diffusing into a planarian's cells. And metabolic water is constantly added to this excess. We might expect that water would accumulate within a planarian's cells, swell against the cell membranes, and eventually burst them. When certain drugs that interfere with the mechanism of active transport are used experimentally on planarians, this is exactly what happens. For freshwater animals, then, excretion of water is necessary to survival.

The same problem faces us. We take in a great deal of fresh water; and, of course, our cells also produce water by metabolic processes. Though (as land animals) we are always in danger of drying out, we are also in danger of

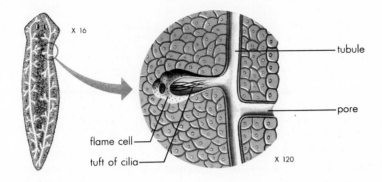

Figure 14 · 21
**Excretory structure in a planarian.**

swelling up with excess water—and in the condition called dropsy this actually occurs. All through our lives we and all other land animals walk a very thin tightrope, balanced between having too much water and too little.

dropsy [Greek: *hydrops* (from *hydor*, water)]

A great variety of structures maintain a water balance within the cells of animals. In planarians this function is performed by a system of tubules spread throughout the body. The functional unit of the system is a *flame cell* Each flame cell, located at the end of a tubule, has a tuft of cilia that projects into the tubule. The waving of the tuft (to early microscopists, this action resembled the flickering of a flame) creates a slight negative pressure, or suction, within the tubule. This tends to draw water from the surrounding tissues and push it along the tubule. The many tubules join and eventually empty into the environment through a pore.

tubule [tōō'bŭl; Latin: *tubulus*, a little tube]

Variations of the flame-cell system are found in some other invertebrates. Most annelids (including earthworms), as well as mollusks and crustaceans, have quite different excretory systems. In these animals the functional unit is a tubule around which there may be a network of blood capillaries. In many cases the tubule connects with the body cavity. Fluid from the body cavity is modified as it passes through the tubule to the outside—more wastes are added and useful materials are absorbed back into the blood or body fluid. In other cases the tubule is blind, so that all substances to be excreted must be transported into it. In vertebrates somewhat similar blind tubules are found in the kidneys.

**Nitrogenous wastes.**    There is considerable evidence that the organs usually called excretory—from flame cells in flatworms to kidneys in vertebrates—have evolved chiefly as water-regulating devices. They still deal with water, but in most animals they also function in the excretion of nitrogen-bearing wastes.

Amino acids, all of which contain nitrogen, are used by cells to build up proteins. When an animal is growing,

Figure 14 · 22

Urea. **(A)** Structural formula. **(B)** Model. How many molecules of urea must a mammal excrete to rid itself of the same amount of nitrogen as does a fish excreting 100 molecules of ammonia?

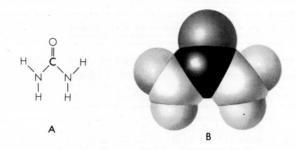

A

B

rather large quantities of amino acids may be required. But often the amino-acid intake is much greater than requirements. This is especially true of animals that are no longer growing. Moreover, some proteins of an animal's body are constantly being broken down into amino acids. Therefore, a surplus of amino acids usually occurs.

Unlike carbohydrates and fats, amino acids (or proteins formed from them) cannot be stored in large quantities. And they cannot be used for the release of energy until the amino group ($-NH_2$) is removed. In vertebrates the removal of amino groups occurs chiefly in the liver.

The ammonia ($NH_3$) that results from this process is quite toxic. It is also quite soluble, and if a large supply of water is available, the ammonia can be carried out of the body in solution. In some aquatic animals this is exactly what happens. If a freshwater fish is placed through a tight-fitting rubber partition so that head and gills are on one side, and tail and the opening from the kidneys are on the other, ammonia accumulates in the water on the "head side" of the partition. In such fishes, then, nitrogenous wastes are excreted through the gills.

In other vertebrates the kidneys are the main avenue through which nitrogenous wastes are excreted. But the wastes are not in the form of ammonia. In birds and reptiles (and in insects, which also are terrestrial animals) amino groups are incorporated into *uric acid*. This rather complex substance is almost insoluble and can be excreted with the loss of only a small amount of water. In most adult amphibians and mammals, however, the amino groups are converted to *urea:* $CO(NH_2)_2$. Unlike uric acid, urea is soluble. It diffuses into the blood, from which it is removed by the kidneys.

Three distinct processes, all of which require the expenditure of energy, occur in a mammalian kidney (Figure 14 · 23). The first step is filtration of blood. This occurs in a *glomerulus,* a ball of capillary-like blood vessels surrounded by the expanded end of a tubule. Each kidney

uric [yŏŏr'ĭk; Greek: *ouron, urine*]

urea [yŏŏ rē'ə]

glomerulus [glō mĕr'yŏŏ ləs; Latin: *a little ball*]

contains many thousand glomeruli. Blood pressure (which represents energy expended by the ventricle in pumping blood) forces some of the fluid of the blood through the walls of the blood vessels and through the thin wall of the expanded end of the tubule. This fluid (filtrate) contains no blood cells or proteins, but otherwise it has the same composition as blood. As the filtrate moves down the tubule, useful substances—such as sugar, amino acids, water, some salts—are reabsorbed by cells in the wall of the tubule (by active transport). These substances are then transferred to the blood in capillaries that surround the tubule. Urea and some other wastes are left behind in the tubule. Some cells of the tubules are able to transfer certain wastes from the capillary blood into the space of the tubule. Thus as the original filtrate moves along the tubule, it is gradually converted—by removal of useful materials and addition of further waste materials—to *urine*.

Constantly, day and night throughout life, urine trickles from each kidney into a urinary bladder. From time to time

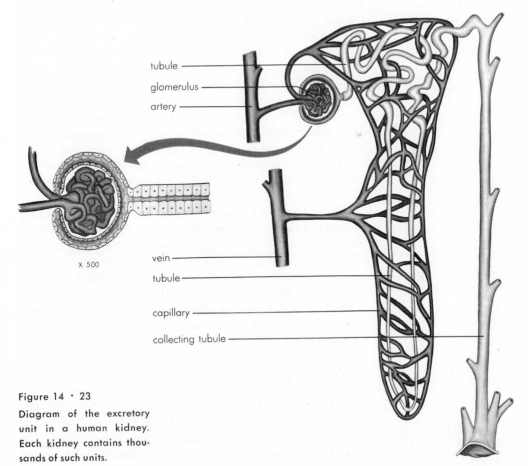

tubule

glomerulus

artery

vein

tubule

capillary

collecting tubule

X 500

**Figure 14 · 23**
Diagram of the excretory unit in a human kidney. Each kidney contains thousands of such units.

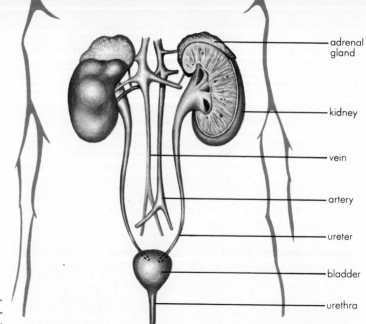

adrenal gland

kidney

vein

artery

ureter

bladder

urethra

**Figure 14 · 24**

Urinary system in man. Adrenal glands are attached to the kidneys but are not a part of this system.

urethra [yoŏ rē′thrə]

the urine is eliminated from the urinary bladder through a *urethra*. It has been estimated that a healthy, normal pair of human kidneys filters some 135 – 150 liters of fluid every twenty-four hours, while only about 1.5 liters of urine are eliminated from the bladder during the same period. In other words, only about 1 percent of the fluid filtered by the kidneys is eliminated.

A kidney is, therefore, a homeostatic organ. It regulates, to a considerable extent, the water content of the body by controlling the amount of water recovered by the tubule. And it prevents the amounts of waste nitrogen, salts, and many other substances in the blood from going above a certain level.

**Other substances.** Excretion of salts involves not only sodium chloride but also many other salts. These enter from the environment faster than they are needed, especially in vertebrates that live in seawater or on land. In land animals, kidneys are the chief excretory organs for salts as well as for nitrogenous wastes. However, on page 504 we took note of the salt-excreting glands near the eyes of sea turtles; and of course our own tears are slightly salty, too. Recently it has been discovered that many seabirds also have salt-excreting glands, but these glands are located in the nostrils rather than near the eyes.

Do you think man could drink seawater if his tear glands produced saltier tears? Why or why not?

There is, then, no one organ that performs all excretory functions in the body of a vertebrate. In our own bodies, water, small amounts of nitrogenous wastes, and salts are excreted through the sweat glands; the liver excretes the remains of dead red blood cells; and almost all the carbon dioxide produced during the release of energy from cells (along with a considerable amount of water) is excreted through the lungs. Excess substances can reach the environment in several ways. But loss of function in both kidneys is always fatal.

## MAINTAINING A STEADY STATE

One of the first ideas that you encountered in this book was the concept of steady state — a never-still, always teetering balance in biological systems held within narrow limits by homeostatic mechanisms.

### ENVIRONMENTS: INTERNAL AND EXTERNAL

We can look at the steady state within a multicellular organism in much the same way we looked at the situation outside the individual. To any one cell within a multicellular organism, the other cells of that body are "outside" — they are part of that cell's environment. In this view, a cell can be likened to an individual, a tissue to a species population, an organ to a community. This analogy can be carried too far, but it can help us to understand some of the things that go on within an organism. The environment of a cell within the body of a multicellular organism is, as the word "environment" implies, external to the cell, but it is internal to the multicellular organism as a whole. Thus we get the rather paradoxical but useful concept of an *internal environment*.

The environment in which an individual cell of a multicellular organism lives is made up not only of neighboring cells but also of body fluids. These fluids are to a cell what the sea is to an individual sea animal: the source of its requirements, the place to which its wastes are returned. In freshwater and land animals the primary function of homeostatic mechanisms is to keep body fluids as favorable and stable an environment for each cell as seawater usually is for each marine organism.

Let us consider an example of homeostasis in an internal environment — the regulation of the glucose content of human blood. After a heavy meal the processes of digestion leave a large amount of glucose in the small intestine. This is absorbed into the blood, but it does not stay there long. Figure 14 · 15 shows that a vessel (called the *hepatic portal*) carries blood (and glucose) from capillaries of the digestive system directly to capillaries in the liver. Here glucose in excess of 0.1 percent is removed and changed to the polysaccharide glycogen, which is then stored in the liver cells. If the meal produces a very large amount of glucose (as it

hepatic    portal    [hĭ păt′ĭk; Greek: *hepar*, the liver, + Latin: *porta*, a gate]

glycogen [glī′kə jən]

may if it contains many carbohydrates), the liver cannot take in all the excess. In this case, glucose is excreted through the kidney.

Now suppose the individual takes part in some kind of exercise, such as basketball or tennis. Muscle cells use a great deal of glucose for energy release at such times. This glucose is drawn from the cells' environment, the body fluids. Reduction of glucose in the body fluids leads to reduction of glucose in the blood. Under these circumstances glycogen in the liver is changed to glucose, which enters the blood. In this manner the liver and the circulatory and excretory systems provide the homeostatic mechanisms that maintain glucose in steady state in the environment of cells.

### INTERNAL STEADY STATE

A homeostatic mechanism requires a means of communication. If the activities within a multicellular organism are to be regulated, some means of communication between cells and tissues within the organism must exist. In most animals this communication occurs in two ways: by means of specialized cells of the *nervous system,* and by means of chemicals that travel through body fluids. In some ways the separation of nervous and chemical communication is misleading, but it is at least convenient for beginning our study.

coordination [kō ôr'də nā'shən; *Latin:* co-, with, + *ordinare,* to arrange]: adjustment of one part with others

### CHEMICAL COORDINATION

That most animals have nervous systems has long been known. Knowledge of the chemical system of coordination, however, has accumulated only within the last century. Just as knowledge of microscopic organisms was dependent on the development of microscopes, so knowledge of chemical systems in organisms has been dependent on the development of chemistry as a science. Today the biochemist plays an important part not only in the study of the activities within cells but also in the study of interrelationships among cells, tissues, and organs and even in the study of interrelationships between individuals and between populations.

**Hormones.** In all multicellular organisms some cells probably secrete chemical substances that in various ways influence the growth, development, or behavior of other cells. We discussed one of these—auxin—in Chapter 13. In general, such substances are called *hormones.*

hormones [Greek: *hormaein,* to stimulate]

As yet very little is known about hormones in most of the animal phyla. They have been studied chiefly in mollusks, arthropods, and chordates. The hormones of the invertebrates influence the same kinds of body processes as the hormones of vertebrates. But the chemical structure of invertebrate hormones is not as well known.

Hormones may be secreted by individual cells scattered among other cells of an animal's body, but usually the secreting cells are grouped into tissues and often into distinct organs—glands. Unlike the glands that secrete tears, sweat, and saliva, the glands that secrete hormones do not empty into a tubule or duct; their secretions pass directly into the circulatory system and are then carried through the body in the blood. Because the hormones from these *endocrine*, or ductless, glands interact with each other, we can say that there is an endocrine *system*, even though its parts are scattered through an animal's body.

endocrine [ĕn′dō krĭn′, ĕn′dō-krĭn; Greek: *endon*, within, + *krinein*, to separate]

**The endocrine glands of vertebrates.** With some relatively minor variations, all groups of vertebrates have similar hormones. However, the same hormone may have quite different functions in animals of different vertebrate classes. For example, the hormone that causes the mammary glands of mammals to secrete milk causes hens to incubate their eggs. Hormones that cause changes in skin color in certain fishes and amphibians are present in us. But human skin does not contain the special color cells that would enable us to match the colors of our surroundings. Within any one vertebrate class, however, a particular hormone has approximately the same effects in most species. Therefore, the results of hormonal experiments on rats, guinea pigs, and dogs, all of which are mammals, can—with caution—be applied to human physiology. The discussion that follows applies for the most part to mammals.

The *hypothalamus* is in the ventral part of the brain and really is a part of the nervous system. But special nerve cells of the hypothalamus produce *neurohormones* that pass through the blood in special vessels to the *anterior pituitary gland*, which lies just below the brain. These hormones cause the anterior pituitary gland to release hormones that control the rate at which some of the other endocrine glands function. Thus the hypothalamus is a major link between the nervous and endocrine systems.

hypothalamus    [hī′pə thăl′ə-məs; Greek: *hypo*, below, + *thalamos*, a chamber (here, a part of the brain)]
neurohormones    [noor′ō hôr′-mōnz; Greek: *neuron*, nerve, + *hormone*]
pituitary [pĭ tū′ə tĕr′ĭ]

All vertebrates have *thyroid* glands. Thyroid hormone regulates the speed of cellular respiration. Too little brings about an increase in weight, since food is stored rather than used in energy release. There are other results, such as slow movement, sleepiness, and lowered body temperature. Too much thyroid hormone increases the rate of cellular respiration. Little food is stored and the individual loses weight, but excess energy results in great activity.

thyroid [Greek: *thyreos*, a shield, + *eidos*, form]

*Parathyroid* glands are found in all vertebrates except

parathyroid    [păr′ə thī′roid; Greek: *para*, beside, + thyroid]

**Figure 14 · 25**

Location of the principal endocrine glands in a human body.

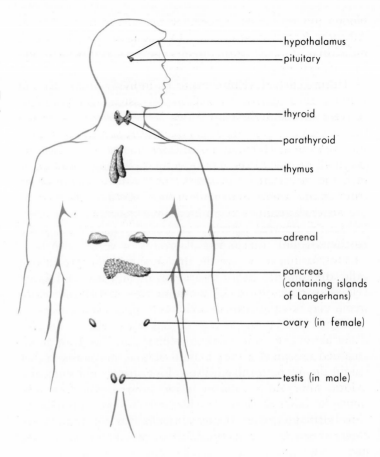

hypothalamus
pituitary
thyroid
parathyroid
thymus
adrenal
pancreas (containing islands of Langerhans)
ovary (in female)
testis (in male)

What other functions might be affected by the control of calcium metabolism?

Langerhans [discovered by Paul Langerhans, 1847–1888, German pathologist]

insulin [Latin: *insula*, island]

adrenal [ə drē′nəl; Latin: *ad*, to, at, + *renes*, kidneys]

adrenalin [ə drĕn′əl ĭn]

fishes, but only in mammals are they embedded in the thyroids. Parathyroid hormone controls the metabolism of calcium, which plays a part in muscle contraction. It is interference with calcium metabolism that brings about death if the parathyroid glands are injured or removed.

The pancreas is a gland with a duct through which a digestive juice is secreted. But embedded in the pancreas are bits of endocrine tissue (the *islands of Langerhans*) that produce *insulin*. This hormone controls the metabolism of glucose, and so lack of insulin results in lack of cellular energy. The unmetabolized glucose is excreted in the urine.

*Adrenal* glands are found in amphibians, reptiles, birds, and mammals. Hormones similar to those produced by these glands are secreted by fishes, but the secreting tissues are not organized into glands. The best-known adrenal hormone is *adrenalin*. Adrenalin raises the blood pressure, speeds up the heartbeat, increases the rate of clotting of the blood, and raises the percentage of glucose in the blood. All these effects increase the chances of survival when an individual is faced with an emergency—particularly one that is likely to result in wounding.

During early development of an individual, the adrenal gland is formed from two different tissues. The part that secretes adrenalin develops from nerve tissue; most of the rest develops from tissue that also gives rise to the reproductive system. Hormones of this latter part of the adrenal gland affect many functions, among them the depositing of fats, the synthesis of proteins, the formation of glucose from amino acids, and the excretion of salt. This part of the adrenal gland is controlled by a pituitary hormone. Obviously, adrenal glands are of vital importance to the biochemistry of an organism.

Ovaries and testes are the organs in which reproductive cells are formed, but embedded in them are endocrine cells. Hormones from these cells control growth, development, and reproductive behavior.

ovaries, testes [tĕs'tēz]: See pages 600–601.

What can you find out about the thymus gland?

**Other kinds of chemical coordination.** Biologists differ about the limits of the endocrine system. Sometimes included are small glands in the walls of the intestine, just below the pyloric valve. When food passes through the pyloric valve, these glands produce *secretin*—the first substance to which the word "hormone" was applied (in 1902). This hormone travels through the bloodstream to the pancreas, where it stimulates the production of pancreatic juice.

secretin [sĭ krē'tĭn]

No biologist would call carbon dioxide a hormone. It is obviously a waste product—an excretion rather than a secretion. But carbon dioxide in the blood plays a part in the coordination of breathing. Numerous experiments have shown that the movements of the muscles in breathing are regulated by the nervous system—specifically, by a part of the brain that lies near the base of the skull. But what determines whether the breathing movements are slow or rapid? Within limits you can voluntarily control your breathing. For a short time you can breathe deeply and quickly—or the reverse, as you may choose. If, however, you hold your breath, the need to start breathing again becomes irresistible. As you hold your breath, the concentration of $CO_2$ in your blood becomes greater and greater. Eventually the increased concentration of $CO_2$ stimulates the nerves to resume the breathing motions in the chest. This chemical control of breathing operates whether you are conscious or unconscious.

Many other kinds of substances that cannot be called hormones aid in coordination of physiological processes.

## NERVOUS COORDINATION

The control of breathing illustrates again how closely nervous and chemical coordination are associated; the

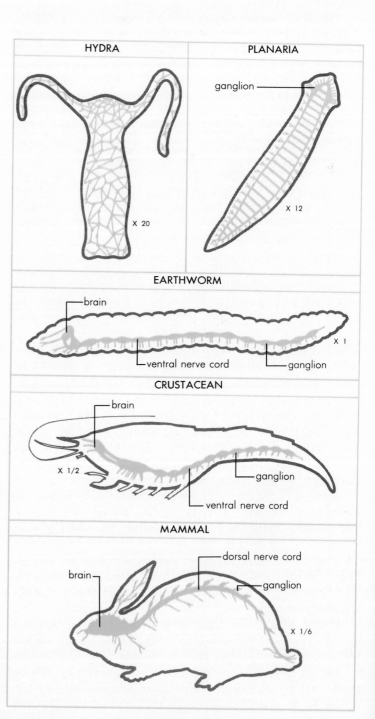

**Figure 14 · 26**

Nervous systems in five diverse kinds of animals.

distinction between the two kinds of coordination is mostly a matter of convenience. In general, however, the more rapid adjustments in animals are usually brought about by the nervous system.

**Kinds of nervous systems.** Sponges have no nervous systems. Indeed, they have nothing that we can call nerve cells. Yet, just as do other organisms without nerve cells (protists and plants), sponges adjust to changes in their environment—they react to *stimuli*.

stimuli [stĭm′yə lĭ]

Coelenterates do have nerve cells, some of which are even specialized to receive only certain kinds of stimuli. The nerve cells are connected in a network that permits local responses as well as some coordinated responses, such as ingestion of food.

Flatworms have nerve networks, too (and even man has such a network, in the walls of the intestines). But a flatworm also possesses a more centralized system. A "nerve ladder," consisting of two cords with interconnecting branches, extends the length of the body. At the anterior end is a rather large mass of nerve tissue, a *ganglion*, a center in which nerve impulses are exchanged. Moreover, a flatworm has cells specialized for receiving stimuli. The eyespots of planarians cannot form images, but they can detect the direction and intensity of light. And the flaps that look like ears can sense food at a distance in the water—which gives flatworms a kind of sense of smell.

ganglion [găng′glĭ ən]

In annelids the nervous system is well developed. The main nerve cord is on the ventral side of the body. Numerous ganglia occur along the cord, and a large ganglion that really deserves to be called a *brain* is found at the anterior end of the body. Although earthworms have no obvious sense organs, a little experimenting will show that they detect many kinds of stimuli. Other annelids have several specialized sense organs, including eyes.

You can devise some simple experiments yourself. See page 535.

Mollusks show a great variety of nervous systems—all basically of the annelid type. Arthropod nervous systems are also essentially like those of annelids, but with a greater variety of sense organs.

The dorsal, tubular nerve cord is a distinctive characteristic of the chordate phylum. In vertebrate chordates the anterior ganglion—the brain—dominates all the rest of the nervous system.

**Nerve cells.** The basic structural unit in all nervous systems is a *neuron*, a nerve cell. Functionally a neuron is a conductor of nerve *impulses*.

neuron [nōŏr′ŏn, nyōŏr′ŏn; Greek: nerve]

Let us take neurons of mammals as examples. Three kinds can be distinguished: *Sensory* neurons receive impulses from a *receptor* (such as the part of the eye that

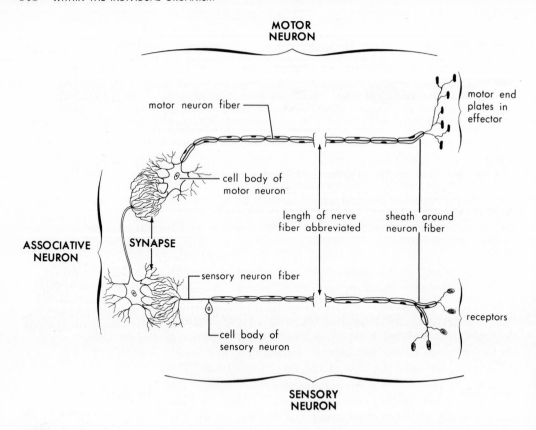

MOTOR
NEURON

motor neuron fiber

motor end
plates in
effector

cell body of
motor neuron

length of nerve
fiber abbreviated

sheath around
neuron fiber

ASSOCIATIVE
NEURON

SYNAPSE

sensory neuron fiber

cell body of
sensory neuron

receptors

SENSORY
NEURON

Figure 14 · 27

Kinds of neurons.

reacts to light) and transmit impulses to another neuron. *Motor* neurons carry impulses to an *effector*—that is, to a muscle or a gland. *Associative* neurons transmit impulses from one neuron to another.

Neurons do not occur singly. The nerves that are visible in a dissected vertebrate are bundles of fibers. In man the fibers of some neurons are almost a meter long. The cell bodies of neurons are mostly in the brain, in the spinal cord, or in the ganglia that occur in pairs along the length of the spinal cord.

Just what a nerve impulse is, physiologists do not completely understand. Complex electrical phenomena are involved, but an impulse cannot be regarded as a simple electric current. Impulses are short in duration—usually only a few ten-thousandths of a second long. Information in the nervous system is usually transmitted by bursts of impulses rather than by single impulses. Under natural conditions an impulse can pass in only one direction in a neuron and is confined to one neuron. Neurons do not directly touch each other. When a sufficiently strong impulse, or rather a burst of impulses, reaches the end of the

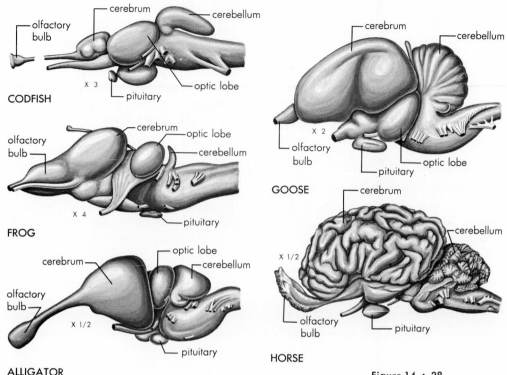

CODFISH
- olfactory bulb
- cerebrum
- cerebellum
- optic lobe
- pituitary
- X 3

FROG
- olfactory bulb
- cerebrum
- optic lobe
- cerebellum
- pituitary
- X 4

ALLIGATOR
- cerebrum
- olfactory bulb
- optic lobe
- cerebellum
- pituitary
- X 1/2

GOOSE
- cerebrum
- cerebellum
- olfactory bulb
- pituitary
- optic lobe
- X 2

HORSE
- cerebrum
- cerebellum
- olfactory bulb
- pituitary
- X 1/2

**Figure 14 · 28**

Brains of animals in five vertebrate classes. Olfactory bulbs are concerned with odor, optic lobes with sight; the pituitary is not part of the brain. From these examples, what generalizations about brains in vertebrates can you make?

fiber of a neuron, it releases a chemical substance that induces an impulse in the next neuron. The very narrow space between two neurons through which this chemical substance passes is called a *synapse*. Synapses occur also between receptor cells and neurons and between neurons and effector cells. Transmission in a synapse can take place only in one direction. Therefore impulses are conducted only in one direction by all neurons.

**Nerves and internal coordination.** Much activity in your nervous system occurs without your being aware of it. Though you have limited control over your breathing, you do not ordinarily think about it. And the rate of your heartbeat, the movements of your stomach and intestines, the secretion of bile by your liver — these are activities of which you are unaware and which you are unable to control. They are under the control of the *autonomic* nervous system, which in turn is controlled through the hypothalamus. The autonomic system consists of interconnecting neurons that operate, for the most part, independently of the external environment but that coordinate activities in the internal environment.

synapse [sĭn'ăps; Greek: *syn-*, with, + *apsis*, a fastening]

autonomic [ô'tə nŏm'ĭk; Greek: *autos*, self, + *nomos*, law]

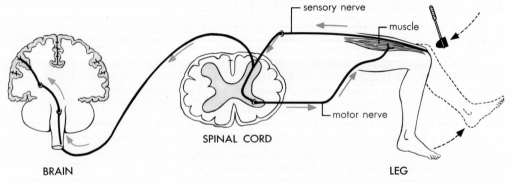

BRAIN

SPINAL CORD

LEG

Figure 14 · 29

Diagram of a reflex. The bending of the leg involves neurons in the leg and spinal cord only. Feeling the tap on the knee involves the brain, but this is not necessary for the reaction to occur.

For example, a steady supply of blood to all tissues is one of the principal requirements for maintaining a favorable internal environment. Suppose that after sitting on the sidelines for the first quarter, you are put into a basketball game. The sudden muscular activity forces blood into the right atrium of the heart much faster than blood is being pumped out, because (for the moment) the heart continues to beat at the normal rate — the rate it maintained while you were sitting on the bench. The walls of the atrium are stretched by the blood that is (so to speak) dammed up. Within the atrial walls are the tips of sensory neurons. They are stimulated by the stretching, and impulses pass over the fibers to the brain. These impulses induce impulses in motor neurons going to the heart, "telling it" to speed up its contractions. This description is somewhat simplified. However, it illustrates the basic functional unit of the nervous system, the *reflex.*

### ADJUSTMENT TO THE EXTERNAL ENVIRONMENT

A need for adjustments in the internal environment usually arises from events outside the body — the basketball game that we discussed, for instance. Such events may result in changes throughout the whole organism. And some of these changes may, in turn, influence events in the outside environment. The overlap between internal and external coordination is great, but the distinction simplifies discussion.

### SENSES

The athlete's heart beat faster because he went into the game, but the endings of the sensory nerves were in the walls of the heart — and they could not receive direct stimulation from the basketball game. Usually we do not think of the internal sensory neurons when we speak of the senses; we consider only the sensory endings that receive stimuli from the external environment. The player heard the whistle and the order of the coach. As a whole organism, he reacted to these stimuli.

Ability to receive and to react to stimuli from the environment is one of the basic characteristics of living things, but the ability is developed to different degrees in different organisms. In most animals different kinds of stimuli are detected by specialized sensory cells—receptors. In man, for example, receptors in the skin of the fingertips are sensitive to pressure but not to light. Receptors in the nose are sensitive to chemical substances but not to light. Only receptors in the eyes are light sensitive, but they are not sensitive to sound waves and other stimuli.

In most animals at least some of the receptors are concentrated in special organs. The principal ones in man are well known—the eyes, the ears, the nose. Other kinds of receptors, such as those sensitive to pressure and heat, are distributed widely in the skin.

Probably no organism can detect all the possible stimuli in its environment. A dog whistle stimulates a dog; but it has no effect on us, because it produces tones that our receptors of sound waves do not detect. Sometimes an inability to detect stimuli—or an ability to detect them and not be affected by them—is to an organism's advantage. How obviously impractical it would be if you were conscious of all the activities and sounds going on around you at this moment! Moreover, probably no organism has specialized receptors for all possible stimuli in the environment. Many cave-dwelling animals have no receptors for light, and we have no receptors for the electromagnetic waves that carry radio and television signals. Lack of sensitivity to light is ordinarily no handicap to cave animals. On the other hand, insensitivity might result in a catastrophe. A man may suffer fatal damage from nuclear radiation without being aware of his exposure, for he has no receptors that can detect it.

How do we become aware of stimuli for which we have no receptors or of those too weak for our receptors to detect?

## MOVEMENT

An animal obtains information about its environment through receptors. But the ability to react—to *do* something about a stimulus received through a receptor—depends on ability to move. Movement is one of the most obvious characteristics of animals. Of course, not all animals move rapidly, and some remain through much of their lives as firmly rooted as any plant—oysters and sponges, for example. But in looking at movement as part of an organism's ability to react to environment, we are not concerned merely with rapid motion or with locomotion. Any motion that helps an individual adjust to stimuli from its environment is important. In animals, motion usually involves specialized cells — muscle tissue.

**Muscles.** As in so many other matters, sponges are an exception among animals: they have no muscle tissues, although individual cells are capable of movement. The larvae swim by means of cilia, just as many protists do.

In coelenterates some of the cells — especially those in the outer layer — have a degree of muscular specialization, though this is usually combined with other characteristics. As a result, coelenterates can elongate and move their tentacles, and many can expand and contract their bodies. In flatworms many cells are further specialized; they are organized into definite muscle tissues, though locomotion is accomplished largely by cilia. In all other animal phyla, muscle tissues are organized into bundles (muscles) and controlled by nervous systems.

There are two general types of muscle, *striated* and *smooth*. Striated muscle is best developed in arthropods and vertebrates; it moves parts of the skeleton and, in general, is capable of more rapid contraction than is smooth muscle. In these phyla smooth muscle is found in such places as the walls of blood vessels, of various ducts, and of the digestive tube. Smooth muscle is usually involved in the regulation of the internal environment; striated muscle, on the other hand, is usually involved in adjustments of the organism to the external environment.

striated [strī′ă təd; Latin: stria, a furrow]

**Figure 14 · 30**

Kinds of vertebrate muscle tissue: (A) Smooth muscle. (B) Striated muscle.

**A** X 315

**B** X 535

A. John Geraci

F. W. Schmidt

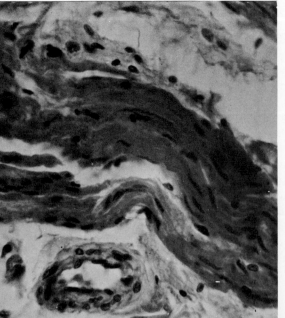

The chemistry of muscular contraction is a very active field of biological investigation. In some recent experiments proteins were extracted from muscle and an artificial fiber was made from them. This fiber was placed in a water bath. When ATP was added, the fiber contracted. Moreover, tests showed that the ATP was changed to ADP in the fiber during contraction. This and many other experiments indicate that proteins make up the contraction apparatus of muscles and that the energy for this action comes from ATP.

Even when an animal appears to be at rest, its muscles are not completely relaxed. The muscles of a healthy organism are always in a state of partial contraction called *muscle tone*. This produces the firmness that can be felt even in "relaxed" muscles.

**Skeletons.** By contracting, muscles in the body of an earthworm produce movement without the aid of a skeleton. In our own bodies, muscles that have no connection to our bones move food along the alimentary canal. But much of the movement of animals—especially locomotion—is a result of muscles and skeletons functioning together.

Skeletons have three main functions: support, protection, and locomotion. In most animal phyla the first two of these are the most important. The skeleton of a sponge consists of small, more or less rigid parts scattered through the soft, living tissues; it probably serves chiefly to support the sponge. Among coelenterates the stony skeletons built up by corals serve both to support and to protect. These two functions also are obvious in echinoderm skeletons; indeed, the skeletons of echinoderms hinder locomotion rather than help it. In mollusks the skeleton (shell) is almost entirely protective, though scallops swim by rapidly opening and closing their shells.

Almost all skeletons adapted for locomotion are found among the arthropods and chordates. Arthropod skeletons are external, with the muscles attached to the inner surfaces. These exoskeletons are composed of chitin, which is rather flexible when thin. In many arthropods calcium compounds, deposited along with the chitin, make the exoskeleton quite hard and strong. It is all one piece, but it is rigid only in sections; thin, flexible chitin joints allow bending.

The chordate skeleton is inside the muscles. It may consist of one or both of two kinds of tissue: cartilage and bone. The hardness of bone is, in part, due to calcium and magnesium compounds. Both cartilage and bone contain cells that secrete these compounds; thus the skeleton can grow as the animal grows. Though the skeleton begins as cartilage, in the majority of vertebrate chordates most of

cartilage: See page 123.

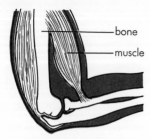

VERTEBRATE

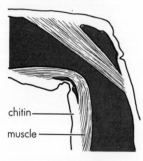

ARTHROPOD

Figure 14 · 31

Relation of muscles to skeletons. Why are *two* muscles shown in each example?

fulcrums [fŭl'krĕmz; Latin: *fulcire*, to prop, support]

Can you think of some disadvantages of being "warm-blooded"?

this cartilage is gradually replaced by bone. At your age this process is well advanced. But it is never completed—the tip of your nose and the external parts of your ears will never become hard bone.

In vertebrates endoskeletons serve all three skeletal functions. However, protection, except in such animals as turtles, is seldom as complete as in most arthropod skeletons. In man the chief protective bones are those of the skull and of the ribs, which form a kind of cage around the organs in the chest cavity.

**Skeletal movement.** The parts of a vertebrate or arthropod skeleton act together as levers. Muscles supply the force to move them, and joints act as fulcrums (points around which movement occurs). A muscle attached to a bone is like a rope attached to a wagon: with a rope we can pull a wagon, but we cannot push it. If we want to move the wagon back to its original position, we must attach a rope to the other end and again move it by pulling. Muscles act in the same way—in pairs. While sitting, you can raise and straighten your leg by contracting one set of muscles, and gravity will pull it back to a bent position. But if you stand and then wish to bend your knee, you will have to use another set of muscles—muscles with an action opposite to that of the ones you used to straighten the leg. By the contraction of opposing sets of muscles, all skeleton movements are performed.

### PHYSIOLOGICAL STEADY STATE AS A WHOLE: AN EXAMPLE

In closing this chapter, we can summarize much of our understanding of animal physiology by considering a case of homeostasis—the regulation of body temperature in "warm-blooded" animals. The chemical reactions of metabolism—like all chemical reactions—are influenced by changes in temperature; they slow down in low temperatures and speed up in high temperatures. Therefore, "warm-bloodedness" is an advantage because it permits an animal to be active when environmental temperatures are low.

The temperature of the skin and even of tissues some distance beneath the skin fluctuates many degrees in most "warm-blooded" animals—birds and mammals. It is only internal body temperature that is held constant. This "deep body temperature" can remain constant only if the rate of heat loss is the same as the rate of heat production. For a control system that can maintain this balance, receptors that respond to changes in temperature are necessary. There are two sets of such detectors. The skin has *thermoreceptors* that detect changes in environmental temperature.

Through nerve impulses these receptors give the hypothalamus "advance notice" that adjustments are necessary if the deep body temperature is to remain unchanged. Within the hypothalamus itself are other thermoreceptors that detect changes in blood temperature. The hypothalamus, with its mixture of nervous and endocrine functions, is the regulator in the homeostasis of temperature control.

What does a "warm-blooded" animal do when the environmental temperature becomes cooler than the body temperature? The first adjustments are usually those that conserve heat. Impulses pass along neurons of the autonomic nervous system, constricting the small arteries of the skin. This reduces the flow of blood to the skin, which, in turn, reduces the amount of heat lost through the skin. Have you noticed that a person is pale when he is cold? He is conserving heat!

At the same time, other impulses along the autonomic nervous system contract the small muscles that control the position of each hair or feather in the skin of the animal. This erects the individual hairs, thus increasing the amount of "dead-air space" between them. And this in turn improves the insulation provided by fur or feathers. These same nerve impulses occur in your body when you become chilly. But the human body no longer has a dense hair covering, although the little hair muscles are still there. The muscles contract, but all you get is gooseflesh.

If these measures fail to prevent a downward change in deep body temperature, the rate of heat production can be increased. This may be accomplished in an almost undetectable manner by increase of metabolic rate in cells. Or it may be accomplished by an involuntary increase in muscle activity—by shivering. This muscle activity itself increases the rate of metabolism. Increase in metabolism increases the release of energy from food. But, of course, this is always accompanied by a "loss" of energy in the form of heat. In this case the additional "lost" energy is useful in maintaining body temperature.

Compare this mechanism of homeostasis with the description on pages 60–61.

In addition to making these internal adjustments most birds and mammals behave in ways that conserve heat. When it is cold, a cat curls up in a ball and covers its nose with its tail. This reduces the amount of surface exposed to the cold air; it also covers an uninsulated surface (the nose), through which heat loss is very rapid. A bird tucks its legs up under its feathers and puts its head under its wing. Many birds can thus cut their heat losses in half. How many times have you put on a sweater almost without thinking, when the air became cool?

What happens when the environmental temperature

Annan Photo Features

Figure 14 · 32
Heat-conserving behavior of a macaw, a tropical parrot.

Figure 14 · 33
What does the position of the cat probably indicate about the environmental temperature?

becomes warmer than the body temperature? Then maintenance of a constant body temperature requires a reduction of heat production, an increase of heat loss, or both. Again impulses on autonomic neurons originating in the hypothalamus activate the mechanisms. The walls of the small arteries in the skin relax and more blood circulates to the skin; thus more heat is lost from the body surface. In some mammals, such as men and horses, the activity of the sweat glands increases. This provides more water on the skin surface. Evaporation of water always requires heat; heat for the evaporation of sweat comes from the body. Dogs have no sweat glands. But a dog can increase the rate of heat loss by increasing the flow of air over the moist surfaces of the upper part of the respiratory system—by panting. There are many behavior patterns that are important in keeping body temperature from going too high.

Heat production through metabolism is reduced by inactivity. In hot weather many mammals and birds are quite inactive during the warmer part of a day. And during that part of a day, most birds and mammals seek the coolness of shade, where heat can be lost rather rapidly. Water conducts heat much more rapidly than air; also the temperature of natural bodies of water is usually lower than air temperature. Therefore bathing, wading, or standing in water increases heat loss.

Thus many homeostatic mechanisms are involved in maintaining the steady state of body temperatures in "warm-blooded" animals. We would find equally extensive mechanisms if we were to examine the maintenance of water content of the body, glycogen content of the liver, salt content of the blood, or any other aspect of internal steady state.

## INVESTIGATION 14.4

### CHEMORECEPTORS IN MAN

#### INTRODUCTION

*Chemoreceptors*—nerve endings sensitive to chemical substances—are common among animals that have well-defined nervous systems. Among arthropods they are often found in the antennae. Among vertebrates they are found mostly in the mouth and nasal passages. Students of human physiology think of chemoreceptors as involving the senses of taste and smell.

The study of chemoreceptors among animals other than man is complicated by a lack of communication: How can we find out just what an animal senses? When studying chemoreceptors in man, we can at least obtain descriptions ("sour," "sweet," "bitter," "spicy," etc.) of particular stimuli. But then there are difficulties in interpreting such reports, so that complete understanding of chemoreceptors—even in man—is not easy.

## MATERIALS AND EQUIPMENT

*For Procedure A*
    *(for each pair of students)*
  Syracuse watch glass or other small container
  Salt solution (10%), 2 ml
  Applicators (toothpicks with small ball of
    cotton wrapped around one end), 4
  Waste jar, 1 for every 6 students
  Beakers filled with water, 2
  Sucrose solution (5%), 2 ml
  Acetic acid solution (1%), 2 ml
  Quinine sulfate solution (0.1%), 2 ml
*For Procedure B*
    *(for each student)*
  Small paper cups, 6
  Sucrose solutions (0.001%, 0.005%, 0.01%,
    0.05%, 0.1%, and 0.5%), 2 to 3 ml of
    each
  Salt solutions (0.001%, 0.005%, 0.01%,
    0.05%, 0.1%, 0.5%), 2 to 3 ml of each
  Beaker filled with water
  Medicine dropper
  Waste jar, 1 for every 6 students
  Chalk, 3 colors
*For Procedure C*
    *(for teams of 3 students)*
  Handkerchief (for blindfold)
  Small paper cups, 3 to 6
  Solutions of orange juice, milk, onion juice,
    vinegar (2%), sugar, dill-pickle juice—any
    3 or all 6

## PROCEDURE A: LOCATION OF TASTE RECEPTORS

During Procedure A students work in pairs.

Student A: Pour about 2 ml of 10% salt solution in a watch glass.

Student B: Make a copy of Figure 14 · 34 and label it *Salt*.

Student A: Dip an applicator into the solution. Drain excess solution from the applicator. Touch the applicator to the tongue of Student B at the point marked *1* in Figure 14 · 34.

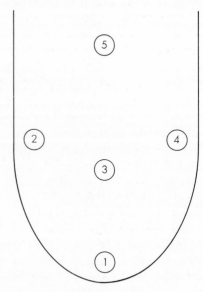

Figure 14 · 34

Student B: At point *1* in your drawing, place a minus sign (−) if you sense no taste of salt, a plus sign (+) if you sense a mild taste of salt, and a double plus (++) if you sense a strong taste of salt.

Student A: As soon as Student B has recorded his sensation, touch the applicator to his tongue at point 2.

Student B: Record your sensation, using the appropriate symbol.

Continue until sensation has been recorded at all five points on the tongue.

Student B: Rinse your mouth with water.

Student A: Break the applicator and discard it. Pour the salt solution from the watch glass into the waste jar. Rinse the watch glass.

Student B: Pour about 2 ml of 5% sucrose solution into the watch glass.

Student A: Make a copy of Figure 14 · 34. Label it *Sweet*.

Student B: Dip an applicator into the glucose solution, drain off excess solution, and touch the applicator to the tongue of Student A at point *1*.

Student A: Record your sensation.

Continue ˙until sensation has been recorded at all five points.

Student A: Rinse your mouth with water.

Student B: Break the applicator and discard it. Pour the glucose solution from the watch glass into the waste jar. Rinse the watch glass.

Student A: Pour about 2 ml of 1% acetic acid solution into the watch glass.

Student B: Make another copy of Figure 14·34 and label it *Sour*.

Student A: Dip a new applicator into the acid solution and proceed to test Student B, following the procedure described above.

Student B: Record sensation, as above.

Following the same procedure for changing solutions and students, test the effects of a 0.1% solution of quinine sulfate. The diagram on which sensation is recorded should be labeled *Bitter*

### PROCEDURE B: TASTE THRESHOLD

Stimuli have different degrees of intensity. The intensity of a stimulus may be so low (weak) that it is not detected by the organism. The degree of intensity that an individual can just barely detect is the *threshold* intensity for that individual. In tests for the taste threshold, intensity is expressed as the percentage of the test substance in a given volume of water.

During Procedure B you will work alone. Using a pencil, mark six paper cups as follows: *0.001%, 0.005%, 0.01%, 0.05%, 0.1%, 0.5%*. From the stock bottles pour into each of the cups 2 to 3 ml of the solutions assigned to you. (Be sure to match the labels on the bottles with the labels on the cups, pouring the 0.001%

solution into the cup marked *0.001%*, and so on.) Arrange the cups in order of increasing concentration. Using a medicine dropper, transfer 2 drops of the 0.001% solution to your tongue. In your data book, write the name of the solution and its concentration. Beside this information write a minus sign if you cannot taste the substance in solution; write a plus sign if you can taste it. Rinse the medicine dropper and follow the same procedure with the solution of next higher concentration. When you reach a concentration you can taste, check by testing the next higher concentration. Then stop testing.

### PROCEDURE C: RELATION OF SMELL TO TASTE

During Procedure C students work in teams of 3. Designate the team members "A," "B," and "C." It is important that the *subject* (the student being tested) be unaware of the identity of the substance.

Student B: Blindfold Student A, the first subject. Obtain a paper cup, labeled *A*, containing a few milliliters of test solution A.

Student C: In your data book, copy the form shown below. Write the letter *A* in the first space under the heading "Solution Presented." Record the name of the solution.

| SUBJECT | SOLUTION PRESENTED | NOSE CLOSED | | NOSE OPEN | |
|---------|--------------------|-------------|----------|-----------|----------|
| | | Taste | Identity | Taste | Identity |
| | | | | | |
| | | | | | |

Student A: *Holding your nose tightly,* sip the solution; report its taste, and try to identify the substance in the solution.

Student C: Record these reports on the form.

Student A: Without holding your nose, sip the same solution; again report its taste, and try to identify the substance.

Student C: Record these reports.

Now repeat the procedure, with Student B as the subject. Student C obtains test solution B, and Student A records the reports. When tests with solution B are completed, repeat the procedure, with Student C as the subject. Student A obtains test solution C, and Student B becomes the recorder.

If time permits a second round of testing, use solutions AA, BB, and CC.

### STUDYING THE DATA

On the chalkboard make four large diagrams of the tongue (Figure 14 · 34). Label them *Salt, Sweet, Sour,* and *Bitter.* Assemble from all students the data obtained in Procedure A. At each test point on the diagrams record the total number of minus, plus, and double-plus responses.   • What are some of the possible causes for variability in the data? (1)   • Which kinds of variability are the result of "errors of observation"? Which kinds are the result of physiological variability? (2)

On the chalkboard assemble the data obtained in Procedure B. Beside each concentration use two colors of chalk to tally separately the number of male subjects and the number of female subjects for whom that concentration represented the taste threshold. Add the two counts and write the total in a third color. For each kind of solution, calculate the *mean* (average) threshold concentration for males, for females, and for the entire class.

On the chalkboard list the solutions (A, B, C, etc.) used in Procedure C. Tally separately the tastes reported with nose closed and with nose open; also tally the identifications of solutions.   • In general, are the kinds of tastes reported with nose open more varied than those reported with nose closed? Less varied? Neither? (3)   • In general, are the identifications made with nose open more accurate than those made with nose closed? Less accurate? Neither? (4)   • What assumption is involved in holding the nose closed? (5)

### CONCLUSIONS

• Do the data from Procedure A support the hypothesis that receptors of the four kinds of taste are unequally distributed on the surface of the tongue? Explain. (6)   • If the data support this hypothesis, where on the tongue is each kind of taste receptor most numerous? (7)

• Do the data from Procedure B support the hypothesis that the taste threshold for sweetness is lower than that for saltiness? Higher? Neither? (8)   • Do the data indicate that the sense of taste in one sex is more acute (that is, has a lower threshold) than in the other? If so, which sex has the lower threshold for sweetness? For saltiness? (9)

• On the basis of the data from Procedure C, write a brief statement concerning the relationship of the sense of taste to the sense of smell. (10)

### FOR FURTHER INVESTIGATION

1. Smell oil of cloves through one nostril, expiring air through the mouth. Hold the bottle containing the oil about 1.5 cm from the nose. How much time passes before the smell of cloves is no longer detected? This is called "olfactory fatigue." Immediately smell oil of peppermint through the same nostril. Is the latter odor detectable?

2. Stick your tongue out and keep it out during the following procedure: Wipe your tongue dry with a piece of gauze or paper toweling. Place a few crystals of sugar on the tongue, and note the time. How much time passes before

the sugar is tasted? Rinse your mouth with water. Again stick your tongue out, but do not dry it before placing sugar crystals on it. How much time passes before the sugar is tasted? Try the same procedure with salt crystals. Again measure the time.

3. To test the hearing threshold, use the ticking of a watch as the stimulus and the distance of the watch from the ear as the measure of intensity. The subject should be blindfolded, and the test should be made where other sounds are at a minimum.

According to the classification used in this book, all animals are multicellular organisms. Most have powers of locomotion at some stage in their life histories. And none of them carry on photosynthesis. As a result of this last characteristic, food-getting is a fundamental activity in all animals.

We have examined the ways in which animals obtain food and other nutrients and prepare them for absorption into cells. We have also considered the means by which animals acquire oxygen. In most animals—particularly the larger ones and those that do not live in marine environments—there are special ways of distributing nutrients and oxygen to all the cells. With nutrients and oxygen delivered, each cell then releases energy for its own use, including synthesis of its complex molecules. Some cells (as in bone and cartilage) secrete materials useful to the organism as a whole.

In doing these things, an organism produces various waste substances, or it may acquire or produce substances in excess of needs. By the processes of excretion, these waste materials are passed from the bloodstream out into the environment. As a result, steady-state conditions for different materials are maintained within the organism.

Adjustment of the individual organism, through homeostatic mechanisms, to maintain steady-state conditions in a changing environment involves both the nervous and endocrine systems. Coordination of the functions of the various parts of an animal's body is brought about by hormones, which move through the circulatory system (if one is present). The more rapid internal adjustments are usually under the control of the nervous system, though there is a close coordination with the hormonal system in such matters.

To react to the environment, organisms must receive stimuli from it. In most animals, parts of the nervous system are specialized as receptors for such stimuli. Reaction usually involves specialized cells of contraction (muscle cells) or of secretion (gland cells), or both.

## GUIDE QUESTIONS

1. Why is eating such an important animal activity?
2. How do the various food-getting devices of animals illustrate structural diversity?
3. What is the function of digestion in maintaining the life of an animal?
4. How is chemical digestion related to the chemical syntheses carried on by cells?
5. In man, where does most of the absorption of digested foods occur?
6. Chyme in the small intestine is semiliquid, yet feces are normally semisolid. Explain.
7. Some salamanders have no lungs. Why is it necessary for them to live in a moist environment?
8. How is air moved into and out of the lungs of mammals?
9. What occurs in the alveoli of lungs?
10. Distinguish between open and closed circulatory systems.
11. What are the differences among arteries, veins, and capillaries?
12. How is blood in mammals kept flowing in one direction?
13. What is blood plasma?
14. How does hemoglobin function in transporting oxygen?
15. In what ways are red and white blood cells and platelets distinguished?
16. Draw a diagram to show how blood clots.
17. How does lymph differ from blood?
18. How can bile be considered both a secretion and an excretion?
19. What are the principal kinds of excreted substances?
20. How does a mammalian kidney function?
21. List places in the human body where excreted substances are eliminated.
22. What is meant by the internal environment of an animal?
23. What are hormones?
24. What are the principal glands of the endocrine system in man?
25. What evidence supports the idea that the endocrine and nervous systems are closely associated?
26. How do sensory neurons differ from motor neurons?
27. How does a synapse function in the transmission of a nerve impulse?
28. What is the autonomic nervous system?
29. What are the principal differences of brain structure in different vertebrate classes?
30. What are the principal kinds of information that vertebrates obtain through their receptors?
31. Distinguish between striated and smooth muscle.
32. How do the skeletons of arthropods and vertebrates function in locomotion?

## PROBLEMS

1. How might you proceed experimentally to show that (a) secretin causes the pancreas to secrete digestive enzymes, (b) *diabetes mellitus* is caused by lack of insulin, and (c) hormones secreted by the pituitary gland affect thyroid and adrenal glands?

2. Antibodies from horse blood can produce some kinds of immunity in man (Chapter 7). Insulin from a cow pancreas can be used in treating human diabetes. Why cannot whole blood of horses and cows be transfused to man?

3. We have implied that excretion is a general biological process essential for maintenance of life in all organisms. Yet we did not discuss the process in Chapter 13, and it is seldom mentioned in botany textbooks. Explain.

4. Blood transports many substances dissolved in the plasma. It can be shown, however, that in mammals less than 10 percent of the carbon dioxide in the blood is dissolved in plasma. How is the rest of the $CO_2$ transported?

5. Describe in detail the route followed by a molecule of oxygen as it moves from the air of your external environment to a mitochondrion in one of your muscle cells.

6. The thyroxin molecule contains four atoms of iodine. What effects would an iodine-free diet have upon a mammal?

7. Hemoglobin acts as a respiratory pigment in animals of several phyla, but there are other such pigments in the animal kingdom. Investigate this matter, considering the following questions: (a) Do all respiratory pigments act in the same way? (b) What are the chemical similarities and

differences among respiratory pigments? (c) Do respiratory pigments provide any clues to the evolutionary relationships among animal phyla? (d) Is there any significance to the chemical relationship between hemoglobin and chlorophyll? To the fact that hemoglobin occurs in the nodules formed by *Rhizobium* on the roots of legumes?

8. A temporary reddening of the skin surface is sometimes called a "flush" and sometimes a "blush." The first term is often used in cases of fever; the second is usually used to describe a reaction to some situation in the external environment. Is the body mechanism the same in both cases? If so, how does it operate? If not, what are the differences?

9. You eat a lettuce and cheese sandwich. Describe what happens to the sandwich from the moment you take the first bite until its remains are passed from the anus. First, you must decide what classes of substances are in the sandwich.

10. In some cases of slow blood clotting, physicians prescribe calcium compounds. Explain. In other cases they prescribe vitamin K. What part does this vitamin play in the clotting process?

11. Many kinds of combustion, such as that in gasoline engines and furnaces, produce carbon monoxide (CO) as well as $CO_2$. Hemoglobin combines readily with CO, and any hemoglobin molecule to which CO is attached cannot combine with oxygen. What effects would an atmosphere containing CO have on a person? Gather facts on carbon monoxide poisoning and suggest a treatment for it.

12. In mammalian physiology the kidney can be regarded as a principal organ of internal homeostasis. Explain.

13. List the principal life functions of animals. Then compare the structures by which each is accomplished in a sponge, a planarian, an insect, and a mammal. Since all of these animals exist in large numbers, we must conclude that despite such diverse structures they all successfully carry on their life functions. Explain how this can be.

14. Instruments may be classed as those by which man increases his powers to *do* things (usually called tools or machines) and those by which he increases his powers to *sense* things. Contrast the abilities of a prehistoric man (who had only the biological receptors) and of a modern man to receive information from the environment. In what ways are instrumental sensors related to biological receptors?

## SUGGESTED READINGS

D'AMOUR, F. E. *Basic Physiology*. Chicago: University of Chicago Press, 1961. (With many anecdotes of physiological discovery and a breezy, sometimes jocular style, this book presents more than basic *human* physiology.)

BURNET, M. "The Thymus Gland," *Scientific American*, November, 1962. Pp. 50–57.

COMFORT, A. *The Process of Ageing*. New York: New American Library, 1964. (Considers aging as a physiological process in animals and its bearing on life-span in man. Fairly easy.)

COMROE, J. H. "The Lung," *Scientific American*, February, 1966. Pp. 56–66.

GORDON, A. S. *Blood Cell Physiology*. (BSCS Pamphlet 8). Boston: D. C. Heath & Co., 1963.

GRAUBARD, M. *Circulation and Respiration: The Evolution of an Idea*. New York: Harcourt, Brace & World, Inc., 1964. (A book of quotations from original investigators with a commentary that shows how physiologists came to understand these processes. Fairly advanced.)

GRIFFIN, D. R. *Animal Structure and Function.* New York: Holt, Rinehart & Winston, Inc., 1962. (This short book is a good next step into animal physiology after the study of our Chapter 14.)

HODGSON, E. S. "Taste Receptors," *Scientific American,* May, 1961. Pp. 135–142.

HUNGATE, R. E. *Cellulose in Animal Nutrition.* (BSCS Pamphlet 22). Boston: D. C. Heath & Co., 1965.

LAKI, K. "The Clotting of Fibrinogen," *Scientific American,* March, 1962. Pp. 60–66.

MONTAGNA, W. "The Skin," *Scientific American,* February, 1965. Pp. 56–66.

RASMUSSEN, H. "The Parathyroid Hormone," *Scientific American,* April, 1961. Pp. 56–63.

RIEDMAN, S. R. *Our Hormones and How They Work.* New York: Collier Books, 1962. (A small book that explains endocrine function, primarily in man. Easy.)

SCHMIDT-NIELSEN, K. *Animal Physiology.* 2nd ed. Englewood Cliffs, N.J.: Prentice-Hall, Inc., 1964. (Concentrates on physiological steady state and the relation of animals to their environment. Lightly written but authoritative. Fairly easy.)

SIMPSON, G. G., and W. S. BECK. *Life: An Introduction to Biology.* 2nd ed. New York: Harcourt, Brace & World, Inc., 1965. Chapters 10–13. (Maintenance and coordination in organisms considered as general biological processes. All organisms—plants, animals, and protists—are discussed, but man is the focus of attention. Advanced.)

SUCKLING, E. E. *Bioelectricity.* (BSCS Pamphlet 4). Boston: D. C. Heath & Co., 1962.

ZUCKER, M. B. "Blood Platelets," *Scientific American,* February, 1961. Pp. 58–64.

# Behavior

## THE STUDY OF BEHAVIOR

The piano has been played for many kinds of audiences, but probably only a biologist would think to play the piano for earthworms. Yet at no time during his performance did this particular inquisitive English scientist — Charles Darwin — feel he was wasting his talent on the worms. He wanted to find out how earthworms behaved when they heard sounds.

Not satisfied with just playing the piano for the earthworms, he blew whistles and shouted. Broadening his studies, he breathed on the worms with a tobacco breath and held red-hot pokers near them. He jumped up and down on the lawn to see if they would retreat into their burrows. He fed them cabbage and onion to test their sense of taste. He sprinkled a field with chips of chalk and thirty years later dug up the field to see how deep the earthworms had buried the chalk. He carefully watched worms drag leaves into their burrows, then obtained some foreign tree leaves and some paper triangles to see if English earthworms could figure out how to maneuver these strange objects. For more than half of his busy lifetime, Darwin observed and was fascinated by the things that earthworms do — by their behavior.

maneuver: to move something about skillfully

### WHAT IS BEHAVIOR?

A botanist once startled his college students by taking them on a twenty-four hour "plant watch." At first the students were reluctant and unexcited about the investigation, because they assumed that plants didn't do anything. Before the end of the study, however, they had made so many question-arousing observations that they pleaded to continue their investigation of plant behavior another day.

In varying degrees, all living organisms—animals, plants, and protists—are doing something, are reacting to stimuli from their environment. Not all these reactions are covered by the term "behavior." Indeed, the word is defined in various ways by biologists, but the concept that it covers is not difficult to understand. When light is directed to a green plant, the plant begins to split water molecules in the light phase of photosynthesis. This is a reaction to a stimulus, but it is not behavior. If the light is directed at the plant from one side, the plant turns its leaves and growing tip toward the light—an easily visible reaction. This is behavior. A cat lies in the sun; muscles move its latest meal through its intestines. This is not behavior. A bird chirps nearby. Unless the cat is deaf, the receptors of the cat's ears react with an impulse to the brain. This is not behavior. The cat's drooping eyelids open, its ears rise, and its tail twitches. This is behavior.

Behavior involves more than the reaction of a cell (unless the individual is a single cell) or of an organ or even of a single organ system. It involves the whole individual, and it is directed toward the external environment of the individual. In considering behavior, we are returning to an external view of the organism. But in the three previous chapters it has become clear that what an organism as a whole *does* depends upon its internal functions—its physiology. In the past both physiologists and ecologists (or scientists with an ecological viewpoint) have contributed to the study of behavior. Today a special science of behavior seems to be developing.

### DIFFICULTIES IN BEHAVIORAL STUDIES

**Observation and experiment.** About a million and a half different species of living things are known to biologists; probably the behavior of no more than 0.1 percent of these has been carefully observed by biologists. At first it might seem that the observation of behavior would be easy. We all observe the behavior of our pets and of other animals, though few of us notice the behavior of plants or protists. But you learned early in this course (Investigation 1.1) that merely looking at or watching something is not necessarily scientific observation. And because behavior is action, observing it is especially difficult. Behavior often occurs so quickly that it is difficult for the observer to determine just what he has seen; paradoxically, in plants it may occur so slowly that the observer may have difficulty determining whether it has occurred at all. Motion pictures

Bert Kempers

Figure 15 · 1
Behavioral study in the field. Recording the voice of an elephant seal.

have helped to solve these difficulties and, at the same time, have provided a basis for the verification that is essential in science.

Where should behavior be observed—in the field or in the laboratory? Study in the field can be very difficult. The organisms that the biologist wishes to study may be hard to find. They may be difficult to observe when they are found; they may be difficult to approach and to keep under observation for a long enough period of time to provide reliable data. The mere presence of an observer may affect the behavior of many vertebrate animals.

In the laboratory organisms can be more easily watched, and the watching can be arranged so that they are unaware of the observer. In the laboratory a biologist can learn much about what an organism *can* do. But behavior in an artificial laboratory environment is not necessarily the same as behavior in a natural environment. A laboratory biologist may still remain ignorant of what an organism *will* do as a part of its ecosystem. And for some purposes such information is important—important, for example, to an understanding of population changes or to an understanding of a species' niche.

As in other branches of science, a behavioral biologist attempts whenever possible to test hypotheses by making observations under controlled conditions. Experiments may be performed either in laboratory or in field, but in field experiments the control of conditions is usually more difficult.

Behavioral scientists called *psychologists* usually do most of their experiments in laboratories, using rather few species

psychologists    [sī kŏl′ə j ĭsts; Greek: psyche, spirit, soul, + logos]

Paul Knipping

Figure 15 · 2

Behavioral study in the laboratory. The behavior of this rat is recorded by a camera on the tripod at the left.

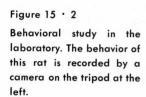

ethologists [ē thŏl'ə jĭsts; Greek: *ethos,* character, habit, + *logos*]

of organisms. Laboratory rats are their favorite subjects. Psychologists have a tendency to emphasize the physiological side of behavior. In the past three decades biologists with an ecological viewpoint also have turned their attention to behavior. These *ethologists* usually work in the field, and they have studied a wide array of organisms in natural ecosystems. Not only their methods are different, but also their concepts—they attach more importance to hereditary factors in explaining behavior than psychologists do. Psychologists and ethologists have sometimes disagreed greatly, but—as has happened before in the history of biology—with increase of knowledge, differences in viewpoint are being reconciled.

**Interpretation.** All biologists have difficulties in drawing conclusions from their data and especially in fitting their conclusions together with those of other investigators. This is the job of interpreting results, giving meaning to them. Behavioral scientists have some special difficulties.

We began this book with a rabbit *hiding* under a raspberry bush. How do we know it was hiding? Perhaps the rabbit was seeking shade or looking for food, or it might just have been resting.

Consider a laboratory experiment. We place on the side of a frog's body some substance that we think unpleasant. Immediately the frog moves its hind foot to rub at the spot where the substance was placed. Aha!, we think, the frog doesn't like the substance and is trying to rub it off. But how do we know that the frog isn't trying to rub it *in* because it enjoys the stuff? The interpretation of this behavior becomes even more perplexing if we destroy the frog's brain; the frog continues to bring its hind foot up to rub at its side. Without a brain, there can be no question of its "liking" or "not liking" the substance.

In observing behavior, we tend to put ourselves in the organism's place, to think that it sees and feels as we do, to explain behavior in human terms. We commonly say that a dog is "angry," a singing robin "happy," a purring cat "contented," a wide-eyed deer "frightened"—that the roots of a cactus are "searching" for water. But we don't know that other organisms have any of these human emotions. This is *anthropomorphism,* the interpretation of the behavior of other organisms as if they were human.

anthropomorphism [ăn'thrə pō- môr'fĭz əm; Greek: *anthropos,* man, + *morphe,* form]

The more we think we know about an organism, the more likely we are to interpret its behavior anthropomorphically. Only a little caution is required to rid ourselves of this way of thinking when studying the behavior of plants. But it is more difficult to resist anthropomorphism when we start to deal with motile organisms—and very difficult indeed when we study organisms that have obvious sense organs.

Behavioral scientists must constantly beware of anthropomorphic interpretations. This is especially difficult because they must discuss their findings in a human language. Human language is a product of the human brain and therefore reflects human ways of reacting to the environment. To use human language to describe and interpret the behavior of other species without introducing human viewpoints is probably impossible, but behavioral scientists try to minimize such viewpoints—and as a result their language often seems strange and obscure to nonscientists.

**Another difficulty.**    Take a walk with a dog. You and the dog go along the street or through the woods. You notice certain smells from freshly cut grass, from flowers, from automobile exhaust. But what a variety of smells there are for the dog, all to be sniffed carefully, all meaning

Figure 15 · 3

Different kinds of photographic films "see" the same scene differently, just as do different kinds of animal eyes. Here a flower garden is shown (*left*) somewhat as many mammals may see it and (*right*) as most insects and primates see it.

Haven Kolb (Both Photos)

something and yet completely unnoticed by you! You have great difficulty imagining the ability to follow the "smell trail" of an animal or man that has passed an hour or a day before. People live in a world that is primarily visual. Our

perceptual [pər sĕp'chŏŏ əl; Latin: *per*, through, + *capere*, to grasp]

perceptual world—what we perceive in our environment—is made up mostly of colors, shapes, and movements. Dogs lack color vision and do not distinguish shapes nearly as well as we do. And dogs hear sounds that we don't; this can be shown with dog whistles, which will call dogs home though we hear nothing.

Why do dogs often howl when certain musical instruments, such as violins and flutes, are played?

If it is difficult to understand the perceptual world of a dog, a fellow mammal with which we live closely, how much more difficult it is to understand the world of a bird, lizard, fish, bee, ant, or octopus. Yet, if we are going to understand the behavior of any organism, we have to know what it perceives in its environment.

Therefore, in studying the behavior of any organism, it is important to determine what kinds of receptors it has and how sensitive they are. Since man often does not perceive stimuli that affect other organisms, a biologist must frequently depend on instruments that can translate things he can't perceive into things he can. Flowers that look white to him may have patterns of color to bees, because bees see by ultraviolet light—light of a wavelength that is invisible to human eyes. He can "see" what the bee sees only by taking photographs with film sensitive to such wavelengths. Similarly, instruments can translate sounds that men cannot hear into lines on a piece of paper; then the biologist can study the characteristics of the sounds even though he cannot hear them.

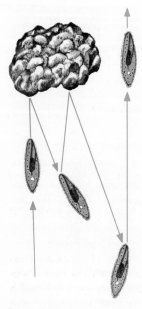

Figure 15 · 4

A *Paramecium* meets an obstacle. How would you describe this behavior? × 60

irritability [ĭr'ə tə bĭl'ə tĭ]

## LEVELS OF BEHAVIOR

All organisms have behavior. *Irritability*, the ability to respond to stimuli, seems to be one of the fundamental characteristics of living substance. This ability allows even the simplest organism to adapt to changes in its environment. But some organisms have differentiated special cells, tissues, or organs in which this fundamental ability is specialized. In general, the greater this differentiation, the more complex the behavior is. Therefore, one way to study behavior is to compare different levels of behavioral complexity.

### BEHAVIOR INVOLVING NO NERVOUS SYSTEM

A slime mold engulfs food particles but flows around inorganic particles; that is, it responds differentially to objects in its environment, just as you respond differentially to a doughnut and a rubber band. But the protist accomplishes this behavior without any nerve receptors or brain or muscles. Many protists show such selectivity in response to objects in their environment.

If a ciliate of the genus *Vorticella* is touched lightly, it usually contracts its stalk. If the stimulus is continued, however, the organism seems to become accustomed to it. If a *Vorticella* is repeatedly touched, it responds in a variety of ways: it may bend away; it may reverse the direction in which its cilia are beating; it may contract; it may even swim away. Thus, the behavior of *Vorticella* is variable.

These protists have no nerve cells or any other cellular differentiation, but they show two characteristics of behavior—selectivity and variability. Plants also lack nerve cells, but they, too, show some basic behavioral characteristics. In general, however, reactions of protists are rapid and reactions of plants are slow.

**Tropisms.** In bryophytes and tracheophytes most behavior is closely associated with growth. We have already studied the behavior called phototropism. There are many such *tropisms*, but in each of them a plant part turns toward (positive) or away from (negative) a stimulus. The phototropism of stems is positive—the stem turns *toward* the light. The *geotropism* of stems is negative, but the geotropism of roots is positive.

Though tropisms represent a somewhat fixed kind of behavior, they are not entirely invariable. The responses sometimes vary with differences in the intensity of the stimulus. Bermuda grass is positively phototropic to weak light but negatively phototropic to strong light.

**Taxes.** Tropisms are responses in sessile organisms. In motile organisms, similar responses are called *taxes* (singular, "taxis"). In a taxis the whole organism moves toward or

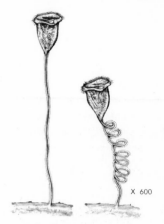

X 600

Figure 15 · 5

*Vorticella:* an individual in feeding position (*left*); same individual after a light touch (*right*).

Vorticella [vôr'tĭ sĕl'ə]

geotropism [jē ŏ'trə pĭz'əm; Greek: *gea,* the earth, + *tropos,* a turning]

taxes [tăk'sēz; Greek: *tassein,* to arrange]

Figure 15 · 6

Leaves of a plant of the genus *Mimosa* as they normally appear (*left*) and a short time after being touched (*right*). How do you think an organism without muscles can perform this response?

Paul Knipping (Both Photos)

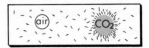

**Figure 15 · 7**

Behavior of small populations of *Paramecium* in response to five environmental stimuli. Using the terms in the text, describe the behavior in each case.

A — Reaction to a drop of 0.5% salt solution.

C — Reaction to a piece of filter paper.

B — Reaction to a drop of weak acetic acid.

D — Reactions to a bubble of air and a bubble of $CO_2$.

away from the source of a stimulus. The kinds of stimuli are quite similar for tropisms and taxes. A *Euglena*, for example, is positively *phototactic*. Near its anterior end is a spot of pigment sensitive to light — a kind of receptor. As *Euglena* swims, its body rotates so that the pigment spot detects the direction of illumination. Somehow this information is transmitted to the flagellum, which then directs the organism toward the light.

## INVESTIGATION 15.1

### TROPIC RESPONSES IN PLANTS

#### MATERIALS AND EQUIPMENT
(for each team)

*Part A*

    Soaked corn grains, 4
    Petri dish
    Cotton
    Scissors
    Heavy blotting paper
    Scotch tape
    Glass-marking crayon

*Part B*

    Flowerpots, about 8 cm in diameter, 4
    Cardboard boxes, at least 5 cm higher than
        flowerpots, 4
    Scissors
    Red cellophane
    Paste
    Blue cellophane
    Scotch tape
    Soil
    Radish seeds, 40

*Part C*

    Test tubes, 25 × 200 mm, 4
    One-hole stoppers, to fit test tubes, 4
    Shoots of *Zebrina*, about 20 cm long, 4
    Melted paraffin in a beaker
    Small brush
    Glass-marking crayon
    Ring stand
    Burette clamps, 4

#### PROCEDURE

• Study the procedure for each part and state a hypothesis appropriate for each. (1)

**Part A.** Place four soaked corn grains in the bottom half of a petri dish. Arrange them cotyledon side down, as shown in Figure 15 · 8. Fill the spaces between the corn grains with wads of cotton to a depth slightly greater than the thickness of the grains. Cut a piece of heavy blotting paper slightly larger than

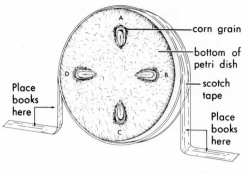

corn grain

bottom of petri dish

scotch tape

Place books here

Place books here

Figure 15 · 8

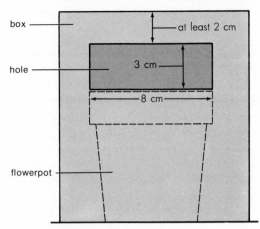

box

at least 2 cm

hole

3 cm

8 cm

flowerpot

Figure 15 · 9

the bottom of the petri dish. Fit it snugly over the grains and the cotton. Hold the dish on its edge and observe the grains through the bottom. If they do not stay in place, repack with more cotton. When the grains are secure in the dish, wet the blotting paper thoroughly. Seal the two halves of the petri dish together with strips of scotch tape.

Place the dish on edge in a location that receives dim light. Rotate the dish until one of the corn grains is at the top. Using a glass-marking crayon, write an *A* on the dish beside the topmost grain; then, proceeding clockwise, label the other grains *B*, *C*, and *D*. Fasten the dish to the table or bench with a long strip of tape, as shown in Figure 15 · 8. If further support is needed, stack books on top of the tape and against the edges of the dish. Do not change the position of the dish until the experiment is completed.

When the grains begin to germinate, make sketches daily for five days, showing the directions in which the root and the shoot grow from each grain.

**Part B.** Number four cardboard boxes *1* to *4* and label each with your team symbol. Turn the boxes bottom side up. Cut a rectangular hole in one side of each of three boxes; use the dimensions shown in Figure 15 · 9. Tape a strip of red cellophane over the hole

in Box 1. Tape a strip of blue cellophane over the hole in Box 2. Leave the hole in Box 3 uncovered. Do not cut a hole in Box 4.

Using a pencil, number four flowerpots *1* to *4* and label each with your team symbol. Fill the pots with soil. In each pot plant ten radish seeds about 0.5 cm deep and 2 cm apart. Press the soil down firmly over the seeds and water the pots. Place the pots in a location that receives strong light but not direct sunlight. Cover each pot with the box bearing its number. Turn the box sides having the holes toward the light. Once each day remove the boxes and water the pots. (Caution: Do not move the pots; be sure to place the boxes back in the same position after each watering!)

When most of the radish seedlings have been above ground for two or three days, record the direction of stem growth in each pot: upright, curved slightly, or curved greatly—and if curved, tell in what direction with respect to the hole in the box.

**Part C.** Fill four test tubes with water and insert a one-hole stopper firmly into each tube. Remove all leaves within 8 cm of the cut ends of four *Zebrina* shoots. Push the cut end of each shoot

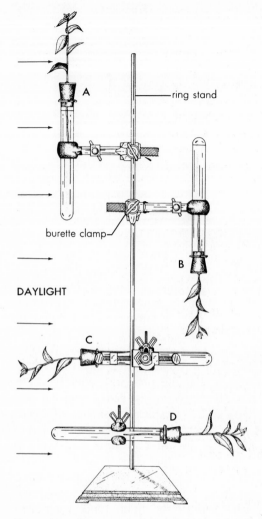

**Figure 15 · 10**

one side. Observe the shoots daily for about a week.

### STUDYING THE DATA

Consider first the data from Part A. • From which end of the grains did the roots grow? (2)   • Did the roots of all grains eventually turn in one direction? If so, what was the direction? (3) • From which end of the grains did the shoots grow? (4)   • Did the shoots of all four grains eventually turn in one direction? (5)   • To what stimulus did the corn roots seem to be responding? Was the response positive or negative? (6)   • To what stimulus did the corn shoots seem to be responding? Was the response positive or negative? (7)

Now consider the data from Part B. • In which pot were the stems nearest to perpendicular? (8)   • Were the stems curved in one direction in any pot? (9) • If so, in which pot, and in what direction? If not, in what direction did *most* of the stems curve? (10)

Finally, consider the data from Part C. • Did any shoots grow without bending? If so, which ones? (11)   • Did any shoots bend as they grew? If so, which ones bent? (12)   • If you noticed any bending, in what direction did it occur in each case? (13)

### CONCLUSIONS

• For each of the hypotheses that you formed at the beginning of the investigation, state as precise a conclusion as your data will allow. (14)

### FOR FURTHER INVESTIGATION

Will centrifugal force overcome the response of plant parts to gravity? To test this idea, you may mount the setup used in Part A on the turntable of a phonograph.

through a stopper until about 5 cm of the shoot is in water. Seal tubes, stoppers, and shoots by applying melted paraffin with a brush. (Caution: The paraffin should be no warmer than is necessary to keep it liquid.) Using a glass-marking crayon, label the tubes *A*, *B*, *C*, and *D*. Attach a burette clamp to each tube; fasten the tubes to a ring stand in the positions shown in Figure 15 · 10. Place the entire assembly in a location that receives bright light from

## BEHAVIOR INVOLVING NERVOUS SYSTEMS

Except for sponges, all animals have differentiated nerve cells (pages 517–519). All organisms that have nerve cells also have differentiated muscle cells—usually organized into tissues or systems that have specialized ability to contract and so bring about movement. The combination of specialized nerve and muscle cells so greatly supplements the responses possible through general irritability and hormones that some biologists restrict use of the term "behavior" to animals that possess such cells.

### INNATE BEHAVIOR

When a male moth emerges from its cocoon, it flies unhesitatingly toward the source of the odor produced by a female of its species. The first time that a tree squirrel encounters a nut, it attempts to bury it—even if it has never seen another squirrel do so and if the nut is lying on the floor of a cage rather than on the ground. Young spiders without any previous experience weave webs as well constructed as those of older spiders.

These are examples of unlearned, *innate*, behavior; they are actions that seem to be inherited just as structures are inherited. Behavior that is brought forth by a particular stimulus in almost all individuals of a species, even in those without any previous experience, is usually considered innate. In tests of such behavior, animals are hatched in isolation; whatever these animals do, they do without following another animal's example. But with mammals there is always at least some chance of learning from the mother, so it is difficult to determine what part of their learning is innate.

innate [in āt'; Latin: *in*, in, + *natus*, born]

Some innate behavior is simply a matter of reflex (pages 519–520. But the behavior of the newly emerged male moth is more complex than a reflex, because many muscles must work in coordination to produce flight. This behavior may be called a taxis, though it is certainly more complex than the taxes in protists.

The behavior of the squirrel with a nut is still more complex; certain muscles must be used in digging, others in pushing the nut into a hole, and others in covering it. Moreover, these actions must be performed in the correct sequence. The construction of a spider web requires even more complex behavior. Yet evidence shows that all these are innate behaviors. They have been called *instincts* or *fixed-action patterns*. The first term is older, but some behavioral scientists think that it is no longer useful because too many false ideas have grown up around it. But the second

Winston Pote from A. Devaney

**Figure 15 · 11**

Any light tap on the side of the nest causes nestlings of many birds to react in the way shown here. This behavior seems to be innate.

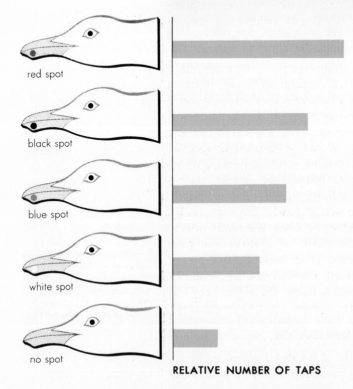

red spot

black spot

blue spot

white spot

no spot

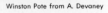

**RELATIVE NUMBER OF TAPS**

**Figure 15 · 12**

Herring-gull nestlings tap at a red spot on the bill of the parent; the parent then feeds them. An ethologist presented different cardboard models (*left*) to newly hatched chicks and recorded the results (*right*). Can you draw any conclusion about this behavior?

Figure 15 · 13
During the nesting season a male European robin raises his head and puffs out his red breast whenever he encounters another male. Here an ethologist has placed a tuft of red feathers in a tree. Without anthropomorphism can you explain the reaction of the bird?

X 1/3

term is somewhat misleading because the behavior is not entirely "fixed," that is, invariable. All behavior depends on an organism as well as a stimulus. A sick squirrel or one that is merely tired may pay no attention to a nut. And spiders to which certain drugs have been given weave very poor webs.

Much behavior, especially behavior of invertebrates, can be classed as instinctive. But this, of course, does not *explain* the behavior. It is necessary for physiologists to explore the nervous and hormonal mechanisms that operate such behavior. And psychologists analyze such behavior by experimental interruptions of the action sequence making up an instinctive behavior.

Many ethologists have been interested in the stimuli that start the chains of physiological reactions in fixed-action patterns. They have found that the stimulus for a complex behavior pattern is often very simple. Such a stimulus —called a *releaser*—acts like a key that unlocks the whole physiological sequence. Like a key, a releaser is specific; only a particular releaser stimulus starts a particular behavior pattern. For example, red-winged blackbirds become very disturbed when a hawk flies over their marsh. But the releaser is not the actual hawk. Experimentally, blackbirds became disturbed even when shown a moving piece of cardboard cut in the shape of a hawk. But when birds were shown a cardboard hawk model moving over them tail first, they exhibited no disturbance reaction. Evidently the tail-first shape was not the right "key" to initiate disturbance behavior.

One flock showed disturbance behavior the first time a plane flew over their marsh. Do you think they would have behaved the same for a helicopter? A balloon? Why or why not?

### LEARNED BEHAVIOR

The nut-burying behavior of squirrels seems to be innate; so, too, is nut opening. A young squirrel opens a nut

**Figure 15 · 14**
Chaffinch.

Just because it is possible, is it *necessary* to do so? Look up "Lloyd Morgan's canon" in Simpson and Beck. See also our page 631.

satisfactorily; but as the squirrel becomes older and more experienced, its efficiency at opening nuts increases greatly. Chaffinches reared from hatching in soundproof rooms develop a song pattern basically like that of wild chaffinches. But the songs never develop all of the notes of the wild song unless the birds are allowed to hear the wild song. Evidently the song pattern is innate, but something is added to the innate behavior during the life of the birds. Both squirrels and birds *learn* behavior.

**What is learning?** This is not easy to describe precisely. Learning depends on the experiences of an individual, and it usually brings about a lasting change in behavior. We must say that learning brings about a "lasting" rather than a "permanent" change in behavior, because forgetting occurs in learned behavior—as every student knows. But some kinds of lasting changes in behavior occur simply as a part of an organism's development. For example, when a tadpole's legs develop and its tail disappears, the change in behavior (from tail swimming to leg swimming) is clearly associated with a change in structure. In other cases it is extremely difficult to determine whether changes in behavior depend on learning or merely on structural development. Isn't experience, practice—that is, learning—necessary before a child can climb stairs? An experiment was tried with identical twins—twins with exactly the same heredity, in whom the rate of development should be the same. At an early age one twin was allowed much practice on stairs; the other was kept on flat surfaces and given no experience with stairs. Yet, when the second was finally allowed to climb stairs, his performance was about as good as that of his experienced twin.

**Do all animals learn?** Thus far, in all experiments with sponges, coelenterates, and echinoderms, it seems possible to explain their behavior without assuming that learning has occurred. But in flatworms there is no doubt that a simple kind of learning does occur. Unlike the other animals mentioned, a flatworm has an anterior end and a posterior end, with a bilaterally symmetrical nervous system and an anterior ganglion (Figure 14 · 26). There may be something about such a structural development that favors the learning process. At least, animals of other phyla in which learning occurs also have central controlling ganglia.

A flatworm does not learn very easily, nor does it learn very much. There is a wide variation in the abilities of different animals to learn. Many kinds of beetles, if put on a tabletop, will crawl to the edge and fall off; and no matter how many times this happens, they never learn about the edge of the table. At the other extreme is the case of a young pilot whale that was captured a few years ago by collectors from Marineland of the Pacific, a large aquarium. When they finally got the whale into a tank, it attempted to dive. It struck its snout on the bottom and thereafter refused to leave the surface. One experience was enough.

**Imprinting.**    Most learning requires more than a single experience. In the 1930's, however, Konrad Lorenz discovered a kind of learning in birds that depends on just one experience—but that experience must come shortly after hatching. Geese follow the first moving object they see after hatching. Normally this is their mother. But geese hatched in an incubator followed Dr. Lorenz. Afterward they behaved toward him as though he were the female goose. He was *imprinted* in the experience of the goslings as "mother."

Konrad Lorenz [lōr′ənz]: 1903————. Austrian biologist and one of the first ethologists

Imprinting resembles the action of a releaser. But the particular stimulus is not recognized innately—it must be learned. Much experimentation has shown that in many cases, the first moving object that a young bird or fish sees later releases many reactions that normally are released by the presence of a parent. This is particularly true if the object also gives appropriate sounds—quacking, in the case of ducks, for instance. If imprinting can be called learning, it is a very simple kind, closely related to innate behavior.

**Conditioning.**    Imprinting was discovered by an ethologist. Conditioning was discovered much earlier by a physiologist. Ivan P. Pavlov was interested in the physiology of mammalian nervous systems. He began to study the reflex involved in the production of saliva in dogs and soon found that the odor or sight of meat was sufficient to start salivation. Pavlov wondered whether other stimuli would produce the salivation response. Just before presenting meat to a dog, he rang a bell. This procedure was repeated many times with the same dog. Before long the dog was beginning to secrete saliva as soon as the bell was rung, before the meat was presented. Eventually Pavlov found that the dog could be made to salivate merely by the ringing of the bell, entirely without the stimulus of the meat. This kind of learning—the transfer of a reflex response from one stimulus to another—is called *conditioning*.

Ivan P. Pavlov [ï vän′ päv′lôf]: 1849–1936. Russian physiologist

Pavlov extended his research in many directions. He showed that the substitute stimulus must come *before* the original stimulus if the response is to be transferred. He also showed that the shorter the time interval between the two stimuli, the quicker the reaction becomes associated with the substitute stimulus. Later biologists have extended Pavlov's principles to other animals, including man.

**Trial-and-error learning.**    In conditioning, the learner is a passive subject. More complicated kinds of learning require movement by the learner. All animals make many kinds of movements. Learning begins when an animal associates certain movements with favorable or unfavorable results. Thus, experimentally, *trial-and-error* learning involves either "rewards" or "punishments," or both.

B. F. Skinner: 1904——. American psychologist

B. F. Skinner has devised a box for investigating trial-and-error learning. A bar in the box releases a pellet of food when pressed. A hungry rat, placed in the box, moves about at random and sooner or later strikes the bar. Before long most rats associate pressing the bar with the reward of food. This device has been used to investigate many questions about learning. For example, what happens if the food pellet is not released after the rat has learned to obtain it by pressing the bar? What happens if the pellet is released sometimes but not always? (If you are curious, refer to Scott's *Animal Behavior,* listed on page 575.)

With any animal that is capable of locomotion, learning can be studied by means of a maze. Basically, a maze is a route with one or more choices of turns leading to a goal that is favorable or unfavorable to the animal. The simplest form is the T maze. How can we know that learning has occurred in a maze? With a T maze we expect that by chance 50 percent of the turns will be to the right and 50 percent to the left. If, after several trials, the animal turns to the right (where food is located) 90 percent of the time and to the left only 10 percent of the time, we might conclude that it has learned. In more complicated mazes, time may be used as a basis for conclusions. At first, an animal

But suppose it went 80 percent leftward, what would your conclusion be? 70 percent? 60 percent?

**Figure 15 · 15**

A learning experiment. Three groups of rats were tested daily in a maze. The route through the maze forked 14 times, and none of the choices could be repeated. The number of errors in choice was counted for each rat, and an average obtained for each group. How do you interpret the results?

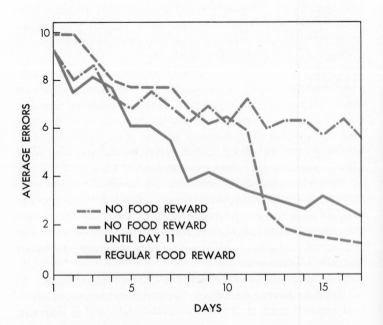

NO FOOD REWARD

NO FOOD REWARD UNTIL DAY 11

REGULAR FOOD REWARD

AVERAGE ERRORS

DAYS

explores blind alleys; as it "learns" the maze, fewer and fewer trips are made down the blind alleys, and the time to reach the "reward" is reduced.

### REASONING

It is difficult to describe what we mean by "reasoning." The process involves situations in which specific stimuli are lacking and trial and error has a very minor part. Perhaps reasoning is best described in an example. In Figure 15 · 16 the raccoon cannot quite reach the food by going directly toward it. First it must go back around stake B. Given enough time, almost any active animal accomplishes the task by trial and error. In this way raccoons learn quickly. But the test of reasoning hinges not on how *quickly* the animal learns by trial and error but on what the animal does on the *first* exposure to the problem.

Figure 15 · 16
A problem.

Put in the raccoon's place, what would you do? You would immediately "size up the situation," walk back around stake B, and reach the food. Chimpanzees and most monkeys do the same thing. This behavior is often described as resulting from *insight*. Many primates apparently do not see A, B, C, and the rope as separate items but as parts of a whole situation—the "meaning" is in the situation, not in the items.

In another kind of experiment, an animal is allowed to watch the experimenter place food under one of two identical cups. After a delay, the animal is released to find the

**Figure 15 · 17**

Another problem—and its solution by a primate. How would you describe this behavior?

food. (Of course, odor must be controlled in such an experiment.) Animals such as rats, cats, and dogs fix their attention on the cup covering the food and go directly to it. But if their attention is temporarily diverted, they do no better than would be expected on the basis of chance. Most primates, however, do not seem to fix their attention on the cup under which the food is placed. Indeed, even if they are removed from the situation and then brought back later, they still go immediately to the correct cup. Does the nonhuman primate mind form some lasting image, such as

Marineland of Florida

"food under right-hand cup"? If so, this behavior closely approaches the language-based behavior of man.

Non-primates apparently do not have insight. Some, such as raccoons, learn quickly, and even an octopus can learn to go around barriers. Often observations of wild animals reveal behavior that seems to demonstrate insight, but of course such behavior may be merely the result of past experience.

Figure 15 · 18

Porpoises learn many things very easily. Is this what we mean by "intelligence"?

## INVESTIGATION 15.2

## BEHAVIOR OF
## AN INVERTEBRATE ANIMAL

### BACKGROUND INFORMATION

Sow bugs and pill bugs are terrestrial crustaceans, relatives of crabs and shrimp. Because they breathe by means of specialized gills and have no way to prevent evaporation of water from their bodies, they must live in habitats where relative humidity remains fairly high. Even in many dry climates such a condition exists under rocks, boards, and logs and in damp leaf litter. Here the animals can frequently be found.

### PURPOSE

Using live sow bugs or pill bugs, you will investigate reactions to different stimuli and then use one kind of stimulus to test the animals' learning ability.

### MATERIALS AND EQUIPMENT
#### (for a team of four)

*Part A*

One-pound coffee can with plastic lid

Mixture of moist soil and leaf litter

Sponge, a cube 2 cm on a side

Carrot or potato

Sow bugs or pill bugs, 10–12

Nail, 8-penny, 1

Glass or metal tray, about 20 × 30 cm

Blotting paper, about 20 × 15 cm

Laboratory desk lamps, 2

Masking tape

*Part B*

Small vials with plastic lids, 4

Mixture of moist soil and leaf litter

Paper towel

Carrot or potato

Glass-marking crayon

Sow bugs or pill bugs, 4

Box, about 10 × 15 × 2 cm, all plastic or with plastic cover

Cardboard, about 12 × 12 cm

Scissors

Roll of masking tape

Laboratory desk lamp

Forceps

### PROCEDURE

**Part A.** Each team will set up a coffee-can terrarium as follows: Place moist soil and leaf litter in the can to a level two-thirds of the distance from bottom to top. Place a few dead leaves on the surface. Add a small piece of moistened sponge and a slice (about 2 × 5 × 1 cm) of carrot or potato. Put in ten to twelve sow bugs or pill bugs and cover with a plastic lid into which 6–8 holes have been punched with a nail. The animals can be kept in the container indefinitely if the sponge is kept moist and the carrot or potato slice is changed every few days.

In subdued light, place all the sow bugs in the center of a large tray. Observe group behavior. • Do the animals tend to remain together? If not, do they wander about aimlessly, or do they move in one direction? (1)

Remove the animals gently and place some moist blotting paper at one end of the tray so that half the bottom is dry and the other half is covered by the moist paper. Place all the animals in the center of the dry end of the tray. Observe the animals for several minutes. • What percentage of the animals remain at the dry half of the tray? (2) • If some animals move to the moist end, do they climb on top of the blotter or move underneath it? (3) • When individuals move, do they move faster in the dry half or in the moist half of the tray? (4) If some animals move under the blotter, wait about five minutes and then pick the blotter up. Observe the distribution of animals on its underside. • Do they tend to be uniformly distributed, or are they clustered in groups? (5)  Make note of any other behavior that you observe.

Set up two lamps of equal intensity about 50 cm apart. Place a sow bug or pill bug equidistant from the two lamps and about 20 cm from the imaginary line running between them.  • If the animal moves, sketch its route in relation to the two lamps. (6) Repeat this several times. Now cover the animal's right eye with a tiny piece of masking tape and repeat the procedure. Again sketch the route in several trials.  • Is there any consistent difference in the routes under the two conditions? (7)  • To what stimulus is the animal reacting? (8)

**Part B.**  Mark four vials *A, B, C,* and *D;* add your team symbol to each vial. Half fill each with moist soil and leaf litter. Add a spiraled strip of moist paper toweling and a small piece of potato or carrot. Into each vial place one sow bug or pill bug. Perforate the lids and cover the vials. Using a plastic-topped cardboard or all-plastic box, prepare a T maze as shown in Figure 15·19. Use strips of cardboard for the inner walls, holding them in place with masking tape. Cut one hole in the box wall at the base of the T and one at the end of each T arm. Place a lamp directly above the T base but do not turn it on.

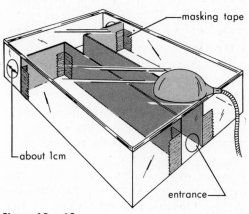

—masking tape

—about 1cm

entrance—

Figure 15 · 19

Place Animal A into the maze through the hole at the base of the T and cover the hole with masking tape. Turn on the lamp.  • How does the animal react? (9)  When the animal reaches the crossarm of the T, it usually will turn in one direction or the other. Note the direction. When it reaches an end of the T bar, remove it immediately and repeat the "test run." Make a total of five "test runs," recording the direction of turn each time. Then return the animal to its vial. Follow the same procedure with Animal B, Animal C, and Animal D. While you are working with the latter animals, Animal A is "resting." Now make five more "trial runs" with each animal, in the same order.

The next day repeat the whole procedure. You should now have the results of twenty trials for each animal. Tabulate the results for each animal, and record on its vial *L* (for consistent left-turner), *R* (for consistent right-turner), or *B* (for an animal that turns in either direction without consistency).

You are now ready to train your animals. Use only the L and R animals. Start with any one of them. Place a lamp at the end of the T arm down which it consistently turned. Do not turn the lamp on yet. Place the animal in the maze as before; but when it reaches the T bar, turn on the light.  • What is the animal's reaction? (10)  Remove the animal from the maze and replace it in its vial. Carry out this procedure with each individual, shifting the location of the light so that it is always at the side of the T arm down which that individual consistently turned during the "trial runs." Then go back to the first individual and repeat the procedure. Continue until each individual has been given ten runs.

Repeat the whole training procedure each day for at least three days. When training has been completed, test each individual in the maze once *without using a light.* Record the direction in which each animal turned.

## DISCUSSION

**Part A.**  • Can the behavior of your animals with respect to moisture be related to their survival? If so, how? (11) • Can the behavior of your animals with respect to light be related to their survival? If so, how? (12)  In Chapter 4 a term was used to describe a structure that seemed to fit an organism to its environment.  • What term might you use to describe the behavior you have observed in this investigation? (13)

Review the discussion of levels of behavior.  • Which term best fits the behavior you have observed? (14)  • What additional information would increase your confidence in your decision? (15)

**Part B.**  • What kind of learning was the procedure used in this investigation designed to produce? (16)  • Did you obtain any evidence of learning in the animals with which you worked? If so, what was the evidence? (17)  • If you obtained evidence of learning in the species, did all individuals learn equally well? (18)  • Do you think that individual differences in ability to learn would have any effect on a population of the animals? (19)

## FOR FURTHER INVESTIGATION

In Chapter 8 it was pointed out that a biologist investigating tolerances has difficulty separating the effects of one factor from the effects of another. In Part A of this investigation the same problem is encountered with respect to stimuli. Criticize the procedure used and then try to design a procedure that would better separate the effects of the stimuli involved.

## SOME PATTERNS OF ANIMAL BEHAVIOR

We have been discussing behavior from the viewpoint of its mechanisms—how it is started and how it is performed. To many biologists another viewpoint is more important: how behavior functions in the survival of individuals and of species. From this viewpoint, the kinds of behavior are so varied that they are difficult to classify. There is behavior associated with adjustment to factors in the abiotic environment—heat, humidity, salinity, for example. There is behavior associated with food-getting, with escape from enemies, with reproduction. None of these kinds of behavior have been fully studied for any species. The study of behavior is a young science.

Rather than attempt a brief glance at many parts of behavioral science, we will restrict the rest of this chapter to a somewhat longer consideration of a few. We will proceed from an aspect of behavior in which attention is primarily upon the reactions of an individual organism, to an aspect in which attention is primarily upon interactions among a group of individuals.

## PERIODICITY IN BEHAVIOR

Almost everyone has observed that many activities of plants and animals do not occur continuously but rather at regular times in each twenty-four hour day. Many birds sing mostly around sunrise. Flowers of some species of plants open in the morning and close at night; those of other species open in the evening. Most species of moths fly at night and rest by day; most butterflies behave in the opposite way.

Most people assume that these daily cycles in activities are the direct result of day and night. To some extent this may be true, but experimentation has shown that it is not entirely true. In 1729 a French scientist took plants deep into a mine. He discovered that for several days (while the plants were still healthy) the leaf movements were very similar to those under natural conditions of day and night. These observations strongly indicated that something within the plant, not something in the environment, was causing these movements to take place.

As so often happens in biology, scientists of the time failed to recognize the importance of these observations. It was not until more than two hundred years later that a German botanist, Erwin Bünning, on the basis of his own investigations and those of others, was able to convincingly support them. He showed that in many organisms — not only plants but animals and protists also — some behavior occurred periodically without regard to changes of light and dark — a kind of innate rhythm of behavior.

Erwin Bünning: 1906——

Figure 15·21 shows the feeding activity of a white-crowned sparrow held under constant conditions (continuous light and uniform temperature). In each twenty-four hour period (a natural day) the bird began to eat about

Hal H. Harrison from National Audubon Society

Figure 15 · 20
White-crowned sparrow.

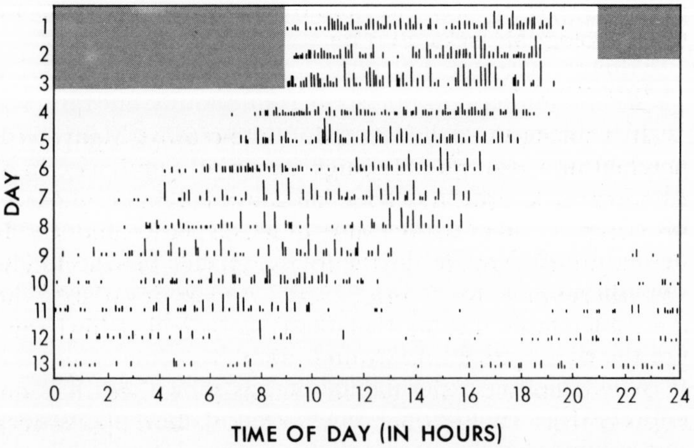

Figure 15 · 21

Feeding activity of a white-crowned sparrow. Shading shows dark periods before the experiment under continuous lighting began. Heights of bars indicate amounts of food consumed each time the bird ate.

TIME OF DAY (IN HOURS)

circadian [sûr′kā′dĭ ən; Latin: circum, around, + dies, day]

one-half hour earlier. He therefore had a periodicity in feeding behavior of about twenty-three and one-half hours. Similar demonstrations have been made with a large variety of organisms and a large variety of activities—for example: leaf movements in plants; cell division in some protists; change in human body temperatures; times of activity in birds, mammals, and insects; changes in metabolic rates in some tissues. Almost all these periodicities turn out to be only approximately twenty-four hours long. They are therefore now referred to as *circadian rhythms.*

Circadian rhythms are innate. But under environmental conditions that provide a light-dark cycle, the rhythms conform to the cycle—the innate mechanism is modified by stimuli from the environment. Thus, under a twenty-four hour light-dark cycle, the feeding rhythm of a white-crowned sparrow becomes a precise twenty-four hour feeding rhythm. This rhythm can adjust to other light-dark cycles. But there are limits. The rhythm cannot conform to a cycle consisting of nine hours of light and nine hours of darkness.

Although details differ in different species, most organisms can readjust circadian periodicities to a new light-dark cycle in a few days. In this era of jet-airplane travel, the problem of adjustment is quite important to man. Consider a traveler who flies by jet airplane from San Francisco to London. At first his circadian rhythms—his "biological clock"—tend to retain San Francisco time. When he appears at a meeting in London at 10:00 A.M., his "biological clock" is still very close to 2:00 A.M., San Francisco time, and he is likely to be an extremely sleepy participant in the meeting. Therefore, persons attending important meetings at places many degrees of longitude distant frequently plan to arrive several days in advance in order to permit their "biological clocks" to reset.

## TERRITORIALITY

It is spring in Alaska. A male white-crowned sparrow is perched in a low tree. He sings. Again and again he sings. Another male appears. Immediately the first male leaves his perch and flies to the bush in which the second sits. If the second does not leave, the first approaches more closely, and there may be a brief fight. Almost invariably the newcomer loses the fight and leaves. The first bird then returns to his perch and resumes singing.

After repeated observation we begin to see that the behavior occurs only when a second male bird approaches within certain limits, that often a second male avoids the vicinity of the conspicuous singing male, and that the presence of a female does not stimulate the same behavior from the singing male.

These Alaskan white-crowned sparrows spend the winter in California. There males and females flock together. At night two males may sit side by side on a roosting perch. There is little or no singing.

In 1920 Eliot Howard published a book in which he described his observations of birds nesting in his garden and orchard. By carefully watching the movements of individual birds, Howard discovered that each male tended to remain within a limited area that was strongly defended against intrusions by other birds of the same species. He interpreted the constant singing of the newly arrived males in the spring as a way of warning other males that particular areas—territories—were already occupied.

Since 1920 many studies of *territoriality* have been made. At first most of the studies were made on birds, and one of the first problems that arose was: How can we explain the change in behavior between summer and winter? By years of experiment with captive birds and years of investigation in the field, some progress has been made toward understanding this problem.

First consider a male white-crowned sparrow in late winter. The days are becoming longer. The lengthening hours of daylight somehow affect the bird's hypothalamus. This, in turn, somehow causes the anterior pituitary to begin releasing the hormones that cause gradual growth and development of the testes. At the same time the hypothalamus stimulates the production of other hormones. These increase the bird's appetite and he takes in more calories than are required for his daily activities in the wintering flock; the excess calories are stored as fat. The

Why would readjustment of the "biological clock" not be necessary on a trip from New York to Santiago, Chile?

Eliot   Howard:   1873–1940. British naturalist

Are "defended" and "warning" anthropomorphic terms? If you think so, can you suggest any better wording?

territoriality   [tĕr′ə tŏr′ĭ ăl′ə tĭ; Latin: *terra*, land]

560

Figure 15 · 22

In herring gulls, only the immediate vicinity of the nest is "defended." This territorial dispute does not affect birds nesting only a few meters away.

combination of these (and perhaps other) hormonal activities brings about nocturnal migratory flights northward. When the reserve of fat is used up, the bird interrupts his migration and restores it.

By the time the male reaches the breeding ground, his testes are producing male sex hormones. One effect of these hormones—together with the sight of the breeding area —is to cause territorial behavior. The response of the bird to another male is completely different from his response a few weeks earlier in the wintering or migratory flock.

As the year proceeds, the days cease to lengthen. The internal mechanism that responded to the lengthening days of spring is insensitive to the long days of June and the shortened days that follow. The hypothalamus no longer causes the anterior pituitary to release hormones affecting the testes. The testes thus shrink in size and discontinue the production of male sex hormones. Without the effect of male sex hormones on the central nervous system, the territorial reaction to other males disappears. Males abandon their territories and assemble with females and young in flocks that move southward.

Territorial behavior appears to have value for the survival of organisms. Animals placed in unfamiliar surroundings have poor chances of avoiding predators; but a territory becomes a familiar area. After the territories are established, little actual fighting usually occurs. Hence individuals have more time and energy to devote to other aspects of daily life. In the kind of territoriality represented by white-crowned sparrows, the conspicuous singing by male birds may increase the chances that unmated females will locate mates. In this kind of territory, also, an area is reserved from which food may be gathered to feed the young. Thus territorial behavior may restrict the size of a breeding population to the number of pairs whose young can be supported by the available food supply.

The territory described for white-crowned sparrows is only one of many kinds now recognized: some are places for mating, some are for nesting, some are for feeding, and others are for various combinations of these activities. The essential fact about a territory is that it is defended — most often by males, sometimes by females, sometimes by mated pairs, and sometimes even by a whole flock.

The study of territoriality is a meeting place for many kinds of biologists. Both nervous and endocrine systems are involved in the physiology of territorial behavior, the interactions of individuals are of interest to ethologists, and the function of territoriality in community structure and in the homeostasis of ecosystems greatly concerns ecologists. It is not surprising that Howard's concept, developed from study of birds in his garden, has now spread far and wide. Territorial behavior of one kind or another has been found among mammals, reptiles, amphibians, fish, and even some invertebrate animals. It is quite probable that the study of territoriality may eventually help scientists to explain some kinds of human behavior.

## INVESTIGATION 15.3

### A METHOD FOR STUDYING TERRITORIALITY

#### PURPOSE

Using field data collected by others, you will work out the territories of breeding birds in a particular ecosystem.

#### BACKGROUND INFORMATION

To determine the nesting territories of breeding birds, a field map of the area to be studied is first prepared. Then the investigator makes a series of field trips through the area. He marks on a copy of the map the location of each singing male of each species encountered, plus the location of any nests found. Females and young birds may also be indicated, but a singing male is assumed to be in a territory with a mate and a nest, though this is not always true. Special symbols are often used to indicate two males of the same species heard singing simultaneously, location of fights between

males, and other helpful data. When all field trips have been completed, the locations of individuals of the various species on each of the field-trip dates are plotted on individual species maps. From study of the data on the species maps, the individual territories are worked out.

You will work with actual, though simplified, field data from a breeding-bird study that was made on a 30-hectare area in Colorado. Most of the vegetation in this area is composed of shrubs. There are some pine groves, some deciduous trees, and some small grassy areas. Sixteen species of breeding birds were found in this area, but you will work with only five of them. Twenty-seven field trips were made to the area; you will consider data from only six — those made at the height of the nesting season.

#### MATERIALS

Graph paper, 5 sheets
Sharp pencil with hard lead (about 4H)

| flicker | solitary vireo | robin | scrub jay | rufous-sided towhee |
|---|---|---|---|---|
| X 1/4 | X 1/2 | X 1/3 | X 1/3 | X 1/2 |
| (98) | (160) | (144) | (127) | (205) |

**Figure 15 · 23**

The five birds of this study. Numbers are used instead of names in Figure 15 · 24.

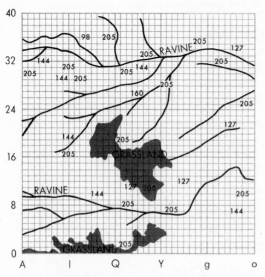

**Figure 15 · 24**

Location of birds on Date 6. (See Figure 15 · 23 for key to numbers.)

### PROCEDURE

On each sheet of graph paper outline a plot 40 × 40 squares. Number the horizontal graph lines upward from 0 at the bottom through 40 at the top. Letter the vertical lines from left to right *A* through *Z*, then *a* through *o*. At the top of each sheet, place the name of one of the species being studied.

In the table of data on page 563, the six dates of observation are represented by numerals 1 through 6. Beside each date (except for 6) is the location on each of the first five dates of an individual bird,

which was usually a singing male. Each location is designated by a number and a letter. For example, 37/c is located at the intersection of line 37 with line c. For Date 6 use the data in Figure 15 · 24, which shows the actual map used in gathering the data on that date (except that data for eleven species are omitted). Also listed is the location of each nest that was found. Many nests were probably not found by the investigators.

Use a separate sheet of graph paper for each species. Plot the location of each bird and nest on the appropriate sheet. Mark the location by placing the date number (1 through 6) at the appropriate intersection of lines.

### STUDYING THE DATA

Compare the five territory maps. • What generalization can you make about the sizes of breeding territories from species to species? Suggest an explanation for this. (1) • Do territories of different species overlap, or is each portion of the study area used only by one species of bird? (2) • How does this relate to the idea of ecological niches? (3) Red-tailed hawks are frequently seen in this area, but no nest has ever been discovered. • What may be the relation of the size of a red-tailed hawk's territory to the size of this plot? (4) In the region where this study was made, robins have a tendency to nest in deciduous trees along ravines, solitary

### Red-shafted Flicker (males)

Date 1: 37/H; 21/F

Date 2: 39/J

Date 3: 38/K

Date 4: 35/M

Date 5: 34/L

Date 6: See Figure 15 · 24

   *Nest:* 35/K

### Solitary Vireo (singing males)

Date 1: 36/B; 29/V

Date 2: 30/B; 29/U

Date 3: 30/U

Date 4: 37/B; 29/X

Date 5: 32/A; 30/a

Date 6: See Figure 15 · 24

   *Nest:* 31/a

### Robin (singing males)

Date 1: 4/F; 17/S; 33/Q; 29/b; 33/j

Date 2: 9/D; 22/Q; 29/Q; 32/Z; 30/i;
   10/o

Date 3: 9/M; 17/U; 32/S; 33/c; 30/k

Date 4: 3/M; 21/N; 33/V; 32/Y; 35/j

Date 5: 2/G; 14/R; 28/R; 27/f; 29/j

Date 6: See Figure 15 · 24

   *Nest:* 29/S; 32/i

### Scrub Jay (males or females)

Date 1: 33/A; 17/J; 1/Z; 23/f; 37/i

Date 2: 29/G; 17/R; 5/Z; 26/g; 39/j

Date 3: 35/M; 18/N; 10/b; 23/1

Date 4: 38/D; 13/S; 4/c; 26/h; 39/1

Date 5: 35/L; 23/R; 6/Z; 27/d; 36/o

Date 6: See Figure 15 · 24

   *Nest:* 9/c; 25/i; 38/n

### Rufous-sided Towhee (singing males)

Date 1: 40/A; 28/F; 37/H; 22/F; 25/I; 28/K; 37/P; 31/S; 25/P; 34/Y; 38/c; 12/Y;
   11/G; 39/g; 34/j; 27/1; 31/e; 25/b; 4/I; 2/Q; 9/N; 15/L; 7/g; 11/m; 17/h; 21/W

Date 2: 36/C; 37/G; 22/I; 28/I; 36/S; 30/R; 24/R; 32/X; 36/d; 37/1; 8/c; 26/1; 12/j;
   30/m; 30/d; 28/z; 12/e; 4/M; 20/Z; 3/S; 14/X; 11/P; 14/P

Date 3: 35/B; 28/A; 33/J; 25/K; 28/M; 33/R; 29/R; 27/V; 31/W; 35/a; 12/X; 37/h;
   31/i; 5/d; 24/j; 29/c; 11/j; 15/f; 27/a; 7/G; 19/U; 4/V; 9/Q; 14/R

Date 4: 32/L; 19/E; 26/M; 27/N; 34/R; 25/S; 30/W; 30/k; 7/e; 25/i; 30/b; 13/h;
   2/L; 18/U; 7/W; 9/S

Date 5: 36/D; 20/G; 34/d; 26/I; 10/Y; 27/K; 36/T; 30/T; 26/U; 33/W; 36/n; 29/j;
   24/h; 32/c; 5/a; 13/d; 28/b; 5/S; 18/Y; 9/O; 17/P

Date 6: See Figure 15 · 24

   *Nest:* 27/U

vireos in ponderosa-pine groves, and scrub jays and rufous-sided towhees in brushland.  • From your examination of the distribution and population density of these four species, tell which of the habitats mentioned is most widespread in this 30-hectare plot. (5) Flickers nest in holes in trees but feed on the ground, mainly on ants. • What might explain the low population density of this species here? (6) The *carrying capacity* of an ecosystem is the maximum population density of organisms the ecosystem can support. • What appears to be the approximate carrying capacity of this area for *adult* rufous-sided towhees during the breeding season? (7) • Why might this same area not have as great a carrying capacity for towhees in the winter season? (8) Compare the population density of scrub jays with that of rufous-sided towhees. • Is the carrying capacity of the area the same for these two species, or are you unable to tell? Explain your answer. (9) • What does the distribution of some of these territories suggest about the habitats in surrounding areas? (10) There is a single record of a rufous-sided towhee at 11/G and a single record of a red-shafted flicker at 21/F. • What could account for these single records during the breeding season? (11) There may be some doubt that in a particular area during the breeding season the day-after-day presence of individual birds or the regular occurrence of a singing male

indicates a nesting territory. • Is there evidence from these territory data that these *are* indicators for nesting territories? If so, what is it? (12)

### FOR FURTHER INVESTIGATION

1. The records of scrub jays are based on sight observations of either male or female adults rather than on sound observations of singing males. You may discover the reason for the difference in method of study by library research on the behavior of scrub jays.

2. You can try some actual fieldwork in your own area, preparing field maps and working out territories of local nesting birds. Such studies can usually be started in late April and ideally should continue into midsummer. The National Audubon Society, 1130 Fifth Avenue, New York, N.Y., 10028, has a leaflet on how to carry out breeding-bird studies. *Field Guide to the Birds* and *Field Guide to Western Birds*, by Roger T. Peterson (Houghton Mifflin Co., Boston), are excellent for field identification, while Peterson's accompanying bird-song records (Houghton Mifflin) are a great aid in recognition of songs.

## COMMUNICATION

We discussed territoriality mostly in connection with the endocrine and nervous mechanisms that bring it about — from a physiological viewpoint. But territoriality is meaningless unless it is also viewed as a kind of interaction between individuals — from an ethological viewpoint. In anthropomorphic terms, a singing male bird is "telling" other males that he "claims" the area around him; he is "telling" females that the area is available for nesting. Communication between individuals is part of territorial behavior.

Any activity on the part of one organism that causes a reaction in another organism can be regarded as communication. In this broad and basic sense, communication must occur in all ecological relationships — among plants and protists as well as among animals. Most biologists,

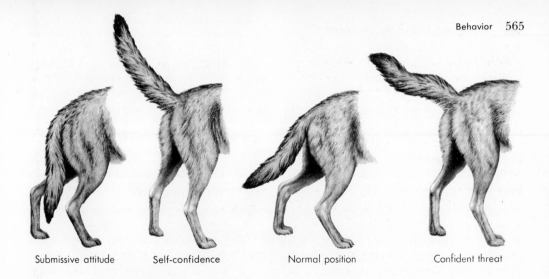

| Submissive attitude | Self-confidence | Normal position | Confident threat |

however, use the term in a narrower sense, though they do not always agree on the limits. In this discussion, communication is restricted to animals.

To be of value for communication, each kind of stimulus must have a "meaning." A biologist can find out what this meaning is only by observing what organisms do when the stimulus is given. A male white-crowned sparrow sings; most other males avoid the vicinity of the singer; many females may approach the vicinity of the singer. In this case the stimulus has one meaning for the males, another for the females. And apparently it has no meaning for the caribou that are grazing nearby, because they show no signs of reacting to it. Many men have reacted to the singing of birds by writing poetry—but most biologists would probably not regard this as communication between bird and man.

Anything that can be sensed by another organism—any kind of stimulus—may serve for communication. Scents, sights, and sounds are the most commonly used stimuli. Scent is used as a means of communication, particularly by mammals and insects. By leaving their scents at various places, some mammals mark the limits of their territories. An ant lays down a "trail" of formic acid from a food source back to its anthill. The formic acid seems to mean, "This is the way." If the formic acid is destroyed, the ants are no longer able to go directly to the food but scurry haphazardly around until they apparently find it again by chance.

Man, having a poor sense of smell, makes little use of communication by scent, but he uses sight—visual communication—extensively. So do other animals in which the sense of sight is present. Usually visual stimuli consist of

**Figure 15 · 25**

Long observation led one investigator to interpret the positions of wolves' tails in this way. To what extent does your observation of the ways dogs act indicate similarity with wolves in "tail communication"?

The poet may communicate with other men, but has the bird communicated with the poet? Explain.

What example of scent as a means of communication was given earlier in the chapter?

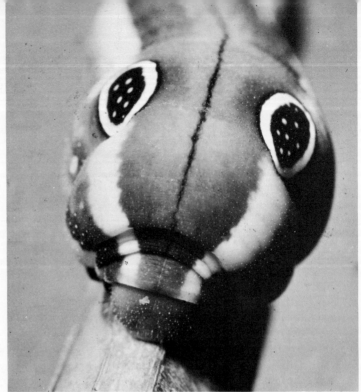

Edward S. Ross

**Figure 15 · 26**

Hornworm, a caterpillar that has false "eyes."

See Figure 8 · 28 for a somewhat similar action in a startled pronghorn.

movements. Often the movements are made more conspicuous by some structure of the body. A startled white-tailed deer communicates its alarm to the rest of the herd by raising its tail, which flashes conspicuously white in contrast to its dark upper side. The giver of a visual stimulus need not necessarily have good vision, because communication may be interspecific—directed toward another species. Some caterpillars have spots that superficially resemble large eyes. The true eyes of a caterpillar are small and probably cannot see the spots on another caterpillar's back. But a food-seeking bird may be "frightened" sufficiently by the large "eyes" to allow the caterpillar to escape. One observer recorded that a bird fell backward off a twig when suddenly confronted with such a caterpillar.

To most people communication by means of sounds means language. Some biologists refer to "animal language," but many psychologists doubt that any organism besides man has a means of communication comparable to human language. We have sounds, such as "ouch," that communicate meaning in much the same way as do the sounds of other animals. But is Lincoln's Gettysburg Address only a series of such sounds? Whatever your answer to that question may be, animals do make a great variety of sounds that result in observable behavior in other animals—sound communication.

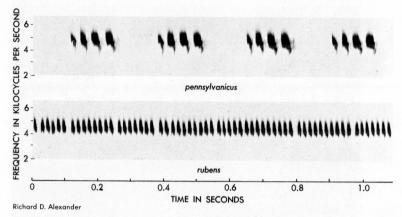

Richard D. Alexander

Figure 15 · 27
"Songs" of two species of
field crickets: *Gryllus penn-
sylvanicus* (above) and G.
*rubens* (below). By such
audiospectrograms, which
put air vibrations into
visible form, details of
animal sound communica-
tion can be clearly com-
pared and verified.

## SOCIAL BEHAVIOR

Any interaction among individuals of the same species could be called "social" behavior. But such a definition is so broad that it has little meaning. The chance meeting of one puma with another on the borders of their kilometers-wide hunting territories, even if it results in some show of hostility, is not usually considered social behavior. Social behavior requires the formation of groups of individuals that are maintained more than momentarily. Oysters form groups, often very close groups; and once formed, the grouping lasts for life. But this is not usually considered social behavior, either.

Sometimes a food supply brings together many animals. When fruit is ripening on a cherry tree, large numbers of birds come together in the tree. Communication occurs; one bird may interact with another, and the grouping may last for several days. This is a simple kind of grouping, but it contains the basic requirements of a social organization.

Of course, a grouping of birds in a fruit tree may be composed of several species. This is not of great importance for many investigations of animal social behavior; but in the remainder of this discussion, we shall deal with groupings containing individuals of a single species.

**Fish schools.** A school of fish represents a fairly simple aggregation. Schooling fish tend to have sleek bodies that glitter as they move. The school's organization and movements are controlled in part by such visual stimuli-releasers; fish that cannot see do not school. A school is usually made up of fish not only of the same species but also of the same size. At any particular instant, all individuals in the school swim in one direction and as a compact group. Pressure receptors along the sides of the fish may receive

At least, not by zoologists. But botanists have somewhat different viewpoints. See Chapter 4 of Oosting (reference on our page 249).

Douglas P. Wilson

**Figure 15 · 28**

A school of mackerel. Can you think of any ways in which this behavior might be an advantage to the fish?

stimuli that tend to keep each fish at a certain distance from the others.

Part of this behavior involves fixed-action patterns, but learning is also definitely involved. Contacts between very young fish increase their ability to swim together in one direction. Older fish, when separated from each other over a period of time, tend to "forget" how to school.

**Insect societies.** When they look at social behavior in other animals, most people probably have human behavior in mind. They are looking for something more organized, more complex than schools of fishes or flocks of birds or even herds of caribou and other mammals. When they look through the animal kingdom for something comparable to human societies, most people find the greatest similarities

**Figure 15 · 29**

Some species of ants feed upon a substance secreted by aphids. They care for the aphids much as man cares for his cows. Why, then, are the behavior of man and the behavior of ants not comparable?  X 4

Alexander B. Klots

in the social behavior of certain insects. Among ants, bees, and termites, large numbers of individuals carry on many kinds of special tasks and seem to work closely together for the good of the group. The more we study these insects, the more similarities we find to human societies. Within a species we find individuals that specialize in different kinds of work: food collectors, fighters, "baby-sitters," even living food bins. Some species cultivate fungi. Some species wage war and make slaves. Some species construct complicated housing projects.

You can easily see the anthropomorphism in the previous paragraph. Psychologists and ethologists do not look at insect behavior in this way. Repeated experiments show that these highly organized invertebrate societies are based primarily on innate behavior.

**Primate societies.** One of the outstanding developments in biology during the last decade has been the large increase in the study of animals usually placed in the same taxonomic order with man—the primates. This has included all parts of primate biology, but it has been especially great in the study of behavior. And it has been marked to an unusual degree by coordination of laboratory and field investigations.

Between laboratory and field have been studies of captive colonies. In one such colony of Japanese macaque monkeys, a female found she could clean dirty sweet potatoes, which they were being fed, by washing them in a stream. Within a few years, all except the baby monkeys and a few oldsters were washing potatoes. These same monkeys were also fed wheat, which was spread about on a sandy beach for them. At first the monkeys painstakingly

macaque [mə käk´]

Paul Knipping

Figure 15 · 30

Laboratory study of primate mother-offspring relationships. Presented with several mother substitutes, this infant monkey clings to an object that is soft and warm and gives milk.

picked up each grain of wheat in their fingers. Then a few monkeys began picking up handfuls of sand and wheat, running into the shallow ocean, and letting the water wash away the sand from the grain. Again, within a few years one-fourth of the monkeys were using this learned and much more efficient technique for obtaining their food. Although similar observations have occasionally been made in other social groups of birds and mammals, in primates a valuable kind of behavior discovered by one individual is especially likely to be learned by its companions.

Clarence Ray Carpenter: 1905——. American psychologist and anthropologist

One of the earlier field studies was made by C. R. Carpenter, who spent almost a year observing howler monkeys on Barro Colorado Island. This island is a forested hill that became isolated when Gatun Lake was formed in the course of the construction of the Panama Canal. Howlers are the largest American monkeys (in body weight) and the noisiest. Cries of howler monkeys can be heard many kilometers away. Their choruses regularly greet the dawn, and they howl at any intruder into their forests.

Carpenter was especially interested in the social organization of the howlers. He found that there were about four hundred howlers on the island, organized into twenty-three clans. Clans varied in size from 4 to 35 individuals, with an average of 17 or 18 individuals—3 adult males, 7 adult females, and young.

persistent [pər sis′tənt]: occurring again and again

The clans were strictly territorial, each staying within a clearly defined area. When two clans came near each other along a territorial border, vigorous howling started—a vocal battle that continued until one band or the other retreated. There were a few solitary "bachelor" males. These, when they tried to join a clan, were shouted off—though Carpenter watched one "bachelor" who, after persistent attempts over several weeks, was finally accepted into a clan.

jealousy [jĕl′ə sĭ]: intolerance of rivals

Carpenter could not find that the clans had leaders. A male was usually in the lead when a clan moved, but sometimes it would be one male, sometimes another. Moreover, the males seemed to show no jealousy over the females, and no instances of fighting within a clan were observed. Among other kinds of monkeys, particularly the Indian rhesus monkeys and the African baboons, there is evidence that one of the males is the recognized leader.

monogamous [mə nŏg′ə məs; Greek: monos, single, + gamos, marriage]

Carpenter also studied gibbons in Thailand. He found them to be organized into monogamous families: each group consisted of one adult male, one female, and one or two young. Gibbons are not monkeys, but apes. Recently, excellent field studies have been made of other apes, particularly chimpanzees and gorillas. In these species groupings

seem larger than single families. Even though these apes are the living animals most similar to man, it is clear that man and the apes have had separate evolutionary histories for a long time. Ape behavior, then, does not necessarily shed direct light on the origin of human societies. Nevertheless, if you visit the primate house in a zoo and watch what occurs on *both* sides of the bars, you will find that not only biologists are interested in primate behavior.

**Figure 15 · 31**

Social behavior in this group of semi-wild Japanese monkeys is easily studied by ethologists.

## INVESTIGATION 15.4

### PERCEPTUAL WORLDS

#### PURPOSE

In studying animal behavior, biologists often use complicated and expensive apparatus. But much can be learned about animal behavior by merely watching—noting what an animal does and under what circumstances it does it. And some kinds of experimentation can be done with very simple apparatus (Figure 15 · 19).

Whether well equipped or not, the student of animal behavior needs first to know something about the stimuli that an animal under study can perceive—something about its "view" of the world. You have already investigated some aspects of the perceptual worlds of a few animals (Investigations 4.3 and 14.1). Now you will try to find out all you can, within the limits of available time, about the perceptual world of one particular kind of animal.

### PROCEDURE

Each team will choose an animal species for study. The species must be one of which a number of living specimens can be obtained. The teacher will provide a list of suitable species.

Plans for studying the perceptual world of any animal will, of course, depend upon the nature of the species. Size, natural habitat, and the obvious sense organs should be considered. Therefore, each team must become generally familiar with its animal before laying plans for studying behavior. Preliminary observations may lead you to suspect senses that were not at first obvious. Consider such matters as reaction to light (intensity and color), sound, gravity, touch, chemical substances (odor and taste); ability to see and the kinds of things seen; awareness of the biotic environment (organisms of its own species and of others). Consider how you will determine whether or not an observed behavior is brought about by a particular factor in the environment. In planning experiments, remember that the best understanding of normal behavior can be gained when the animal is disturbed as little as possible.

When your team has laid its plans, draw up a short, simple list of materials and equipment. The list will be reviewed by the teacher. The listed items should be assembled and made ready for use before the laboratory periods in which the experimenting is to be done.

### SUMMARY

Prepare a team report on the perceptual world of the animal studied. The report should clearly indicate how each bit of information in it was obtained.

---

The ability to react to stimuli from the environment is a characteristic of all living things. Such reactions, behavior in a broad sense, enable individual organisms to adjust to changes in their environment. Behavior can be studied from the point of view of the anatomical and physiological processes that make it possible. It can also be studied from the viewpoint of its function in the life of the organism. Though physiology and ecology must both be kept in mind for any complete understanding of behavior, these two approaches have usually characterized separate groups of biologists.

The behavior of organisms that lack nervous systems is rather limited. The nervous and muscular systems of animals allow a much wider variety of responses. But this variety introduces difficulties into the study of animal behavior. Because the activities of animals sometimes resemble human behavior, it is difficult to resist the tendency to interpret their behavior in human terms. We are inclined to see human senses, human emotions, and human thought patterns in animals; thus, we often misinterpret even when we observe carefully.

The behavior of animals can be conveniently divided into innate behavior and learned behavior, though in practice it is often difficult to distinguish the two. Both innate and learned behavior frequently involve endocrine mechanisms as well as the nervous system. Reflexes, taxes, and instincts are innate. All animals show innate behavior to a greater or lesser degree. But the more highly developed the nervous system, the less important such behavior tends to be. Some degree of learning seems to be possible in every animal having a nervous system with a central controlling ganglion. Reasoning seems to be confined to the larger primates.

The kinds of animal behavior can be grouped in many ways. We have discussed four aspects of animal behavior: periodicity, territoriality, communication, and societies.

## GUIDE QUESTIONS

1. What is behavior?
2. How, in general, do behavioral studies by ethologists differ from behavioral studies by psychologists?
3. Why is anthropomorphism a danger in studying the behavior of animals?
4. What other difficulties does the behavioral scientist encounter?
5. How is irritability related to behavior?
6. How does a tropism differ from a taxis?
7. What do we mean when we say that a kind of behavior is innate?
8. What is a "releaser"?
9. What evidence is there that much behavior is the result of both fixed-action patterns and learning?
10. What difficulties are involved in defining "learning"?
11. How does imprinting differ from other kinds of learning?
12. What is conditioning?
13. How is trial-and-error learning studied?
14. How does insight differ from learning?
15. What functions may territorial behavior have in the ecology of an organism?
16. What kind of stimuli most often serves in communication between animals?
17. How can a biologist determine the "meaning" of a communication stimulus?
18. What factors are usually present in behavior that is called "social"?
19. What kinds of behavior can be recognized in the schooling of fish?
20. Why do behavioral biologists regard insect societies as only superficially like human societies?

## PROBLEMS

1. A human infant clutches at anything that touches its hands, and the strength of its grasp is great enough to support its weight. This grasping reaction appears to be innate. Would you call it a reflex or an instinct? Explain. What adaptive value might this behavior have had in the past? Do you think it has any adaptive value now?

2. The following are examples of behaviors that have been called instinctive: (a) the web-building of spiders; (b) the nest-building of birds; (c) the comb-building of bees; (d) the dam-building of beavers. Suggest ways in which it might be possible to obtain evidence showing to what extent these activities are innate and to what extent they are learned.

3. Prepare a list of animals arranged in order of the care given the young—from least to most. You should have a variety of phyla and classes represented on your list. List the same animals in order of numbers of young produced—from most to least. Explain any relationships you can find between the two lists.

4. In embryonic mammals movements of the diaphragm and muscles attached to the ribs do not occur. At birth, however, these movements begin immediately. Does the young mammal *learn* this behavior, or are there other ways to explain it? Relate this problem to the distinction between innate and learned behavior.

5. The behavior of an animal results from a complex interaction between the environment and the physiology of the animal. Find out what is known about the relation of environmental factors to the migratory behavior of birds. What environmental factors influence this behavior? How do they act on the physiology of the birds? How do physiological changes bring about changes in behavior? How do changes in behavior affect the physiology of the birds?

6. Can an understanding of animal behavior have any value in understanding human behavior?

7. Biologists have found evidence of organization in even the simplest groupings of animals—for example, in herds of domestic cattle. What is a social hierarchy? How is it formed? How is it maintained? What is the effect on the hierarchy of introducing new individuals to the group? What effect do hormones have on hierarchy behavior?

## SUGGESTED READINGS

BATES, M. *The Forest and the Sea.* New York: Random House, Inc., 1960. Chapters 12 and 13. (Discussion of animal behavior in a conversational style that can raise many questions in the mind of a thoughtful reader.)

BEST, J. B. "Protopsychology," *Scientific American,* February, 1963. Pp. 54–62.

BROWN, F. A., JR. *Biological Clocks.* (BSCS Pamphlet 2). Boston: D. C. Heath & Co., 1962.

CARR, A. *Guideposts of Animal Navigation.* (BSCS Pamphlet 1). Boston: D. C. Heath & Co., 1962.

COLLIAS, N. E. *Animal Language.* (BSCS Pamphlet 20). Boston: D. C. Heath & Co., 1964.

DETHIER, V. G., and E. STELLAR. *Animal Behavior, Its Evolutionary and Neurological Basis.* 2nd ed. Englewood Cliffs, N.J.: Prentice-Hall, Inc., 1964. (Considers animal behavior primarily as an expression of the organization of the nervous system. Rather advanced.)

DILGER, W. C. "The Behavior of Lovebirds," *Scientific American,* January, 1962. Pp. 88–98.

EIBEL-EIBESFELDT, I. "The Fighting Behavior of Animals," *Scientific American,* December, 1961. Pp. 112–116.

FARNER, D. S. *Photoperiodism in Animals.* (BSCS Pamphlet 15). Boston: D. C. Heath & Co., 1964.

HARLOW, H. F., and M. K. HARLOW. "Social Deprivation in Monkeys," *Scientific American,* November, 1962. Pp. 136–146.

LORENZ, K. Z. *King Solomon's Ring.* New York: The Thomas Y. Crowell Co., 1952. (Excellent scientific research lies behind this book, but the material is not presented in textbook style. Easy.)

MEYERRIECKS, A. J. *Courtship in Animals.* (BSCS Pamphlet 3). Boston: D. C. Heath & Co., 1962. (An easily read account of animal courtship, from insects to mammals.)

MOMENT, G. B. *General Zoology.* 2nd ed. Boston: Houghton Mifflin Co., 1967. Chapter 2. (One of the best summaries of animal behavior in any college textbook of zoology. Fairly easy.)

PALMER. J. D. "How a Bird Tells the Time of Day," *Natural History,* March, 1966. Pp. 48–53.

Scott, J. P. *Animal Behavior.* New York: Doubleday and Co., Inc., 1963 — originally published in 1958 by University of Chicago Press. (Considers animal behavior from a wider viewpoint than do Dethier and Stellar. Not a textbook.)

Shaw, E. "The Schooling of Fishes," *Scientific American,* June, 1962. Pp. 128–134.

Simpson, G. G., and W. S. Beck. *Life: An Introduction to Biology.* 2nd ed. New York: Harcourt, Brace, & World, Inc., 1965. Chapter 14. (Considers behavior from a wider viewpoint than does Moment. Somewhat advanced.)

Tinbergen, N., and Editors of LIFE. *Animal Behavior.* New York: Time, Inc., Book Division, 1965. (A well-illustrated consideration of many aspects of behavior.)

Van Lawick, J., and H. Van Lawick. "New Discoveries among Africa's Chimpanzees," *National Geographic Magazine,* December, 1965. Pp. 802–831.

# Section Five    CONTINUITY
## OF THE
## BIOSPHERE

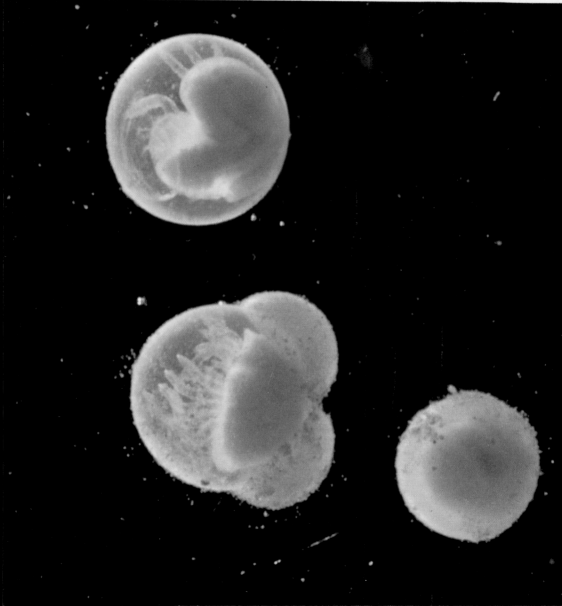

Once again we shift our point of view. In Section Four we were looking *into* organisms. We were concerned with the way in which a living individual is constructed and with the internal chemical and physical processes that distinguish living from nonliving matter. Much current research centers on problems of this "inner" biology—on anatomy, physiology, biophysics, biochemistry. What biologists learn about such matters is of importance to all of us. But its importance becomes evident only when internal processes show up in external actions—behavior. So even in Section Four we had to return at the end to the whole organism, with its internal homeostasis, maintaining a steady state in an unsteady environment.

Individual organisms exist in populations. Through natality and mortality individuals come and go, but populations of organisms exist for long ages. And, as we saw in Chapter 10, the evidence from fossils indicates that the biosphere itself has endured perhaps three billion years. Thus there is continuity in the biosphere. There is continuity, but there is also change. Again the fossil record is the evidence; it indicates that change has been slow and, in general, orderly. There is homeostasis between populations of organisms and their abiotic environment.

How do populations achieve continuity? How are individuals replaced? How are characteristics maintained generation after generation? And on the other hand, how do characteristics change over many generations, so that ecosystems of today are recognizably different from those of past ages? These are some of the questions we shall consider in Section Five.

To start the discussion, we shall have to look again at cell units, at "inner" biology. But we shall soon return to individual units, to "outer" biology. As you come to appreciate the continuity of the biosphere, so also you may recognize the continuity between "inner" and "outer" biology.

# 16

# Reproduction

## WHY REPRODUCTION?

One statement about living things that has no exception is: They die. Life can end in a wide variety of ways: An organism may be eaten, may be killed by parasites, may starve, or may be destroyed by natural events—frozen in a blizzard, boiled in lava, crushed in an avalanche. Very few die of old age.

Obviously, since individuals die, life would eventually disappear unless new individuals were continually being formed. There are two possibilities: nonliving substances may somehow come alive spontaneously, or bits of organisms may detach themselves and become new individual living things. The first possibility is referred to as spontaneous generation. The second is called *reproduction*.

Consider first the possibility of spontaneous generation. We have already looked at the matter of the beginning of life on Earth (pages 345–347). The conditions assumed by Oparin may well have existed hundreds of millions of years ago—but they certainly have not occurred more recently.

Yet many people have believed that living things can arise from nonliving materials—by spontaneous generation. For example, some think that in spring the mud in marshes turns into frogs. Suddenly, after a warm spring rain, the marshes—frozen and apparently lifeless in winter—swarm with frogs, which make their presence known with unmistakable loud calls. Eyes and ears agree that the warming mud has turned into frogs. The conclusion is wrong, mainly because the observations are not carried far enough. Some digging in the mud beneath the frozen covering of the winter marsh would reveal that dormant frogs were present from the previous autumn.

Figure 16 · 1

Redi's experiment: (A) Maggots developed in meat
left in a vessel. (B) Another
vessel was covered with
cloth, and no maggots de-
veloped in the meat. How-
ever, on the cloth, flies'
eggs were found—from
which maggots hatched.

Francesco Redi [rĕ′dĭ]: 1626?
—1698. Italian poet and
naturalist

Since the seventeenth century, when Francesco Redi performed the experiment illustrated in Figure 16 · 1, biologists have not believed in the spontaneous generation of larger organisms. The discovery of microorganisms by Leeuwenhoek revived interest in spontaneous generation—until Pasteur's experiments showed that these organisms, too, come from others of their kind. Reproduction became the only way to account for the appearance of new individuals.

For a species, reproduction answers the problem of death. For an individual, there is no answer to death. And for an individual, there is no need for reproduction. Therefore reproduction is a life process somewhat different from the life processes discussed in Section Four. Reproduction concerns not the maintenance of individuals, but the continuity of species.

## KINDS OF REPRODUCTION

All organisms have the same basic life functions, but we have seen that they perform these functions in many different ways, using a great diversity of structures. Diversity of structures and of processes also characterizes reproduction. Reproduction may occur in two ways, differing greatly in their effects upon the continuity of species: *asexually* or *sexually*.

### ASEXUAL REPRODUCTION

It is easier to describe asexual reproductive processes than to define asexual reproduction. But we can say that when one or more new individuals are produced by a single parent, the process—with a few exceptions—is asexual.

Most organisms that reproduce asexually have sexual methods also. But in deuteromycetes sexual reproduction is unknown, and in a few other groups it is rare. Species that

Lynwood M. Chace

**Figure 16 · 2**

Vegetative reproduction of a strawberry. The young plant (*left*) will eventually lose its connection with the parent.    × 1/8

See Figure 13 · 28.

X 1

**Figure 16 · 3**

Vegetative reproduction of *Bryophyllum*. Small new plants develop in notches of the leaf.

depend primarily upon asexual reproduction are close to the end of the evolutionary road; that is, they have little chance of changing to meet new environmental conditions. Why this is so will become clear in Chapter 18.

**Vegetative reproduction.**    In spring, potato farmers in Maine prepare for planting. Potatoes are cut into pieces, each piece with an "eye" (actually, a bud). After planting, the bud develops into a leafy shoot, drawing upon the foods stored in the rest of the piece. Soon roots appear at the end of the shoot, and before long a new plant is established. From one potato a number of new plants have developed.

In Honduras, plantation workers cut the shoots that grow up from underground stems of banana plants and set them out to begin a new crop. In Hawaii, shoots that appear below the fruit of the pineapple plant are used in the same way to start a crop. Everywhere, nurserymen take cuttings from a wide variety of woody plants, root them in moist sand, and so start new trees and shrubs.

Multicellular organisms have an ability, called *regeneration*, to replace lost parts. This is one aspect of the general process of growth. You have the ability to regenerate lost pieces of skin. In the cases described above, this ability is simply developed to an extreme degree: a small part, separated from one individual, can grow into a completely independent new individual.

In plants a bud or a branch may take root; on the other hand, a piece of a root may sprout a stem. In either case, a whole new plant may eventually be formed. Many plants reproduce in this way without aid from man. The long shoots of black raspberry plants arch over until the tips touch the ground, roots form at these tips, and a new plant is established. This is *vegetative* reproduction.

A similar form of reproduction occurs among animals. Because starfish eat oysters, it was once a common practice among oystermen to chop up starfish that they caught and throw the pieces back into the water. But the power of regeneration in starfish is great. Each arm that had a piece of the center portion attached grew into a whole new starfish, and the oystermen were actually multiplying starfish!

But starfish do not reproduce by breaking themselves up in separate pieces. In fact, few animals do. Exceptions occur among some species of freshwater annelids, which regularly reproduce by simply breaking in half. The anterior piece then grows a new posterior section, and the posterior piece grows a new anterior section.

**Fission.**    Among the single-celled organisms—diatoms, many green algae, and most protists—reproduction is often merely a matter of cell division. Two offspring result, but

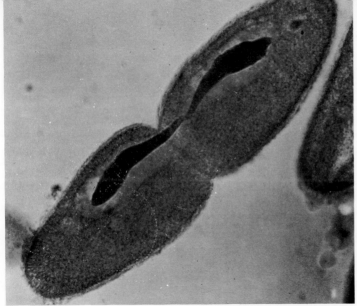

**Figure 16 · 4**

Fission of paramecium as seen in a stained specimen.

× 600

the parent loses its identity in the process. This kind of reproduction is called *fission*. It may occur at a certain stage in the life history of an organism that reproduces by some other means at another stage. But some organisms apparently always reproduce by fission.

fission [fĭsh′ən; Latin: *findere*, to split, cleave]

Fission usually involves the process of mitosis, but there are exceptions in ciliates, bacteria, and blue-green algae. It was long thought that bacteria had no organized nuclear material. Now the electron microscope has revealed a structure that is at least similar to a nucleus; and indirect evidence from studies of heredity indicates that each bacterium has a single chromosome. But mitosis (at least as described in Chapter 11) does not seem to occur. And in the blue-green algae nothing even resembling a nucleus has yet been demonstrated.

**Budding.** In some protists, plants, and animals, a projection grows from the body of an adult. As the projection enlarges, parts differentiate until a duplicate of the

**Figure 16 · 5**

The process of budding in a hydra.

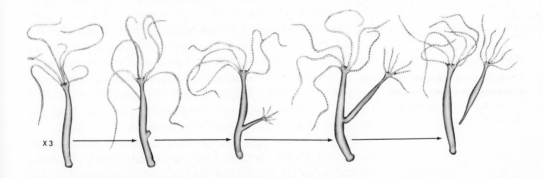

X 3

parent is formed. Eventually the offspring may break free from the parent and become an independent individual. You saw such budding in yeasts, in Investigation 2.2.

**Reproduction by spores.** In vegetative reproduction and budding, a new individual is simply an outgrowth of some structure or tissue that normally functions in the nonreproductive life of the parent organism. In fission, also, there is no differentiated reproductive structure; a cell that has been functioning as an individual simply divides. But in most multicellular organisms (and some unicellular ones, also) there are specialized reproductive parts.

One kind of reproductive structure is called a *sporangium* (spore case). Within a sporangium many spores are produced, each consisting of a single thick-walled cell. When the sporangium breaks open, the tiny spores may be carried long distances by currents of air or water without damage, and they can survive long periods of time in dry air with little loss of water. If a spore reaches a favorable environment, it germinates and develops into a new organism. Though spore-formation does not occur among animals, it is very common in the plant kingdom.

*Can you see any similarities between budding and the vegetative reproduction of multicellular plants?*

*sporangium [spō răn'jĭ əm; Greek: spora, a seed, + angeion, a small container]: The derivation is misleading; for distinction between spore and seed see page 168.*

## INVESTIGATION 16.1

### VEGETATIVE REPRODUCTION

#### PURPOSE

You will try to answer this question: To what extent does coleus—a plant that does not naturally reproduce vegetatively—have the ability to do so under experimental conditions?

#### MATERIALS AND EQUIPMENT
(for each team)

Flowerpot (shallow form), 15- to 20-cm diameter
Stone or piece of broken pot
Sand, enough to fill flowerpot
Saucer or shallow pan
Pot labels, 4
Live coleus plant, in a pot
Scalpel
Plastic bag
String

#### PROCEDURE

Place a large stone or a piece of broken pot over the drainage hole in the empty flowerpot. Pour sand into the pot to a level within 2 cm of the rim. Place the pot in a saucer or shallow pan, and water the sand thoroughly. Pour excess water from the saucer. Using a pencil, divide the surface of the sand into quarter sections. Mark four pot labels *A, B, C,* and *D*, and place one along the outer edge of each section (see Figure 16·6).

You are to obtain four cuttings from the coleus plant. Three of these (*A, B, C*) must each have three pairs of leaves and a terminal bud; the fourth cutting (*D*) must be at least 5 cm long and must be taken from *between* pairs of leaves. (If possible, obtain *D* and one of the other cuttings from the same branch.) Using a scalpel, make the necessary cuts.

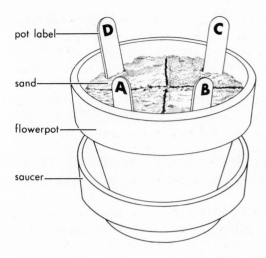

pot label

sand

flowerpot

saucer

**Figure 16 · 6**

From Cutting A remove the bottom pair of leaves. With a pencil, make a hole in the center of Section A in the pot; the depth of this hole should be about 1 cm less than the distance from the base of Cutting A to the lower pair of remaining leaves. Insert Cutting A (cut end first) into the hole so that the lower pair of leaves is just above the sand. Press the sand together around the cutting.

From Cutting B remove the tip of the branch and all but the uppermost pair of leaves. Make a hole in the center of Section B; the depth of this hole should be about 1 cm less than the distance from the base of Cutting B to the remaining pair of leaves. Insert Cutting B so that its leaves are just above the sand. Press the sand together around the cutting.

Prepare Cutting C just as you did B, and plant it in Section C. Then remove its remaining pair of leaves. Press the sand together around the cutting.

Plant Cutting D, placing it so that at least 5 mm projects above the level of the sand.

Cover the cuttings with a plastic bag, and close the bag's open end around the rim of the pot with string. Set the pots containing the coleus plant and the cut-

tings in a place where they will receive abundant light. Add water to the saucers whenever necessary.

After about three weeks, examine the plant from which the cuttings were taken. • What, if anything, has happened at the points where cuttings were removed? (1)   Remove the plastic cover from the pot containing the cuttings and examine them. • Which ones seem to be alive? In each case, what is the evidence for your decision? (2)

Loosen the sand and remove Cutting A.   • Have roots developed? If so, at what points on the cutting? (3)   • What, if anything, has happened to the cut surface? (4)   • What, if anything, has happened to the tip of the cutting? (5)

Loosen the sand and remove Cutting B.   • Have roots developed? If so, at what points? (6)   • What, if anything, has happened to the end that was in the sand? (7)   • What, if anything, has happened to the exposed end? (8)

Loosen the sand and remove Cutting C.   • Have roots developed? If so, at what points? (9)   • What, if anything, has happened to the end that was in the sand? (10)   • What, if anything, has happened to the exposed end? (11)

Loosen the sand and remove Cutting D.   • Have roots developed? If so, at what points? (12)   • What, if anything, has happened to the end that was in the sand? (13)   • What, if anything, has happened to the exposed end? (14)

**CONCLUSIONS**

First consider only the plant from which the cuttings were taken. • What evidence do you have that coleus has the ability to regenerate parts lost by injury? (15)

Now consider the evidence from the cuttings. • To what extent might the accidental breaking up of a coleus plant (by a hailstorm, for example) result in the reproduction of coleus plants? (16)

## FOR FURTHER INVESTIGATION

1. Use this procedure to investigate and compare the abilities of other plant species—tomato, household geranium, begonia, bean, pepper, marigold, zinnia, for example—to reproduce vegetatively.

2. Rooting is likely to proceed more slowly in cuttings of woody plants than of herbaceous plants. Investigate the effects of various "growth substances" (see Figure 13 · 28) on the rate of root forma-

tion in several species of woody plants.

3. Does the age of a plant (or the age of a plant part) have an effect on its ability to regenerate?

4. Among animals, planarians have considerable ability to regenerate. To what extent is it possible to obtain vegetative reproduction in planarians? For methods consult Moog, F. *A Laboratory Block on Animal Growth and Development.* Boston: D. C. Heath & Co., 1963.

## SEXUAL REPRODUCTION

The main point in sexual reproduction is quite simple: A new individual organism begins with the union of two cells—*fertilization*. But the consequences of this simple event are great. They affect heredity, the mechanisms of evolution, and much of the behavior of organisms.

**Gametes and zygotes.** Only certain cells can unite in the process of fertilization. They are called *gametes*. In some unicellular organisms, gametes look just like other cells of the same species. In some multicellular organisms, gametes differ from other cells only in number of chromosomes. In such cases, gametes can be distinguished only by what they do—their uniting to form new individuals.

In most cases not only are gametes differentiated from other cells, but the two cells of any uniting pair are visibly

gametes [gə mēts′; Greek: gamos, marriage]

Figure 16 · 7

Comparison of asexual and sexual reproduction in black bread mold, *Rhizopus nigricans.* x 15

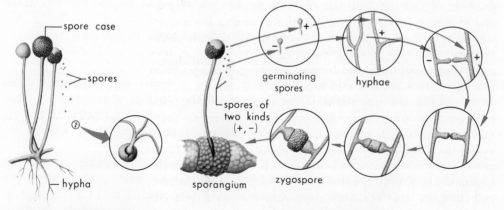

spore case

spores

hypha

**ASEXUAL REPRODUCTION**

germinating spores

hyphae

spores of two kinds (+, −)

sporangium

zygospore

**SEXUAL REPRODUCTION**

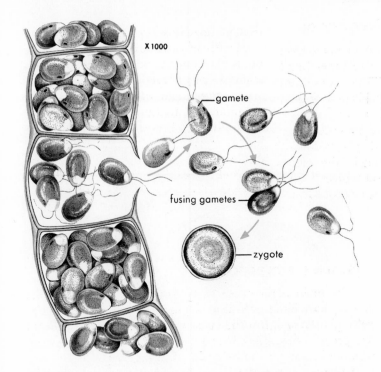

X 1000

gamete

fusing gametes

zygote

Figure 16 · 8
In the algal genus *Ulo-thrix*, gametes develop flagella. Are these sperm cells?

different from each other. One kind, the *sperm* cell, is usually smaller, carries very little reserve food, and is motile. The other kind, the *ovum* (egg cell), is usually larger, carries a reserve food supply, and is nonmotile. The differences between sperm and ova are somewhat variable, but they are the basis for defining sexes. An organism (or any part of an organism) that produces ova is called *female;* an organism (or any part) that produces sperms is called *male.*

In some organisms no differences between uniting gametes can be seen. However, there is evidence that even when visible differences are lacking, biochemical differences may exist. For example, in black bread mold (Figure 16 · 7) the hyphae that unite in sexual reproduction are not just any two hyphae; they must be from two different varieties (strains). Because the two strains appear alike, they cannot be called male and female. Mycologists simply refer to them as plus (+) and minus (−).

A cell produced by the union of gametes—by fertilization—is a *zygote.* After zygote-formation there are many pathways of development. In a unicellular organism a zygote is itself a complete new individual, but in a multicellular organism a zygote is merely a beginning. From this beginning a new individual develops by repeated mitotic cell divisions. But these divisions may not occur immediately. In some species a zygote produces a thick covering

zygote [zī'gōt; Greek: zygon, a yoke]

that is resistant to heat and drying; in this form it may remain dormant for months or even years. In some species a zygote develops into an embryo, which then becomes dormant. In still other species a zygote develops without pause through embryo and young stages to adult.

**Meiosis.**   If both gametes contain the same number of chromosomes, the resulting zygote will have twice that

Figure 16 · 9

Comparison of some eggs (ova) and sperms. Notice the very different magnifications. In chicken, snake, frog, and fish, the ova are surrounded by other materials (*shown in outline*).

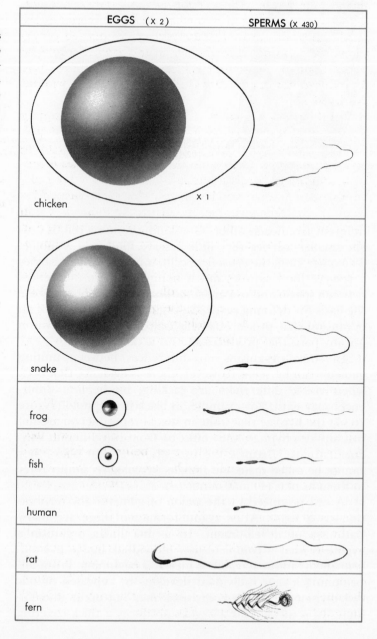

| EGGS (X 2) | SPERMS (X 430) |
|---|---|
| chicken   X 1 | |
| snake | |
| frog | |
| fish | |
| human | |
| rat | |
| fern | |

number. The new individual develops from the zygote by means of mitotic cell divisions. And each of these mitotic divisions results in two daughter cells, each with the same number of chromosomes as the parent cell. Therefore, whatever the number of chromosomes in a zygote, that number appears in the cells of the individual that develops from the zygote. When the individual matures, it, too, forms gametes. When one of these gametes unites with another, will not the number of chromosomes be doubled again in the zygote? And will not *every* following generation redouble the number of chromosomes? Chromosomes are small; but by this process, after only a few hundred generations the mass of chromosomes in the zygotes would be larger than the largest-known cells. Yet organisms have reproduced for many thousands of generations without this happening.

Truth in science cannot be established by reasoning alone. But in this case reasoning is supported by evidence. By 1890 cell biologists had shown that normally the number of chromosomes of the body cells in any species is constant. Counting chromosomes is a difficult and tedious job, but the chromosome number has now been determined for many species. For example, in corn the number is 20; in the housefly, 12; and in man, 46. Clearly at some step in the life cycle of a sexually reproducing organism the number of chromosomes must be reduced. How and when does this occur? Most of the solution to this problem was worked out just before the beginning of the twentieth century. Answers to the "how" part of the question turn out to be rather similar for all sexually reproducing organisms—a process called *meiosis*. But the answers to the "when" part vary a great deal.

Meiosis consists of two nuclear divisions. As you read the following description, refer often to Figure 16·10.

The first division of meiosis begins somewhat like a mitotic division. A spindle forms. Chromosomes become visible as double threads, each pair of chromatids held together by a kinetochore. However, before moving toward the equator of the spindle, each chromosome pairs with a similar chromosome. And since each chromosome consists of two chromatids, a pair appears to be *four* strands—often twisted together. After the pairs of chromosomes move to the equator, the kinetochores do not divide. As a result, whole double-chromatid chromosomes move to the poles of the spindle—one member of each pair to one pole, the other member of each pair to the other pole. Therefore, the number of chromosomes gathering at each pole is *half* the number present in the original cell.

In what branch of human knowledge is truth established by reasoning alone—not regarding observational evidence?

tedious [tĕd´ē əs; Latin: *taedet*, to be disgusted with]: here, boring but requiring close attention

meiosis    [mī ō´sĭs;    Greek: *meioun*, to make smaller]

The cytoplast may now begin to divide, but the chromosomes do not fade from view as they do at the end of mitosis. Instead, another division begins in each chromosome group. This division is much like mitotic division. The chromosomes gather at the equator of the new spindle, the kinetochores break, and the chromatids (now chromosomes) move to the poles of the spindle. New nuclei are formed, and usually the cytoplast divides. The result of the whole process is four new nuclei, each with half the number of chromosomes that the original cell possessed. The

**Figure 16 · 10**

Diagrammatic representation of meiosis. In this case what is the diploid number of chromosomes?

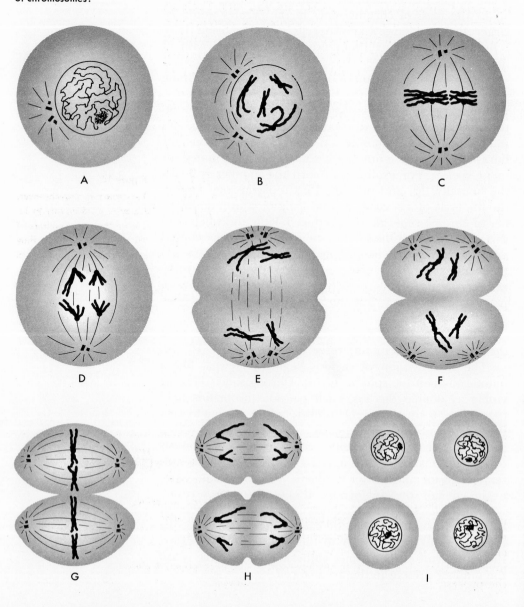

A    B    C

D    E    F

G    H    I

number of chromosomes before meiosis is called the *diploid* number; the number after meiosis is called the *monoploid* number. Gametes contain the monoploid number of chromosomes for a particular species; union of gametes restores the diploid number.

diploid [dip'loid; Greek: *diploos*, double, + *eidos*, form, shape]

To simplify the description, one important event in the first meiotic division was omitted. When chromosomes are paired in the first meiotic division, the chromatids often break where they are twisted together. When the paired chromosomes begin to separate, the upper part of one chromatid may join with the lower part of another, and the remaining upper and lower parts may also join. Such an exchange of chromatid parts is known as *crossing-over*. There is no way to predict where the breaks will occur. But the process occurs quite regularly—much more often than not. And it is of great importance to our later study of heredity.

monoploid [Greek: *monos*, single]: A synonym is "haploid" [Greek: *haploos*, single, simple].

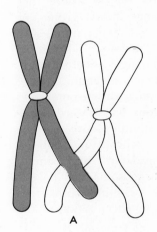

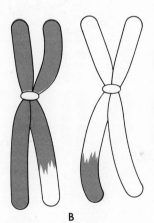

Figure 16 · 11

Two steps in crossing-over. Color is used merely to indicate the two members of the chromosome pair; they are indistinguishable in living or stained cells.

A                                    B

## INVESTIGATION 16.2

### A MODEL OF MEIOSIS

#### PURPOSE

Many biological events are easier to understand when they are explained by means of models. By duplicating the nuclear events of meiosis in a model, this investigation will help you to understand the process.

**MATERIALS AND EQUIPMENT**
(for each team)

Poppit beads, two colors,
   36 of each color
Pipe cleaners, 2
Scissors
Wrapping paper, 2 pieces
Crayon

## PROCEDURE

Begin the construction of the meiosis model by making up eight strands of poppit beads as follows:

2 eight-bead strands, all of the first color

2 eight-bead strands, all of the second color

2 ten-bead strands, all of the first color

2 ten-bead strands, all of the second color

Each strand of beads represents a chromatid. Using short pieces of pipe cleaner to represent kinetochores, fasten the like chromatids together, as shown in Figure 16·12, to form chromosomes.

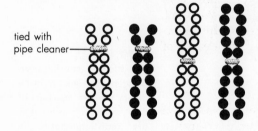

tied with pipe cleaner

Figure 16 · 12

Strands of poppit beads that have been joined to represent chromosomes.

On a large sheet of wrapping paper, draw a spindle large enough to contain the chromosomes you have made. Assume that the early events of the first division have already occurred — the formation of the spindle, the disappearance of the nuclear membrane, the formation of the chromosomes from the nuclear material.

Arrange the four chromosomes along the equator of the spindle in pairs. Since gametes contain only half the number of chromosomes characteristic of a species, we can assume that any individual received one chromosome of each pair from its male parent and one of each pair from its female parent. The chromosomes of such a *homologous* pair cannot be distinguished from each other under the microscope. In this investigation, however, one color can be used for the chromosomes from the male parent, the other color for those from the female parent.

In each homologous pair the chromatids of one chromosome usually overlap the chromatids of the other at one or more points. Show this by overlapping the strands of beads representing the chromatids of each homologous pair. To show crossing-over, break the strands at the points where they cross and exchange beads from one chromosome with an equal number of beads from its homologue. The colors will make the exchange visible throughout the rest of the investigation.

Now begin to move the chromosomes of each homologous pair toward opposite poles of the spindle. Move them by grasping the kinetochores and pulling; the strands of beads will trail behind. Each moving chromosome will have a distinctive shape, resulting both from its length and from the position of the kinetochore.

When the chromosomes of each pair reach the two poles, draw two more spindles. These two spindles should be centered on the poles of the first, and their axes should be perpendicular to the axis of the first. The model is now ready for the second division of meiosis.

Place the chromosomes along the equators of the two new spindles. Unfasten the kinetochore of each chromosome. Grasping each chromatid at the kinetochore, pull the chromatids to opposite poles of their spindles. If there are four members of your team, all the chromatids can be made to move at once, as they do in a living cell.

Discard the wrapping paper and reassemble the chromosomes as they are shown in Figure 16·12. Using a new sheet of paper, repeat the process of meiosis without referring to the directions printed here.

## SUMMARY

• How would a mitosis model differ from this one? (1)   • What are some advantages of using a model to visualize a process? (2)   • What are some disadvantages? (3)

## PATTERNS OF REPRODUCTION

Thus far we have been considering basic similarities in the reproductive processes of all organisms. But there are also some well-defined differences, which are most conspicuous in multicellular plants and in animals. We shall, therefore, select some examples from these groups of organisms to show some of the diversity in the details of reproduction.

### PLANT REPRODUCTION

In the plant kingdom asexual methods of reproduction are more frequent than in the animal kingdom. And in plants sexual methods are more closely associated with evolutionary history—and therefore with classification—than in animals.

Why are characteristics associated with evolutionary history likely to be of importance in classification?

### SOME CHARACTERISTICS OF PLANT REPRODUCTION

Both asexual and sexual methods of reproduction occur in most plant species, but in some species sexual reproduction is rarely observed. In some algae and fungi, for example, zygotes are formed only under unfavorable environmental conditions—such as the approach of winter.

In bryophytes and tracheophytes (and often in the red and brown algae) there is a regular alternation of sexual and asexual methods of reproduction—one generation reproducing sexually and the next, asexually. Such *alternation of generations* occurs in all the familiar plants; however, it is not easily observed, because usually during one of the generations a plant is microscopic.

Where sexual methods occur in the plant kingdom, the gametes may be alike and motile (Figure 16·8). Or they

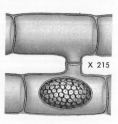

**BEGINNING OF CONJUGATION**  **UNION OF GAMETES**  **ZYGOTE FORMED**

**Figure 16 · 13**

Nonmotile gametes develop from undifferentiated cells in the algal genus *Spirogyra.* This kind of sexual process is referred to as *conjugation.*

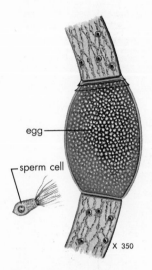

egg

sperm cell

X 350

**Figure 16 · 14**

Gametes of the algal genus *Oedogonium.* The egg cell forms from an undifferentiated cell in the algal filament.

embryological [ĕm′brē ə läj′ĭ-kəl]

Embryophyta [ĕm′brĭ ŏf′ĭ tə]

antheridia [ăn′thə rĭd′ĭ ə; Greek: *anthos,* flower, + *idion,* little]

archegonia [är kə gō′nĭ ə; Greek: *archos,* first, chief, + *gonos,* offspring]

may be alike and not motile. But most often the two gametes are unlike; only in this case is it possible to use the words "sperm" and "ovum." One major difference between sexual reproduction in plants and in animals is the timing of meiosis—the "when" part of the question on page 587. In animals meiosis occurs during the formation of gametes; in plants it often occurs much earlier.

In one-celled plants there is, of course, no embryological development. Botanists speak of embryos only in the bryophytes and tracheophytes; in these plants an individual that develops from a zygote is dependent—at least for a time—on its parent.

### EXAMPLES OF PLANT REPRODUCTION

Several times in this chapter we have referred to reproductive processes of fungi and algae. Now we shall look at bryophytes and tracheophytes, which are often linked together as the subkingdom Embryophyta.

**A moss.** In looking at the life cycle of a moss (Figure 16 · 15), we may start with spores. If a spore reaches a favorable environment—usually a moist soil surface—the wall bursts open. Immediately the cell within begins to divide by mitosis, forming a long green thread from which arises the familiar moss plant. This new individual has a stalk, tiny leaflike structures, and rootlike threads that penetrate the soil.

At the tips of such plants, *antheridia* (sperm-producing structures) and *archegonia* (egg-producing structures) are formed. In some species a single plant produces both kinds of gametes; in other species the sexes are separate. During wet weather, sperm cells swim to an egg cell and fertilization occurs in an archegonium.

The zygote begins to divide immediately, forming an embryo within the archegonium. The embryo grows out of the archegonium and may become taller than the parent. It often forms chlorophyll and produces food, but it must obtain water and dissolved minerals from its parent, to

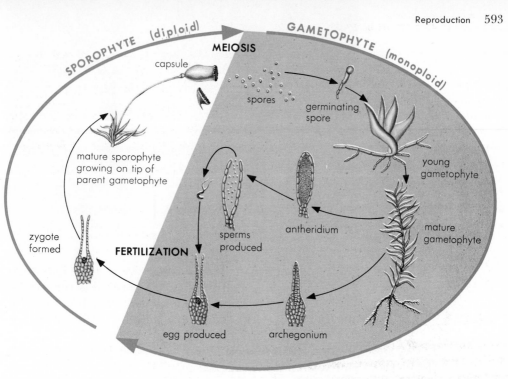

SPOROPHYTE (diploid)    GAMETOPHYTE (monoploid)

MEIOSIS

capsule

spores

germinating spore

young gametophyte

mature gametophyte

mature sporophyte
growing on tip of
parent gametophyte

antheridium

zygote
formed

FERTILIZATION

sperms
produced

egg produced        archegonium

Figure 16 · 15

Reproductive cycle of a
moss. The parts are drawn
to different scales.

which it remains attached. Eventually a spore case develops
at its tip. Within this case meiosis occurs, and cells with the
monoploid number of chromosomes develop into spores.
This completes the cycle.

Two points will be useful for comparison with the life
histories of other plants. First, the moss cycle involves two
generations. Because meiosis occurs when spores are
formed, the "leafy" plant developed directly from a spore
must be composed entirely of monoploid cells. This mono-
ploid organism is called a *gametophyte* because it produces      gametophyte [gə mē′tə fīt′]
gametes. When the gametes unite, a diploid zygote is
formed; and the plant developed from it is called a *sporo-*
*phyte* because it bears spores. Second, fertilization requires      sporophyte [spōr′ə fīt′]
a liquid in which the sperms may swim; in terrestrial mosses
it can only occur when there is rain or dew.

**Selaginella.**  The genus *Selaginella* (subphylum Lycop-      *Selaginella* [sə lăj′ə nĕl′ə]
sida) is composed of small plants that are often found com-
peting with grass in moist and shaded lawns. They also
grow as weeds in greenhouses. They look somewhat like
mosses; but being tracheophytes, they have vascular systems and, therefore, true roots, stems, and leaves.

At the tips of some of the branches, many very small,
overlapping leaves are produced. On the inner surfaces of

Figure 16 · 16
*Selaginella douglasii.*

X 1/2

FPG

these leaves are spore cases. These are of two kinds—and each kind produces its own kind of spore. As in the mosses, meiosis occurs during spore-formation, which means that the spores have the monoploid number of chromosomes.

In the smaller kind of spore (*microspore*), the single cell divides without breaking the spore wall. The structure that develops in this tiny space may be thought of as a minute gametophyte. It forms a single antheridium; indeed, the whole male gametophyte is scarcely anything more than an antheridium. By the time the microspore leaves the parent plant, it contains within its antheridium many flagellated sperms.

Ripon Microslides Laboratory

Figure 16 · 17

Photomicrograph of a longitudinal section through sporangia of *Selaginella.* On the left are two sporangia that contain microspores; on the right are two with megaspores.      X 30

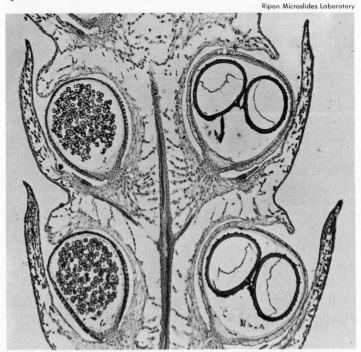

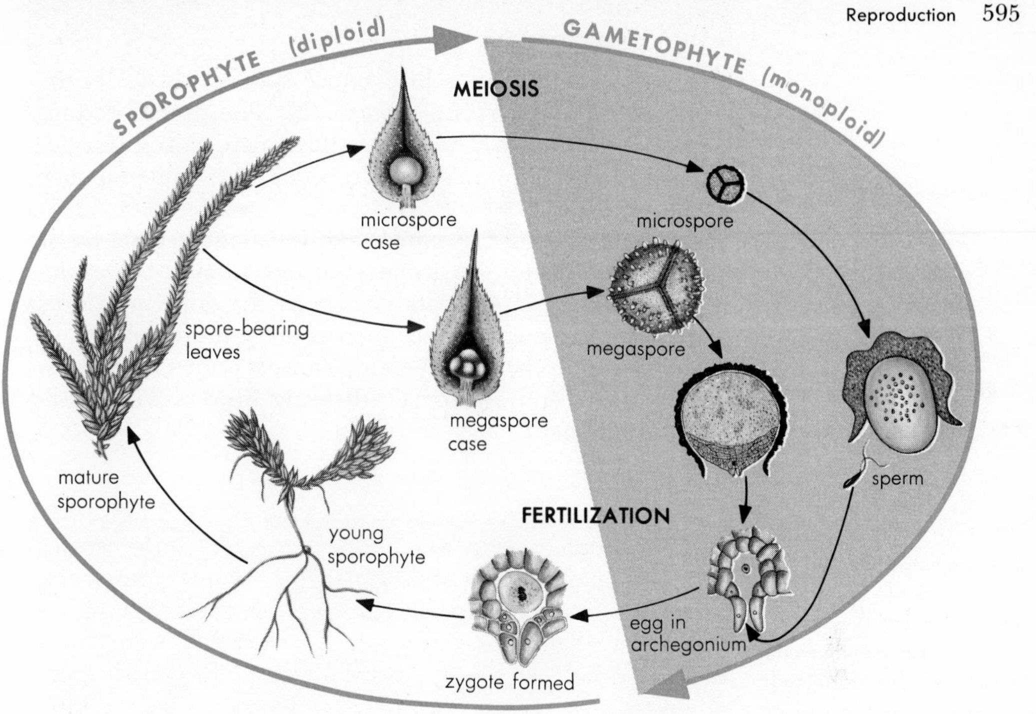

Figure 16 · 18
Reproductive cycle of *Selaginella*. The parts are drawn to different scales.

megaspore [Greek: *megas*, great, mighty, + *spora*]

The larger kind of spore (*megaspore*) becomes the female gametophyte, which is larger and more complex than the male. The female gametophyte forms several archegonia, each with an egg cell. Fertilization depends on dew or rainwater, through which sperm cells are able to swim to the eggs. As the zygote develops into a young plant, the female gametophyte nourishes it with food originally stored in the megaspore. Eventually the new sporophyte forms roots and chlorophyll-bearing leaves and so becomes independent.

In the life history of *Selaginella* are several similarities to the life history of a moss: First, meiosis occurs just before spore-formation; second, there is an alternation of generations; third, water is necessary for fertilization. On the other hand, the spores of *Selaginella* are of two kinds, one producing a male gametophyte and the other a female gametophyte. Also, the gametophytes are tiny in comparison with the sporophyte. Keep these points in mind as you consider reproduction in a flowering plant.

**An angiosperm.** To understand the principles of angiosperm reproduction, we need to focus attention on the pistils and stamens in the characteristic angiosperm structure, the flower. Think of the pistils and stamens as

Refer to Figure 5·5.

highly modified leaves that produce spores (just as do the slightly modified leaves of *Selaginella*). The pistils produce megaspores and the stamens produce microspores; thus we can call the pistil a female structure and the stamen a male structure.

In many angiosperms, male and female structures occur in the same flower. In some—the oak family, for example—they occur in separate flowers on the same individual plant. In a few angiosperms, such as holly, individual plants are either entirely male (bearing flowers with stamens but no pistils) or entirely female (bearing flowers with pistils but no stamens).

How does this statement relate to the explanation of "male" and "female" given on page 585?

Ripon Microslides Laboratory

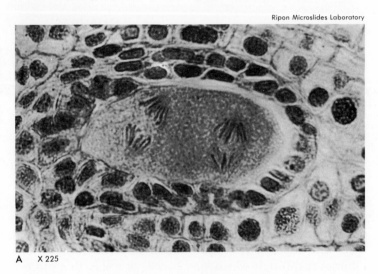

A    X 225

**Figure 16 · 19**

The gametophyte of an angiosperm (a lily). (A) Meiosis in the developing ovule. (B) The mature ovule ready to be fertilized; the egg nucleus is one of those on the left.

B    X 225    Ripon Microslides Laboratory

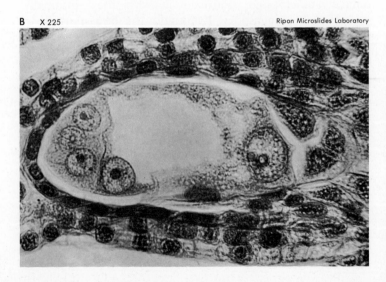

Meiosis occurs before megaspores are formed, and megaspores develop into gametophytes within the spore case, as in *Selaginella*. But in angiosperms a whole gametophyte consists of only a few cells and remains within a pistil. A gametophyte together with some enclosing tissues is called an *ovule*. Within an ovule several nuclei form in a single cytoplast. One of these nuclei is the egg nucleus.

In the stamen tip many microspores are produced by meiosis. Each microspore divides into two cells; then the spore wall around them thickens, and the result is a *pollen grain*. If fertilization is to occur, a whole pollen grain must be transported to a pistil of a flower of the same species. Because most flowers have both stamens and pistils, it might seem that this would be an easy matter—the pollen has only to fall from the stamen onto the pistil of the same flower. Such *self-pollination* does occur, but in many plants various devices prevent it. Though pollen may be transported from flower to flower by wind, a large proportion of angiosperms are pollinated by insects.

There is usually a sticky area on the pistil, and pollen grains adhere to it. Each pollen grain begins to grow a *pollen tube*, which penetrates into the pistil. The pollen grain and its tube (which sometimes reaches a length of several centimeters) can be considered the male gametophyte, a structure even simpler than the female gametophyte. It produces two sperm nuclei which are carried along in the pollen tube as it grows (Figure 16 · 20). Thus angiosperms (and gymnosperms, which also have pollen grains) are not dependent upon water for fertilization.

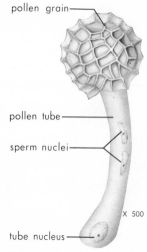

pollen grain —

pollen tube —

sperm nuclei —

X 500

tube nucleus —

**Figure 16 · 20**

**Male gametophyte of an angiosperm.**

The relationship between insect and plant is mutualistic. Explain.

**Figure 16 · 21**

The reproductive cycle of gymnosperms is somewhat like that of angiosperms. **(A)** Pollen-producing (microspore) structures (X 2) , and **(B)** ovule-producing (megaspore) structures (X 3) in

A

Ross E. Hutchins

B          pine.          Ross E. Hutchins

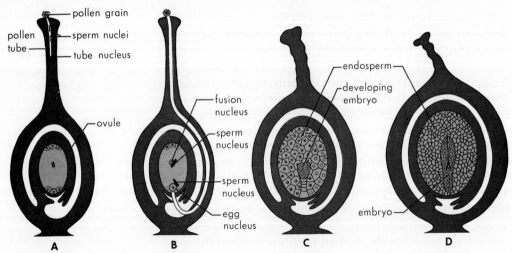

A    B    C    D

**Figure 16 · 22**

Stages (A to D) in fertilization and embryo development of an angiosperm.

triploid [trip′loid; Latin: *triplus*, threefold]

**Figure 16 · 23**

Reproductive cycle of an angiosperm. The parts are drawn to different scales. An *embryo sac*, inner part of an ovule, can be called a female gametophyte.

Eventually a pollen tube reaches an ovule, where one of the sperm nuclei unites with the egg nucleus. The second sperm nucleus unites with another nucleus in the ovule. Unlike the monoploid egg nucleus, this nucleus is diploid; by uniting with a sperm nucleus, it forms a *triploid* nucleus—one with *three* sets of chromosomes. In most plants this triploid nucleus gives rise to a mass of food-storing

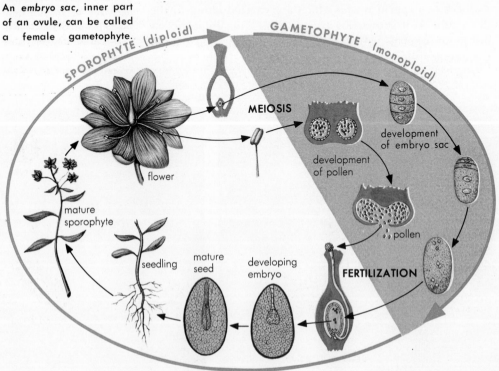

cells, the endosperm. The zygote nucleus, formed by the union of sperm nucleus and female egg nucleus, develops into a small plant, the embryo.

Unlike an embryo of *Selaginella*, an angiosperm embryo becomes dormant. With its food supply and a coat formed from ovule tissues, it is a seed. The pistil and (sometimes) the receptacle of a flower develop into a fruit. Eventually a fruit, containing one or more seeds, leaves the "parent" plant—at least, "parent" is the customary term. But if you have carefully followed the description and understood the previous examples, you know that the plant bearing the seed is actually the *grandparent* of the embryo in the seed. The *parents* of the embryo within the seed were the microscopic gametophytes within the pollen grain and ovule. But the gametophyte generation is so difficult to see in angiosperms that it is usually overlooked, and so generations of angiosperms are counted only from one spore-bearing plant to the next.

## ANIMAL REPRODUCTION

In the animal kingdom reproduction is primarily sexual. Even in species that have asexual methods, as do many coelenterates, sexual reproduction takes place frequently.

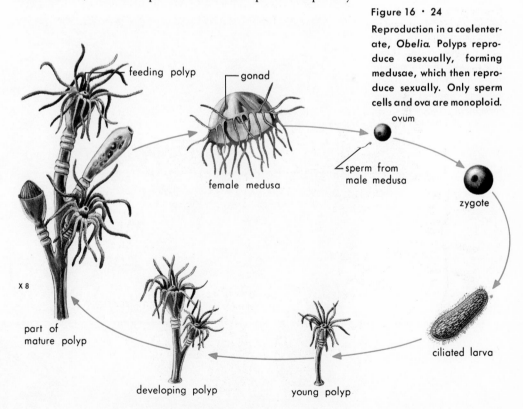

**Figure 16 · 24**

Reproduction in a coelenterate, *Obelia*. Polyps reproduce asexually, forming medusae, which then reproduce sexually. Only sperm cells and ova are monoploid.

In animals, alternation of monoploid with diploid generations is unknown. In coelenterates there is an alternation of a sexual generation with an asexual generation, both diploid. Furthermore, in animals, gametes are always of two kinds, and meiosis occurs just before or during gamete-formation.

### SOME CHARACTERISTICS
### OF ANIMAL REPRODUCTION

**Gamete-formation.** In all animals except sponges, meiosis and gamete-formation occur in special structures called *gonads*. Gonads that produce ova are *ovaries;* those that produce sperm cells are *testes.* The two kinds of gonads are usually distinct, though in American oysters gonads produce ova one year and sperms the next.

gonads    [gŏn'ădz;    Greek: gonos, offspring]

How would you describe the sex of an oyster?

We have seen how the process of meiosis results in the division of one cell into four. In the testes each of these four cells becomes a sperm. Because there is no period of growth between the two meiotic divisions, only a small cytoplast surrounds the nucleus in each of these cells. Most of the cytoplast is in the form of a tail by which the sperm cell swims; the head of the sperm consists mainly of the nucleus.

Edward Roosen-Runge

**Figure 16 · 25**

Photomicrograph of a section through a rat testis. Sperm cells are formed in the walls of tubules. Cells between tubules secrete hormones.    X 375

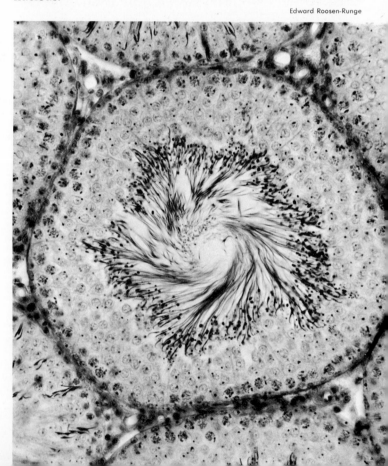

In egg-formation the substance of the cytoplast is distributed somewhat differently during meiosis. In the first meiotic division almost all of this substance goes to one cell, resulting in one large and one small cell. In the second meiotic division the same thing happens to the larger cell. The outcome is the formation of one large cell, which has almost all of the cytoplast of the original cell, and three small cells. The one large cell becomes an ovum; the others die. In many species egg cells increase in size after they are formed, but there is enormous variation in the size of fully developed animal egg cells (Figure 16·9).

**Sex in animals.** In most familiar kinds of animals, any one individual has ovaries only or testes only, not both. If it has ovaries, the individual is female; if testes, male. Often this difference in the gonads is reflected by differences in other characteristics—secondary sexual characteristics. These may be differences in appearance, or they may be differences in voice or behavior. In some animals, on the other hand, only differences in the gonads distinguish the sexes.

In some animal phyla, an individual has both ovaries and testes. This is true of earthworms. It is also true of many other annelids, most flatworms, and some crustaceans. An individual animal that has both ovaries and testes is called a *hermaphrodite*. Even among vertebrates, hermaphroditic individuals occasionally occur, though they are not normal in any vertebrate species.

hermaphrodite, [hûr mǎf′rə-dīt′]. This word is not used by botanists, but essentially the same condition is very frequent among angiosperms. Can you give some examples?

**Fertilization.** The tails of most animal sperms make it possible for them to swim like tadpoles, but of course there must be some liquid in which to swim. Animals that live in water can release eggs and sperms directly into the environment. But sperm cells contain only a very small amount of stored food. Hence they can survive only a short time (usually not more than a few days) after being released from the parent. Obviously, then, if there is to be any reasonable chance of a sperm's uniting with an ovum, both must be released at approximately the same time and place.

Consider the striped bass (Class Osteichthyes) that annually ascend all the large rivers of the Atlantic coast and some of the Pacific. The trip upriver brings the fish into shallow pools, where females lay eggs and males deposit sperm cells at the same time. What factors bring male and female bass to the same place at the same time, with eggs and sperms ready to be shed? Can water temperature play a part? Or variations in salinity? These are important biological questions, and biologists are far from fully answering them.

striped bass: See Figure 16·31.

Apparently, sexually reproducing animals never release eggs and sperms at random, leaving the meeting of the two

Richard W. Emery

**Figure 16 · 26**

From March to July, always a day or two after full moon, grunions come to the beaches of southern California, where their eggs are laid and fertilized. What may time this meeting of the sexes? × 1/3

parthenogenesis [pär′thə nō-jĕn′ə sĭs; Greek: parthenos, maiden, + genesis, origin]

to pure chance. In many phyla the meeting of gametes is still further ensured by *internal* fertilization. The male places sperms into the body of the female, where they meet the ova at some point between the ovary and the opening to the environment.

Among aquatic animals such internal fertilization is not necessary, but it occurs among many crustaceans and all cartilaginous fishes. Among terrestrial animals internal fertilization is a necessity. But there is still the matter of timing. If, when sperms arrive, the ova have not yet reached a proper stage of development, fertilization will not occur, because sperms are short-lived. There are exceptions to this, however. For example, in some insects the sperms are stored in a special sac after they have been deposited within the reproductive system of the female. There they remain alive and are released as eggs are laid — in bees, sometimes several years later!

**Parthenogenesis.** In some animals, and under certain conditions, an ovum may develop into a new individual without fertilization by a sperm cell. Such reproduction by *parthenogenesis* occurs, for example, among aphids. During summer, generation after generation of aphids is produced in this manner. Then fertilization produces zygotes, which remain dormant throughout the winter.

About 1900, experimental biologists discovered they could bring about parthenogenesis artificially. Many factors, such as treatment with weak organic acids or simply pricking with a sharp glass needle, were found to cause the

**Figure 16 · 27**
This parthenogenetic turkey had lived to the age of 161 days when the photograph was taken. In several ways it was abnormal. Note the crooked toes.    × 1/7

ova of various animals to begin development without fertilization. Usually such development is incomplete, but occasionally individuals from such ova are even raised to adulthood. Early work on parthenogenesis was done with invertebrates, but during the last few decades ova of frogs and even of rabbits have been stimulated to develop without fertilization. Until recently it was believed that parthenogenesis does not occur naturally among vertebrates. Then biologists of the Agricultural Research Center at Beltsville, Maryland, found that a small percentage of the eggs laid by a new breed of turkey are parthenogenetic, though development rarely continues until hatching.

Do you consider parthenogenesis a sexual method of reproduction? Why or why not?

### EXAMPLES OF ANIMAL REPRODUCTION

In multicellular organisms fertilization is merely the beginning of reproduction. Only when a zygote has developed into an embryo and the embryo has become an individual capable of feeding and maintaining itself — only then has reproduction been accomplished. *Embryology* is, therefore, a basic part of the study of reproduction. In the following examples of animal reproduction, emphasis is placed on embryology. The examples also show a small part of the great diversity in animal reproductive processes.

embryology [ĕm′brĭ ŏl′ə jĭ]

**Hydra.** Through much of the year, hydras reproduce asexually, by budding. But under certain conditions they

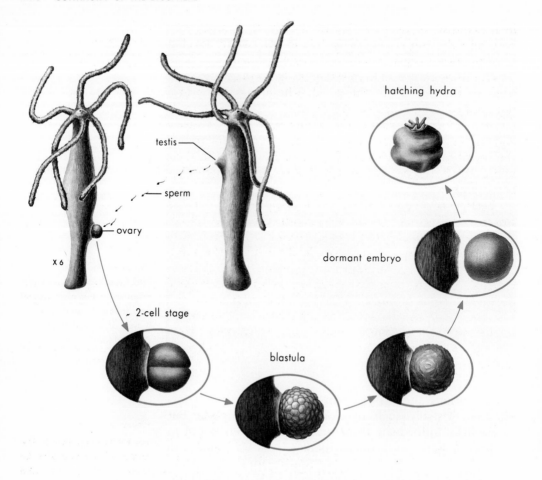

**Figure 16 · 28**
Stages in the embryology
of a hydra.

How many parents may a
sexually reproduced hydra
have?

cleavage [klē′vĭj]

blastula [blăs′chŏŏ lə; Greek:
*blastos*, a sprout]

produce ovaries and testes. Most species are hermaphroditic. The testis is a conical elevation on the outer body wall,
and sperms are released from it through a small pore at its
tip. The ovary is a rounded, swollen structure, also on the
outer body wall. Only one ovum is formed in each ovary; at
maturity it bursts the ovary wall but remains attached to the
parent hydra.

If an ovum is fertilized, the zygote splits into two cells of
equal size. Each of these splits, forming four cells; the four
form eight, and so on. This process is called *cleavage*. As the
number of cells increases, a hollow ball, the *blastula*, is
formed. Further divisions inside the blastula fill the hollow
space with cells. Thus the embryo includes an outer layer
of cells and an inner mass of cells. The body of an adult

hydra consists of only two layers of cells: the (outer) *ecto-derm* and the (inner) *endoderm*. These two layers develop from the two groups of cells in the early embryo.

ectoderm [Greek: *ektos*, out-side, + *derma*, skin]
endoderm [Greek:    *endon*, within, + *derma*]

At this point the embryo separates from the parent and sinks to the bottom of the pond, where it remains in a dormant condition, protected by a thick wall secreted by its outer cells. As time passes, the protective wall breaks away and the embryo elongates; a hollow space appears among the inner cells, tentacles develop at one end, and in their midst a mouth appears. Development of the new hydra has been completed.

**Earthworm.**    Earthworms are hermaphroditic, but the ova in an individual are not fertilized by the sperm cells of the same individual because tubes from the ovaries lead to the surface of one segment, while those from the testes lead to openings in an adjoining segment. Fertilization is internal. Two earthworms *copulate;* sperms of one individual are deposited in a special sac of the other individual, and likewise, sperms from the second individual are deposited in the sac of the first individual. Later, as ova move from the ovary they pass the sac; from it sperm cells are released, and the ova are fertilized.

copulate [kŏp′yə lāt;    Latin: *copulare*, to unite, couple]

How many parents must an earthworm have?

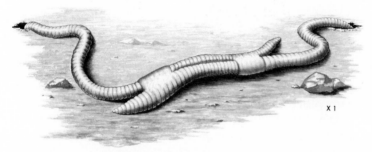

X 1

Figure 16 · 29
Earthworms copulating. The thickened bands aid in the transfer of sperms and later secrete a protective coating around the developing embryos.

Earthworm zygotes are enclosed in a tough case secreted by the worm. Within this case cleavage begins. The first cells formed are not of equal size. As a result, the cells of the blastula have a kind of spiral arrangement; this is characteristic in many animal phyla, from flatworms to arthropods, but not in echinoderms or chordates.

An earthworm embryo also differs from the embryo of a hydra in having a third layer of cells, the *mesoderm* (Figure 16 · 30). All animal phyla except sponges and coelenterates have such a third embryonic layer. From the three layers all the organ systems of the animal body are derived. The earthworm embryo requires two or three weeks for development, after which it escapes from its case as a small copy of the adult.

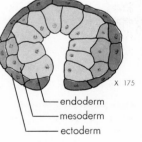

X 175

endoderm
mesoderm
ectoderm

Figure 16 · 30
Section through a *gastrula* (stage following the blastula) of an earthworm embryo.

mesoderm [měz′ə dûrm′; Greek: *mesos*, middle, + *derma*]

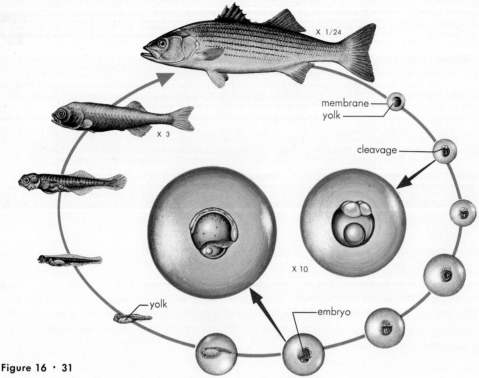

**Figure 16 · 31**

Stages in the embryonic development of a striped bass.

**Striped bass.** Female striped bass deposit their eggs in shallow pools; males follow behind and release sperms over the eggs. Thus fertilization is external, as it is in hydra and many other aquatic animals.

Development of the zygote is rapid. Within a few hours after fertilization, two or more cell divisions occur. In cleavage the divisions are approximately equal (this is characteristic of echinoderms and chordates), but they do not involve the whole zygote. As Figure 16 · 31 shows, new cells are formed only on the top of the zygote. The *yolk* (food supply) remains undivided and nourishes the embryo.

The illustration shows a feature that we did not encounter in hydras or earthworms. Surrounding the ovum is a fluid enclosed in a membrane. Thus, the embryo develops in a somewhat protective environment. Three cell layers—ectoderm, mesoderm, and endoderm—are formed early in development. Within thirty-six hours a tadpole-like embryo is visible on top of the yolk; twelve hours later this tiny, undeveloped organism has "hatched" through the enclosing membrane and is wriggling about in the water. But the hatchling is not a fully developed fish. It has no mouth, and for many days it lives on the food supply still in

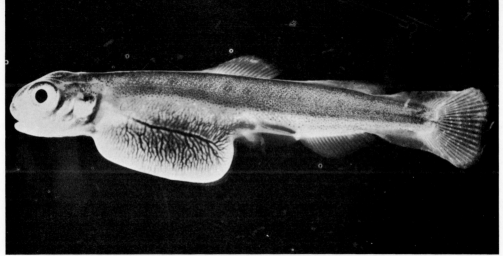

the yolk. In about a month the striped-bass larva has gradually developed the appearance of a young fish.

**Chicken.** Because animal sperms swim, land animals cannot simply shed sperms and eggs into the environment: fertilization must be internal. Many land animals—including all birds—then deposit the fertilized eggs, and development of the embryos occurs outside the body of the female parent. This is possible only if the fertilized egg is protected from drying out. We find, therefore, that fertilized eggs of terrestrial *oviparous* (egg-laying) animals have various kinds of coverings that enclose the developing embryo in a moist environment. Among terrestrial chordates one of these coverings is the amnion, which was discussed on page 363. Chicken eggs have additional coverings present at the time of laying; the amnion develops later.

In a female chicken there is one ovary, with an *oviduct* that leads from the ovary to the outside. Males secrete a fluid, *semen*, in which the sperms swim. During copulation semen is deposited in the oviduct. The sperms swim up the oviduct and meet an ovum in the upper end of the oviduct, where fertilization occurs. Then, as the fertilized egg descends, glands in the wall of the oviduct secrete the various coverings that we find around the "yolk" of a chicken egg when it is laid.

**Figure 16 · 32**

Larva of Chinook salmon, about 90 days after fertilization. It is still living on food stored in the yolk, in which numerous blood vessels can be seen.    × 3

oviparous [ō vǐp′ə rəs; Latin: *ovum*, egg, + *parere*, to bear young]

oviduct [ō′vǐ dŭkt; Latin: *ovum* + *ducere*, to lead]

semen [sē′mən; Latin: *semen*, seed]

## INVESTIGATION 16.3

## CHICK EMBRYOLOGY

### PURPOSE

By direct observation you will investigate the embryology of a common vertebrate animal.

### MATERIALS AND EQUIPMENT
#### (for each team)

A. *Unincubated Egg*

Fertilized chicken egg, unincubated

Finger bowl (about 250 ml)

Stereomicroscope

B. *Two-Day Embryo*

Paper towels

Finger bowl

Egg incubator

Chicken egg, incubated 48 to 52 hours

Scissors (fine-pointed)

Forceps

Medicine dropper

Stereomicroscope or hand lens

Watch with a second hand

Filter paper

Syracuse watch glass

Physiological saline solution

Heat source

Thermometer ($-10-$ $+110°C$)

Monocular microscope

C. *Five-Day Embryo*

Paper towels

Finger bowl

Egg incubator

Chicken egg, incubated 5 to 6 days

Scissors (fine-pointed)

Forceps

Medicine dropper

Stereomicroscope or hand lens

D. *Later Stages of Development*

Egg incubator

Chicken egg, incubated 10, 14, 18, or 21 days

Scissors

Forceps

Finger bowl

Physiological saline solution

Heat source

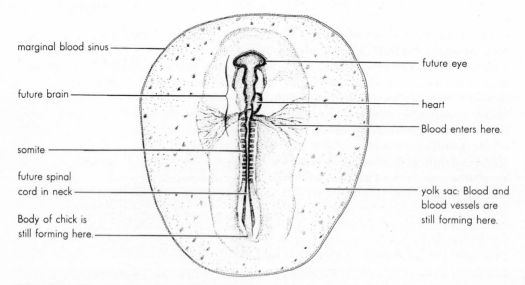

marginal blood sinus

future brain

somite

future spinal cord in neck

Body of chick is still forming here.

future eye

heart

Blood enters here.

yolk sac: Blood and blood vessels are still forming here.

**Figure 16 · 33**

Chick embryo after 33 hours of incubation. At this stage the yolk sac is about 1 cm in diameter and is growing along its entire edge.

Thermometer (−10 to +110°C)
Hand lens

## PROCEDURE

In a freshly laid bird's egg the embryo consists of a few cells on the surface of the yolk. After the egg is laid, further development of the embryo is usually delayed until the egg is incubated by the body heat of an adult bird. You will work with eggs that have been artificially incubated at a temperature of approximately 38°C. But first you will examine an egg that has not yet been incubated.

**A. Unincubated egg.**  Crack a fresh, fertilized chicken egg crosswise. Holding the cracked side up, with your thumbs on each side of the crack, gradually pull apart the two ends and let the contents drop gently into a finger bowl. Observe the albumen ("white"), which is made up largely of protein and water.  • Where is it most dense? (1)  The embryo appears as a white area on the surface of the yolk.  • Describe its appearance under the stereomicroscope. (2)  Examine the inside of the shell and the membrane that lines it.  • At which end of the egg is the membrane not closely attached to the shell? (3)  • What occupies this space between membrane and shell? (4)  • List in order the structures added around the fertilized ovum as it passes down the hen's oviduct. (5)  • Suggest a function for each structure. (6)

**B. Two-day embryo.**  Figure 16 · 33 shows a chick embryo after 33 hours of incubation. At this stage the embryo is still so thin that the parts shown in the drawing can be observed only if stained. *Somites* are blocks of tissue from which vertebrae and muscles develop. Notice that only the head and neck regions of the chick have begun to form. Refer to this figure for comparison as you observe a 48- to 52-hour embryo.

Crumple one or two paper towels into a finger bowl and hollow out a space

A. Carefully insert point of scissors at x, barely penetrating the shell.

B. Carefully and slowly clip the shell completely around the egg.

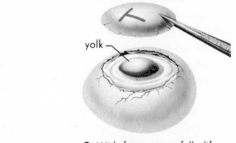

yolk

C. With forceps carefully lift the loose piece of shell and discard.

yolk

embryo

shell

D. Draw off albumen with medicine dropper until yolk is not covered.

Figure 16 · 34

Steps in exposing a chick embryo in an early stage of development.

in the center of them for support of an egg.

Obtain an egg that has been incubated 48 to 52 hours. Before removing it from the incubator, mark a *T* on the top of the egg. Then carry the egg to your work space, holding the marked side up. Keeping that side up, place the egg in the hollow of the paper.

Hold the egg gently but firmly. To expose the embryo, follow the steps shown in Figure 16 · 34. If you have not rotated the egg since taking it from the incubator, the embryo should be on the top of the yolk. If it is not, *gentle* pushing with the medicine dropper may rotate the yolk until the embryo is on top—but great care must be taken that the yolk is not broken.

When the embryo is exposed, you can observe the extent of the *yolk sac* by noting the blood vessels on the surface of the yolk. • Approximately what percentage of the yolk is now covered by the yolk sac? (7) • What do you think is the function of the yolk sac? (8) Using a stereomicroscope or hand lens, examine the embryo. Locate the heart by looking for pulsating movement. • How fast is the heart beating (pulsations per minute)? (9)

Further observation will be easier if you remove the embryo from the yolk. To do this, follow the steps shown in Figure 16 · 35. Before placing the filter-paper ring on the yolk, make sure that none of the albumen is on the surface of the embryo. If it is, repeat Step D, Figure 16 · 34.

After the embryo has been transferred to the watch glass, the saline solution may become cloudy. If this happens, draw off the saline with a clean medicine dropper and replace it with fresh, warm saline. Place the watch glass on the stage of a monocular microscope and observe under low power. Since you are not using a cover slip, you must be careful to

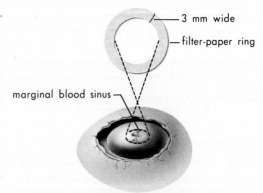

A. Measure diameter of marginal blood sinus. On filter paper, draw a ring that has inner diameter slightly less than diameter of marginal blood sinus. Cut out ring and place over edges of sinus.

B. Grasp ring and edge of membrane. Clip membrane all the way around ring. Slowly lift ring, membrane, and embryo away from yolk.

C. Place ring, membrane, and embryo in Syracuse watch glass containing physiological saline solution (3 mm deep) at 38°C.

Figure 16 · 35

Steps in removing a chick embryo from the yolk.

keep the objective from touching the surface of the liquid. • Which of the structures shown in Figure 16·33 can you see? (10) • Compare the general shape of the embryo with that of the 33-hour embryo. (11)   Most of the large mass of tissue adjacent to the heart will become brain. This part of the embryo may appear to have a membrane, the developing amnion, over it. You may be able to see an ear opening; this was not visible in the 33-hour embryo. Examine the heart carefully.   • Can you trace the pathway of the blood through the heart? If so, describe it. (12)   A slowing of the heartbeat indicates that the temperature of the saline solution is falling. If this occurs, draw off the saline with a medicine dropper and replace it with warm saline.

**C. Five-day embryo.**   Using the technique shown in Figure 16·34, open an egg that has been incubated 5 days. (Caution: The yolk is quite watery at this stage, and some of the delicate membranes are close to the shell; therefore, it is important that you insert only the *tips* of the scissors beneath the shell.)

Compare the amnion in this embryo with the one in the two-day embryo. • Describe any differences. (13)   Gently probe the surface of the amnion with a blunt pencil.   • Is anything besides the embryo inside? If so, what? (14)   Next to the amnion and apparently attached to it by a stalk is a bladder-like membrane covered with blood vessels. This is the *allantois.* Later in development it enlarges and eventually lines the whole inner surface of the egg. Through it the embryo obtains oxygen and excretes carbon dioxide. Observe the extent of the blood vessels on the surface of the yolk. • Approximately what percentage of the yolk is now covered by the yolk sac? (15)

Using forceps and scissors, carefully cut away the amnion, exposing the embryo.   • Compare the size of the eyes with the size of the head. (16)   This size

**A.** Crack the large end of the egg with scissors or scalpel handle.

**B.** Use forceps to pick away the shell. Avoid breaking shell membrane if possible.

**C.** After part of the shell has been removed, put the egg in finger bowl of physiological saline (at 38°C) and pick off the remainder of the shell.

**Figure 16 · 36**

**Steps in exposing a chick embryo in a late stage of development.**

relationship is a characteristic of bird embryos in contrast to mammalian embryos. Look for the two pairs of *limb buds*, the parts that will become the appendages. • How is it possible to distinguish wings from legs at this stage? (17) • Describe any other differences you can see between a two-day and a five-day chick. (18)

**D. Later stages of development.** Eggs incubated 10, 14, 18, and 21 days are to be opened by different teams. For opening eggs in these later stages of development, use the technique shown in Figure 16·36. Try not to break any of the membranes.

When the shell has been removed, you will notice that it is lined with a continuous membrane containing blood vessels. This *chorioallantoic* membrane results when the allantois is extended and united with another embryonic membrane, the *chorion*. • What substances, then, probably pass through it? (19)

Using scissors and forceps, carefully remove the chorioallantoic membrane. • Can you find the yolk sac? How is it connected to the embryo? (20) • How is the food in the yolk transported to the embryo? (21)

Remove the amnion from around the embryo. • Note all features that indicate the organism is a bird. Look for characteristics that you know occur in a hatched chick (beak, feathers, wings, claws, scales on the feet). (22)

After each team has studied its embryo, exchange embryos until all teams have seen each stage of development. • Note (with the day of incubation) features that you were unable to see in your own embryo. (23)

**SUMMARY**

• List all the structures you have observed, in the order of their first appearance during development. (24)

Using the observations you made in this investigation as a basis and supplementing these with any other information you can find, consider the following questions: What characteristics of a chicken egg are adaptations that enable it to develop on land? If the egg developed within the hen instead of outside, what structures would be less important? What explanations can you give for the early development of heart, blood, and blood vessels? How do your observations support the statement (page 127) that chordates show segmentation? What other observations of chordate characteristics did you make (if any)? • Write a summary statement on chick-embryo development that includes your thinking on these questions. (25)

FOR FURTHER INVESTIGATION

1. What effect would incubation at higher or lower temperatures have on the development of a chick embryo? Experiment to test your hypotheses.

2. Pigeon eggs may be incubated artificially, but because the embryos are rather small, handling and observing them is difficult. Even if you cannot make a step-by-step comparison with chicken development, a useful comparison is the state of development at hatching. How do the differences in hatching development relate to parental care? In which bird is development at hatching most like that of turtles at hatching?

3. The development of frog embryos can be studied fairly easily. With frogs you can begin with fertilization and follow development past hatching into the formation of tadpoles. Such a study should include at least two kinds of comparison: the characteristics that are related to aquatic (in contrast to terrestrial) development and the ways in which structures arise during development. For procedures, see the reference given at the top of page 584.

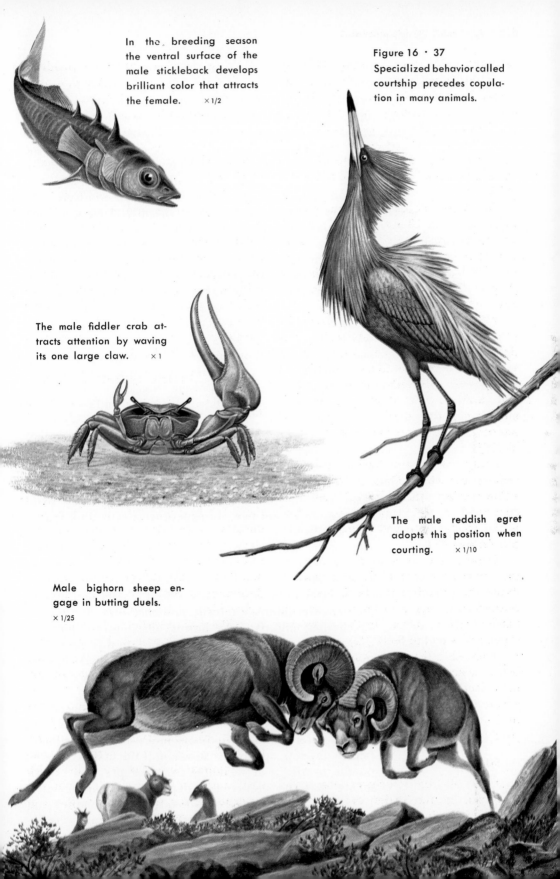

In the breeding season the ventral surface of the male stickleback develops brilliant color that attracts the female. ×1/2

Figure 16 · 37 Specialized behavior called courtship precedes copulation in many animals.

The male fiddler crab attracts attention by waving its one large claw. ×1

The male reddish egret adopts this position when courting. ×1/10

Male bighorn sheep engage in butting duels. ×1/25

viviparous [vī vĭp'ə rəs; Latin: *vivus*, alive, + *parere*]

Can you find out how the embryos of *ovoviviparous* animals develop?

uterus [ū'tə rəs]: In nontechnical language this is called the "womb."

estrous [ĕs'trəs]

**Man.** Among mammals only monotremes are oviparous. All other mammals are *viviparous;* fertilized eggs are retained in the body of the female parent and embryonic development occurs in a *uterus,* a thick-walled part of the tubes that lead from the ovaries to the outside.

Most animals reproduce only at certain times of the year. This is true even in a stable climate, such as that of the tropical rain forest. Many animals have a single annual reproductive season; a good example is the white-crowned sparrow discussed on pages 557–561. Among domesticated birds and mammals such seasonal reproduction is much less clearly marked than in wild animals, but even such animals as chickens and cattle breed more frequently at some seasons than at others. Among primates, however, there is a tendency toward continuous breeding. Apes and man reproduce at any time during the year.

In addition to the general seasonal reproductive cycle, which usually affects both sexes, female mammals have a shorter cycle of reproductive activity—the *estrous* cycle. Though an annual cycle of reproduction is lacking in man and apes, a female cycle is present. No clear understanding of mammalian reproduction is possible without careful consideration of it.

A cycle of physiological activity implies controls. And we might expect that we can look to the nervous and endocrine systems for such controls.

Early efforts of physiologists to work out the mechanisms of these controls indicated that the pituitary gland plays an important part. In experiments with adult female rats, the pituitary glands were removed. Development of eggs in the ovaries ceased, and thickening of the lining in the uterus, a usual event in the cycle, failed to occur. These results raised a number of questions: Does the pituitary gland exert a direct effect upon both ovaries and uterus? Or does the pituitary directly influence only the ovaries, which then influence the uterus? Or does the pituitary directly influence only the uterus, which in turn influences the ovaries? And, if removal of the pituitary gland stops the functioning of ovaries and uterus, why are they not continuously active when the pituitary is present?

Other experiments provided information concerning these questions. When rat ovaries are removed, leaving both the uterus and the pituitary intact, the uterine lining fails to develop; apparently function of the uterus depends on the ovaries. But we know from the previous experiments that the uterus also depends on the pituitary. In still another set of experiments, both pituitaries and ovaries were removed from rats. Then the rats were in-

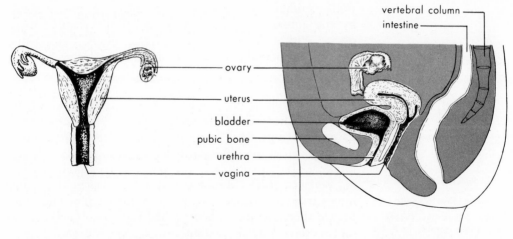

vertebral column
intestine

ovary

uterus

bladder

pubic bone

urethra

vagina

jected with hormones from ovaries of other rats, and thickening of the uterine lining followed. It was concluded that pituitary hormones influence the ovaries and that ovarian hormones influence the uterus.

By many experiments such as these, physiologists have come to understand the female reproductive cycle in mammals. As in other studies of physiological processes, most of this experimental evidence can be applied to humans. However, in humans and other primates of the subfamily Hominoidea the cycle differs enough from that in other mammals to have another name—the *menstrual* cycle.

It is convenient to begin a description of the menstrual cycle at the time when the lining of the uterus is thin and

**Figure 16 · 38**

Human female reproductive system in a sectional view (*right*), and the principal organs in a frontal view (*left*).

menstrual [mĕn'strŏŏ əl; Latin: *mensis*, month (because the cycle's average length is 28 days, the lunar month)]

**Figure 16 · 39**

Cross section of a rat ovary, showing numerous follicles. An egg cell can be seen in the follicle at lower center (*arrow*).    ×26

Eric Grave/Charles A. Ely, Columbia Univ. from Photo Researchers

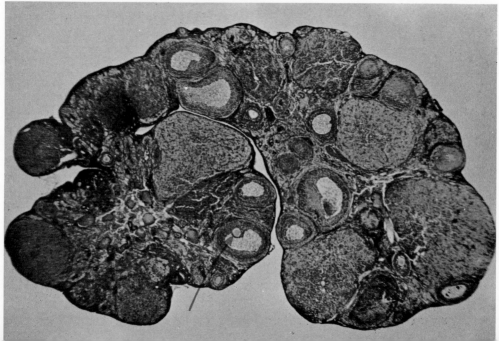

nonfunctional. Secretion of *follicle stimulating hormone* (*FSH*) by the pituitary causes development of a *follicle* in an ovary. Within the follicle an ovum develops. Usually one ovum is developed in each cycle. If an ovum is developed in the right ovary during one cycle, then usually during the next cycle an ovum is developed in the left ovary, and so forth. Ovum and follicle enlarge and move to the surface of the ovary, and the follicle begins to secrete the hormone *estrogen*. Estrogen brings about the thickening of the uterine lining and also causes the pituitary to cease producing FSH. In addition, estrogen stimulates the pituitary to secrete *luteinizing hormone* (*LH*). LH brings about *ovulation*: the ovum bursts from the follicle and enters the adjacent oviduct. The follicle then becomes a body called the *corpus luteum*. This, too, secretes a hormone, *progesterone*, which greatly speeds growth of glands and blood vessels in the uterine lining, causing it to become still thicker.

When the follicle bursts at ovulation, its production of estrogen ceases. *If the ovum is not fertilized,* there is no longer estrogen in the blood stimulating the pituitary to produce LH. Without LH, the corpus luteum ceases forming progesterone. And with no more progesterone, the thickened lining of the uterus is no longer maintained; it breaks down. The discharge of blood and the sloughed uterine

estrogen [ĕs'trə jən]

luteinizing [lōō'tĭ ə nī'zĭng; Latin: *luteus*, golden-yellow]

ovulation [ō'vyə lā'shən]

corpus luteum [kôr'pəs lōō'tĭ-əm; Latin: *corpus*, body, + *luteus*]: In many mammals this body is yellow.

progesterone [prō jĕs'tə rōn']

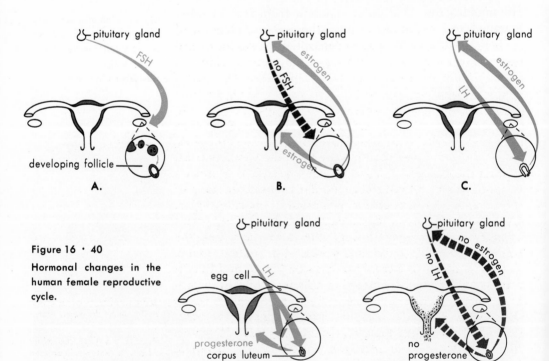

**Figure 16 · 40**

Hormonal changes in the human female reproductive cycle.

lining through the *vagina* is called *menstruation*. Meanwhile, decline in concentration of estrogen and progesterone in the blood apparently affects the nervous system, through which the output of neurohormones from the hypothalamus is increased. This, in turn, permits the pituitary to secrete FSH, thus starting a new cycle.

But what happens if the ovum *is* fertilized? This requires the presence of sperm cells, so we turn to the male reproductive system.

vagina [və jī'nə]

Can you recall other physiological processes in which neurohormonal stimulation of the pituitary is important?

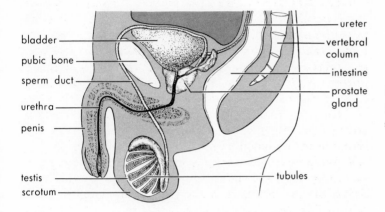

**Figure 16 · 41**
**Human male reproductive system in sectional view.**

In human males there is a continuous production of sperm cells. They are produced in coiled tubules in the two testes, which lie outside the body wall in a sac of skin, the *scrotum*. From the testes, sperm cells pass through a series of ducts that lead up into the body cavity. Along the way secretions produced by three sets of glands are added to the sperm cells; thus semen is formed. The duct from each testis unites with the urethra, which passes through the *penis*.

scrotum [skrō'təm]

penis [pē'nis]

As a result of sexual stimuli, veins in the penis contract, slowing the flow of blood, which consequently accumulates in spongy tissue within the penis. This causes stiffening of the penis so that it is able to penetrate the female vagina. Upon further stimulation semen is discharged. The sperms swim from the vagina through the uterus and into the oviducts; there, if an ovum is present, fertilization occurs.

The pituitary of a male produces both FSH and LH. In a male LH stimulates endocrine cells in the testes to produce hormones called *androgens*. FSH apparently increases the amount of these hormones, which maintain the functioning of the entire male reproductive system. However, they do not appear to affect the hypothalamus; thus there is no cycle in the reproductive organs of a human male.

androgens [ăn'drə jəns; Greek: andr, man, + genes, born]

How do you think this might differ in a male white-crowned sparrow?

618

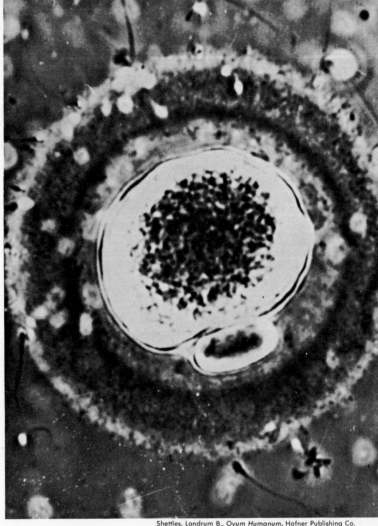

Shettles, Landrum B., *Ovum Humanum*, Hafner Publishing Co.

**Figure 16 · 42**

Human ovum surrounded by sperms. In fertilization only one sperm cell penetrates the membrane of the ovum.

pregnancy [Latin: *pregnans,* heavy with young]

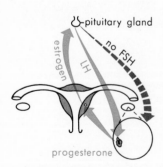

**Figure 16 · 43**

Female hormonal relationships during early part of pregnancy.

Now we can return to the female. If an ovum is fertilized, the menstrual cycle is interrupted. The zygote is moved along the oviduct. When it reaches the uterus, it sinks into the soft, spongy lining, and *pregnancy* begins.

But what prevents the breakdown of the uterine lining and the sloughing of the embryo? The embryo causes glands in the uterine wall to produce estrogen. Uterine estrogen functions just as does follicular estrogen: it prevents production of FSH and stimulates production of LH by the pituitary gland. LH, in turn, causes the corpus luteum to continue to produce progesterone, which maintains the thick lining of the uterus. As long as progesterone is produced, menstruation does not occur, pregnancy is maintained, and no new ova develop in the ovaries.

Very early in pregnancy, embryonic membranes appear. A chorion develops against the uterine wall and,

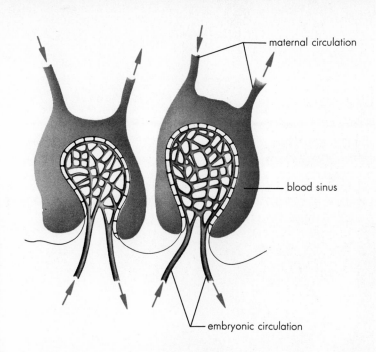

maternal circulation

blood sinus

embryonic circulation

**Figure 16 · 44**

A diagrammatic section through a placenta. The circulations of embryo and mother are separate but close to each other. Blood of the embryo passes through networks of capillaries that are surrounded by small pools of maternal blood.

together with an outgrowth of the uterine wall itself, forms the *placenta*. Through this placenta, which eventually lines much of the uterus, the embryo receives food and oxygen and discharges wastes and carbon dioxide. All exchanges between parent and embryo are by diffusion through the placenta. An allantois grows out from the embryo, and its blood vessels connect the embryo with the placenta through the *umbilical cord*. A yolk sac appears, but it is not functional; a mammalian egg has very little yolk. However, an amnion develops around a human embryo, just as it does around a chick. It is liquid-filled, protecting the embryo from mechanical shock.

Complex hormonal controls continue during pregnancy. The developing chorion, for example, secretes a hormone that stimulates the corpus luteum to continue secreting progesterone; this maintains the uterine lining until the placenta begins to secrete both estrogen and progesterone. Eventually the placenta secretes sufficient amounts of hormones to maintain pregnancy even if the ovaries are removed.

By the ninth month (280 days) of human pregnancy, the baby's head is usually turned downward. How the process of birth is initiated is not fully understood. It begins when muscle layers in the wall of the uterus start to alternately contract and relax. At first, the muscular activity is just strong enough to move the baby slowly toward the vagina. At this stage the amnion usually breaks, and its

placenta [plə sĕnt′ə;  Greek: *plax*, anything flat and broad]

In marsupial mammals placentas do not fully form. How does this affect the development of marsupial embryos?

umbilical [əm′bĭl′ĭ kəl;  Latin: *umbilicus*, the navel]

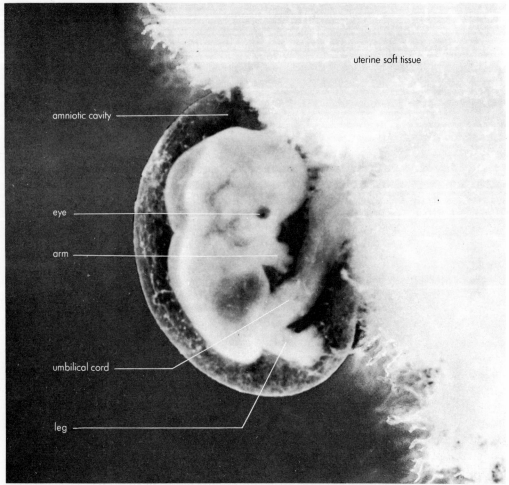

uterine soft tissue

amniotic cavity

eye

arm

umbilical cord

leg

Gesell Institute of Child Development

**Figure 16 · 45**

Human embryo attached to the wall of the uterus.

× 3

fluid contents are released. Contractions in the muscles of the uterus become stronger and more frequent, and the baby, still attached to the placenta by the umbilical cord, is pushed out through the vagina. Muscular contractions of the uterus continue until they push out the placenta, commonly called the "afterbirth."

Late in pregnancy the mammary glands undergo changes that prepare them for producing milk after the baby is born. If the baby does not feed from its mother's breasts, the glands soon stop secreting milk. Usually when milk secretion stops, the menstrual cycle begins again.

For an organism to survive as an *individual*, reproduction is an entirely unnecessary life process. Only for the survival of a *species* is reproduction essential—and this is because individuals die.

Methods of reproduction are almost as diverse as the kinds of organisms themselves, but they can be grouped as either sexual or asexual.

The distinguishing event in sexual reproduction is fertilization, the union of two cells (gametes) to form one (a zygote). At some time before the next fertilization, the number of chromosomes in the zygote—the diploid number—is reduced by half to the monoploid number by the process of meiosis.

Asexual reproduction involves no union of gametes. A single cell or a many-celled fragment merely separates from the parent and develops into an independent individual. Asexual reproduction is rare in the animal kingdom, frequent in the protist and plant kingdoms. The blue-green algae seem to be the only phylum in which sexual reproduction is still unknown.

We have examined some of the principal methods of reproduction that occur in the plant and animal kingdoms. An alternation of asexually reproducing and sexually reproducing generations is characteristic of reproduction in the bryophytes and tracheophytes. However, in gymnosperms and angiosperms the gametophyte generation has become very inconspicuous and dependent upon the sporophyte generation; indeed, we would scarcely recognize the gametophyte without knowledge of such plants as mosses and *Selaginella*. Hermaphroditism and parthenogenesis, variations in sexual reproduction, are found in both the plant and the animal kingdoms, but they are not normal among vertebrates.

Internal fertilization increases the chances that gametes will meet. In terrestrial organisms it also enables gametes to pass easily from one individual to another without a water environment between them. When fertilization is internal, a zygote may develop through an embryonic stage protected within the body of a parent.

The processes of reproduction and embryonic development are probably always closely controlled by chemical mechanisms that are often influenced by environmental conditions. These have been most thoroughly investigated in mammals, and we have used man as our chief example.

## GUIDE QUESTIONS

1. How did Redi show that maggots are not spontaneously generated?
2. From the viewpoint of the individual organism, how does reproduction differ from other life processes?
3. How does vegetative reproduction occur among tracheophytes?
4. What is fission?
5. What is a sporangium?
6. What is the basic event in the process of sexual reproduction?
7. What is the basic biological distinction between the terms "male" and "female"?
8. How is a zygote formed?
9. In what ways does meiosis differ from mitosis?
10. In chickens the diploid chromosome number is 18. What is the number in the cells that result from meiosis?
11. What is meant by the phrase "alternation of generations"?
12. In what ways does the reproductive process of a moss differ from that of a primitive tracheophyte as represented by *Selaginella*?
13. Compare the characteristics of the gametophyte generation in mosses, *Selaginella*, and angiosperms. Compare the characteristics of the sporophyte generation, using the same three examples.
14. Why can pollen-bearing plants be considered more completely adapted to life on land than other terrestrial plants such as mosses and ferns?
15. What two botanical terms can be considered equivalent to the zoological terms "testis" and "ovary"? Can you see any reason for retaining both these pairs of terms?
16. How does the formation of sperm cells following meiosis in animals differ from the formation of egg cells?
17. What is a hermaphroditic animal?
18. Under what circumstances is internal fertilization necessary? Why?
19. With respect to parentage, how does parthenogenesis differ from the usual methods of sexual reproduction?
20. A blastula stage occurs in the embryonic development of many animals. How is the blastula of a hydra formed?
21. From what three embryonic cell layers do the organs of most animals' bodies develop?
22. Where does the food of most animal embryos come from?
23. In chickens where does fertilization occur? How do the sperms reach the ova?
24. How does the reproduction of oviparous vertebrates differ from that of viviparous vertebrates?
25. When an ovum is not fertilized after it breaks from its follicle, what series of events brings about menstruation in the human female?
26. What is the function of androgens?
27. How is the thick lining of a uterus maintained during pregnancy?
28. How are the embryos of most mammals nourished?
29. What is the average length of human pregnancy?
30. How does birth begin?
31. What is the "afterbirth"?

## PROBLEMS

1. What experimental procedures could be used to show that progesterone in a particular mammalian species is secreted by the placenta?
2. Testes of vertebrates develop in the body cavity. In man, if they do not descend into the scrotum they produce no live sperm cells. In some mammals with seasonal breeding, they descend into the scrotum only during the breeding season; during the nonbreeding season they are in the body cavity and produce no sperm cells. If temperatures around the scrotum of an experimental animal are kept the same as the internal body temperature, sperm cells either are not produced or are weak. Yet the testes of birds never leave the body cavity, and birds have, on the average, a higher internal temperature than most mammals. Can you explain these data?
3. What are the advantages to man of propagating plants by rooting portions of an older plant instead of planting seeds? What is the relation of grafting to this propagation by cuttings?

4. Sexuality is usually discussed in terms of "male" and "female," but we have seen that these terms are not always meaningful—as in some molds. In some protists the situation becomes even more complicated. Investigate "mating types" in the genus *Paramecium* and try to explain the situation as a special case of sexuality.

5. Investigate the ways in which self-pollination is prevented among gymnosperms and angiosperms. Are there, on the other hand, plants in which self-pollination always occurs? Can you see any advantages to the plant either in self-pollination or in cross-pollination?

6. Describe *apomixis*. To what process in animals is this comparable?

7. From your understanding of plant reproduction, explain each of the following: (*a*) Seeds will not develop in the yucca unless a certain small species of moth lives in the area. (*b*) Berries do not develop on holly trees unless two trees are planted together; even then, berries do not develop on both and may develop on neither. (*c*) In 1839 a single individual of the plant *Alchornea ilicifolia*, bearing only pistillate flowers, produced abundant seeds in the Kew Gardens, near London. The nearest male plant of the species was in Australia. (*d*) Some kinds of flowers open only at night. (*e*) Orchardists often keep apiaries as a sideline. (*f*) Pea plants, even when grown in an insect-free greenhouse, produce seeds.

8. Each egg of a bony fish is enclosed in a single membrane. A number of membranes develop during the embryonic life of a bird or mammal. Investigate the development and function of embryonic membranes in all the vertebrate classes.

## SUGGESTED READINGS

ALLEN, R. D. "The Moment of Fertilization," *Scientific American*, July, 1959. Pp. 124–130.

ETKIN, W. "How a Tadpole Becomes a Frog," *Scientific American*, May, 1966. Pp. 76–80+.

GABRIEL, M. L., and S. FOGEL (eds.). *Great Experiments in Biology.* Englewood Cliffs, N.J.: Prentice-Hall, Inc., 1955. (Reprints of original papers in which biological discoveries were announced. Especially recommended: Redi, pp. 187–189; Loeb, pp. 201–203; Driesch, pp. 210–214; and Spemann, pp. 215–219.)

GREULACH, V. A., and J. E. ADAMS. 2nd ed. *Plants: An Introduction to Modern Botany.* New York: John Wiley & Sons, Inc., 1962. Chapters 15 and 16. (Clear and accurate general account of reproduction among plants. Fairly easy.)

MICHELMORE, S. *Sexual Reproduction.* New York: The American Museum of Natural History, 1965. (Descriptive accounts of reproduction and embryology in various animal groups. Fairly easy.)

MOMENT, G. B. *General Zoology.* 2nd ed. Boston: Houghton Mifflin Co., 1967. (Reproduction in many kinds of animals is described; use the index. Somewhat advanced.)

SIMPSON, G. G., and W. S. BECK. *Life: An Introduction to Biology.* 2nd ed. New York: Harcourt, Brace & World, Inc., 1965. Chapters 5 and 8. (An excellent general account of the reproductive process. Advanced.)

SUSSMAN, M. *Animal Growth and Development.* 2nd ed. Englewood Cliffs, N.J.: Prentice-Hall, Inc., 1964. (An excellent discussion of the main features of animal embryology.)

WILSON, K. A. "Biology of Reproduction in Ferns," *Natural History*, June, 1965. Pp. 52–59.

# Heredity

### INHERITANCE

"Who does he look like?" For every infant born, some-one asks this question. That a child can be expected to resemble in many ways his parents and his grandparents was certainly one of the first biological ideas developed by man. And still today no biological idea is of more interest. How do we inherit our characteristics of appearance and action and intelligence? Every family is curious about such matters as where Junior's red hair comes from and why Aunt Sarah's large nose appears in Johnny but not in Jane. And we also want to know what the chances are that daughter Mary will have a feeble-minded child if she mar-ries Jim, whose great-uncle on his father's side was feeble-minded.

Man has had other interests in the processes of inheri-tance. For thousands of years pedigreed animals and plants have been prized. Such individuals are valued for one major reason: Their offspring are much more likely to possess desired characteristics than are offspring that have unknown ancestry. A farmer wants pedigreed cattle from which to breed his milk cows; cows from a pedigreed par-entage can be depended on to give abundant and rich milk. The stability of pedigreed lines of organisms—the likeli-hood that offspring will be like parents—is the result of careful selection over many generations. For example, wool-growers have sent sheep that produced poor wool to market as mutton and have selected the best wool-producers as the parents of future flocks. Corn-growers have saved as seed for the next crop ears of corn that had the largest and most numerous grains. Such *selective breeding* has, in

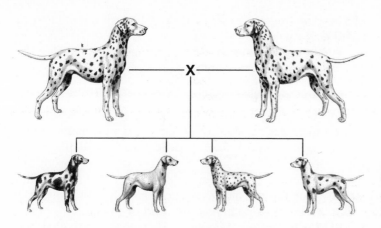

Figure 17 · 1
Variation in the offspring of small-spotted Dalmatian dogs.

many cases, improved the inherited characteristics that are most wanted by man.

Frequently, however, very little success has been obtained from selective breeding. Breeders of Dalmatian dogs have wanted animals with many small and distinct black spots. Year after year they have selected for breeding animals that have just the right pattern. But generation after generation, regardless of the pattern of the parents, pups are born with various amounts of spotting. In short, man long knew that many characteristics *are* inherited, but he did not know *how* they are inherited.

Dalmatian [dăl mā′shən]

The development of modern science, with its emphasis on experiments, led to much experimentation on heredity through the eighteenth and early nineteenth centuries. But until a little over a hundred years ago, no biologist was able to make any sense from the results he obtained.

## THE WORK OF MENDEL

The principles by which the characteristics of organisms are inherited were first explained in 1865 by Gregor Mendel, who had discovered them through a long series of experiments with garden peas. Mendel's success stemmed in large part from the fact that he was trained in mathematics as well as in biology—a combination most unusual for his day. With this background, he planned experiments that differed in three important respects from those of his predecessors.

Bettmann Archive

Figure 17 · 2
Gregor Mendel: 1822 – 1884. Austrian priest and biologist.

First, he did not attempt to study everything about the offspring at once. Instead, he limited each study to a single characteristic.

predecessors   [prĕd′ə sĕs′ərz, prĕd′ə sĕs′ərz]: one who precedes another in an office, position, etc.

Second, instead of studying only the relatively small number of offspring obtainable from a single mating, Mendel used many identical matings. He then pooled the results

pooled: summed, put together

of these matings as if the offspring had all resulted from a single mating.

Third, by working with large numbers of offspring, he was able to apply mathematics to the results.

### MENDEL'S EXPERIMENTS

For his experiments Mendel selected garden peas because numerous varieties of garden peas with many different *traits* (hereditary characteristics) were available. Also, they were easy to cultivate and to breed, and they produced a new generation in a reasonably short time. Finally, the structure of the pea flower is such that Mendel thought it could not be cross-pollinated by wind or insects.

At the beginning Mendel had to make sure that the plants he was to use in his experiments were *pure-breeding* for the traits he wished to study. He did this by letting the plants pollinate themselves for a number of generations. He examined each new generation to make sure that all offspring were alike and like the parent plants with respect to the trait being studied.

Mendel then made hundreds of experimental crosses. If he wished to pollinate one plant with pollen from another plant, he removed the stamens from the flower to be cross-pollinated *before* its own pollen was mature. Later, when the pistil was mature, he transferred pollen from another plant (chosen as the male parent) to this pistil. Thus he was able to control the parentage of the next generation of pea plants.

For one series of crosses, Mendel pollinated plants of a variety that produced only round seeds—a variety purebred for round seeds—with pollen from a variety that produced only wrinkled seeds—purebred for wrinkled seeds. He observed that *all* the offspring of this cross had

**Figure 17 · 3**

Although the pistil and the stamens in peas are surrounded by the keel petal, later investigators have shown that Mendel was wrong in supposing that cross-pollination cannot occur in peas.

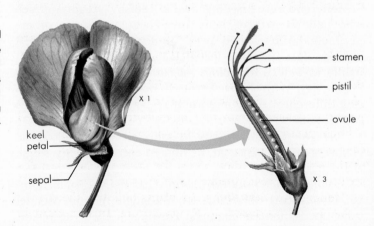

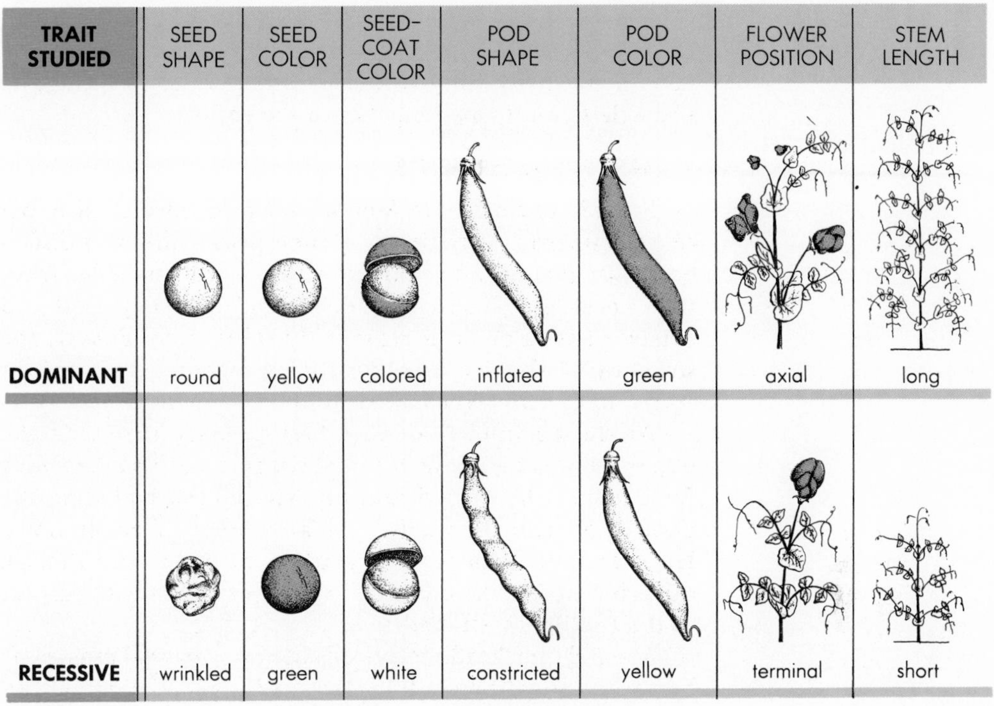

| TRAIT STUDIED | SEED SHAPE | SEED COLOR | SEED-COAT COLOR | POD SHAPE | POD COLOR | FLOWER POSITION | STEM LENGTH |
|---|---|---|---|---|---|---|---|
| DOMINANT | round | yellow | colored | inflated | green | axial | long |
| RECESSIVE | wrinkled | green | white | constricted | yellow | terminal | short |

Figure 17 · 4

The seven traits of garden peas studied by Mendel.

round seeds, none wrinkled ones. Moreover, no matter whether the round-seeded parent contributed the sperm nucleus (by way of the pollen) or the egg nucleus, the off-spring were always round-seeded. And there were *no intermediate* kinds; the seeds of the offspring were just as round as those of the one parent and without any trace of the wrinkling of the other parent. One trait seemed to rule out, or dominate, the other. Mendel therefore called *dominant* those traits that appeared without exception in the *hybrids* (offspring of a cross between parents with con-trasting traits). A summary of the cases in which Mendel found dominance is given in Figure 17 · 4.

When a cross is made between two organisms that are pure-breeding for a particular trait, the parent generation is called the $P_1$ generation. The offspring resulting from the $P_1$ cross are called the first filial generation ($F_1$). In plants that have alternation of generations, such as garden peas, the whole sporophyte-gametophyte cycle is considered a single generation, because meiosis and fertilization occur only once in the cycle—and these are the important things in the study of heredity. Thus, the cross we have just de-scribed is a $P_1$ cross, producing an $F_1$ generation.

Mendel then let the hybrid plants pollinate themselves —that is, he produced an $F_2$ generation. In the example

dominant [Latin: *dominus*, mas-ter (of a house, *domus*)]

hybrids: This word has a spe-cial meaning in the study of heredity; the more common meaning is "offspring of par-ents belonging to different species," as on page 67.

filial [fil′i əl; Latin: *filius*, son]

| | P₁ CROSS | F₁ PLANTS | F₂ PLANTS | ACTUAL RATIO |
|---|---|---|---|---|
| 1. | round X wrinkled seeds | all round | 5,474 round<br>1,850 wrinkled<br>7,324 total | 2.96:1 |
| 2. | yellow X green seeds | all yellow | 6,022 yellow<br>2,001 green<br>8,023 total | 3.01:1 |
| 3. | colored X white seed coats | all colored | 705 colored<br>224 white<br>929 total | 3.15:1 |
| 4. | inflated X constricted pods | all inflated | 882 inflated<br>299 constricted<br>1,181 total | 2.95:1 |
| 5. | green X yellow pods | all green | 428 green<br>152 yellow<br>580 total | 2.82:1 |
| 6. | axial X terminal flowers | all axial | 651 axial<br>207 terminal<br>858 total | 3.14:1 |
| 7. | long X short stems | all long | 787 long<br>277 short<br>1,064 total | 2.84:1 |

**Figure 17 · 5**
Mendel's data from self-pollination of his F₁ plants.

recessive [Latin: re-, back, + cedere, to yield]

used here, he found that most of the seeds in the $F_2$ generation were round, but some were wrinkled. Mendel called wrinkledness a *recessive* trait, because it had "receded" into the background for a generation. He noted again that there were no intermediate forms; the new seeds were either round or wrinkled. In the other six characteristics he was studying, he obtained the same results; the trait that had appeared in all of the $F_1$ generation—the dominant trait—appeared in *most* of the $F_2$ generation, but some $F_2$ generation individuals showed the opposite trait.

A summary of the results that Mendel obtained when he permitted the $F_1$ generation to produce an $F_2$ generation by self-pollination is given in Figure 17 · 5.

## INVESTIGATION 17.1

### PROBABILITY

#### PURPOSE

You will investigate experimentally two principles of probability that are important in understanding Mendel's work.

#### BACKGROUND INFORMATION

The mathematics of probability was originally developed by persons interested in gambling—in games of chance. "Chance" is a term used to describe any situation in which the factors affecting the outcome are so numerous and (taken individually) so weak that we can never hope to determine one "cause." "Random" is another term used for such situations. The expression "choosing at random" means choosing entirely by chance.

The basic question in probability is: How often should we *expect* a particular event in a given number of events? Of course, the gamblers who first worked out the mathematics of probability would have liked to know exactly when, for example, the ace of spades would appear in a deal of cards. But the best that the mathematics of probability can ever do for gamblers or for scientists is to tell what expectation will *least often* be disappointed. In the language of gamblers, it gives us the "odds."

The simplest way to express probability mathematically is by means of fractions. When a coin is tossed into the air, it may come up "heads" or "tails." The number of possibilities is the denominator of the fraction—in this example, two. What is the probability that "heads" will come up when you toss the coin? In this question you are looking for *one* specific event; this is the numerator of the fraction. Thus, the probability of a coin's landing "heads" up is 1/2.

We can also write this as 0.5 or 50%, but the common fraction is the starting point.

Some further examples: There are 52 cards in a deck, 13 of each suit. What is the probability that you will draw a spade from a shuffled deck? There are 52 possibilities in the deck, of which 13 meet the conditions of the question. Therefore the probability is 13/52, or 1/4, or .25, or 25%. What is the probability that you will draw the ace of diamonds? Again there are 52 possibilities, but this time only one meets the conditions of the question; the probability is 1/52. A die (singular of "dice") has six sides. What is the probability that an even number will come up on one throw of the die? Since there are three even numbers on the die—2, 4, and 6—there are three ways in which the conditions of the question may be met; therefore the probability is 3/6, or 1/2.

#### MATERIALS AND EQUIPMENT
(per pair of students)

Pennies, 2 (one shiny, one dull)
Cardboard box

#### PROCEDURE

Students will work in pairs.
*Tossing a Single Penny*

Student A: Prepare a score sheet containing two columns. Label one column *H* ("Heads"); label the other *T* ("Tails").

Student B: Toss a penny 10 times. Toss into a cardboard box to prevent rolling.

Student A: Use a slash mark (/) to tally the result of each toss in the appropriate column on the score sheet. After the tenth toss, draw a line across the columns of the score sheet and pass the sheet to Student B. Take the penny and make 10 tosses.

Student B: Tally the results of Student A's tosses. Draw a line across the score sheet.

Continue reversing the roles until the results of 100 (ten series of 10) tosses have been tallied.

*Tossing Two Pennies Together*

Student A: Prepare a score sheet containing four columns: *Both H, Both T, Dull H / Shiny T,* and *Dull T / Shiny H.* (H = "heads"; T = "tails")

Student B: Choose two pennies that can be easily distinguished—one dull and one shiny. Toss both pennies together 20 times.

Student A: Tally each result in the appropriate column of the score sheet.

Reverse roles once (this will result in a total of 40 tosses).

### STUDYING THE DATA

**Tossing a single penny.** • What does the mathematics of probability lead you to *expect* in a series of 10 tosses of the coin? (1)  • In any set of 10 throws, did you ever obtain the expected results? If not, how close did you come? (2)

*Deviation* is a measure of the difference between expected results and observed results. To calculate deviation, first determine the difference between the number of "heads" you expected and the number of "heads" you observed. Then determine the difference between the number of "tails" you expected and the number of "tails " you observed. Add the two differences together, and divide the sum by the total number of tosses.

Calculate the deviation for each set of 10 tosses. Add the ten sets and calculate the deviation for your team. Add the data of all teams in your class and calculate the class deviation. If your school has more than one biology class, combine the data of all classes and calculate the deviation. Finally, calculate the *average* deviation of sets, teams, classes, and the school.  • How does increasing the number of tosses affect the average size of the deviation? (3)   You have just worked out an important principle of probability.

**Tossing two pennies together.** On the chalkboard record the data from all teams and total each column of the chart.  • In how many columns do data concerning "heads" of a dull penny appear? (4)  • In what fraction of the total number of tosses did "heads" of the dull pennies occur? (5)  • In how many columns do data concerning "heads" of a shiny penny occur? (6)   In what fraction of the total number of tosses did "heads" of the shiny pennies occur? (7)  • In how many columns do "heads" of both dull and shiny pennies appear? (8)  • In what fraction of the total number of tosses did "heads" of both pennies appear at the same time? (9)  • Is this fraction closest to the *sum,* the *difference,* or the *product* of the two fractions for heads on one penny at a time? (10) You have just worked out a second important principle: the relationship between the probabilities of *separate* events and the probability of a *combination* of events.

## MENDEL'S THEORY

Mendel was probably puzzled by the results of his experiments, because they did not fit any theory of heredity known at the time. It then became necessary for him to develop a new theory—a theory that would account for the facts he had obtained from his experiments.

**His reasoning.**   First Mendel assumed that the roundness trait of pea seeds was due to a dominant "element," which may be symbolized by **R** (read this as "big R"). The trait of wrinkled seeds, he assumed, was due to a recessive "element," represented by **r** (read "small r"). Since about 1910 such genetic "elements" have been called *genes*. This is the term we will use.

genes [jĕnz; Greek: *genos*, breed, kind]

Next Mendel reasoned that each plant had a *pair* of genes for each trait. He was forced to this conclusion because in the F₁ generation parent plants showing the dominant trait produced some offspring that showed the recessive trait. Mendel had to assume that these parents could have the dominant *trait* only if they had at least one dominant *gene*. Yet how could they have produced offspring that showed the recessive trait without having at least one recessive gene? Each F₁ plant that produced offspring with wrinkled seeds must, therefore, have had genes for *both* round and wrinkled seeds, **R** and **r**. Of course, an F₁ plant might have had more than one of each, but it was simplest to assume that for each trait there was a single pair of genes, one of each kind. In science the simplest explanation that *fits all the facts* is always preferred.

Morgan's canon (page 548) is a special illustration of this principle.

Then to be consistent, Mendel had to assume that plants of the P₁ generation also had two genes. A plant that bred true for round seeds could be symbolized by **RR**, meaning

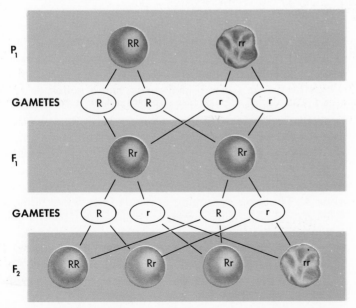

**Figure 17 · 6**
Mendel's theory illustrated by seed shape in peas.

genotype [jĕn′ə tīp′]

that it had two genes for round seeds and none for wrinkled seeds. And a plant that bred true for wrinkled seeds could be represented by **rr**, meaning that it had two genes for wrinkled seeds and none for round. Today the pattern of inherited genes indicated by such paired symbols is called an organism's *genotype*. Notice that this is a matter of theory, not of direct observation.

From these assumptions, from further consideration of the data, and from his knowledge of the mathematics of probability, Mendel was led to an important generalization: The two members of each pair of genes separate when gametes are formed; only one gene of each pair enters any one gamete.

**Testing the reasoning.** It is rather difficult to follow Mendel's reasoning from his data to his generalization. But we can test the generalization by applying it. We shall use Mendel's assumptions and our own knowledge of probability gained from Investigation 17.1 to see how the generalization explains Mendel's data.

allele [ə lēl′; Greek: *allelon*, of one another]

Three new words will make our discussion easier, though they were not used by Mendel. The first, *allele*, refers to each of the members of a gene pair. For the gene pair **Rr, R** is an allele of **r,** but **R** is not an allele of **Y** (a symbol we might use for the gene of yellow seed color). **R** and **Y** are symbols for genes controlling different traits. The other two words refer to pairs of allelic genes. If a pair is formed of like genes (for example, **RR**), then it is referred to as *homozygous* and an individual organism having such a genotype is also called homozygous. If the pair is formed of different genes (for example, **Rr**), then it is referred to as *heterozygous*.

homozygous    [hō′mə zī′gəs; Greek: *homos*, the same, + zygon, a yoke]

heterozygous [hĕt′ər ə zī′gəs; Greek: *heteros*, the other, + zygon]

We shall continue to use the trait of seed shape as an example. According to Mendel's reasoning, the $P_1$ plant that bred true for round seeds had a genotype **RR.** It was homozygous for this pair of alleles. The other parent plant, which bred true for wrinkled seeds, had a genotype **rr.** It was homozygous for this pair of alleles.

When gametes were formed in the reproducing plants, Mendel reasoned, the genes of the pair **RR** must separate, one going to one gamete and the other going to another gamete. Since both genes of the pair are alike, all the gametes produced by this homozygous parent are alike, having gene **R.** The same reasoning applies to the other homozygous parent. All of its gametes are alike; all have the gene **r.** Therefore, at fertilization, when the gametes combine, all the zygotes formed by crossing an **RR** plant with an **rr** plant have the gene pair **Rr**—the **R** from one parent, the **r** from the other. Thus, all the zygotes are heterozygous for this pair of alleles. Yet Mendel found that all the $F_1$ plants produced seeds just as round as those of the homozygous **RR** parents. If his reasoning was correct, plants could *appear* alike in a trait even though they had different genotypes. The appearance of an organism, regardless of its genotype, is referred to as its *phenotype*.

phenotype [fē′nə tīp′; Greek: *phainein*, to show, + type]

Now, consider the result of breeding one member of the $F_1$ generation with another member of the $F_1$ generation. (In pea plants we get the same result by allowing the flowers to self-pollinate.) We begin our reasoning by writing down the kinds of gametes and their probabilities. Notice that the situation is the same as that for pennies. There are two possibilities: **R** and **r** instead of "heads" and "tails."

Why is self-pollination equivalent to breeding one $F_1$ individual with another?

Gametes produced by one **Rr** parent: $1/2$ **R** + $1/2$ **r**.

Gametes produced by the other **Rr** parent: $1/2$ **R** + $1/2$ **r**.

Now zygotes are formed by combining gametes. Therefore, we use the mathematical principle for a combination of separate probabilities by multiplying:

$$(1/2 \ \mathbf{R} + 1/2 \ \mathbf{r}) \times (1/2 \ \mathbf{R} + 1/2 \ \mathbf{r}) =$$
$$1/2 \ \mathbf{R} \ (1/2 \ \mathbf{R} + 1/2 \ \mathbf{r}) + 1/2 \ \mathbf{r} \ (1/2 \ \mathbf{R} + 1/2 \ \mathbf{r}) =$$
$$1/4 \ \mathbf{RR} + 1/4 \ \mathbf{Rr} + 1/4 \ \mathbf{Rr} + 1/4 \ \mathbf{rr}.$$

Expected zygotes: $1/4$ **RR** + $1/2$ **Rr** + $1/4$ **rr**.

Of course, in applying probability to this situation, we are assuming (and Mendel did also) that the gametes unite at random.

The genotypes **RR** and **Rr** produce the same phenotype — that is, both the homozygous **RR** plants and the heterozygous **Rr** plants have round seeds. By adding the **RR** fraction of the zygotes to the **Rr** fraction, we see that we can expect $3/4$ of the offspring to have round seeds and only $1/4$ (those with the genotype **rr**) to have wrinkled seeds — in other words, a $3:1$ ratio. Figure $17 \cdot 5$ shows that Mendel's results from experiments on seed shape $(2.96:1)$ were very close to the ratio that his theory predicts. And likewise the observed ratios for the other six traits that he studied were very close to the expected $3:1$. In other words, Mendel's theory fitted his observations very closely.

**The theory applied to two traits.**    Mendel went on to consider problems involving two traits at the same time. Such combinations are called *dihybrid* crosses. For example, if plants that are purebred for both seed shape and seed color are crossed, what should be the combinations of shape and color, and in what ratios? We can use algebraic multiplication to work out such problems.

dihybrid [dī hī′brĭd; Greek: *dis*, twice, + hybrid]

This time we shall leave Mendel's data and use an example in the animal kingdom. In some breeds of guinea pig, hair may be either short or long, either black or brown. If a

guinea [gĭn′ĭ]

purebred animal having short, black hair is crossed with a purebred one having long, brown hair, all the $F_1$ offspring have short, black hair phenotypically. Thus short hair (**S**) is dominant to long hair (**s**) and black hair (**B**) is dominant to brown (**b**). Therefore, individuals of the $F_1$ generation are genotypically **SsBb.**

Now, two individuals of the $F_1$ generation are mated. Using the same method shown previously, we can work out the hair-length possibilities, ignoring hair color; then we can work out the hair-color possibilities, ignoring length.

**Ss** mated with **Ss** gives us 1/4 **SS** (homozygous short), 1/2 **Ss** (heterozygous short), and 1/4 **ss** (long). **Bb** mated with **Bb** gives us 1/4 **BB** (homozygous black), 1/2 **Bb** (heterozygous black), and 1/4 **bb** (brown). Combining the two sets of results, we multiply algebraically to find what the probabilities will be:

$$(1/4\,\textbf{SS} + 1/2\,\textbf{Ss} + 1/4\,\textbf{ss}) \times (1/4\,\textbf{BB} + 1/2\,\textbf{Bb} + 1/4\,\textbf{bb})$$

Work this out and check your results with the following summary:

| Fraction | Genotype | Phenotype |
| --- | --- | --- |
| 1/16 | **SSBB** | short-haired, black |
| 1/8 | **SsBB** | short-haired, black |
| 1/16 | **ssBB** | long-haired, black |
| 1/8 | **SSBb** | short-haired, black |
| 1/4 | **SsBb** | short-haired, black |
| 1/8 | **ssBb** | long-haired, black |
| 1/16 | **SSbb** | short-haired, brown |
| 1/8 | **Ssbb** | short-haired, brown |
| 1/16 | **ssbb** | long-haired, brown |

Phenotypically, the dihybrid cross produces a characteristic ratio, which we can obtain from combining the above data.

9/16 short-haired, black (dominant-dominant)
3/16 long-haired, black (recessive-dominant)
3/16 short-haired, brown (dominant-recessive)
1/16 long-haired, brown (recessive-recessive)

Thus, the expected ratio of phenotypes in the $F_2$ generation of a dihybrid is 9:3:3:1.

Mendel made similar calculations for dihybrid crosses in garden peas. In doing so he was making an assumption: that the genes of the two traits were sorted out (*assorted*)

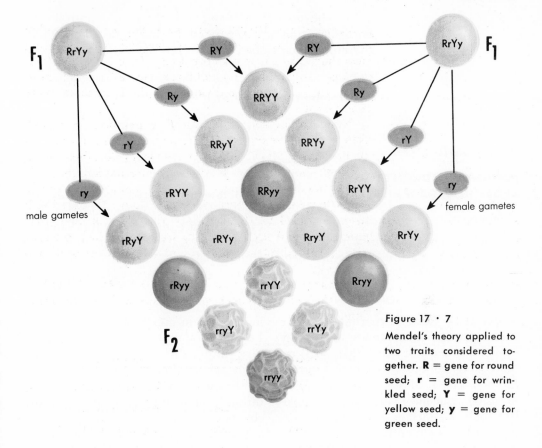

Figure 17 · 7

Mendel's theory applied to two traits considered together. **R** = gene for round seed; **r** = gene for wrinkled seed; **Y** = gene for yellow seed; **y** = gene for green seed.

independently of each other during gamete-formation. But his experimental results justified this assumption. In one experiment, for example, 556 $F_2$ seeds were obtained, as follows: 315 round, yellow; 108 round, green; 101 wrinkled, yellow; 32 wrinkled, green. Compare these data with the numbers based on calculation: $9/16 \times 556 = 312.75$; $3/16 \times 556 = 104.25$; and $1/16 \times 556 = 34.75$.

### MENDEL'S CONCLUSIONS

1. Inheritance of traits is determined by genes.

2. In zygotes and the individuals that develop from them, genes that control a particular trait are in pairs; genes of a pair may be alike or different.

3. In gametes only one gene of each pair is present. At fertilization gametes unite randomly, which results in a predictable ratio of traits among offspring.

4. The *principle of dominance:* when genes controlling a particular trait (alleles) are different, the effect of one is observed (dominant), while the other one remains hidden (recessive).

5. The *principle of segregation:* the genes controlling a particular trait are separated during gamete-formation; therefore, each gamete carries only one gene of each pair.

6. The *principle of independent assortment:* when two pairs of traits are studied in the same cross, they are found to assort independently of each other.

## INVESTIGATION 17.2

### MENDELIAN MONOHYBRID CROSS IN *DROSOPHILA*

#### PURPOSE

Using twentieth-century techniques, you will conduct a breeding experiment to test some of Mendel's principles.

#### BACKGROUND INFORMATION

Mendel's basic experiments have been repeated many times with many organisms, many of which (like peas) require long periods of time to produce the necessary $F_1$ and $F_2$ generations. But by using fruit flies, you can see the results of a Mendelian monohybrid cross in less than one month.

There are many species of fruit flies in the genus *Drosophila.* The most abundant and widespread species is *Drosophila melanogaster* (drō sŏf'ə lə mĕl'ə nō găs-tər). It occurs in almost every part of the world during the warmer seasons and is found on overripe fruit, such as bananas, grapes, and plums. It is particularly common around fruit markets and warehouses.

For many reasons, *Drosophila* is an excellent organism for studies of heredity: (*a*) It is easy to raise in the laboratory because it has simple food requirements, takes up little space, and is fairly hardy. (*b*) It can complete its life cycle in about twelve days at room temperature. (*c*) It produces large numbers of offspring. (*d*) It has many kinds of hereditary variations that can be recognized with low-power magnification.

Before using fruit flies in experiments, you must understand their life cycle, practice techniques for handling them, and learn to distinguish males from females.

The eggs of *Drosophila* are small, ellipsoidal objects, which are usually laid on the surface of food. The eggs hatch into larvae in about twenty-four hours. Larvae eat almost continually; in laboratory culture their black mouthparts can easily be seen moving back and forth in the medium. Because they channel through the medium while eating, many channels indicate successful growth of a culture. Mature larvae in laboratory culture usually climb up the side of the bottle or onto a paper strip in the bottle. There they *pupate*—that is, they enter an inactive stage during which they change to adult flies. When the adults emerge from pupal cases, they are fragile, light in color, and do not have fully expanded wings; but within a few hours the body color darkens and the wings expand. Adults may live a month or more. Females do not mate for about ten hours after emerging from the pupae. During mating they store considerable quantities of sperms; fertilization occurs later, at the time the eggs are laid.

Male (♂) fruit flies are usually smaller than females (♀), but there are a number of more reliable characteristics by which the sexes may be distinguished. Figure 17·10 shows these characteristics.

## MATERIALS AND EQUIPMENT
### (for each team)

*For All Parts of the Procedure*
Etherizer (see Figure 17 · 8)
Ethyl ether, in dropping bottle
Examination plate (square of white
    plastic bathroom tile)
Water-color brush, small
Stereomicroscope
Morgue (see Figure 17 · 9)
Glass-marking crayon

*For Examining Fruit Flies*
Cultures of wild-type flies, in glass vials, 2
Cultures of mutant flies, in glass vials, 2
Culture bottles containing fresh food
    supply, 5

*For the $P_1$ Mating*
Culture of wild-type flies from which all
    adults have been removed eight hours
    previously
Culture of mutant flies from which all adults
    have been removed eight hours previously
Culture bottle containing fresh food supply

*For the $F_1$ Generation*
Culture bottle containing offspring of $P_1$ cross

*For the $F_1$ Mating*
Culture bottle containing flies of $F_1$
    generation
Culture bottle containing fresh food supply

## PROCEDURE

**Examining fruit flies.** Your team will be given two cotton-plugged vials containing *Drosophila* cultures. Label both vials with the team symbol. The flies in one culture differ in some conspicuous trait from the flies in the other. One culture (marked *W*) contains wild-type. flies bearing the form of the trait that is normal in wild populations. The other culture (marked *M*) contains flies bearing the trait in a form that has appeared in laboratory populations. To determine the difference, you must compare the flies in the two cultures.

You can compare flies only when they are immobile. They must be *anesthetized*. Refer to Figure 17 · 8 as you watch the teacher demonstrate the following procedure:

1. Place a finger beneath the neck of the funnel. Put several drops of ethyl ether in the funnel and close the upper end of the neck. Avoid using too much ether. You need ether *vapor* in the etherizer; liquid ether will kill the flies. When the ether trickles down the neck and reaches your finger, place the funnel in the glass.

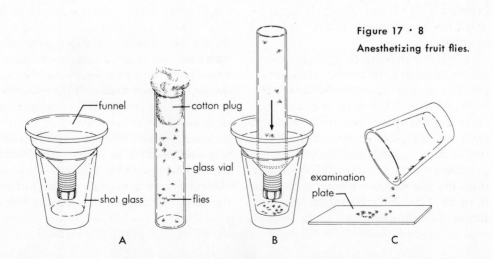

**Figure 17 · 8**
**Anesthetizing fruit flies.**

funnel
cotton plug
glass vial
shot glass
flies
examination plate
A          B          C

2. Gently but rapidly tap against your knee the bottom of the glass vial containing the wild-type flies. This temporarily forces the flies to the bottom of the vial. Quickly remove the cotton plug, invert the vial, and place it firmly in the funnel.

3. Holding vial, funnel, and glass firmly together, tap the bottom of the glass sharply against your hand or knee. This dislodges the flies into the glass.

4. The flies will be overcome within a few seconds and will fall to the bottom. Watch them through the side of the glass. *As soon as* the last fly stops moving, remove the funnel and empty the flies onto the examination plate. (Caution: The flies should not remain in the etherizer more than a minute; over-anesthetized flies will die.)

The flies are easily injured. Use a small brush when moving them about on the examination plate. Anesthetized flies recover in about five minutes. They may be re-anesthetized if necessary. Flies that are accidentally killed should be placed in the morgue.

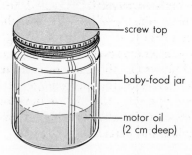

Figure 17 · 9
Morgue for fruit flies.

screw top

baby-food jar

motor oil
(2 cm deep)

Examine the flies in the W culture, noting differences between males and females (Figure 17 · 10). When you have finished, return the flies to the original vial or discard them in the morgue or

use them to start a new culture — whichever the teacher directs.

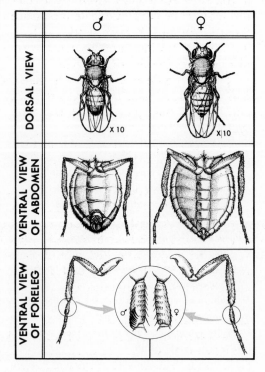

Figure 17 · 10
Comparison of male and female fruit flies.

Examine the flies in the M culture. Record the trait in which all these flies differ from all the wild-type flies. The teacher will give you the name used for this trait.

**The $P_1$ mating.** Use cultures from which all adults have been removed not more than eight hours previously. Using the technique described in the preceding part, anesthetize the flies in the culture designated by the teacher. Pick out two or three females. Do not select flies having a very pale color or incompletely expanded wings; these flies have recently emerged and are easily injured. Place the selected females in a culture bottle containing a fresh food supply. Return the other flies to the original vial.

Now anesthetize the flies in the other vial (the W culture if you selected females from the M culture; the M culture if you selected females from the W culture). Select two or three male flies, place them in the new culture bottle containing the female flies, and return the remaining flies to the original vial.

On the bottle containing the mated flies mark the date, the cross (the sex and trait of each parent), and the team symbol.

Seven or eight days after the mating, remove the parent flies and place them in the morgue.

**The $F_1$ generation.** About ten or twelve days after the mating, the adult flies of the $F_1$ generation should begin to emerge. Anesthetize them, examine each for the trait you are studying, and place them in the morgue. Tally each fly on a chart similar to the one below.

| Date of Mating _____ | | |
| Date Parents Removed _____ | | |
| $P_1$ ♂ _____ X ♀ _____ | | |
| Generation _____ | | |
| DATE | WILD-TYPE | MUTANT |
| --- | --- | --- |
|  |  |  |
|  |  |  |
| ↓ | ↓ | ↓ |
|  |  |  |
| Total |  |  |

Each day examine the adult flies that have appeared during the previous twenty-four hours; discard them and tally the counts. Do not count beyond the ninth day after the emergence of the first $F_1$ flies. You might then run into some individuals of the $F_2$ generation.

**The $F_1$ mating.** On the fifth or sixth day of counting, place five or six males and five or six females from the $F_1$ generation in a bottle containing a fresh food supply. Mark the bottle with the date, team symbol, and traits of the parent flies. After seven or eight days remove the adult flies and place them in the morgue.

After ten or twelve days adults of the $F_2$ generation should begin to emerge. When they do make daily counts and record the results on a chart like the one used before.

### STUDYING THE DATA

• With respect to the trait you are studying, how many phenotypes occur among the $P_1$ flies? (1)  • How many phenotypes occur among the $F_1$ flies? (2) • What Mendelian principle is illustrated by the results of this cross? (3)  Compare results obtained by teams that used wild-type males with results obtained by teams that used wild-type females in the $P_1$ mating.  • Is the number of $F_1$ phenotypes the same in both cases? If not, try to explain the difference. (4)  • In making the $F_1$ mating, why was it unnecessary to follow the precautions of the $P_1$ mating to insure that only previously unmated females become the parents? (5)  • With respect to the trait you are studying, how many phenotypes occur among the $F_2$ flies? (6)  • On the basis of your team's data, calculate the percentage of each phenotype in the $F_2$ generation. (7) • Now combine the data of all teams and calculate the percentages. (8)

### CONCLUSIONS

Are the observed percentages close enough to those expected by Mendel's theory to give you confidence that only chance has produced the difference? This question cannot be answered easily. It is similar in form to the question that every scientist repeatedly faces: Are the numbers obtained in my experiment close enough to the numbers expected from my hypothesis to allow a reasonable degree of confidence that only chance caused the difference and not some defect in the hypothesis or the procedure? In other words, is the difference between the actually observed numbers and the expected numbers a chance difference? Is it the same kind of difference that occurs when we toss a penny ten times and get 4 "heads" and 6 "tails" instead of the expected 5 and 5?

Consider an example. A biologist who crossed two kinds of tomato plants hypothesized that half the offspring would have green leaves, half yellow. In certain kinds of tomatoes this is a reasonable expectation. In one experiment he obtained 1240 seedlings, 671 with green leaves and 569 with yellow leaves; the expected numbers from a total of 1240 are, of course, 620 of each kind. Is this a minor difference, a matter of chance? Or is it so large that the biologist ought to suspect that something is wrong with his hypothesis?

In Investigation 17.1 you saw one way to express deviation. A better way was invented in 1900 by Karl Pearson (1857–1936), an English mathematician. He called this measure *chi-square* (pronounced "kī square"). It is symbolized by the Greek letter *chi* and the square sign, thus: $X^2$. Chi-square is found as follows: For each class of objects, obtain the difference between the number expected and the number observed; square this difference; divide by the expected number; finally, add all the quotients together. The sum is the value of $X^2$.

In mathematical form this is:

$$X^2 = \Sigma \frac{(O - E)^2}{E}$$

where $\Sigma$ means "the sum of," $O$ = observed number, and $E$ = expected number. In the example, the difference for the first class of objects, green-leaved

plants, is $671 - 620 = 51$; squaring this, we get 2601; dividing by the expected number, 620, we get the quotient 4.2. The difference for the other class of objects, the yellow-leaved plants, is $569 - 620 = -51$; squaring this, we get 2601; dividing by 620, we get 4.2. Added together, the two quotients come to 8.4, the value of $X^2$.

But what does this value mean? By solving an elaborate equation, mathematicians have provided the information needed to judge whether a $X^2$ value represents the sort of difference that occurs *very probably* by chance alone or *very improbably* by chance alone, or at probabilities between these extremes. A table prepared from the equation allows us to see how often (in 100 cases) a given value of $X^2$ could have been produced by chance alone.

For two classes of objects, the $X^2$ value of 8.4 goes beyond the table, which means that there is less than 1 chance in 100 that the deviation between the observed and expected numbers could have been caused by chance alone. When the probability that a difference occurs by chance alone is less than 5 in 100, then the difference is said to be *significant*—in other words, we may reasonably suspect that the difference did *not* occur by chance alone.

In this case, further experimentation showed that the difference from the expected numbers was caused by a loss of yellow-leaved plants. They were less sturdy than the green-leaved plants; fewer of their seeds germinated and lived.

When more than two classes occur among the results of an experiment, it is necessary to use other lines in the table. For example, to test the significance of the 9:3:3:1 ratio of a dihybrid cross, $X^2$ for four classes is needed.

Now use the combined data of all teams to calculate chi-square for the $F_2$

| X² for four classes | .115 | .352 | .584 | 2.366 | 3.665 | 6.251 | 7.815 | 11.341 |
|---|---|---|---|---|---|---|---|---|
| X² for three classes | .020 | .103 | .211 | 1.386 | 2.408 | 4.605 | 5.991 | 9.210 |
| X² for two classes | .0002 | .004 | .016 | .455 | 1.074 | 2.706 | 3.841 | 6.635 |
| Times in 100 that chance alone could have been responsible for the difference | 99 | 95 | 90 | 50 | 30 | 10 | 5 | 1 |

Figure 17 · 11

Table of chi-square values.

generation of fruit flies. • Are the data significantly different from the numbers expected by Mendelian theory? (9) • If the difference is not significant, what conclusion can you make? (10) • If the difference is significant, how can you explain it? (11)

### FOR FURTHER INVESTIGATION

Once you have learned the techniques of handling fruit flies and used chi-square to test the significance of breeding results, you can carry on many genetic experiments. Here are some questions you can investigate: (a) What is the result of mating an $F_1$ individual with a purebred dominant? (b) With a purebred recessive? (c) What is the result of allowing all individuals of the $F_2$ generation that show the dominant characteristic to mate? (d) Are two traits considered together always inherited independently of each other?

## FURTHER DEVELOPMENTS IN MENDEL'S PRINCIPLES

Mendel's theory fitted the results of his experiments. But important questions remained: Would the theory fit results of other experiments? If such things as genes really exist, where are they? And do they indeed behave in the manner described by the theory? For a long time such questions remained unanswered. In fact, they were not even asked, for the report of Mendel's work lay neglected on library shelves.

Biologists continued to breed plants and animals experimentally and to attempt — without success — to explain their results. Most did not seem to know of Mendel's work. Those few who had read Mendel's paper either did not understand his mathematics or, perhaps, were unwilling to believe that a biological question could be explained mathematically.

Then, some years after Mendel's death, came one of the most striking coincidences in biological history. Three biologists in three different European countries, working independently on problems of heredity, each found Mendel's work. Each recognized the importance of that work, and each reported it—all in the same year, 1900. From that year the modern science of genetics is dated.

genetics [jĭ nĕt′ ĭks; Greek: *gignesthai*, to be born]: Genetics is the branch of biology that deals with heredity.

### LOCATION OF GENES

During the thirty-five years in which Mendel's work was unheeded, much progress was made in the study of cells. In this period biologists developed new staining techniques that permitted close observation of the nuclear substance of cells. As a result, chromosomes were discovered, and during the 1870's and 1880's details of mitosis and meiosis became known to biologists. Within two years of the discovery of Mendel's work, the close agreement between the events of meiosis and the actions of Mendel's hypothetical genes was being pointed out. First to show this clearly was a young graduate student at Columbia University, Walter S. Sutton.

### THE CHROMOSOME THEORY

**Sutton's reasoning.** The initial step in Sutton's thinking was not new (in science, first steps rarely are). The links between parents and offspring in all organisms that reproduce sexually are sperms and eggs. These reproductive cells must, therefore, contain whatever it is that controls heredity. Furthermore, Mendel had found that it makes no difference which parent—male or female—contributes dominant or recessive traits; the ratios among the offspring are the same. Therefore, the sperm and egg must contribute equally to the heredity of the offspring. Since a sperm cell consists of little but nucleus, and the nucleus of the egg is to all appearances the same as the nucleus of the sperm, it may be concluded that the nuclear material controls heredity.

Victor A. McKusick

Figure 17 · 12

Walter S. Sutton: 1876–1916. American geneticist.

Now, it is from within the nucleus that the chromosomes appear in both mitosis and meiosis. Sutton continued reasoning as follows:

1. At the conclusion of meiosis, the number of chromosomes going into each sperm or egg is just half the number found in cells of the body. This corresponds to Mendel's theory that one gene of each pair is present in each gamete.

2. The union of sperm and egg, each with its single (monoploid) set of chromosomes, reestablishes for the new organism the double (diploid) set of chromosomes present in the body cells of the parent organisms. This corresponds to Mendel's requirement that the genes be contributed equally by each parent.

3. An individual chromosome retains its structure and identity throughout the various cell divisions of meiosis and, later, throughout the numberless mitotic cell divisions that occur as a new organism develops. This preservation of the individuality of the chromosome is comparable to the preservation of each gene throughout the generations of body cells and gametes.

4. During meiosis each pair of chromosomes separates independently of every other pair. Suppose, in any one pair, we designate one chromosome (of the monoploid set received from the male parent) as **A** and the like chromosome (of the monoploid set received from the female parent) as **A'**. And suppose we designate another pair as **B** (from the male parent) and **B'** (from the female parent). In meiosis we would find that **A** does not always go to the pole that **B** goes to, nor does **A'** always end up with **B'**. Instead, at the poles we get **AB**, **A'B**, **AB'**, and **A'B'** — and with equal frequency. This chromosome behavior during meiosis parallels the principle of independent assortment in Mendel's theory.

In summary, then, Sutton reasoned that the genes are small particles located in chromosomes. This is the *chromosome theory of heredity*. But what kind of convincing evidence could be gathered to support the theory? Could it be "proved"?

**Meaning of "proof."**   A scientist gradually accumulates data by many steps and with many doubts. At intervals — when, on the basis of the data gathered, it seems reasonable — he tries to interpret his findings. He seeks some pattern that will organize the data into a reasonable whole. Such an interpretation of accumulated data is what we call a theory.

A theory can do no more than take into consideration all the data that exist *at the time it is formed*. If it does this without any omissions or distortions, it is a good theory. The surest way to test a theory is to make a prediction on the basis of the theory and then to check the data to see whether the prediction holds true. Thus an important effect of a theory is to spur scientists to search for new data. When new data are found, the theory must be reexamined. If the new data do not support the theory, then the theory must be revised or discarded.

distortions [dĭs tôr′shənz; Latin: *dis-*, apart, + *torquere*, to twist]: here, twisting facts away from their meaning

In biology, then, as in all science, a theory is never "proved" once and for all. But if it continues to account for new data as they appear, it becomes increasingly convincing. In short, "proof" of a scientific theory means simply this: The theory continues to account for new evidence as it arises.

See Problem 15, page 671.

## EVIDENCE FOR THE CHROMOSOME THEORY

**Numbers of genes and chromosomes.** Mendel had found that each trait he studied was inherited independently. When he considered two traits at a time (a dihybrid cross), the phenotype ratio in the $F_2$ generation closely agreed with the 9:3:3:1 ratio predicted by the principle of independent assortment. According to Sutton's reasoning, then, each of the traits that Mendel studied must have been controlled by genes located on different pairs of chromosomes.

But Sutton realized that if there were just one gene pair to each pair of chromosomes, the number of traits under genetic control in an organism would be limited to the number of pairs of chromosomes. Since some organisms have only two or three pairs of chromosomes, and man—a very complex organism—has only 23 pairs, the number of hereditary traits would be limited, indeed. When the great number of inheritable traits possessed by an organism is considered, it is clear that many different genes must be located on each chromosome.

So Sutton made a prediction: If genes for two different traits are carried on the same pair of chromosomes, they should not be able to assort independently. Traits controlled by such *linked* genes should appear together in the offspring, and the ratio of phenotypes should *not* be 9:3:3:1.

As early as 1906, $F_2$ dihybrid ratios that differed radically from the 9:3:3:1 predicted by Mendel's theory were found, though none were simply 3:1, as might be expected if the two genes were *always* held together on one chromosome. The new evidence was a kind of confirmation of the chromosome theory, but it also raised a new problem: Why were the ratios of $F_2$ phenotypes neither 9:3:3:1 nor 3:1? This was not explained until several years later.

**Sex in the fruit fly.** Meanwhile, in the laboratory where Sutton had worked, the study of heredity was placed on an entirely new basis. Thomas Hunt Morgan began to experiment with the fruit fly, *Drosophila melanogaster*. Careful work on the cells of *Drosophila* showed that only three of the four pairs of chromosomes are identical in males and females (Figure 17 · 14). In the fourth "pair" the rod-shaped chromosome was named the X chromosome; the hook-shaped one was named the Y chromosome.

Female flies always have two X chromosomes; male flies always have one X and one Y chromosome. Thus, from the fourth chromosome pair females can contribute only X chromosomes to the gametes, but males can contribute

California Institute of Technology

Figure 17 · 13

Thomas Hunt Morgan: 1866–1945. American geneticist.

either X or Y chromosomes to the gametes, since the members of chromosome pairs separate from each other in meiosis. Thus sex, a clearly visible trait in the individual, could be definitely associated with a visible characteristic of its cells: the unlike pair of chromosomes. Here was the best evidence yet that an inherited trait is determined by something involving the chromosomes.

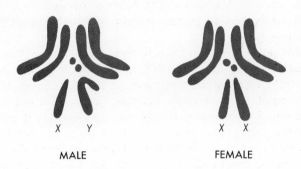

MALE                    FEMALE

Figure 17 · 14

Chromosomes of *Drosophila melanogaster* arranged in pairs (as during meiosis).

**Sex-linkage.** *Drosophila melanogaster* normally has red eyes. But while examining thousands, Morgan found one, a male, that had white eyes. He mated this male with a normal red-eyed female. The $F_1$ generation produced from this mating consisted entirely of red-eyed flies. Next, he allowed the members of the $F_1$ generation to mate and produce an $F_2$ generation. Among these he noted a ratio of three red-eyed flies to one white-eyed. This, of course, was expected. But Morgan noticed an odd thing—*all* the white-eyed flies were males; none were females. Here was a trait related in some way to sex—a "sex-linked" trait.

Further thought shows that the case of the white-eyed fruit flies provided precise evidence for the location of genes. Since the Y chromosome differs from the X chromosome in appearance, we might assume that it differs in whatever genes (if any) it carries. Suppose, then, we hypothesize that the genes for eye color are located in the X chromosome and have no counterpart in the Y chromosome. What might we expect in a breeding experiment?

Let **R** stand for the normal dominant red-eye gene, and let **r** represent the recessive white-eye gene. But we must associate the gene symbols with chromosomes. Since we have hypothesized that these genes occur only on the X chromosomes, we can write $X^R$, $X^r$, and Y for the three kinds of chromosomes. Thus, the genotype of the original white-eyed male found by Morgan must have been $X^rY$, and that of the normal red-eyed female with which it was

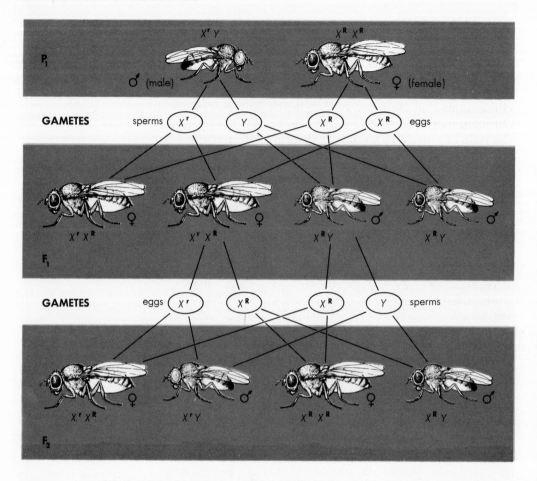

**Figure 17 · 15**

Inheritance of the "white-eye" trait in *Drosophila*. Compare this with the results of one of Mendel's crosses diagrammed in Figure 17 · 6.

Calvin B. Bridges: 1889–1938. American geneticist

nondisjunction [Latin: *non*, not, + *dis-*, apart, + *jungere*, to join]

mated must have been $X^R X^R$. With these symbols, Figure 17 · 15 shows the results that should be expected according to our hypothesis. Clearly, these are like the results Morgan actually obtained. Hence, the evidence supports our hypothesis that the gene for eye color is located on the X chromosome.

**Nondisjunction.** The work of Morgan resulted in a firm basis of evidence for the chromosome theory. But still more evidence has been obtained by others. In 1915 Calvin B. Bridges discovered *nondisjunction*. This means that a pair of chromosomes, which normally separate during meiosis, do not do so. Instead they end up together in one daughter cell, leaving the other daughter cell without a chromosome representing the pair. The result is the production of gametes that either have one more than the monoploid number of chromosomes or one less.

In studying fruit flies, Bridges found that nondisjunction occurs rather frequently in the tiniest chromosome

pair of *Drosophila*. Zygotes formed from such gametes have either three dot chromosomes or one dot chromosome. Such zygotes develop into adult flies that have visible abnormalities. From the presence of a particular abnormal trait in a fly, Bridges could predict the number of dot chromosomes in its cells. And from the number of dot chromosomes in the cells of a parent fly, he could predict the ratio of normal to abnormal offspring. The experimental verification of his predictions—from chromosomes to genetic trait and from genetic trait to chromosome makeup—eventually convinced geneticists that the chromosome theory of heredity is true.

**Figure 17 · 16**

*Drosophila* chromosomes, showing a result of nondisjunction of dot chromosomes during meiosis.

abnormalities [ăb'nôr măl'ə tĭz; Latin: *ab*, from, + *norma*, a rule]: characteristics different from those usually present

### MENDELISM MODIFIED

By 1915 Morgan's fruit flies had become the center of genetic research, but heredity in maize (corn), guinea pigs, mice, and many other organisms was also being investigated. From this research came great quantities of data—and not always agreeing with Mendel's data. It thus became necessary to modify some of the ideas Mendel had held. But the basis he had laid for the chromosome theory still remains the foundation of genetics.

**Nondominance.** In all Mendel's experiments, one allele was dominant over the other. Thus, a pea plant with

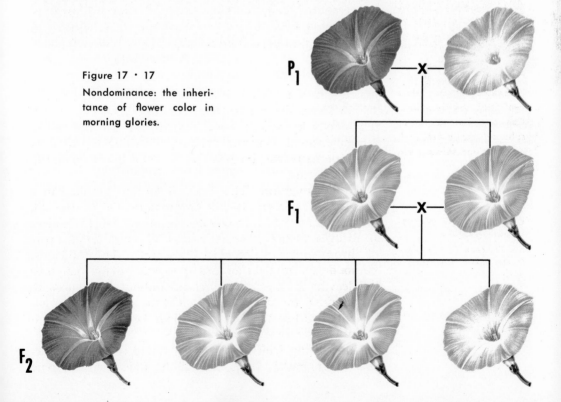

**Figure 17 · 17**
Nondominance: the inheritance of flower color in morning glories.

$P_1$

$F_1$

$F_2$

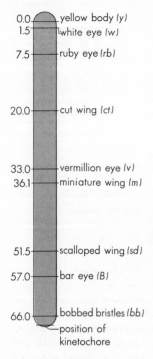

Figure 17 · 18

The relative position of some gene loci on one of the chromosomes of *Drosophila*. The numbers at the left are determined by the percentage of recombinations observed in experimental breeding. They indicate, for example, that trait *bb* is much more likely to be separated from trait *y* by crossing-over than is trait *w*.

locus [lō′kəs; Latin: a place]: plural, loci [lō′sī]

Can you explain why this is so?

a genotype **YY** (homozygous yellow-seeded) could not be distinguished from an individual with the genotype **Yy** (heterozygous yellow-seeded). Seeds of both individuals were equally yellow; the phenotype was the same, even though the genotypes were different. But today many cases are known in which neither allele dominates the other. In such an instance, the hybrid organisms show an *intermediate degree* of the trait: heterozygous individuals are phenotypically different from both their homozygous parents. The alleles are said to be *nondominant*. An example is given in Figure 17·17.

**Linkage.** Early in the twentieth century cases had been found that failed to support Mendel's Principle of Independent Assortment. These cases had been used to support the chromosome theory, but they left a puzzling problem: Shouldn't the ratios in the $F_2$ generation of dihybrid crosses be *either* 9:3:3:1 (when the genes are on different chromosomes) *or* 3:1 (when the genes are linked together on the same chromosome)?

The solution to this problem lies in the crossing-over that occurs during meiosis. Suppose we are studying two traits—one determined by genes **A** (dominant) and **a** (recessive), the other by genes **B** (dominant) and **b** (recessive). Suppose further that the genes for these two traits are on the same chromosome but the *locus* (position) of **A** (or **a**) is at one end of the chromosome and the locus of **B** (or **b**) is at the other end. Figure 17·19 shows what happens if crossing-over occurs in 20 percent of the cells during meiosis. Instead of 50 percent having **A** linked with **B** and 50 percent **a** linked with **b**, only 45 percent of the gametes have the first linkage, and 45 percent the second. Five percent have **A** on the same chromosome with **b**, and 5 percent have **a** linked with **B**. The new linkages are called *recombinations*. If zygotes are formed from such gametes, the two dominant traits are not *always* associated—nor are the two recessive traits. Instead, some zygotes have combinations of dominant and recessive genes—**Ab** and **aB**. Instead of two kinds of phenotypes in a 3:1 ratio, there are four kinds—but in a ratio very different from 9:3:3:1.

In this example the break was near the middle of the chromosome, and the two loci were at opposite ends. If the loci of **A** and **B** were closer together, we might suppose that a break between them would be less likely and would therefore occur less frequently. In general, then, the farther apart two loci are on the same chromosome, *the more likely* the genes are to be separated by crossing-over and the more frequently recombinations will occur. Therefore, in a dihybrid cross, the more the ratio of phenotypes departs

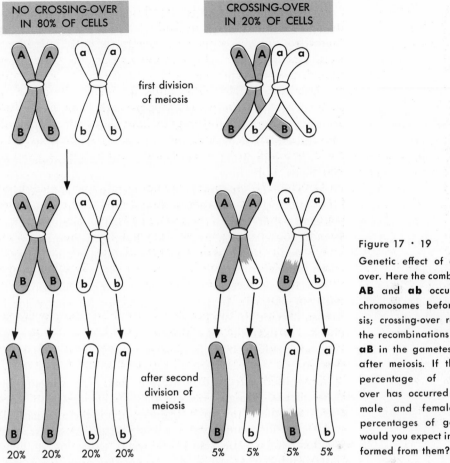

**NO CROSSING-OVER IN 80% OF CELLS**

first division of meiosis

**CROSSING-OVER IN 20% OF CELLS**

after second division of meiosis

20%   20%   20%   20%          5%   5%   5%   5%

Figure 17 · 19

Genetic effect of crossing-over. Here the combinations **AB** and **ab** occur in all chromosomes before meiosis; crossing-over results in the recombinations **Ab** and **aB** in the gametes formed after meiosis. If the same percentage of crossing-over has occurred in both male and female, what percentages of genotypes would you expect in zygotes formed from them?

from the 9:3:3:1 ratio, the farther apart the genes must be on the chromosome. If two loci are very close together, crossing-over may be so infrequent that some experiments show *no* recombinations; then a 3:1 ratio of phenotypes will result.

This principle has enabled geneticists to construct "maps" of chromosomes, which locate the genes in relation to each other. This can be done only with organisms that have been used in hundreds of genetic experiments involving many thousands of offspring. In the case of fruit flies, corn, and a few other species, the mapping of chromosomes has been quite thorough.

**Multiple alleles.**   Mendel never found more than two alleles for a given trait. There were **R** and **r** (round and wrinkled) and **Y** and **y** (yellow and green), but there was never a case of **Y, y,** and **Y'** (the **Y'** representing some other

Under what abnormal circumstances could an individual have three alleles for a specific gene locus?

albino [ăl bī′ nō; Latin: *albus*, white]

chinchilla [chĭn chĭl′ə]

Himalayan [hĭ mäl′yən, hĭm′ə-lā′ən]

X 1/10

CC

c c

c$^{ch}$ c$^{ch}$

c$^h$ c$^h$

Figure 17 · 20
Four phenotypes of coat color in domestic rabbits. From top to bottom: normal ("wild type"), albino, chinchilla, Himalayan. Genotypes are shown beneath each animal.

color, such as purple)—*three* possible alleles. Today, however, we know that there may be several alleles available within a *population* of organisms to occupy a particular locus in a chromosome. Normally an *individual* has only two alleles for any trait—one gene derived from its male parent, the other from its female parent.

For example, four genes determining coat color are available in the total population of domestic rabbits: **C, c, c$^{ch}$,** and **c$^h$.** These genes occur at a single locus—they are alleles. Any individual rabbit has just two chromosomes with this locus and, therefore, only two of the genes for coat color. The combination **CC** causes a normally colored coat. The homozygous recessive **cc** causes an *albino* coat (without pigment—therefore, appearing white). The gene **c$^{ch}$,** when homozygous (**c$^{ch}$c$^{ch}$**), produces a light-gray color over the entire body (called the chinchilla pattern). The gene **c$^h$,** when homozygous (**c$^h$c$^h$**), produces a white body with color on the tips of the ears, nose, tail, and legs (called the Himalayan pattern). In general, the genes for coat color in rabbits may be considered dominant in the order **C, c$^{ch}$, c$^h$,** and **c.** For example, in a rabbit with the genotype **Cc$^h$,** the coat is normal in color. In a **c$^h$c,** the coat has the Himalayan pattern.

**Combined effects of different loci.** To simplify his experimental design, Mendel deliberately chose to work with traits that show only distinct phenotypic alternatives: wrinkled and round seeds, yellow and green seeds. With nondominance, one locus can yield three phenotypes. Cases of more than three phenotypes can result from multiple alleles. But multiple alleles cannot account for many characteristics that seem to have a quite continuous variability—the length of dogs' ears or the color of human skin, for example. These may appear in dozens of variations—dozens of phenotypes.

To account for such continuously varying traits, twentieth-century geneticists developed the hypothesis that several pairs of nonallelic genes—that is, genes occupying several loci—may affect one characteristic of an organism. Suppose that gene **X** at one locus produces a certain degree of red coloring and is nondominant. Suppose also that genes **Y** and **Z** at other loci have the same effect as gene **X.** In addition, suppose that **x, y,** and **z** produce no color. In such a case, an organism with the genotype **xxyyzz** would be entirely white. But the genotype **XXYYZZ** would have six color-forming genes and would thus be very red. **Xxyyzz,** with one dose of red pigment, would be a light shade of pink. **XXyyzz, xxYYzz,** and **xxyyZZ,** each with two "red" genes, would be a shade darker, and so on through seven possible shades. This is actually the way seed color is inherited in wheat, as a Swedish geneticist showed in 1908.

**Heredity and environment.** Mendel had one variety of pea that produced short vines and another that produced tall vines. But a little observation shows that the size of plants is generally related to the kind of soil in which the plants grow. Mendel controlled this variable by growing all his plants in the same soil. In many instances, however, it may be difficult to determine to what extent the phenotype of an individual organism is the result of its genotype, and to what extent the phenotype has been influenced by the environment.

## INVESTIGATION 17.3

### SEEDLING PHENOTYPES

#### PURPOSE

To what extent does an environmental factor (light) influence the color of tobacco seedlings? You will investigate this problem experimentally.

#### MATERIALS AND EQUIPMENT
(for each team)

Paper towels

Scissors

Petri dishes, 2

Beaker filled with water

Tobacco seeds, 60

Forceps, 2

Glass-marking crayon

Box (large enough to cover half the dishes used by the class)

Medicine dropper

Hand lens

#### PROCEDURE

Cut eight disks of paper towel to a size that fits snugly into the bottom of a petri dish. With a pencil write a large *A* on one disk and a large *B* on another. Place four disks (with A on top) in one petri dish and four (with B on top) in another. Pour water into each dish.

When the paper is thoroughly soaked, pour off the excess water.

Sprinkle 30 tobacco seeds into each dish. Using forceps, arrange the seeds so that none lie on the labels. No seed should be closer than twice its own length to another seed.

Cover the dishes and label with the team symbol. Put both dishes in a warm place that receives strong light, but not in direct sunlight. Cover the B dishes of all teams with boxes or other devices that will keep them in darkness. Check the dishes each day to make sure the paper does not dry out. If it begins to do so, add water with a medicine dropper.

When at least half the seeds have germinated, examine them with a hand lens. Each young tobacco plant consists of a colorless root and two tiny leaves, the cotyledons (Figure 17·21). Usually the root appears first, but in this experiment you are concerned only with the cotyledons. Some seedlings have green cotyledons and some have creamy or yellowish cotyledons. Count the number of each kind in each dish. At least two members of the team should take counts; recount if the two disagree. Use a form

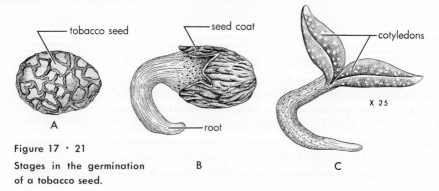

A

B

C

X 25

tobacco seed

seed coat

cotyledons

root

Figure 17 · 21
Stages in the germination
of a tobacco seed.

like that shown below; record the counts opposite "Day 1." Replace the lids on the dishes; return the dishes to the assigned location, covering the B dishes as before.

On the following day (Day 2) take another count. The number of germinated seedlings may have increased; but if the number of seedlings of either kind is smaller, then an error in counting must have been made on one of the days. Record the counts. To calculate percentages of yellow seedlings, divide the number of seedlings having yellow cotyledons by the total number of seedlings that have cotyledons. Make this calculation for each dish. Return the dishes to the assigned location, but *do not* cover the B dishes; allow all dishes to remain exposed to light.

On Day 3 count the seedlings again. Record the counts and return the dishes to their assigned place, allowing all dishes to remain exposed to the light.

· On Day 4 make final counts and calculate the percentage of seedlings with yellow cotyledons in each dish.

## STUDYING THE DATA

From the data obtained on Day 2, compare the percentages of yellow seedlings in Dish A and Dish B.   • In what ways are they different? (1)   • What experimental variable may be associated with this difference? (2)   • Can this variable be considered the cause of yellow color in tobacco seedlings? Why or why not? (3)

Compare the percentage of yellow seedlings in Dish B on Day 4 with the percentage on Day 2.   • What striking change has occurred? (4)   • What experimental variable is associated with this change? (5)   • Can this variable be considered the cause of yellow coloration in tobacco seedlings? Why or why not? (6)   • How can you account for the difference among the seedlings in Dish A? (7)

## CONCLUSIONS

• Do any data support the statement "Yellow color of tobacco seedlings is caused by environment"? If so, which data? (8)   • Do any data support the statement "Yellow color of tobacco seedlings is caused by heredity"? If so, which data? (9)   • Try to formulate a statement that accounts for all the data. (10)

| DAY | DISH A | | | DISH B | | |
|---|---|---|---|---|---|---|
| | Green | Yellow | % Yellow | Green | Yellow | % Yellow |
| 1 | | | | | | |
| 2 | | | | | | |
| 3 | | | | | | |
| 4 | | | | | | |

## HUMAN HEREDITY

From garden peas, guinea pigs, fruit flies, and other organisms, geneticists have learned much about the way in which traits are passed from an organism to its offspring. This knowledge, applied to the breeding of cattle, corn, and many other domesticated plants and animals, has resulted in about as much improvement in agricultural production during the past fifty years as had all the genetic improvement of the previous two thousand years. But what of man?

### EVIDENCE FOR HUMAN HEREDITY

Biologists have learned a great deal about human physiology from studying guinea pigs and rats; there is no reason to doubt that human genetics follows the same principles found in rabbits and fruit flies. But the principles tell us nothing about specific traits. Black hair is dominant to brown in guinea pigs, but this is not true in rabbits. We cannot make predictions about the inheritance of a trait in one species by studying that trait in another. Each trait must be newly worked out for each species.

Figure 17 · 22
The same trait may be inherited differently even in different populations of the same species. (A) Phenotypes produced by combinations of the two allelic genes I and i in leghorn chickens. (B) Phenotypes produced by the same genes in the Castillana nigra breed. How would you describe dominance for this trait?

Poultry Dept., Iowa State Univ.

A        II                    Ii                    ii

B        II                    Ii                    ii

To discover how a trait is inherited — whether it is recessive, dominant, nondominant, or the result of multiple alleles — geneticists make the kinds of crosses that give them the most reliable information. But this is impossible with human beings. Geneticists cannot pick and choose individuals for mating. Furthermore, man takes a long time to get from a $P_1$ generation to an $F_2$ generation. And worst of all, from the geneticist's viewpoint man (unlike pea plants and fruit flies) cannot produce the numbers of offspring needed for mathematical analysis.

Thus, for knowledge of human heredity the geneticist must depend in large part on family histories and pedigrees. But such information is often questionable; it requires the investigator to rely on human memory. Do you know whether your maternal great-grandmother was blonde or brunette, short or tall?

maternal [Latin: *mater*, mother]

Reliable or not, such information is gathered together in the form of a pedigree chart (Figure 17 · 24). From the study of large numbers of pedigrees, some deductions can be made concerning the ways in which human traits are inherited. For example, a completely dominant trait seldom skips a generation. A sex-linked trait possessed by a man cannot be passed to his sons, but a sex-linked recessive trait carried by a woman will go, on the average, to half her sons — and to none of her daughters (unless she marries a man who also has the trait).

Can you explain these statements?

### GENETICS OF SOME HUMAN TRAITS

From the study of many pedigrees, geneticists have gained considerable information about hundreds of human hereditary traits. Man is still far from understanding his own genes as thoroughly as he understands those of fruit flies. But here are a few examples, arranged roughly according to the completeness of the available evidence:

**Sex.** As in fruit flies, determination of human sex is a "whole chromosome" inheritance. Males have an X and a Y chromosome; females have two X chromosomes. Because such different organisms as mammals and insects have this kind of sex inheritance, you might think that it is the same in all animals. This is not the case; in birds females have X and Y chromosomes and males have two X's.

**Blood types.** Probably no human trait is better understood genetically than blood types. When techniques for transfusing blood from one person to another were developed at the end of the nineteenth century, it was discovered that this could be done safely in some cases and not in others. Karl Landsteiner, an Austrian physician, worked out a system for distinguishing the kinds of human blood

transfusing [Latin: *trans*, across, + *fundere*, to pour]

Karl Landsteiner [lănd'stī'nər]: 1868 – 1943. Austrian (later, American) physician

that were important in transfusions. These were designated Type A, Type B, Type AB, and Type O. In hospitals all over the world millions of persons have had their blood typed. From this great mass of data geneticists have deduced the inheritance of these blood types.

Other blood types, resulting from other loci, are known. Most are unimportant medically, but see pages 182—185 in G. B. Moment's *General Zoology* for the Rh factor.

These "ABO" types are determined by genes at one locus, but three alleles exist in the human population. They are: gene **Iᵃ**, which causes formation of blood factor "A"; gene **Iᵇ**, which causes formation of blood factor "B"; and gene **i**, which does not cause either of these blood factors to form. The table below shows how the alleles may combine to give various blood types:

| GENE COMBINATIONS | BLOOD TYPE |
|---|---|
| **Iᵃiᵃ** or **Iᵃi** | Type A |
| **Iᵇiᵇ** or **Iᵇi** | Type B |
| **Iᵃiᵇ** | Type AB |
| **ii** | Type O |

What does the chart show about the dominance relationships of these alleles?

**Phenylketonuria.**   This is a condition in which there is extreme mental deficiency accompanied by the excretion of phenylpyruvic acid. This substance is not found in the urine of "normal" persons. It is not known whether the mental deficiency results from the accumulation of phenylpyruvic acid itself or from some substance derived from it. In any case, the condition is probably caused by the lack of an enzyme, and it is known to be transmitted in a simple Mendelian way by a recessive gene.

phenylketonuria    [fē′nĭl kē′tə-nyoōr′ē ə]

phenylpyruvic [fē′nĭl pī roō′vĭk]

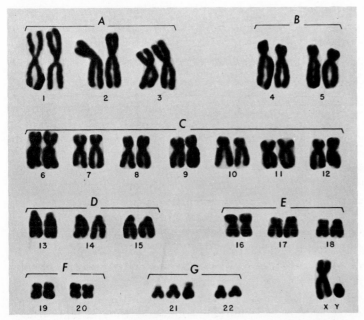

Figure 17 · 23

Chromosomes in mongolism. To make this chart, a photomicrograph of a cell during mitosis was taken; then the picture was cut apart and the chromosomes rearranged in pairs. Was this a female or a male?

**Mongolism.** This form of mental deficiency, which is accompanied by a characteristic facial appearance, results from nondisjunction during formation of gametes by meiosis. A zygote formed from such a gamete has *three* of the chromosomes designated as number 21 (Figure 17 · 23). Abnormal meiosis seems to occur more frequently in older parents than in younger.

**Eye color.** This is a complex trait, not completely understood at present. It seems that a person with pure-blue eyes is a homozygous recessive at a certain locus. Heterozygotes or homozygous dominants have pigmented eyes. (Here we must take "pigmented" to mean an eye with even the least spot of brown, together with so-called hazel, green, and gray eyes.) Then there probably are genes at other loci that have lesser effects on eye color provided at least one "pigment gene" is present.

**Skin color.** The amount of dark pigment is controlled by genes at four to eight loci, with nondominance at each locus, so that many degrees of skin color can occur. In certain individuals, additional reddish and yellow pigments are controlled by other genes. Environmental factors (such as sunlight) also alter the amount of dark pigment.

**Resistance to tuberculosis.** Probably many genes, as well as environmental conditions, play a part in establishing this trait.

**Intelligence.** This is a very difficult matter to investigate. In the first place, we are not sure whether intelligence is a single trait or many traits combined — most probably it is the latter. Second, results of intelligence tests are not a certain indication of whatever we may mean by "intelligence." But it seems clear that both heredity and environment influence the intelligence of an individual.

Can you show how each of these examples of human heredity resembles one of the examples given earlier for other organisms?

## INVESTIGATION 17.4

### HUMAN INHERITANCE

#### PURPOSE

You will investigate some methods of reasoning used by geneticists.

#### PROCEDURE

You will be given a number of facts and asked to answer questions based on the facts. The answers to one set of questions lead to the next set of facts, so you must move step by step through the procedure.

**Percentages of male and female infants.** With respect to the sex chromosomes, females can be designated XX, males XY. • Considering only the sex chromosomes, how many kinds of gametes can females produce? (1) • How many kinds of gametes can males produce? (2)

The frequency of any particular characteristic within a group is expressed as a fraction. Thus, in a group of 100 marbles containing 20 red and 80 blue marbles, the frequency of red marbles is $20/100 = 1/5 = 20\% = 0.2$. The frequency of blue marbles is $80/100 = 4/5 = 80\% = 0.8$. Regardless of the way the fractions are written, their sum (whether expressing two frequencies, as in this case, or more) must always be equal to 1:

$$20/100 + 80/100 = 100/100 = 1$$
$$1/5 + 4/5 = 5/5 = 1$$
$$20\% + 80\% = 100\% = 1$$
$$0.2 + 0.8 = 1.0$$

It is customary to represent two frequencies with the letters p and q. Thus for any group of red (R) and blue (B) marbles, frequencies of the two kinds may be written as "pR + qB."

Any population of sperms, then, may be represented by the mathematical expression pX + qY.  • Using your knowledge of meiosis, calculate the values of $p$ and $q$. (3)  The same kind of mathematical expression may be used to represent the population of eggs produced by a female. • What are the values of $p$ and $q$ for the egg population? (4)

The frequencies of males and females among human offspring may be predicted in the same way you predicted the percentages of "heads" and "tails" when tossing coins. Use algebraic multiplication to calculate the expected frequencies of the zygotes:

| sperms | eggs | zygotes |
|--------|------|---------|
| $(pX + qY) \times (pX + qY) =$ | | ? |

• What percentage of zygotes do you expect to be male? (5)  • What percentage do you expect to be female? (6)

When calculating these percentages you are making two assumptions: (a) that X-carrying sperm and Y-carrying sperm have exactly equal chances of reaching and fertilizing an egg, and (b) that XX and XY zygotes have equal chances of developing to birth stage. The two assumptions seem natural, and they are commonly made. But available data do not support your predictions. Data on

deaths of embryos and on deaths during birth show that males have a much poorer chance of developing and of surviving birth than do females.  • In the light of these data which assumption must you reject? (7)  • If you still accept the other assumption, how must the expected percentages of male and female infants be changed? (8)   Data on live births show that for every 100 females born, between 105 and 106 males are born. • What do these data suggest about the other assumption? (9)

**Inheritance of red-green color blindness.** In Figure 17·24 are pedigree charts showing occurrence of red-green color blindness in two families. A

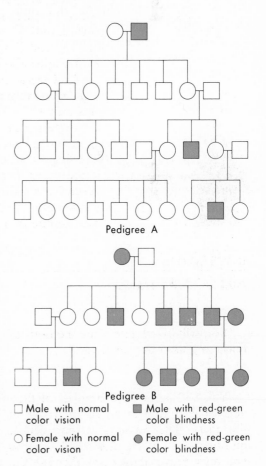

Pedigree A

Pedigree B

☐ Male with normal color vision        ■ Male with red-green color blindness

◯ Female with normal color vision        ● Female with red-green color blindness

**Figure 17 · 24**

person with this visual defect is unable to distinguish red from green. Study the two charts. • Is the gene for this trait dominant or recessive? Explain your reasoning. (10)

You can apply your understanding of sex-linkage in *Drosophila* to the study of red-green color blindness in the human pedigrees. • Is the trait sex-linked? What evidence supports your answer? (11)

**Inheritance of hemophilia.** Hemophilia is a condition in which the blood platelets have great stability, so that normal clotting does not occur. It is a sex-linked trait.

Figure 17 · 25 shows, in part, the occurrence of hemophilia among the royal families of Europe during the nineteenth and twentieth centuries. Study the chart. • Then list the mothers who *must* have been carriers, that is, heterozygous. (12)

The chart shows the actual occurrence of hemophilia in a pedigree. Now consider the frequencies (expressed as percentages) of hemophiliacs — persons afflicted with hemophilia — that we may *expect* among the offspring of certain marriages.

First, consider the marriage of a hemophiliac man and a woman homozygous for normal blood clotting. • What percentage of their male offspring do you expect to be hemophiliacs? (13) • What percentage of their female offspring do you expect to be hemophiliacs? (14) • What percentage of females do you expect to be carriers? (15)

Second, consider the marriage of a man whose blood clots normally and a woman who is a carrier of hemophilia. • What percentage of their male offspring do you expect to be hemophiliacs? (16) • What percentage of their female offspring do you expect to be hemophiliacs? (17) • What percentage do you expect to be carriers? (18)

Figure 17 · 25
Inheritance of hemophilia in descendants of Queen Victoria of England.

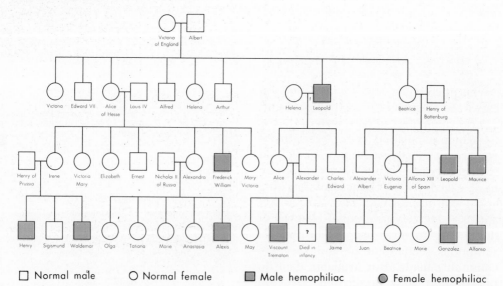

□ Normal male    ○ Normal female    ■ Male hemophiliac    ● Female hemophiliac

## THE SOURCE OF NEW TRAITS

The basic fact of heredity is that offspring resemble their ancestors. But when we consider the fossil evidence outlined in Chapter 10, it is quite clear that new heritable traits must have appeared in organisms from time to time in the past; otherwise, there could have been no changes in organisms through geological time. This deduction from reasoning is supported by abundant genetic evidence that new traits continue to appear today.

### MUTATIONS

New heritable traits are called *mutations*. Morgan's white-eyed fly was almost certainly a mutation. But not *all* characteristics that seem new are mutations. This can be illustrated by a trait in man, feeble-mindedness. It is difficult to trace most human families for more than a few generations, and some kinds of feeble-mindedness are the

mutations [mū tā′shənz; Latin: *mutare*, to change]

**Figure 17 · 26**

Mutations in mink. (A) Normal color. (B) A mutant called "pastel" by mink ranchers. (C) A mutant called "palomino." (D) "Sapphire" results from mutations at two loci.     x 1/10

Richard M. Shackelford (All Photos)

A

B

C

D

result of rare recessive genes that may have been hidden for many generations. For these reasons, feeble-mindedness may appear to be a new trait in a family when in fact it has been inherited. But feeble-mindedness may also occur as a result of lack of oxygen during or shortly after birth. In this case the cause is environmental, not genetic, and the trait cannot be inherited by the next generation. Finally, feeble-mindedness can be produced by mutation.

How do mutations arise? According to the chromosome theory of heredity, they should result from changes in chromosomes. We might, then, look for visible changes in the chromosomes and associate such changes with the appearance of new traits in organisms. And in fact, this is what Bridges did when he discovered nondisjunction. In addition to nondisjunction, many other chromosomal changes have been discovered.

From time to time a part of one chromosome may become attached to another chromosome. Or a part may break off and become reversed before reattaching to the original chromosome. Or a small piece may become lost. Still other accidents may befall chromosomes—and when such accidents happen, changes usually occur in the traits of the organism that bears such chromosomes. Once changes in chromosomes are made, they are carried on in mitosis and meiosis from one generation to another—they are heritable. Mutations of this sort are called *chromosomal mutations*.

Often, however, mutations occur without any visible change in the chromosomes. It seems reasonable to assume that such mutations are due to changes in the invisible genes within the chromosomes. For example, a gene that normally leads to the formation of a red pigment might change so that a purple pigment or no pigment at all is formed. A gene that brings about the change of sugar to starch in a corn grain might change so sugar accumulates in the grain. Such mutations are called *gene mutations*.

## A THEORY OF GENE MUTATIONS

replicate [rĕp′lə kāt′; Latin: re-, back, again, + *plicare*, to fold]

Mendel's experiments showed that genes must have three characteristics: (*a*) they must be separate particles; (*b*) they must carry "information" about traits from one generation to another; and (*c*) they must be able to replicate themselves—to produce copies of themselves, so that every time a cell divides, each daughter cell contains each gene. Mendel himself did not try to explain genes any further, but since 1900 many geneticists have attempted to construct mental models of genes. Now a large amount of evidence, mostly accumulated during the past fifteen years,

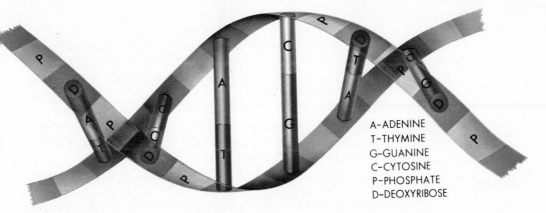

A-ADENINE
T-THYMINE
G-GUANINE
C-CYTOSINE
P-PHOSPHATE
D-DEOXYRIBOSE

**Figure 17 · 27**

**Diagram of a small part of a DNA molecule.**

has resulted in the belief that each gene is a molecule of deoxyribose nucleic acid or part of one.

DNA was long known to be constructed of nucleotides, but the way in which the nucleotides were joined was not explained until 1953. Then, on the basis of X-ray studies by M. H. F. Wilkins, a model of a DNA molecule was proposed by J. D. Watson and F. H. C. Crick. They visualized a DNA molecule as a long, double-spiral structure. Each spiral is a string of nucleotides joined together by bonds between deoxyribose and phosphate groups. The spirals are joined to each other by bonds between the bases of the nucleotides (Figure 17 · 27).

Maurice    H.    F.    Wilkins: 1916——. English biochemist

James D. Watson: 1928——. American biochemist

Francis H. C. Crick: 1916——. English biochemist

This model of DNA can be used to explain the replication that must be possible for a gene. The bonds between bases are rather weak. If a DNA spiral flattens out, the double strand may break apart between the bases. Then if nucleotides are present in the cell, they may attach to the open bases, building up two new double strands—two new DNA molecules. Since only a cytosine base can attach to a guanine, and only an adenine to a thymine, each new molecule would be exactly like the original one.

This model of DNA can also be used to explain the way in which a gene carries "information." The bases along the length of a single DNA strand may have any sequence, such as AGCT . . . or TAGA . . . or CGTT . . . . (The bases along the opposite strand of the DNA double spiral would, in these cases, be TCGA . . . ATCT . . . GCAA . . . .) Because the molecule is very long, the possible number of sequences is almost unlimited. We can imagine the arrangement of bases within a DNA molecule as a kind of code that carries "information" from one cell generation to the next.

A DNA molecule, if the Watson-Crick model is correct, satisfies the requirements for a Mendelian gene: (*a*) it is a

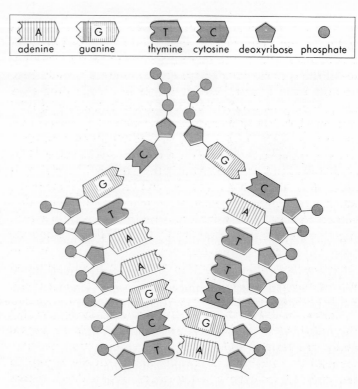

**Figure 17 · 28**
Replication of DNA. The strands come apart at the bonds between the nucleotides. New nucleotides —which temporarily bear extra phosphates—will be added one by one, eventually producing two new DNA molecules.

*Notice the use of anthropomorphic language. Is this as dangerous in biochemistry as in the study of behavior?*

separate particle; (*b*) it can carry "information"; (*c*) it can replicate itself. During the past decade abundant, though indirect, evidence has confirmed both the model and the assumptions concerning its replication and transmission of "information."

Now how does this concern gene mutations? During mitosis and meiosis each DNA molecule exactly replicates itself along its whole length. But we may assume that occasionally chemical accidents happen. One of the bases might be destroyed or lost, leaving a gap in the code. Or it might be replaced by a different base, changing the "meaning," just as the meaning of "CAT" changes when the "C" is replaced by an "R." Thus, the "information" carried by the changed molecule would be different from that in the preceding cell generation. The new cell (or, if the cell happened to be a gamete, the resulting new individual) would then have new "instructions" for its development—a mutation would result.

### LETHAL GENES

Most mutations are harmful. At first this may seem unreasonable. But let us look at the matter by means of an analogy.

The fact that a species exists in considerable numbers within its environment is an indication that the set of genes it contains is adapted to that environment. If this were not so—if the species did not fit its environment—it would have become extinct, or at least it would be in the process of disappearing. An individual of a successful species can be compared with a well-constructed watch: it is balanced; it "runs" smoothly. Now suppose we bring about a random change in the watch by poking a needle into its works. This *might* cause the watch to run better. But is it likely? It is much more likely that whatever happened would make the watch run *less* well or even cause it to stop running altogether. So it is with a mutation. A random change in a gene *might* make an organism "run" better—that is, operate more effectively in its environment. But unless the environment is changing, the probability is high that a mutation will cause the organism to function less effectively. It might even cause the individual to die.

Many mutations that occur in gametes do, in fact, kill the individuals formed from such gametes. These mutant genes are termed *lethal.* Lethal genes may stop development of an individual at various stages—in the zygote, in the embryo, or even in later stages. When death occurs before birth (or hatching or germination), lethal genes reduce the number of expected offspring and change the ratios of expected phenotypes. From study of such changes, H. J. Muller was able to calculate the rates at which mutations occur.

George Schwartz

Figure 17 · 29

Hermann J. Muller: 1890–1967. American geneticist who developed methods of measuring mutation rates by analysis of lethal traits in fruit flies exposed to X-rays.

lethal [lē′thəl; Latin: *letum,* death]

### RATES AND CAUSES OF MUTATIONS

In the main, genes are quite stable; they usually replicate themselves exactly for hundreds of cell generations. It has been calculated that on the average a particular gene changes only once in every 100,000 to 1,000,000 gametes. Of course, mutations *per gamete* are not so infrequent. If a gamete carries 10,000 different genes, and if the individual genes mutate at the rate just stated, the probability that a gamete will contain at least one mutant gene is between 0.1 and 0.01. Or, expressed as rate, between one mutant per 10 gametes and one mutant per 100 gametes. This is a basic rate of mutation—a rate that occurs without any known cause. But the rate can be increased by certain factors in the environment of an organism.

First, mutation rate is increased by heat. Within the range of temperature that a given organism can tolerate, the higher the temperature, the greater the mutation rate. This observation supports the idea that mutation is basically a chemical change, since a rise in temperature usually increases the rate of chemical reactions. But with higher temperatures the mutation rate increases more rapidly than do ordinary chemical reactions.

Second, certain chemicals have been shown to speed up the rate of mutation. A common laboratory preservative, formaldehyde, is one of these. Mustard gas (a poisonous gas used in warfare), nitrous oxide, and phenol (carbolic acid) are others. Especially effective are compounds whose molecules closely resemble in chemical structure the bases of nucleotides.

Third, mutation rates are strikingly increased by high-energy radiations, such as X-rays, beta and gamma rays resulting from atomic changes (and from atomic explosions), and even by ultraviolet light. In a world where such radiations are becoming a more frequent part of the environment, this source of mutation is probably increasing.

## MECHANISM OF GENE ACTION

Experiments led to the theory that heredity is controlled by some particle—a gene—in the nucleus of a cell. Further experiments showed that genes must be located in chromosomes. Finally, we have seen that genes may be molecules of deoxyribose nucleic acid. A major question remains: How do genes, whether DNA or something else, bring about the development of traits? Put in another way: How does a chemical particle in a cell nucleus cause a pea plant to develop round rather than wrinkled seeds, a guinea pig to develop brown rather than black hair, a man to develop Type A rather than Type O blood?

Studies of an ascomycete mold, *Neurospora crassa,* provided the first clear evidence on the mechanism of gene action. This mold grows easily in a test tube containing a medium made up of a dilute solution of minerals, some table sugar, and a single vitamin called biotin. The growing mold develops hyphae beneath the surface of the medium; then tufts of pink or orange spore-bearing threads grow upward through the surface.

If the mature mold plant is analyzed chemically, we find that it is made up of a wide range of proteins, carbohydrates, lipids, a large number of vitamins, nucleic acids, pigments, and so on. The mold must have produced these complex chemical compounds from the simple raw materials in the test tube—the minerals, sugar, and biotin. The materials taken from the environment must have been put together in just the way that would make the new mold plant resemble its parent.

In the early 1940's George W. Beadle and Edward L.

formaldehyde [fôr măl′də hīd′]
nitrous [nī′trəs]
phenol [fē′nŏl]

Neurospora crassa [nyŏŏr ŏ-spər′ə krăs′ə]

biotin [bī′ə tĭn]

George W. Beadle: 1903——.
American geneticist

Tatum, at Stanford University, treated spores of *Neurospora* with X-rays. Then they germinated the spores and raised the plants. They found that some spores could not grow at all on the simple medium. Some kind of lethal mutation had occurred in these spores. The two investigators hypothesized that the lack of growth by the mutant spores was due to need for some substance that was lacking in the medium. So they devised a medium containing additional nutrients, particularly vitamins and all the amino acids known to be required for synthesizing proteins—what they called a "complete" medium. On this medium almost all spores grew, confirming their hypothesis.

The next step was to find which substance (or substances) in the complete medium was required by a particular mutant. Figure 17·30 shows the procedure that was used. It was found that the production of almost every substance normally synthesized by *Neurospora* can be blocked by an X-ray-produced mutation.

How can synthesis of a substance be blocked? We have seen that synthesis is controlled by enzymes. Beadle and Tatum suggested that each failure by a mutant to synthesize a substance resulted from the lack of a specific enzyme.

Edward L. Tatum: 1909———.
American biochemist

**Figure 17 · 30**

Procedure used to discover mutations in the ability of *Neurospora* to synthesize various substances. In this case the mold has lost the ability to synthesize substance C.

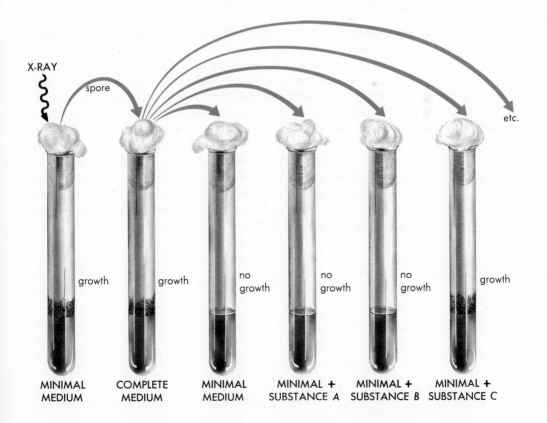

X-RAY

spore

etc.

growth    growth    no growth    no growth    no growth    growth

MINIMAL MEDIUM    COMPLETE MEDIUM    MINIMAL MEDIUM    MINIMAL + SUBSTANCE *A*    MINIMAL + SUBSTANCE *B*    MINIMAL + SUBSTANCE *C*

Further investigation produced definite evidence in many cases that this was so. Therefore, each gene change—each mutation—was linked to an enzyme.

Enzymes are proteins, and proteins are synthesized in the ribosomes of cells. The genes are in the nuclei of cells. But the ribosomes are closely associated with ribose nucleic acids (RNA) in cell cytoplasts. An RNA molecule can be visualized as something similar to one strand of a DNA molecule except that ribose is substituted for deoxyribose, and a base called uracil takes the place of thymine. Many experiments by biochemists during the past decade have shown that RNA is formed in cell nuclei by DNA molecules in much the same way that DNA molecules replicate themselves. Thus the sequence of bases in a DNA molecule is repeated in an RNA molecule (except that uracil substitutes for thymine). For example . . . AGT . . . would form . . . TCA . . . in an opposite strand of DNA, but it would form . . . UCA . . . in a strand of RNA. RNA molecules then move to ribosomes in a cell's cytoplast. Here amino acids are gathered to synthesize proteins.

In a series of brilliant experiments, a team of biochemists at the National Institute of Health, in Bethesda, Maryland, showed in 1961 that the base sequence UUU in RNA (formed by the sequence AAA in DNA) always added the amino acid called phenylalanine to a forming protein. Since then many other three-base sequences in DNA have been linked with specific amino acids in proteins.

phenylalanine [fĕn′ĭl ăl′ə nēn′]

Today the theory of gene action is clear. Genes are sequences of bases on DNA molecules; these sequences form a code that directs the way in which amino acids are put together to form proteins; proteins—particularly those that are enzymes—determine the biochemistry and ultimately the structure of an organism. Put very simply, this means that the difference between a rabbit and a raspberry bush—and the difference between you and your neighbor—is the difference in the sequence of bases of the DNA molecules in their cells.

## INVESTIGATION 17.5

### GENETIC DIFFERENCES IN PEAS

#### PURPOSE

You will investigate three seed characteristics in peas: a macroscopically visible characteristic, a microscopically visible one, and a biochemical one.

#### MATERIALS AND EQUIPMENT
(for each team)

*Day 1*

Small bottles, 2

Glass-marking crayon

Balance (0.1-g sensitivity)

Peas of the genetic strains "round" and "wrinkled," 25 of each

*Day 2*

Bottles of soaked peas (from Day 1), 2

Paper towels, 2

Balance (0.1-g sensitivity)

Glass-marking crayon

Microscope slide

Medicine dropper

Scalpel

Soaked peas, round and wrinkled, 1 of each

Monocular microscope

Dry peas, round and wrinkled, 10 g of each

Mortar and pestle

Graduated cylinder

Cheesecloth

Beakers (250-ml), 2

*Day 3*

Glass-marking crayon

Petri dish containing glucose agar

Extracts of round and wrinkled peas (from Day 2)

Medicine droppers, 3

Watch

Paper towel

Forceps

Iodine–potassium-iodide solution ($I_2KI$)

#### PROCEDURE

**Day 1.** An apple or a potato wrinkles as it dries out. Therefore, when you first observe round and wrinkled peas together, it may occur to you that some

have simply dried more than others. You can investigate this matter in reverse by determining whether the two kinds of peas take up the same amount of water when they are soaked.

Select two bottles, each of such a size that 25 peas will occupy no more than half of it. Label one bottle $R$ (round) and the other $W$ (wrinkled). Label both bottles with the team symbol. Rinse the bottles and shake out the larger drops of water. Weigh each bottle separately and record the weights in a table like the one below. Place 25 round peas in Bottle R and 25 wrinkled peas in Bottle W. Now weigh each filled bottle. Record the weights. Fill the bottles with water and allow them to stand overnight.

a. Weight of dried round peas + bottle. . . _____ g

b. Weight of bottle . . . . . . . . . . . _____ g

c. Weight of dried round peas (a-b) . . . _____ g

d. Weight of soaked round peas + bottle. . _____ g

e. Weight of soaked round peas (d-b) . . _____ g

f. Water absorbed by round peas (e-c) . . _____ g

g. Weight of dried wrinkled peas + bottle . _____ g

h. Weight of bottle . . . . . . . . . . . _____ g

i. Weight of dried wrinkled peas (g-h) . . _____ g

j. Weight of soaked peas + bottle. . . . . _____ g

k. Weight of soaked wrinkled peas (j-h) . . _____ g

l. Water absorbed by wrinkled peas (k-i) . _____ g

**m.% increase in round peas (f ÷ c x 100) . _____ %**

**n. % increase in wrinkled peas (l ÷ i x 100)_____ %**

**Day 2.** Pour the water from each bottle. Place the round peas on one paper towel, the wrinkled peas on another. Shake the larger drops of water from each bottle. Return each group of peas to its bottle. Weigh each bottle with the peas it contains. Record the weights.

Using a glass-marking crayon, label one end of a microscope slide *R* and the other end *W*. Place a drop of water at each end of the slide. Using a sharp scalpel, cut through a soaked round pea. Scrape the cut surface and mix the scrapings into the drop of water at the R end of the slide. Clean the scalpel thoroughly. Cut through a soaked wrinkled pea. Scrape the cut surface and mix the scrapings into the drop of water at the W end of the slide.

Using the low power of a monocular microscope, examine the scrapings from both peas. Look for starch grains in each. Carefully compare the starch grains from the two kinds of peas, moving the slide back and forth from one drop to the other. Record the appearance of the starch grains from each kind of pea. The following are some terms you may find useful: "compound," "simple," "divided," "whole," "oval," "spherical." Make sketches of a few grains in each sample.

Weigh out 10 g of dried round peas. Using mortar and pestle, grind the peas in 10 ml of water. Filter the mixture of water and ground peas through two layers of cheesecloth into a beaker. Mark the beaker *R* and add the team symbol to it.

Weigh out 10 g of wrinkled peas. Grind and filter as directed for the round peas. Mark this beaker *W* and add the team symbol. Store both beakers in the refrigerator overnight.

**Day 3.** Using a glass-marking crayon, draw a line dividing into halves the bottom of a petri dish that contains glucose agar. Mark one half *R* and the other half *W*. The marks should be visible through the agar when you turn the dish right side up. Remove the cover of the dish. Using a medicine dropper, place four small drops of the extract from round peas on the R half of the agar surface. Space the drops as widely

as possible. Note the time. Using a different medicine dropper, place four small drops of the extract from wrinkled peas on the W half. Note the time.

At the end of ten minutes, use a small piece of paper towel held in forceps to blot up one drop of the round-pea extract. (Caution: Do not disturb the other drops!) Using a third medicine dropper, place a drop of $I_2KI$ solution on the spot from which the extract has been removed. Immediately carry out the same steps with one drop of the wrinkled-pea extract.

Three minutes later, use a piece of paper towel and forceps to blot up both drops of $I_2KI$ solution. Look beneath the surface of the agar for evidence of a positive starch test. Record the time; sketch each drop, accurately showing the size and shape of any blue area.

Continuing at ten-minute intervals (twenty, thirty, and forty minutes after the drops of extract were first placed on the agar), blot another drop of extract on each half of the petri dish and repeat the starch test.

### STUDYING THE DATA

Complete the calculations in the table of data obtained from soaking the two kinds of peas.

• Do round pea seeds differ from wrinkled pea seeds in ability to absorb water? If so, which kind absorbs more water in proportion to dry weight? (1)

• Assuming that the cells in all developing pea seeds have approximately the same water content, which peas—round or wrinkled—lose the greater amount of water as they mature? Or do they lose equal amounts? (2)

Compare all the data on the shape of starch grains in round and wrinkled peas. • Is there a consistent difference? If so, would it enable you to predict seed shape from starch-grain shape, and vice versa? (3)

Compare the data of all teams on the production of starch from glucose.    • Is there a consistent difference between enzyme extracts of round and wrinkled peas in speed of starch production? (4) • In amount of starch produced? (5)

## SUMMARY

You have investigated differences between round and wrinkled pea seeds at three levels of observation.    • Which characteristics, if any, were always associated with roundness? (6)    • Which characteristics, if any, were always associated with wrinkledness? (7)    • Is association between characteristics conclusive evidence that they are effects of one gene? Why or why not? (8)    • If your answer to the last question is No, what additional evidence might change it? (9)

By studying one at a time pairs of contrasting traits in crosses between varieties of peas, Gregor Mendel discovered the fundamental principles of heredity. First, heredity is determined by stable units in cells, now called genes. Second, the two genes of each pair segregate into different gametes, which combine at random into zygotes. Third, the members of different gene pairs assort independently of each other. Mendel also observed dominance of traits in heterozygous individuals.

Since the rediscovery in 1900 of Mendel's reports, the science of genetics has become one of the fundamental divisions of biology. The chromosome theory of heredity, which developed from the combination of Mendel's experimental results and the discoveries of cell biologists, has been supported by investigation of sex-linkage and nondisjunction. Mendel's principles have been supplemented by the discovery of nondominance, linkage, multiple alleles, and the combined effects of genes at different loci. Intensive study of linkage and crossing-over has provided a way to map the locations of genes in chromosomes. Most of these discoveries in the first half of the century came about through experimentation with fruit flies and American corn (maize).

New traits result from changes in genes and chromosomes. Such mutations occur randomly, but the rate at which they occur can be increased by exposure of cells to X-rays and other high-energy radiations, to high temperatures, and to certain chemicals.

In more recent years great progress has been made in biochemical genetics. DNA is now known to be the fundamental substance in chromosomes. The structure of DNA molecules has been shown to provide a possible explanation of gene differences and gene action. Studies with the mold *Neurospora* have indicated that genes control the production of enzymes.

Meanwhile, the analysis of many kinds of evidence has greatly improved understanding of heredity in man. Though experimental study of human genetics is impossible, geneticists have learned much by such techniques as the study of pedigrees. Human traits are inherited in the same ways as are traits in other organisms, and the inheritance of many human traits is now well known.

## GUIDE QUESTIONS

1. How did Mendel's experimental methods differ from earlier ones?
2. With what kind of events does the mathematics of probability deal?
3. Why did Mendel believe each individual contains a *pair* of genes?
4. Using one of the traits studied by Mendel as an example, explain the difference between a homozygous and a heterozygous individual.
5. Using one of the traits studied by Mendel as an example, explain the difference between genotype and phenotype.
6. What was Mendel's experimental evidence for the principle of independent assortment?
7. Why have fruit flies been used so frequently for experiments in genetics?
8. For what purpose does a scientist use the chi-square test?
9. How does observed behavior of chromosomes in mitosis and meiosis parallel Mendel's theory about behavior of genes in heredity?
10. What do we mean when we say that the chromosome theory of heredity has been *proved?*
11. How did the inheritance of white eye color in fruit flies convincingly link the inheritance of a particular trait with a particular chromosome?
12. When nondisjunction occurs during meiosis, what result is visible in the chromosomes of a zygote?
13. What is nondominance?
14. In the $F_2$ generation of a dihybrid cross, the ratio of phenotypes often is neither 9:3:3:1 nor 3:1. Why?
15. How can the inheritance of traits that show great variability in phenotypes be explained by the gene theory?
16. Why may there be apparent differences in a trait among individuals that have the same genotype for that trait?
17. What difficulties are involved in the study of human heredity?
18. Give an example from human heredity of each major kind of inheritance.
19. What is a mutation?
20. How does a chromosomal mutation occur?
21. How does the Watson-Crick model of DNA structure fit the theory of the gene?
22. Why are many mutations lethal?
23. What factors in the environment are known to affect the *rate* of mutation? What factors affect the *kind* of mutation?
24. How was it shown that genes control the biochemistry of cells?
25. What biochemical syntheses do genes control?

## PROBLEMS

1. The *polled* (hornless) trait in cattle is dominant; the horned trait is recessive. A certain polled bull is mated to three cows. Cow A, which is horned, gives birth to a polled calf. Cow B, also horned, produces a horned calf. Cow C, which is polled, produces a horned calf. What are the genotypes of the four parents?
2. In shorthorn cattle, when a red bull (**RR**) is crossed with a white cow (**rr**), the offspring are *roan* (intermingled red and white hairs). How could a rancher go about establishing a herd of roan cattle?
3. In sheep, white coat is dominant; black is recessive. Occasionally a black sheep appears in a flock. Black wool is worthless. How could a farmer eliminate the genes for black coat from his flock?
4. In summer squash, white fruit color is dominant; yellow is recessive. If a squash plant that is homozygous for white is crossed with a homozygous yellow, what will be the appearance of the $F_1$ generation? Of the $F_2$? Of the offspring of a cross between an $F_1$ individual and a homozygous white individual?
5. The shape of the root in radishes may be long or round or oval. In a series of experiments, crosses between long and oval produced 159 long and 156 oval. Crosses between round and oval produced 199 round and 203 oval. Crosses between long and round produced 576 oval. Crosses between oval and oval produced 121 long, 243 oval, and 119 round. Show how root shape is inherited in radishes.
6. What are the possible blood types of children in the following families?

a. Type A mother, Type A father
b. Type A mother, Type O father
c. Type B mother, Type AB father
d. Type AB mother, Type AB father
e. Type A mother, Type B father

7. In tomatoes, red fruit color is dominant to yellow; round-shaped fruit is dominant to pear-shaped; and tall vine is dominant to dwarf vine. We cross a pure-breeding tall plant bearing red, round fruit with a pure-breeding dwarf plant bearing yellow, pear-shaped fruit. What is the appearance of the $F_1$ generation? Assuming that the genes controlling the three traits are in three different pairs of chromosomes, what are the possible genotypes in the $F_2$ generation? What are the expected ratios of the phenotypes?

8. Suppose that you discover in *Drosophila* a mutation that appears to result from a single dominant gene. Devise a procedure to determine on which chromosome the locus of the mutant gene is to be found.

9. How would you go about improving the characteristics of the seedless orange?

10. Very rarely nondisjunction of human sex chromosomes occurs, and individuals having three sex chromosomes may result. What do you think would be the sex of each of the following cases: (a) XXX, (b) XXY, (c) XYY? Further reading on this problem will show something of its complexity. For example, a larger number of habitual criminals are XYY than would be expected by chance. Can you suggest any explanation for this?

11. Before Mendel the chief theory of heredity was "blood-line inheritance." According to this theory, the parents' traits are blended in the offspring, just as two liquids blend when mixed together. Mendel's theory rested on the idea that traits are transmitted by particles (genes) and and do not blend. Give evidence in support of the older theory. Then show how the results of Mendel's experiments fail to fit that theory.

12. At the present time there is no such thing as an all-blue tulip. The first one found will be quite valuable. How might a Dutch tulip-breeder increase his chances of finding a blue tulip in his fields?

13. Emphasis is usually put upon mutations in reproductive cells because such mutations affect later generations. But mutations can occur in any cell. Suppose that during the development of a human embryo, a mutation that increases the production of pigment occurs in a cell of the right anterior ectoderm. What effect will this have upon the appearance of the infant? Will this trait be inherited by the infant's future offspring?

14. The Himalayan coat pattern in domestic rabbits is influenced by environment. Find out what factor is involved and as much as you can about the way it works. Then write a comparison between this case and your results from Investigation 17.3.

15. How does proof in science differ from proof in mathematics?

## SUGGESTED READINGS

BEARN, A. C., and J. L. GERMAN. "Chromosomes and Disease," *Scientific American,* November, 1961. Pp. 66–76.

BONNER, D. M., and S. E. MILLS. *Heredity.* 2nd ed. Englewood Cliffs, N.J.: Prentice-Hall, Inc., 1964. (A short book, with heavy emphasis on the molecular and biochemical aspects of heredity. Advanced.)

CRICK, F. H. C. "The Genetic Code," *Scientific American,* October, 1962. Pp. 67–72.

DEERING, R. A. "Ultraviolet Radiation and Nucleic Acid," *Scientific American,* December, 1962. Pp. 135–138.

GOLDSTEIN, P. *Genetics Is Easy.* New York: The Viking Press, Inc., 1961. (Especially written for high school students. Easy.)

HARTMAN, P. E., and S. R. SUSKIND. *Gene Action.* Englewood Cliffs, N.J.: Prentice-Hall, Inc., 1965. (The relationship of DNA to the gene concept and the chemical links between gene and organism. Advanced.)

McKUSICK, V. A. *Human Genetics.* Englewood Cliffs, N.J.: Prentice-Hall, Inc., 1964. (This book describes the methods and results of genetic study applied to man. Rather advanced.)

————. "The Royal Hemophilia," *Scientific American,* August, 1965. Pp. 88–95.

NIRENBERG, M. W. "The Genetic Code," *Scientific American,* March, 1963. Pp. 80–86.

PETERS, J. A. *Classic Papers in Genetics.* Englewood Cliffs, N.J.: Prentice-Hall, Inc., 1959. (Includes [pages 2–20] a translation of Mendel's original article on his experiments and twenty-seven other important reports by geneticists from 1903 to 1955. Advanced.)

SIMPSON, G. G., AND W. S. BECK. *Life: An Introduction to Biology.* 2nd ed. New York: Harcourt, Brace & World, Inc., 1965. Chapters 6 and 7. (A good account of genetics on the college level, with special attention to reasoning from experimental results to principles. Rather advanced.)

SINSHEIMER, R. L. "Single-stranded DNA." *Scientific American,* July, 1962. P. 186.

# Evolution

## CHARLES DARWIN AND EVOLUTION

The Galápagos Islands are a bleak volcanic archipelago, straddling the equator in the Pacific Ocean far off the west coast of Ecuador. Their shores are fringed by broken black lava rocks crowded with shaggy marine lizards, and behind are arid hills guarded by ranks of towering tree cacti. Mists often cover the humid forests on the higher peaks. Touched mainly by buccaneers, whalers, and explorers in the past, these islands brought forth few compliments—"a shore fit for Pandemonium" was one English sea captain's comment. For biologists the most revealing statement was about the land tortoises of the archipelago: with a glance at a tortoise's body, shell plates, and size, you could tell which of the islands it came from.

Galápagos [gə lä'pə gōs']
archipelago [är'kə pĕl'ə gō']: a group of islands

Pandemonium [păn'də mō'ni-əm; Greek: *pan*, all, + *daimon*, a demon]: in the poetry of John Milton, the capital of hell

Late in the year of 1835 a British exploring vessel, HMS *Beagle*, arrived in the Galápagos. Almost the first person ashore was the ship's naturalist, Charles Darwin. This young Englishman, who had already spent nearly four years of fruitful scientific exploration in the rich lands and waters of South America, was fascinated by the harsh landscape of the islands. For the next three weeks he roamed the cluster of islands, observing and collecting the tortoises and lizards, the shells and insects, the birds and plants. Many things roused his curiosity—the varied tortoises, one of which he rode at the alarming speed of 360 yards an hour; and the mockingbirds, which seemed to differ from island to island—but nothing made a more lasting impression than a group of small, dull-colored finches.

See Figure 4 · 15.

George E. Lindsay, California Academy of Sciences (Both Photos)

**Figure 18 · 1**

Landscapes in the Galá-
pagos Archipelago. *Above:*
Baltra Island. *Below:* Cactus "forest" on Santa Fé
Island.

These birds reminded Darwin of ones he had seen in
Ecuador. But what diversity there was among the Galápagos finches! Some islands had several species; others, a few
or one only. Some of the finches were small; some were
much larger. But the greatest diversity among the many
species appeared in the shape of their beaks.

Finches ordinarily are seed-eaters. Indeed, some of the
Galápagos finches did eat seeds; but others fed on the
fleshy parts of cacti. There was even one that used a cactus
spine, held in its beak, as a tool to extract insects from
under the bark of tree cacti. This was especially interesting,

X 1/2

X 1/2

Figure 18 · 2

The Galápagos finches, the birds that aroused Darwin's interest in variation and adaptation.

since Darwin noticed that there were no woodpeckers on the islands—in fact, there were few land birds of any sort except the finches. And every available ecological niche seemed to hold finches: big and little; ground finches, tree finches; seed-eaters, fruit-eaters, insect-eaters; and a "woodpecker" finch!

In his notebook Darwin jotted down all his observations; in his mind he recorded vivid pictures of the island scenes. There in the Galápagos an idea began to form. But not

**Figure 18 · 3**

Charles Darwin eighteen years after the voyage of the *Beagle*. At this time he had sketched out his theories but had not yet published them.

Edinburgh [ĕd′ ən bûr′ō], Scotland

Alexander von Humboldt [hŭm′bōlt]: 1769–1859. German explorer, geographer, and naturalist

John S. Henslow: 1796–1861. English botanist

until twenty-three years after the *Beagle*'s masts disappeared from the Galápagos' horizon would the world hear of Darwin's idea—and never be the same again!

### THE RELUCTANT SCIENTIST

The work of the scientist may take place anywhere. Some problems require an air-conditioned laboratory, some a telescope on a far mountain peak, some only a pencil and a piece of paper. The work of the scientist may occur at any time. Men scarcely out of their teens have made important discoveries; others have labored for years with meager results. The work of the scientist may call to anyone. Many have been led to the study of nature in childhood; some have made careers in other fields before turning to science; others, drifting aimlessly from one occupation to another, have been enlisted in science only by accident.

Charles Darwin had been one of the drifters. There were no science scholarships in his day, no search for science talent, no science fairs. And it is doubtful that he would have benefited from them. He was an unenthusiastic student who, as his father once commented, cared "for nothing but shooting, dogs, and rat-catching." But he early came to enjoy travel, liked to read, and collected everything he could get his hands on, though doing little of scientific value with what he collected. Encouraged by his brother, he became so interested in chemistry that he was known as "Gas" Darwin in his neighborhood of mid-England Shrewsbury.

His attempt to follow in his father's footsteps by studying medicine at the University of Edinburgh was a failure. He found the medical lectures as dull as the lecturers themselves and became sick at the two operations he attended. So his father suggested that he study to be a clergyman. With this in mind, Darwin was sent to Cambridge University. Here he avoided dull classes, spending his time instead in shooting, collecting beetles, carousing with young colleagues, and dreaming of making a world cruise like that of Alexander von Humboldt. But at Cambridge, Darwin was fortunately befriended by several teachers, especially a botanist named Henslow who enjoyed taking groups of students on field trips. Finally Darwin graduated—and through Henslow received a tantalizing offer.

A British naval expedition, setting out to survey the coast of South America, had room for an unpaid naturalist, who would observe and collect plants, animals, and geological specimens. The invitation from Henslow was vehemently objected to by Charles' father—five years as an unpaid naturalist, indeed!—and the expedition's captain took an initial dislike to young "Gas" because of the shape of his nose. Nevertheless, on December 27, 1831, at the age of twenty-two, Darwin put to sea from Plymouth aboard the *Beagle*.

## THEORIES FORMING

Five years later, having sailed entirely around the world, the *Beagle* docked in England. There, as he prepared his official report (which became a best seller), Darwin relived the sights and sounds of the trip. First in the comfort and leisure of London, and then at his country estate in Kent, he began to see patterns among the queries hastily jotted down during the voyage.

All the tremendous variety of life forms that Darwin had encountered seemed to require some explanation. Those odd finches on the Galápagos, for example—all so similar, yet each with some peculiar characteristic of its own. And the geological problems—the origin of islands in the open ocean, for instance. Could there be any connection between the biological and geological problems? Sir Charles Lyell, whose *Principles of Geology* had accompanied Darwin around the world, had already gathered evidence showing that the rocks of the earth are subject to change.

queries [kwir′iz]: brief questions, especially those expressing doubt

Sir Charles Lyell [lī′əl]: 1797–1875. British geologist

**Figure 18 · 4**

The red jungle fowl, a wild bird of Southeast Asia, is thought to be the species from which the many breeds of domestic chickens have been developed. Which breed do you think retains the most of the wild bird's traits?

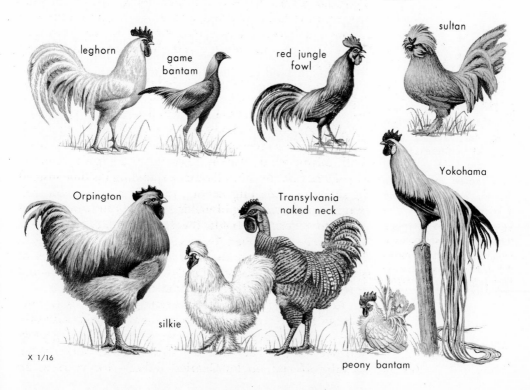

X 1/16

And Darwin had checked this evidence throughout South America. If rocks, islands, and continents could change, might not time also bring about changes in living things? Indeed, domesticated animals and plants *have* changed considerably in the relatively short time that man has been breeding them. How have such changes occurred?

Already richer than any other English naturalist in firsthand knowledge of the breadth and variety of the living world, Darwin now began patiently to collect examples of variation among domesticated animals and plants. He went directly to the sources of information—to seedsmen, to farmers, to animal-breeders. And he undertook experiments of his own.

At the same time, he dug deeper into the accumulated knowledge of geology. He checked the geological evidence that series of fossils taken from older to younger rocks showed gradual changes. Could the older fossils be the ancestors of the later forms? Lyell himself had not dared to believe this, but Darwin found more and more evidence that made him think so. Moreover, the manner in which present-day plants and animals are distributed over the surface of the earth could be linked to the past distribution of their possible ancestors. So Darwin sifted through the reports of exploring expeditions that had charted the geographical distributions of organisms. His library shelves became filled with scientific books from all over the world, their margins scribbled with his comments.

See pages 370–371.

Though he had little contact with laboratory biology, Darwin recognized that the structures of organisms now living might hold clues to the structures of their ancestors. Then, too, the ways in which modern organisms develop as individuals might reveal something about how their ancestors had changed. So Darwin studied anatomy and embryology. He became the world's greatest authority on

**Figure 18 · 5**

Under domestication, species of the genus *Cucurbita* have developed a wide range of fruit forms. Shown here are some obtained from native gardens in Bolivia. Working with the domesticated forms of *Cucurbita* nearly a century ago, the French botanist Charles Naudin proposed the biological definition of "species."

Dr. Hugh C. Cutler

Figure 18 · 6

Comparative embryology of some vertebrates. Zygotes are shown on the left, adult animals on the right, and comparable embryological stages between. Drawings are not on the same scale. Darwin's theories greatly stimulated the development of embryological science.

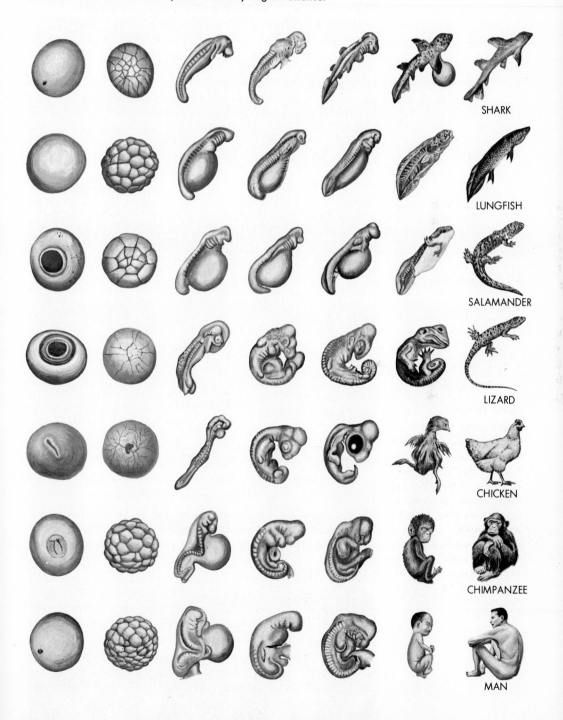

SHARK

LUNGFISH

SALAMANDER

LIZARD

CHICKEN

CHIMPANZEE

MAN

barnacles and triumphed when he found that the larva of a barnacle, unlikely as it might seem, was a free-swimming form quite similar to the larva of a shrimp or a crab. Were the barnacles, then, crustaceans that had long ago settled down to live attached to the rocks?

As the years went by, from a hill of suspicion a mountain of facts arose. All pointed to the conclusion that individuals within species vary and that from these variations great changes in the species inhabiting the earth have occurred. Still lacking, however, was a guiding principle. To produce changes that would result in populations adapted to their environment (as species populations are) variations had to take some direction. Or if all sorts of variations occurred, then some of them had to be preserved and others not. What directed change?

If Darwin had known only the peaceful English countryside, he might long have pondered this question. But still fresh in his mind was the lush and teeming life of the Brazilian rain forest. In a variety of ways, the rich plant life of the tropical forest seemed to struggle upward to reach the light. Having seen this, Darwin could detect in all kinds of habitats the struggle to obtain the necessities of life. Moreover, not long after he returned to England, he chanced to read Malthus' little book, *An Essay on the Principle of Population* . . . . Malthus had written that man tends to produce more offspring than can be supported. If this were true of all sorts of living organisms, wouldn't there be a struggle for existence among them? Under such circumstances, wouldn't the offspring best fitted for survival be the ones most likely to grow up and produce offspring like themselves? So it seemed to Darwin. The breeder of domestic animals culls from his flocks and herds those animals that fail to show the characteristics suited to his purpose, and he selects those animals that have such characteristics. In a like manner, the struggle for existence in nature might cull the unfit from each generation so that they would leave fewer offspring; the fit would be left to produce a larger percentage of the next generation. Darwin thought this idea of natural selection might explain how variations are guided.

*Malthus: See pages 38–39.*

*culls: picks out for discard*

## THE THEORIES PUBLISHED

It is one thing to convince one's self; it is something else to convince one's fellow scientists and the public. As patiently as he gathered evidence supporting his idea, Darwin also gathered objections to it. Contrary evidence was examined. Flaws in reasoning were worked over. Alternative methods of explaining the facts were tried. Nearly a quarter of a century passed. During this time, Darwin published books on a number of biological subjects, but only a few friends knew about his theory of evolution through natural selection.

Then quite unexpectedly, on June 18, 1858, he received a scientific paper from a young man who had been exploring in Malaya. The explorer, A. R. Wallace, requested Darwin to read it and, if it seemed "sufficiently novel and interesting," to send it on to the geologist Lyell for his comment. Imagine Darwin's surprise when he discovered that Wallace had worked out ideas on evolution almost identical to his own, that he had even been influenced by a chance reading of Malthus! Darwin realized that in good conscience he could not now, with fairness to Wallace, publish a summary of his own ideas. But Darwin's friends Lyell and the botanist Joseph Hooker prevailed upon him to prepare a summary of his theories and make a joint presentation with Wallace. Thus, on July 1, 1858, the Darwin and Wallace papers were presented before a meeting of the Linnaean Society of London, though neither Wallace nor Darwin was present.

The next year Darwin assembled his accumulated studies in a book, *The Origin of Species by Means of Natural Selection*. In it he proposed two theories. First was the theory that the living species of today are direct but modified descendants of species that populated the earth in bygone ages. This idea was far from new. It had been held by some of the ancient Greeks. And during the eighteenth and early nineteenth centuries quite reasonable attempts had been made to explain the fossil evidence that was then beginning to accumulate. But Darwin was the first to present such an enormous body of carefully sifted evidence to support this theory. Within a decade many of the biologists of the world were convinced that this theory—the theory of organic evolution—was as "true" as any theory can be. The second theory attempted to explain what makes evolution occur. This *theory of natural selection* became widely but not universally accepted by the biologists of Darwin's time.

In 1809 Jean de Lamarck had published a theory to explain organic evolution, based on the idea that changes in an individual brought about by influences in its environment could be inherited. Thus an animal that browsed on twigs and leaves of trees would stretch its neck to reach food, and, generation after generation, the offspring would be born with longer and longer necks. In this manner, said Lamarck, giraffes could have developed from ancestors similar to antelopes.

Bettmann Archive

**Figure 18 · 7**
**Alfred Russel Wallace:**
**1823–1913. English naturalist.**

Joseph Hooker: 1817–1911. English explorer and botanist

See page 643.

Lamarck: See page 379.

Darwin tried to reject this idea. He believed that variation was a basic characteristic of living things and that all kinds of variations occurred. The giraffe's ancestors probably included both shorter-necked and longer-necked individuals. Darwin agreed that, over a long period, the average neck length of the population would increase — but only because, *on the average,* the longer-necked individuals would survive in greater numbers (being better able to reach food). And, *on the average*, they would therefore produce a larger proportion of the offspring. But Darwin was still troubled. What made the variations occur in the first place? Could continual use of a part of the body (or failure to use it) have anything to do with this?

Unfortunately, Darwin was never able to explain how hereditary variation occurs. Apparently he never ran across the work of the Austrian monk who was experimenting with inheritance in garden peas and applying his mathematical training (which Darwin lacked) to the results. But perhaps Mendel's work would not have helped. At that time almost nothing was known about mutation.

### THE PROCESS OF EVOLVING

All the evidence Darwin presented in support of his theory of natural selection was indirect. And the evidence would always have to be indirect because the theory, as stated by Darwin, depended upon long periods of time. No person could live long enough to observe the processes of evolution occurring — or so it seemed to Darwin and to biologists for more than half a century after him.

*Biston betularia* [bĭs′tən bĕt ū-lā′ri ə]

They were wrong. Consider the case of *Biston betularia*, the peppered moth, a common inhabitant of English woodlands. To a casual observer all peppered moths look alike; but if we examine a large number of them carefully, we find — as in any population — many individual differences. A few have shorter antennae than most. Some have longer legs. The most noticeable difference, however, is in coloration: some individuals are light and others dark.

For a long time the collecting of moths has been a popular hobby in Britain as well as a part of biological research. Thus, many specimens from all periods of time during the last century and a half are available for study. When we examine these specimens, we see that the variations among moths caught in, say, 1850 are mainly the variations seen in a modern collection. There is one exception. Collections made in recent decades show more dark moths than light ones; in 1850 there were many more light than dark.

Biologists have made some additional observations. If they examine separate recent collections from rural southern England, they find the proportion of light and dark moths is still very much like that of 1850. It is when they examine collections from the smoky, heavily industrialized Midlands of England that they find very few light moths. Undoubtedly the coloration is controlled genetically, but why should light moths predominate in one region, dark moths elsewhere? And why should dark moths apparently have been rarer in the past than now?

The information they already had was sufficient to lead the biologists to develop a hypothesis, which they proceeded to test. In the Midlands they placed both light and dark moths on smoke-blackened tree trunks in the position moths take during their daytime rest. They soon observed that birds preying on the moths ate many more light than dark moths. Then they placed both light and dark moths on trees of the kind common in southern England—soot-free and encrusted with whitish lichens. Here the birds ate more dark than light moths.

The conclusion is clear: the increase of dark moths during industrialization has been a result of better adaptation of the dark moths to the increasingly soot-covered tree trunks. During the last century Darwin's "natural selection" favored the moths most protectively colored in the new

*Before reading further, can you state a hypothesis of your own?*

**Figure 18 · 8**
The basis for natural selection in the peppered moth (*Biston betularia*). *Left:* Dark and light forms on a tree blackened by soot. *Right:* The two forms of the moth on a tree covered with light-colored lichens.    × 4/5

American Museum of Natural History

environment. Meanwhile, the white form remained successful in rural areas where tree trunks were not sooty.

## CHARACTERISTICS OF THE EVOLUTIONARY PROCESS

What can we make of this directly observed example of evolution? Starting with the situation in 1850, we can note four important points.

First: An evolutionary event is a change in a *population*, not a change in just one or a few individuals. A century ago the population included only a few dark moths. The change that occurred during the next hundred years was in the frequency of dark coloration in the population.

For this usage of the word "frequency," see Investigation 17.4, page 656.

Second: On the whole, change is not the dominant note in an evolutionary event. All the individuals were much alike in 1850. Today they are still much alike. Most of the rare differences noted in 1850 are still rare, and few new variations have been discovered. Only the coloration characteristic has changed in frequency. There is a *stability factor* in evolution.

Third: An evolutionary event must have a basis to work on—some "raw material," so to speak. Before the rise in frequency of dark moths, there were already a few dark individuals in the moth population—and their darkness was genetic. An evolutionary event, then, requires genetic variations as its raw material. Thus there is a *change factor* in evolution.

Finally: An evolutionary event does not involve *all* the raw materials available. There were many hereditary varia-

### Figure 18 · 9

Screech owls occur in the two color forms shown here. The red form is common in New England but is less so elsewhere in the East; it is rare or absent in the West. Can you propose a hypothesis to explain this situation?

Lynwood M. Chace

tions in the moths of a century ago, but only one, the dark color, became the basis for a change in the population. The others remained more or less unchanged in frequency. Evolution is a selective change, with environmental factors (the soot and the birds, in our example) guiding the selection. Thus there is a *guiding factor* in evolution.

## THE STABILITY FACTOR

What tends to keep organisms much the same from generation to generation? We already know a part of the answer—the mechanism of heredity and reproduction. The many characteristic structures and functions of a living organism develop according to the set of genes it inherits. These genes, for all their great chemical complexity, are generally quite stable molecules. Not only the genes themselves, but also the mechanisms by which genes are duplicated, portioned out, and passed on to offspring, are wonderfully exact. Mitosis and meiosis rarely "go wrong."

Neither Darwin nor Mendel knew about any of this, other than that offspring resemble their parents. Their contemporaries, who discovered mitosis and meiosis, *did* guess the importance of the chromosomes for the stability of hereditary characteristics. But it was not until the twentieth century that another aspect of the stability factor in evolution became known.

contemporaries [Latin: *cum*, with, + *tempus*, time]: persons living in the same period of time

Darwin supposed that hereditary variations disappear permanently when opposite types mate. This is still a common idea among people who have not studied the behavior of genes in populations. They think—and speak—of heredity as being a mixing of "blood." That is, they think of it as a mixing of liquids. From your study of Mendel's work, you know that heredity does not act in this way. However, doesn't common observation tell us that when populations differing in some characteristic interbreed, succeeding generations show a blending of the traits? Wouldn't the result be a loss of variety? Let us investigate this problem.

## INVESTIGATION 18.1

### THE HARDY-WEINBERG PRINCIPLE

#### PURPOSE

By studying a hypothetical situation mathematically, you may develop an appreciation of one factor in the genetic stability of populations.

#### PROCEDURE

Consider a hypothetical species of beetle. Assume that it lives in a stable environment. Assume that among the variations in this hypothetical species are two hereditary color types—one black, the other white speckled with black. Assume that the difference in color is determined by a single pair of allelic genes and that black (**B**) is dominant over speckled white (**b**). Finally, assume that the species population consists of 1000 beetles, with equal numbers of males and females. Among the beetles of each sex, 250 are homozygous black (**BB**) and 250 are homozygous speckled white (**bb**).

• Using the symbol ♂ for male and the symbol ♀ for female, diagram all the possible phenotypic matings in this hypothetical population. (1)   • Now list all the possible kinds of matings in terms of genotypes—for example, **BB** × **bb**. (2) • Beside each kind of mating write all the kinds of genotypes that can occur among the offspring. (3)   • Does any cross produce more than one kind of offspring? (4)

Assume that the offspring generation also consists of 1000 beetles and that each kind of mating you listed for (2) contributes equally to this population.   • What will be the ratio of black beetles to white beetles in the offspring? (5)   • Is this phenotypic ratio the same as that in the first generation? (6)

Recall the mathematical way to write frequencies used in Investigation 17.4. Now consider the two genes **B** and **b**.   • What were their frequencies (expressed as decimal fractions) in the original population? (7)   • What are their frequencies in the offspring population? (8)   • How do the frequencies in the two generations compare? (9)

Now make the same calculations for a third generation. You can do this by mating every genotype with every other genotype *in proportion to their frequencies.* But this becomes complicated and tedious. You can obtain the same result by using the "gene-pool" method: First, set down the frequencies of all the kinds

of gametes in the second generation. (In this case, they are equivalent to the frequencies of genes in Item 8.) Then assume random combination of these gametes. The frequency of **B** plus the frequency of **b** will represent the total sperm population. Likewise, the frequency of **B** plus the frequency of **b** will represent the total egg population. By algebraic multiplication (page 657) the third-generation genotypes and their frequencies can be obtained.

Use the gene-pool method to answer the following questions:   • What are the frequencies of the genotypes in the third generation? (10)   • Assuming again a population of 1000 beetles, what are the frequencies of **B** and **b** in the third generation? (11)   • Is the phenotypic ratio the same as that in the second generation? (12)   • Are the gene frequencies the same as those in the second generation? (13)

Will similar results follow regardless of what the original frequencies of **B** and **b** might be? Letting all other assumptions remain unchanged, assume that the original population contains 400 homozygous black beetles and 600 homozygous white beetles, each group containing males and females in equal numbers.   • What are the frequencies of the two genes among males in the population? (14)   • Among females? (15) • By multiplication determine the frequencies of the three genotypes among the offspring. (16)   • What are the frequencies of the two genes in the offspring population? (17)   • Calculate the frequencies of the genes in a third generation. (18)

## CONCLUSION

• In a single sentence try to state a conclusion concerning gene frequencies in populations. (19)

If you have been successful in formulating your sentence, you have stated the basic idea of the *Hardy-Weinberg principle.* In 1908 Godfrey H. Hardy, an English mathematician, and Wilhelm R. Weinberg, a German physician, independently worked out the effects of random mating on the frequencies of allelic genes in a population where neither selection nor mutation occurs. You have just done the same.

Godfrey H. Hardy: 1877 – 1947. English mathematician

Wilhelm R. Weinberg: 1862 – 1937. German physician

## THE CHANGE FACTOR

Without *some* changes in hereditary traits of individuals, there could be no evolution of populations. What are these changes, and how do they arise?

First, there are alterations in the chromosomes and genes — mutations. Among the millions of individuals making up a population, and among the thousands of genes each individual possesses in each of its cells, there is no predicting where the next mutation will occur. Furthermore, our inability to make such a prediction is probably not a result of mere ignorance. Evidence suggests that the answers to "*Which* gene will mutate?" and "When?" are matters of chance. Mutation is a random process.

The *effect* of a particular mutation appears (according to present evidence) to have nothing to do with the forces that affect the rate at which mutations occur. If the mutation rate is raised by high temperature, the changes made in the organism may make it *less* able to live in high temperatures or *more* able to live in high temperatures, or they may have nothing whatever to do with adjustment to temperature.

A second source of change lies in the recombination of mutations. Suppose we look at a population in which only two mutations — *A* and *B* — have occurred. How much variety will *A* and *B* provide as raw material for evolution? How many different kinds of offspring can be produced? A little thought tells us that there are four kinds: those with neither mutation, those with *A* only, those with *B* only, and those with both *A* and *B*.

The combination of two mutations may produce an individual as different from an individual with one mutation as either of these is from an individual with neither mutation. For example, a combination of very big bones and very strong muscles would produce a giant among men, while very big bones with ordinary muscles might produce a cripple, and ordinary bones with very strong muscles might do likewise.

Thus, recombination can yield a wide variety of individuals from relatively few mutations. Sexual reproduction, by

Recall the statement regarding evolution of organisms that reproduce only asexually, pages 579–580. Explain the meaning of the statement.

the recombining of mutations in zygotes and the crossing-over process during meiosis, greatly multiplies the effect of the change factor in evolution.

Summing up, we can say that the change factor in evolution has two bases: first, the mutation of chromosomes and genes; second, the recombination of differences produced by mutation. Mutation supplies the raw materials for evolution, while recombination casts it into new combinations. But no evidence has been found that they supply needed or desirable changes only. Just changes—any changes.

## THE GUIDING FACTOR

Fossil evidence clearly shows us that evolution, unlike mutation and recombination, has not occurred at random. The organisms that have developed through geological time are not merely a helter-skelter collection of changes. On the contrary, the combinations of traits that they exhibit are, in most cases, well-organized, beautifully coordinated *sets* of traits. All or most of these combinations are nicely adapted to the environment in which the organisms live, or lived, and are nicely fitted to one another. How did this internal harmony and external adaptation arise from random mutation?

nicely: here, finely, delicately, exactly

The theory devised to answer this question is the most important accomplishment of Charles Darwin. As we have noted, many others had pointed out the evidence for evolution—though none so thoroughly and logically as he. Only Lamarck had supplied a theory to explain the direction of evolution. Lamarck's theory, though plausible enough in the case of the giraffe's neck, failed to explain many other cases of adaptation. (Thus, it was weak as a theory, because it explained only *part* of the available evidence.) Darwin's theory of natural selection, however, supplied reasonable, natural causes for the guiding factor of evolution; it was worked out to apply to most of the evidence then available to naturalists. And the new evidence of twentieth-century genetics has continued to support it.

plausible [plô′zə bəl]: seeming to be true or reasonable

What additional weaknesses does Lamarck's theory have in the light of twentieth-century genetics?

We have already seen how the idea of natural selection developed; now let us summarize the theory. First, in every species there are many hereditary variations. In many species, indeed, it is safe to say that no two individuals are exactly alike genetically. Second, in most cases the process of reproduction operates so that each generation is more numerous than the one before. Clearly, if increase were to go on unchecked, the number of individuals in any species would soon be greater than the available nutrients could possibly support. Third, it is clear that this increase *is* checked. The *net* population of a species does not increase sharply over long periods of time. Many members of each generation die, from one cause or another, before reaching the age of reproduction.

Review Investigation 2.1.

Thus there is a kind of struggle for survival—a competition among individuals of a species for the available food, light, water, or any other factors that may be important in the environment. This intraspecific competition takes place among individuals that are genetically different from one another. Often it is these heritable differences that determine which individuals survive and which do not.

On the average, *in any particular environment* individuals having characteristics that improve their ability to survive will more often reach reproductive age than will individuals lacking such characteristics. Thus, in each generation we should expect a slight increase in the proportion of individuals having high *viability*—that is, having many characteristics favorable to survival. That is what Darwin called *survival of the fittest*.

viability  [vī′ə bǐl′ə tǐ;    Latin: vivere, to live, + ability]

Now let us see how the theory of natural selection works out in the example of evolution described earlier—the peppered moths. In the clean forests that existed before industrialization, the birds ate more dark moths than light ones—just enough more to balance the increase of dark ones by mutation. So dark moths remained very rare in the population. But after industrialization the dark moths in the sooty woods were eaten *less* often than the light ones —their darker color was better adapted to the new environmental conditions. And more of the dark moths survived to have dark offspring than did light ones to have light offspring. So over the years, in generation after generation,

**Figure 18 · 10**

The varying hare (*left*) has a nearly white coat in winter, although it is brown in summer. The coat of the cottontail rabbit (*right*) changes little from summer to winter. Which species is likely to survive better in Georgia? In Ontario?    x 1/8

Lynwood M. Chace

Leonard Lee Rue III from Annan

the ratio of dark moths to light ones in the population slowly increased; eventually, the light moths became rare, and the dark moths—the fittest ones in the new environment—became common.

Note that fitness is not a characteristic of an organism alone. It is an ecological characteristic, the *interaction* of a *particular organism and a particular environment*. Blackness of the moths does not fit them to living everywhere—only to places where the tree trunks are dark. A different example: In most environments the possession of wings is obviously an advantage to a fly. But in the southern Indian Ocean, far from any other land, is an island swept all year by savage winds. Flies are present on this island, but none have wings. It is easy to imagine what would be likely to happen to any mutant winged fly on this island.

So far in this consideration of the guiding factor in evolution, the importance of adaptations for a particular environment has been stressed. However, not every characteristic of every organism is obviously adaptive. Natural selection can act only on *whole* organisms. If genes of poor adaptive value and genes of high adaptive value are closely linked, selection can sort them out only after recombinations have separated them. And often, since each gene mutation has several or even many effects, harmful effects

Many flightless land birds live on islands, but some do not. Look up some examples and try to explain their survival as species.

Figure 18 · 11

Irish elk (artist's reconstruction from fossil skeletons).

may be linked inseparably with beneficial effects. If the *overall* effect is favorable, the seemingly harmful effect is carried along. The antlers of the now-extinct Irish elk evolved to such gigantic size that they probably became a serious hindrance to the animal. But bigger antlers tend to go with bigger body size. Perhaps, in this case, the bigger body had been a greater advantage to the elk than the oversized antlers were a handicap. Perhaps the Irish elk became extinct when the advantage of its big size was no longer sufficient to compensate for the disadvantage of its huge antlers.

compensate [kŏm′pən sāt′]: to make up for, to counterbalance

Now one final important point. Superior ability to survive—viability—is not the only factor in natural selection. Equally important is superior *fertility*—the ability to produce offspring. High viability and high fertility do not always go together. The most fertile individuals in a population are not always the biggest, the strongest, or even the healthiest ones. Differences in viability and differences in fertility add up to *differential reproduction:* On the average, populations whose members produce the most offspring capable of living to maturity tend to survive and increase in size.

## INVESTIGATION 18.2

### SICKLE CELLS AND EVOLUTION

#### BACKGROUND INFORMATION

In 1910 James B. Herrick, a Chicago physician, examined the blood of a boy ill with a mysterious disease. The red blood cells of the boy were shaped like crescents—"sickle-shaped" (Figure 18 · 12). Soon after Dr. Herrick's account of his discovery was published, other physicians uncovered more cases of the same illness.

In this disease, called "sickle-cell anemia," newly formed red blood cells are normal in shape; but when the oxygen in their hemoglobin is released to body tissues, most of these red blood cells change to the abnormal sickle shape. The sickle cells are destroyed in the

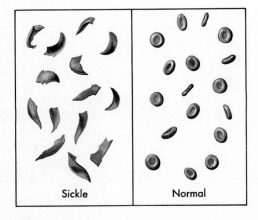

Sickle                    Normal

Figure 18 · 12
Human red blood cells.      x 500

spleen. This reduction in the number of red blood cells cuts down the amount of oxygen available for body cells. Also, because sickle cells are much less flexible than normal red blood cells, they do not pass through capillaries as easily. By clogging the capillaries, sickle cells further reduce the efficiency of the circulation. Persons with sickle-cell anemia usually die in childhood.

Individuals with less severe cases of sickling may produce sickle cells when the supply of oxygen is low (as at high altitudes) or when their need for oxygen increases (as during strenuous exercise). Such persons are said to have the "sickle-cell trait," and this is not usually fatal.

### PROCEDURE

Figure 18 · 13 is a pedigree of a family in which sickling occurs. • How many phenotypes are there in the family? (1)  • If the trait is determined by a single pair of allelic genes—one for normal hemoglobin and one for the hemoglobin of sickling—what kind of inheritance must be involved? (2)  The gene for normal hemoglobin may be symbolized as $H^n$ and the gene for the hemoglobin of sickling as $H^s$.  • What,

then, is the genotype for Individual 1 in the pedigree? (3)  Recall that the sickle-cell trait is a mild form of sickling. • What, then, is the genotype of Individual 2? (4)  • Of individual 3? (5)  • If Individual 4 marries a man with a genotype like her own, what percentage of her children may be expected to have sickle-cell anemia? (6)

The gene that brings about the formation of the hemoglobin associated with sickling is rare in most human populations. In some parts of Africa, however, the sickle-cell trait is found in as much as 40 percent (0.4) of the population.  • In such a population, what is the probability that any one heterozygous individual will marry another heterozygous individual? (7)  • What percentage of their offspring may be expected to be homozygous for the sickle-cell gene? (8)  • On the average, then, which would you expect to leave more offspring —individuals with the sickle-cell trait or individuals with normal red blood cells? (9)  • How many sickling genes are lost from the gene pool when a child with sickle-cell anemia dies? (10)  • What effect would you expect the death of children with sickle-cell anemia to have on the frequency of the gene for sickling in any population? (11)  You have described an evolutionary change in terms of modern genetics.  • How would Darwin have described this situation? (12)

Actually, there is no evidence that the frequency of the gene for sickling is becoming less in African populations. Therefore, a biological problem arises: How can the frequency of the gene for sickling be maintained at such a high level when selection works so strongly against the gene?

Now, after several months in this course, you know that the scientist begins his attack upon such a problem by devising hypotheses—explanations that

Figure 18 · 13

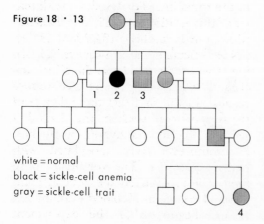

white = normal
black = sickle-cell anemia
gray = sickle-cell trait

may be tested by making suitable observations or by carrying out suitable experiments. Biologists have developed at least three hypotheses to account for the high frequency of the sickling gene in African populations. One is based on mutation rates, a second on fertility, a third on resistance to disease. • Using these clues, devise three hypotheses to explain the persistently high frequency of the sickling gene in African populations. (13) (14) (15) *Write these down before reading further.*

Through genetic reasoning and mathematical techniques, it is possible to calculate the rate at which genes are lost from the population gene pool by natural selection. For the **H$^s$** gene, this rate is about 100 times the average rate of mutation at any known locus in human chromosomes. Geographically, mutation rates vary only slightly. • Does this information support or weaken your first hypothesis? Explain. (16)

At present there is no evidence that individuals with the sickle-cell trait produce more children than do individuals with normal red blood cells. • Does this information support or weaken your second hypothesis? Again explain your answer. (17)

As data on sickling were collected, the frequencies of the sickle-cell trait in various populations were plotted on maps; it became clear that the gene is most common in a belt extending across central Africa. In the same region malaria and hookworm disease are common. • From your knowledge of these two diseases and from your knowledge of the part of the body affected by sickling, which of the two diseases would you think more likely to be associated with sickling? (18) • The foregoing question—and its answer—provides new information for your third hypothesis. How might you now word it? (19)

To test this hypothesis, one investigator examined the blood of 290 children in an East African tribe where both malaria and sickling were common. The results are given in Figure 18·14. • Calculate the percentage of "sicklers" (heterozygotes plus recessive homozygotes) with malaria and then the percentage of "nonsicklers" with malaria. (20)

|  | WITH MALARIA | WITHOUT MALARIA | TOTAL |
|---|---|---|---|
| SICKLERS | 12 | 31 | 43 |
| NONSICKLERS | 113 | 134 | 247 |
| TOTAL | 125 | 165 | 290 |

Figure 18 · 14

The chi-square ($X^2$) test can be used to determine whether the difference between "sicklers" and "nonsicklers" with respect to malaria is significant. In this case, however, the method of calculation is somewhat more complex than that in Investigation 17.2. You must consider *four* combinations: (a) "sicklers" with malaria, (b) "sicklers" without malaria, (c) "nonsicklers" with malaria, and (d) "nonsicklers" without malaria. To obtain the "expected" values for each combination, multiply the totals in the far-right column by a ratio obtained from the totals in the third line. For "sicklers" with malaria, this is $125/290 \times 43$; for "sicklers" without malaria, this is $165/290 \times 43$, etc. • Now calculate the chi-square. (21) In the table on page 641 use the $X^2$ for *two* classes. • Reasoning from the chi-square results, do you find that these data tend to support or weaken the hypothesis? (22) To test the hypothesis further, 30 volunteers were inoculated with malaria parasites. The volunteers were men of approximately the same age and physical condition. A blood examination at the beginning of the experiment showed that none of the 30 had malarial parasites, 15 had the sickle-cell trait, and 15 had normal red blood cells. Two of the "sicklers" and 14 of the "nonsicklers" developed malaria. • Apply the chi-square test to see whether the difference between the "sicklers" and the normal individuals with respect to malaria infection is significant. (23) • Does the result tend to support the hypothesis in Item 19? (24)

The present frequency of the sickle-cell trait in the parts of Africa from which the ancestors of American Negroes came indicates that the early American-Negro population contained about 22 percent "sicklers." • Would mixture with the European population and the American-Indian population have caused this frequency to increase, to decrease, or to remain the same? (25) In the United States, man has almost completely eliminated the vector of malaria, the *Anopheles* mosquito. • Do the heterozygotes still have a survival advantage over the homozygotes in this country? (26) • Recalling that an individual homozygous for sickling usually dies before reaching reproductive age, and considering your answer to Item 25, what would you expect to happen to the frequency of the gene for sickling in the United States? (27)

## CONCLUSIONS

• How are the factors in the evolutionary process illustrated in the case of the sickle cells? (28) • How does this investigation show that evolution involves interaction between the genetic makeup of an organism and its environment? (29)

Hereditary traits (and the genes that determine them) are sometimes described as "beneficial," "good," "harmful," or "bad." • Keeping in mind all the ideas developed in this exercise, comment on such use of these terms. (30)

## SPECIATION

Darwin called his book *The Origin of Species*. But so far in our description of evolution, no species have originated. Mutation and natural selection have merely brought about changes in the ratios of different kinds of individuals in a population. Today the population of peppered moths in industrial England is composed mostly of dark individuals, but there are some light-colored individuals with which they may interbreed. As we move away from the industrial areas into less sooty parts of England, the percentage of light individuals gradually increases. We may say that the population in industrial areas is a *variety*. But we cannot say that it is a new species—the process of *speciation* may have begun, but it has not been completed.

To become a new species, the moths in industrial areas would have to become a *reproductively isolated* population —that is, a population that does not interbreed with individuals from other populations. This statement fits the definition of a species (pages 65–67). But black moths still *can* interbreed with white moths, and white moths are still abundant in nonindustrial England. Therefore, genes can be exchanged fairly freely. Even if the few white moths in an industrial area were all eaten by birds, genes for whiteness could still come into this population if it interbreeds with rural populations that still have many white moths. As long as dark moths interbreed with light ones and produce offspring as vigorous and as capable of reproduction as their parents, a new species has not originated.

Present-day industrial processes tend to reduce the amount of soot produced by factories. What effect may a continuance of this trend have on peppered-moth evolution?

## MECHANISMS OF ISOLATION

How can reproductive isolation of a population develop? Obviously, something must happen that will interrupt the flow of genes from one population to another. Since reproductive isolation has not yet occurred in *Biston betularia,* we must turn to other species to find examples.

### ISOLATION BY TIME

At present, perhaps the most completely known fossil record of any evolutionary line is that of the horse family. The earliest organism that can be definitely identified as a member of the family was an Eocene animal scarcely larger than a fox terrier. It had a short muzzle and low-crowned teeth and probably browsed on bushes. It had four toes on each front foot and three on each hind foot, each toe with a tiny hoof. The modern horse has a long muzzle, with a wide gap between the front and rear teeth. Its teeth are high-crowned, with ridges of resistant enamel, a fine adaptation for grazing on the coarse, dry grasses of prairies. On each foot it has only one toe, which ends in a large hoof. There are many other differences, also, between the Eocene and the modern horse.

*Hyracotherium:* See Investigation 10.1.

muzzle: the projecting nose and jaws of an animal

The fossil record shows that all these differences are the result of a series of many gradual changes. Populations of horses, and thus numbers of horse genes, have always been great. Indeed, the paleontologist George Gaylord Simpson has estimated that during every epoch between the Eocene and the present, 150,000 *favorable* mutations of every horse gene could have occurred! Each change that became established through natural selection must have been very slight; only when many such changes accumulated did they result in detectable differences.

George Gaylord Simpson: 1902——. American paleontologist and geologist

Now how can this sequence of horses be divided into species? We cannot breed the extinct species of the family with the modern ones—horse, ass, and zebra; nor can we breed the extinct ones with each other. Yet the skeletal differences between many of the extinct populations were enormously greater than the differences between horse, ass, and zebra. If there are many differences, and if they

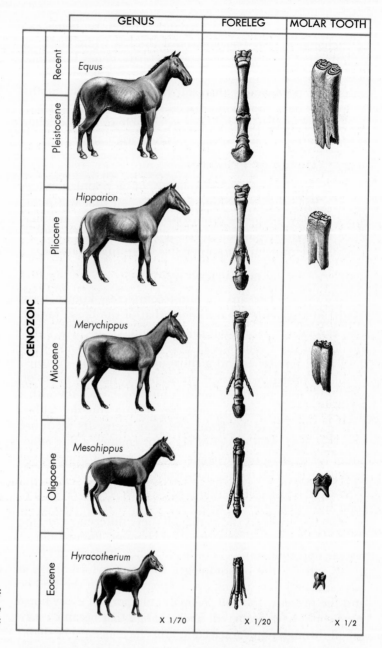

| | | GENUS | FORELEG | MOLAR TOOTH |
|---|---|---|---|---|
| **CENOZOIC** | Recent | Equus | | |
| | Pleistocene | | | |
| | Pliocene | Hipparion | | |
| | Miocene | Merychippus | | |
| | Oligocene | Mesohippus | | |
| | Eocene | Hyracotherium | | |
| | | X 1/70 | X 1/20 | X 1/2 |

Figure 18 · 15

Some characteristics of five genera of the horse family, from five levels of geological time.

are great enough, most paleontologists agree to call the populations of two very different times different species. But the populations of any one time must have given rise to later populations; these, in turn, gave rise to still later generations—and so on. Thus a species, over a long period of time, was gradually transformed into a new species through the accumulation of genetic differences. And this happened many times in the horse family. So the horse family in the past sixty million years must be viewed as a succession of many species.

### GEOGRAPHIC ISOLATION

**Islands.**   The finches of the Galápagos interested Darwin because they all seemed much alike and much like the finches on the distant mainland of Ecuador—yet they had many different forms of beaks.

It is easy to suppose that a few finches might have been carried by storms from the coast of Ecuador to the Galápagos. The islands are close enough to each other so that at one time or another finches might have been carried in this way to all the islands. Yet the islands are far enough apart to make interbreeding between populations on different islands a rare event. Therefore, mutations occurring in a population on one island are not likely to be carried into the populations of other islands. By the accumulation of mutations over hundreds of years, the *gene pool* on each island would become different from the gene pool on other islands. If the populations became different enough, they would not be able to interbreed even if brought together again. The populations on each island would have become separate species.

It is difficult to believe, however, that the evolution of new species has taken place only on groups of islands.

**Variation on continents.**   In species that have wide geographic ranges, traits often vary from one part of the range to another. The variation may be in the frequency with which a characteristic occurs in different populations of the species, or it may be in both the frequency and the intensity of the characteristic. If, by moving in a particular

Figure 18 · 16
Seven species of honeycreepers from the Hawaiian Islands. Why doesn't this arrangement illustrate the same idea as the arrangement of horses in Figure 18 · 15? What ideas does it suggest to you?

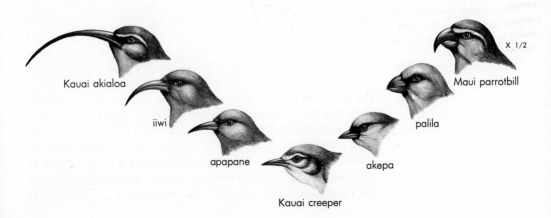

Kauai akialoa

iiwi

apapane

Kauai creeper

akepa

palila

Maui parrotbill

X 1/2

A　　　John H. Gerard from National Audubon Society　　B　　　Lynwood M. Chace from National Audubon Society

**Figure 18 · 17**

The (A) silver and (B) red forms of *Vulpes fulva,* the red fox.

cline [Greek: *klinein,* to slope]

direction through the range, we find that there is a continuous increase or decrease in the variation, the variation is called a *cline.*

For example, in North American red foxes there is an incompletely dominant mutation that affects coat color. If an individual bears the mutant gene in the homozygous

**Figure 18 · 18**

Cline in the frequency of the **I^b** gene (see page 655) in the human population of western Asia and Europe. This cline, of course, is not externally visible.

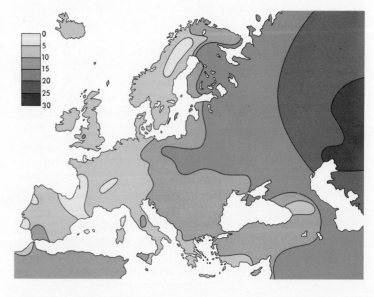

| 0 |
| 5 |
| 10 |
| 15 |
| 20 |
| 25 |
| 30 |

X 1/2

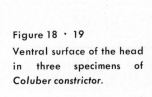

Figure 18 · 19
Ventral surface of the head in three specimens of *Coluber constrictor*.

(A) New York        (B) South Carolina        (C) Florida

condition, a beautiful silver fur is produced. If the individual is heterozygous, a fur with mingled red and silver hairs is produced (the "cross" fox). The silver coat is by far the most frequent in the north, the red in the south. The cross is most common between these regions. This north-south cline—from silver to red—is probably related to natural selection. A silver fox may be less conspicuous when hunting its prey on the edge of the tundra than a red fox would be, and a red fox may be less conspicuous when hunting along the edge of the deciduous forest than a silver fox would be.

When traits are inherited by the interaction of genes at several loci in the chromosomes, clines show variation in intensity as well as in frequency. In North America there is a cline in size among white-tailed deer. In general, when populations are measured in a series of more and more northerly localities, the average height is found to increase. The largest white-tailed deer in the Florida Keys measures 53 cm high at the shoulder; in northern Michigan the largest on record is 104 cm.

**From clines to subspecies.**   Variation within a cline is not always gradual. This is shown in the cline for a characteristic of the snake known as the racer (*Coluber constrictor*). Along the Atlantic coast of the United States, this snake varies in the number of white scales on the ventral surface of the head (Figure 18 · 19). In the New York population, the average number of white scales is low; in Florida populations, the average number of white scales is high. But the cline is not even. From central Florida to Georgia, the decline in the number of white ventral scales is steep, but the change northward from Georgia is slight.

Within the range of a widespread species there may be clines in many traits—but the clines do not necessarily coincide in location, direction, and intensity. Sometimes, when several clines *do* coincide, and when distinct changes

*Coluber constrictor* [käl′yə bər kən strĭk′tər]

coincide [kō′in sīd′]: to occupy the same place

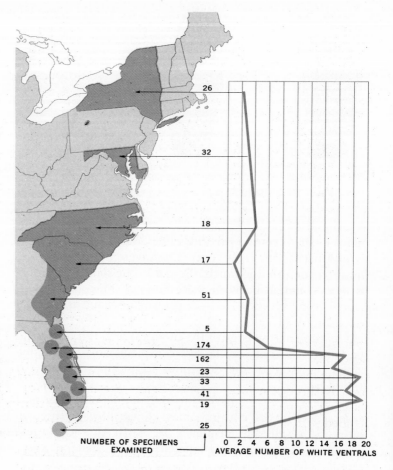

**Figure 18 · 20**

Cline in the trait shown in Figure 18 · 19. The areas from which population samples were taken are shown in color. The graph shows the average number of white or partly white scales in specimens from each population.

NUMBER OF SPECIMENS EXAMINED

26
32
18
17
51
5
174
162
23
33
41
19
25

0  2  4  6  8  10 12 14 16 18 20
AVERAGE NUMBER OF WHITE VENTRALS

in intensity occur in several clines at about the same place, it is possible to describe subspecies within a species.

**Subspecies into species?** Figure 18·21 shows the distribution of some of the subspecies of the racer in the eastern United States. This map records facts—facts of geographical variation in the traits of this species of snake. Using these facts, let us make a supposition. Suppose that the sea invades the Mississippi Valley (as it has done, according to geological evidence), destroying all the populations of *Coluber constrictor* intermediate between the subspecies *flaviventris* and the subspecies *constrictor*. At first the two subspecies might still be capable of interbreeding, but they would be prevented from doing so by the wide water barrier between them. Therefore, new mutations that occurred in *flaviventris* and in *constrictor* could not be exchanged. And with the accumulation of different mutations over a long period of time, wouldn't the two eventually become sepa-

*flaviventris* [flā′vǐ věn′trəs]

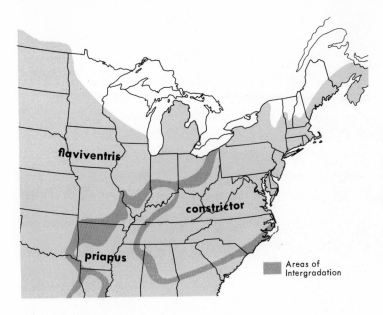

Figure 18 · 21

Distribution of subspecies of *Coluber constrictor* in a part of eastern North America.

Areas of
Intergradation

rate species? Perhaps so—but let us examine some further evidence.

The indigo bunting (*Passerina cyanea*) is a small bird that breeds throughout the eastern United States. The lazuli bunting (*Passerina lazuli*) breeds over much of the western United States. Both nest in bushes and small trees of brushy habitats. One hundred fifty years ago, both were apparently absent from the Great Plains (between the Mississippi River and the Rocky Mountains), where trees and brushy habitats were rare.

The biological names of these birds indicate that taxonomists consider them to be closely related. It seems possible that there was at one time a single bunting species, spread across the United States in the continuous forest environment that probably once existed. Then the development of the treeless plains—habitat unsuitable for buntings—may have separated the eastern and western populations. During this separation, visible genetic differences have arisen—at least in the males. In contrast to the male indigo (Figure 2 · 31), the male lazuli has white wing patches and red-orange breast and sides; there are also differences in the songs.

Now man has transformed the prairies and plains. Patches of trees and shrubs surround hundreds of farmhouses and line miles of streets in towns. Indigo buntings have spread westward from the deciduous forest, and lazuli buntings have spread eastward from the mountains. Here, then, we have a case in actuality that is much like the one

*Passerina cyanea* [păs′ə rĭn′ə sī ā′nē ə]

*lazuli* [lăz′yōō lī′]

How do the names show this?

See Figure 8 · 47.

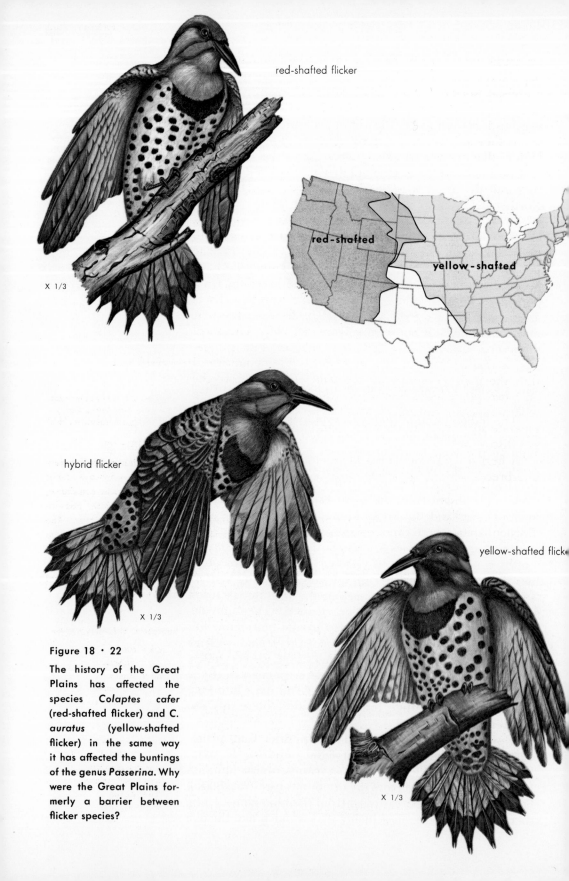

red-shafted flicker

X 1/3

red-shafted

yellow-shafted

hybrid flicker

X 1/3

yellow-shafted flicker

X 1/3

Figure 18 · 22
The history of the Great Plains has affected the species *Colaptes cafer* (red-shafted flicker) and *C. auratus* (yellow-shafted flicker) in the same way it has affected the buntings of the genus *Passerina*. Why were the Great Plains formerly a barrier between flicker species?

we could only imagine with the racer: the reunion of two populations that have acquired genetic differences in geographical isolation. What has happened? In many places male lazuli buntings have mated with female indigo buntings, and vice versa. Hybrids have been produced. And it seems they are fertile, though their fertility may not be as high as that of their parents.

Consider now the case of another bird species, the herring gull (*Larus argentatus*). The geographic range of this Northern Hemisphere bird is circumpolar (Figure 18 · 23); but breaks are present in the clines of traits—breaks that allow taxonomists to distinguish a series of subspecies and to draw "boundaries" between them. Of course, intermediate populations occupy the regions where the boundaries have been drawn, so genes can be passed, by interbreeding, from population to population. But in western Europe there is an exception. Here the chain of subspecies from the west meets the chain of subspecies from the east. The small differences have accumulated from subspecies to subspecies, so that the gulls of subspecies *fuscus* do not interbreed with the gulls of subspecies *argentatus*. If these were the only two populations known, we would say that they are separate species. Indeed, taxonomists long considered them separate species—until the ring of intermediate subspecies was discovered.

A herring-gull population in any one part of the range interbreeds with neighboring populations, and genes are

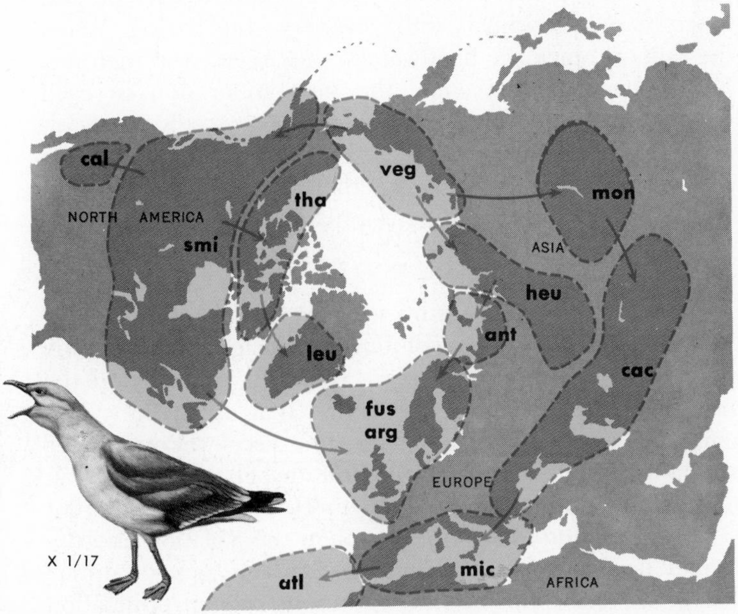

On the basis of this evidence, do *you* consider these populations to be separate species?

*Larus argentatus* [lă′rəs är′jən-tä′təs]

*fuscus* [fŭs′kəs]

They are still listed as separate species in some books. Can you give any explanation for this?

**Figure 18 · 23**

**Distribution of *Larus argentatus*. Approximate limits of the subspecies are shown, but intermediate populations usually occur. The subspecies vegae can be considered a central one from which differentiation has occurred in several directions.**

X 1/17

**Subspecies of *Larus argentatus***

**ant** = antelius
**arg** = argentatus
**atl** = atlantis
**cac** = cachinnans
**cal** = californicus
**fus** = fuscus
**heu** = heuglini
**leu** = leucopterus
**mic** = michahellis
**mon** = mongolicus
**smi** = smithsonianus
**tha** = thayeri
**veg** = vegae

exchanged. But so great is the distance around the habitable parts of the Northern Hemisphere that mutated genes have not been able to "flow" (the term used by geneticists for gene-exchange between populations) fast enough to prevent the two "ends" of the ring from developing great differences. And the differences are sufficient to prevent interbreeding (hence, the flow of genes) at the two ends.

## OTHER KINDS OF ISOLATION

Perhaps geographic isolation is always necessary to get populations started toward the formation of new species. Many biologists think so. But certainly other factors are involved in reaching permanent reproductive isolation.

Sometimes two populations may be isolated because they live in different habitats—ecological isolation. For example, in Michigan there are two populations of deer mouse (*Peromyscus maniculatus*), one of which inhabits the shoreline of the Great Lakes, the other the wooded areas. Between the shore area and the woods is a zone of meadowland that both populations avoid, so they rarely meet. However, there is good reason to suppose that if individuals from the two populations did meet, they could still interbreed. They are considered to be subspecies.

Sometimes the behavior of a species tends to isolate populations. The salmon of the Pacific Northwest live most of their lives in the ocean. When they mature, they enter rivers and swim upstream toward the headwaters—each individual swimming toward the small stream where it was hatched. How each individual knows where to turn off and enter its own stream is still a mystery—but it does. When the salmon reach the headwaters, they breed and then die. Because of this behavior, the new generation in each stream must obtain its genes from the preceding generation of the *same* stream. Therefore, though the salmon in the ocean have been living together for years, they are not really a freely interbreeding population.

## THE OUTCOME OF ISOLATION

Looking at the organisms now living around us, we can see many stages in the evolution of species—that is, many stages of reproductive isolation. Anything that hinders the free flow of genes in a population—that is, anything that tends to prevent free interbreeding—sets the stage for speciation. Geographical, ecological, or behavioral isolation may fail; mating may occur between individuals of different populations. But the more complete the isolation and the longer it continues, the greater will be the genetic differences between populations. Mutations in one population

X 1/3

**Figure 18 · 24**
**Deer mouse.**

*Peromyscus maniculatus* [pĕr ə-mĭs′kəs mə nĭk′yə lä′təs]

But the salmon population of each small stream is not considered a separate species. Can you explain the reasoning of taxonomists in this case?

will not spread through the other, and vice versa. Ultimately gene and chromosomal differences become so great that interbreeding becomes impossible.

When we recall that genes seem to direct the biochemistry of cells (pages 664–666), it is easy to see that differences in just a few genes from different parents might give conflicting biochemical "instructions" for development. In such cases gametes may form, but the zygotes fail to develop. Or a zygote may develop, but the resulting individual is weak and fails to reach reproductive maturity. Sometimes no zygotes are formed. The sperms of a duck or goose do not survive in the reproductive tract of a female chicken. In flowering plants, pollen grains from one species often burst and die when they start growth on the pistil of a flower of a different species. In these cases biochemical differences have become so great that mere contact between different cells is lethal.

In all of these cases, gene flow between populations is impossible. When any two populations develop such complete genetic isolation, the populations are distinct species; speciation has been completed.

## ABRUPT ORIGIN OF NEW SPECIES

In each of the examples given so far, a considerable amount of time has been necessary to bring about reproductive isolation. But there are instances in which new species have emerged quite rapidly.

Sometimes, especially in plants, meiosis is so abnormal that gametes are formed with two whole sets of chromosomes; the gametes are diploid. If fertilization is accomplished by a normal monoploid gamete, the new individual has three sets of chromosomes—that is, it is triploid. Occasionally even higher numbers of chromosome sets may occur; the general term for this situation is *polyploidy*.

polyploidy [pŏl'ĭ ploi'dĭ]

Charles M. Rick

**Figure 18 · 25**

Effects of varying numbers of sets of chromosomes on tomato leaves. *Left to right:* Average leaves from monoploid, diploid, triploid, and tetraploid plants.

When an Asiatic species of cotton (in which the monoploid number is 13) is crossed with a wild American species of cotton (monoploid number also 13), the hybrid is sterile. This sterility occurs because the 13 chromosomes from the two parents are, apparently, so different from each other that they fail to pair during meiosis. If, however, chromosome doubling occurs in the hybrids, each resulting cell has two sets of chromosomes from each of the species—a total of four sets (*tetraploid*). In such cells, each chromosome from the Asiatic cotton has an identical chromosome to pair with, as does each chromosome from the American cotton. Therefore, normal meiosis can occur. Each gamete formed then receives a complete set of the Asiatic and a complete set of the American chromosomes. By self-fertilization, these gametes can again produce a tetraploid plant. And such a hybrid is completely self-fertile. But if the hybrid is crossed with either ancestral species, only sterile offspring are produced, because a diploid gamete uniting with a monoploid gamete produces a triploid in which normal pairing cannot occur during meiosis. Thus, a new, tetraploid species—reproductively isolated from its parents—may arise suddenly, in only two generations.

The fine cultivated cottons of today are all polyploids that have come into existence in this way. So are the cultivated tobaccos and wheats. Among flowering plants, many wild species seem also to have arisen by polyploidy.

## INVESTIGATION 18.3

### A STEP IN SPECIATION

#### PURPOSE

Using data selected from an actual speciation study, you may gain an understanding of the way in which some kinds of evolutionary problems are investigated.

#### BACKGROUND INFORMATION

The small salamanders of the genus *Ensatina* are strictly terrestrial. Even their eggs are laid on land, and there is no aquatic larval stage. Nevertheless these salamanders require a rather moist environment and do not thrive in arid regions. In California *Ensatina* has been intensively studied by Dr. Robert C. Stebbins of the University of California (Berkeley). He has studied the animals in the field and has collected specimens of the species *E. eschscholtzii* in many parts of the state.

## MATERIALS

Outline map of California
Set of colored pencils

## PROCEDURE A

Imagine that you are working with Dr. Stebbins' specimens of salamanders, some of which are pictured below. In the following list, the parentheses after

**Figure 18 · 26**

Specimens of the salamander species *Ensatina eschscholtzii.*

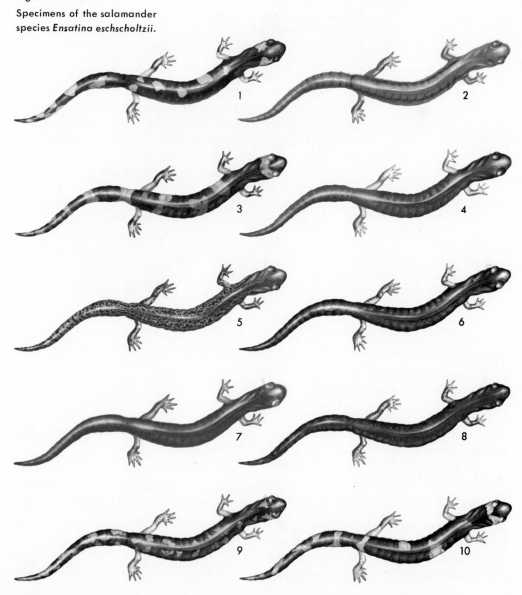

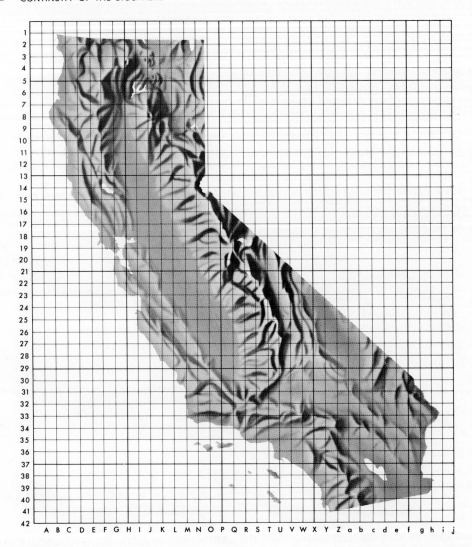

**Figure 18 · 27**
Map of California with the grid to be used in
plotting the distributional data for *Ensatina eschscholtzii*.

each of the subspecies' names contain a number and a color. The number is the total number of individuals that Stebbins had available for his study; the color is for you to use in designating the subspecies. Following this is a list of collection localities, indicated by a code that fits the map of California shown in Figure 18·27. For example, 32/R means that one or more *E. e. croceator* specimens

were collected at the intersection of line 32 and line R.

1. *croceator* (15; brown): 32/R, 32/S, 30/T, 31/T

2. *eschscholtzii* (203; red): 30/M, 32/O, 34/S, 35/V, 36/W, 35/Z, 38/Y, 40/Z

3. *klauberi* (48; blue): 36/Z, 38/a, 40/a, 39/a

4. *oregonensis* (373; pink): 9/B, 7/E, 6/E, 13/C, 10/C, 7/D, 15/D

5. *picta* (230; yellow): 2/B, 2/C, 3/C, 4/C

6. *platensis* (120; green): 8/J, 10/J, 11/M, 13/M, 15/M, 15/O, 17/M, 15/P, 20/Q, 24/S, 21/R, 25/T, 26/U

7. *xanthoptica* (271; orange): 17/G, 17/F, 19/H, 19/O, 20/I, 20/J, 21/I

On an outline map of California marked with the same grid as in Figure 18 · 27, plot the collection localities for each subspecies by making a small **X** mark with colored pencil.

### STUDYING THE DATA

You now have a distributional map of the subspecies of *Ensatina eschscholtzii* in California. • Is the species uniformly distributed throughout California? Use your knowledge of the species' ecological requirements to offer an explanation for the distribution. (1) Now consider the physiography of California (Figure 18 · 27). • Does this species of salamanders seem more characteristic of mountain areas or of large valley areas? (2) • Do you expect any order in the distribution of subspecies? Why or why not? (3)

Examine the pictures in Figure 18 · 26. Note that some subspecies have yellow or orange spots and bands on a black body; some have a fairly plain, brown-orange body; one has small orange spots on a black background; and one has a faintly orange-brown body marked with yellow and with small black blotches. There are other differences as well; for example, some of the seven have white feet. Now refer to your distributional map. • Does there appear to be any order to the way these color patterns occur in California? For example, Do the spotted forms occur only along the coast? Do spotted forms occur in the north and unspotted ones in the south? (4) • Sub-

species *eschscholtzii* and *klauberi* are very different from each other. What relationship (if any) is there between their distributions? (5)

### PROCEDURE B

At this point in your study you may begin to wonder whether there might not be salamanders in some of the areas for which you have no records and whether there might be additional subspecies for which you have no specimens in your collections. The biologist faced with these questions would leave his laboratory and go into the field to collect more specimens. Imagine that you do so, too, and return with the following additional data:

*eschscholtzii* (16; red): 36/Z, 41/Z, 33/M, 34/W, 34/U

*klauberi* (23; blue): 40/b, 40/Z, 36/a

Unidentified population #8 (44; black and green): 4/I, 5/H, 7/H, 7/F, 6/J, 9/F

Unidentified population #9 (13; black and red): 28/T, 27/T, 26/T, 28/S, 29/T

Unidentified population #11 (131; black and blue): 23/J, 24/K, 24/I, 29/M, 25/J, 25/I

Unidentified population #12 (31; black and yellow): 6/C, 7/C, 6/B

Mark with an 0 the following places which were searched for *Ensatina* without success: 11/I, 14/I, 17/K, 19/K, 22/N, 26/Q, 5/M, 32/U, 32/a, 35/f.

Specimens of #8 and #9 are shown in Figure 18 · 26; there are no illustrations for #11 and #12.

### STUDYING THE DATA

According to Dr. Stebbins, the unidentified populations are not additional subspecies. • What, then, is the probable genetic relationship of populations #8, #9, and #11 to the subspecies already plotted on the map? (6) • On this basis, describe (or, better, make a colored drawing of) the appearance you would expect specimens of population #11 to have. (7) • Why is it unlikely that you would ever find individuals combining characteristics of *picta* and *xanthoptica?* (8)

Now consider *eschscholtzii* and *klauberi*. Look at the distribution of the original collections. • What reasons were there for making efforts to collect additional specimens from extreme southwestern California? (9) • How do the results of the additional collections differ from the results in other places where two different populations approach each other? (10) • Does the distributional pattern of *eschscholtzii* and *klauberi* remind you of any examples that you have read about in this book? If so, which ones? (11) Bear in mind the biological definition of a species and also the appearance and distribution of the seven named populations of *Ensatina*. • Which one of these populations could best be considered a species separate from *E. eschscholtzii?* (12) This population was

indeed once considered by biologists to be a separate species.

Now imagine that while examining another museum collection, you find the specimen shown in Figure 18·26, #10. Compare its characteristics, especially the pattern of spotting, with those of the named populations. Also consider the distribution of these populations. • Between which two is this specimen most likely a hybrid? (13) On your map draw a line along which you might expect to collect other specimens like this one.

## CONCLUSION

• In a brief paragraph explain why Dr. Stebbins concluded that there is but one species of *Ensatina* in California. (14)

### FOR FURTHER INVESTIGATION

When we consider the effect of wide valleys and deserts on the distribution of *Ensatina*, the collection of *xanthoptica* at locality 19/0 raises a problem. State the problem and suggest some possible explanations for it.

---

The idea of evolution—that kinds of living things change as time passes—is very old. But a clear explanation of how evolution occurs was not developed until a little more than a century ago. In 1858 Darwin and Wallace set forth the theory of natural selection to explain the evolution of living things. To Darwin and Wallace, natural selection was a sufficient explanation for the origin of species. They saw the wonderful adaptations of species to their environments as the main feature to be explained. But the tremendous unfolding of biological sciences (especially of genetics) in the twentieth century has revealed that natural selection is not the only significant factor in the mechanism of evolution. It is, however, a *guiding* factor—the factor that explains the existence of adaptations. Like all theories, then, the theory of natural selection has had to take into account new discoveries as they occur, and it has been modified accordingly.

The recent history of the moth *Biston betularia* in England shows the first steps in the development of a new species. We have seen that stability, not change, is the general rule among populations. The frequencies of allelic genes and genotypes present in a population may be maintained by random interbreeding from generation to generation (the Hardy-Weinberg principle). But mutations and the recombination of mutant genes are constantly introducing variations—the "raw material" for evolutionary change. And when the environment changes, natural selection alters the proportions of allelic genes in favor of those that (on the average and in the long run) result in greater viability and fertility. Finally, when genetic differences develop through isolation of changing populations, a new species may appear. The isolation may be brought about simply by differences in the time when the species exist or by geographic, ecologic, or behavioral barriers. And sometimes genetic separation of populations occurs abruptly, through polyploidy.

## GUIDE QUESTIONS

1. How did Charles Darwin become a biologist?
2. What experiences in Darwin's life helped to form his theories?
3. What kinds of evidence did Darwin gather to develop his theories?
4. What event hastened the publication of Darwin's theories?
5. How did Lamarck explain the changes that occur in evolution?
6. What important part of Darwin's reasoning remained unexplained during his lifetime?
7. What has been the basis for natural selection in the peppered moth?
8. Why cannot a single individual organism indicate an evolutionary change?
9. How do reproductive processes tend to keep organisms genetically stable?
10. What is the Hardy-Weinberg principle?
11. What are the bases for the change factor of evolution?
12. What is the reasoning that leads to the theory of natural selection?
13. Why must the environment as well as the organism be considered in describing fitness?
14. Why must fertility as well as viability be taken into account when natural selection in a population is studied?
15. If we are to recognize that speciation has occurred, what must happen to a population of organisms?
16. How is time a factor in the process of forming new species?
17. How might a small species population, carried to an archipelago, develop into a number of separate species?
18. What is the relationship between clines and subspecies?
19. How might geographical isolation of subspecies lead toward speciation on continents?
20. In addition to geographical isolation, what other kinds of isolation may lead toward speciation?
21. How can the process of polyploidy produce new species suddenly?

## PROBLEMS

1. Sexually reproducing organisms are most likely to adapt rapidly to changing environments. Self-fertilization and parthenogenesis reduce the adaptability of populations. Explain these statements, using your knowledge of both reproductive and evolutionary mechanisms.

2. How do you explain the much greater variability of domesticated organisms than of similar or the same species in the wild (for example, dogs *vs* wolves;

chickens *vs* red jungle fowl; pigeons *vs* rock doves)?

3. *Polydactyly* (in which more than the normal number of digits are present) is carried by a dominant gene, but it is quite rare phenotypically in the human population. Type O blood results from a recessive gene; yet in some populations of North American Indians, as many as 97 percent of the individuals may have Type O blood. Explain these two statements.

4. Look back at the question in the caption to Figure 8 · 11. Do you recall how you answered the question? Would you answer it differently now?

5. It is sometimes said that an organism that has only asexual reproductive methods (domesticated bananas, for example) has reached the "end of the evolutionary road." To what extent do you think this is true?

6. In many species of birds, it has been found that populations living at higher latitudes lay more eggs per clutch than do populations living at lower latitudes. Would you expect the former gradually to replace the latter? Why or why not?

7. What effects may modern medicine have upon the future evolution of man? The facts needed for investigating this problem are to be found in biological science, but the *interpretation* of the facts lies outside the realm of verifiable conclusions. Therefore it is necessary to distinguish carefully between the facts and your interpretation of them.

8. The discussion of speciation has centered on terrestrial organisms. The same principles can be applied to speciation in the oceans, but fewer examples of the process are known there. Apply these principles to the oceans, using hypothetical cases —or real ones, if you are able to find them.

9. In Cambrian rocks, brachiopods have been found that are indistinguishable from the modern *Lingula* (Appendix II). Modern cockroaches are very similar to those of the Carboniferous period. Turtles of the genus *Caretta* occur in Cretaceous rocks and in the modern seas. Yet, during these same long years, other organisms have changed greatly. How can you explain such great differences in *rate* of evolution between species?

10. You are collecting grasshoppers in the vicinity of a canyon. The canyon is 80 km long and averages 800 m deep but in several places is only about 300 m from rim to rim. Along one rim of the canyon most of the grasshoppers have yellow wings; along the opposite rim most have orange wings. How can you account for this difference? Where would be the most likely place to look for grasshoppers with intermediate wing coloration?

11. Deep-sea animals and cave animals both live in lightless environments. Few, if any, deep-sea animals are blind, and a great many are bioluminescent (Chapter 9). Few, if any, cave animals are bioluminescent, and most are blind. Try to explain these facts from an evolutionary viewpoint.

12. What might be the evolutionary consequences of a worldwide nuclear war?

## SUGGESTED READINGS

ALEXANDER, R. D. *Singing Insects: Four Case Histories in the Study of Animal Species.* Chicago: Rand McNally & Co., 1967. (Steps in the process of speciation are shown by examples of familiar American insects. Fairly easy.)

BROWER, L. P., and J. V. Z. BROWER. "Investigations into Mimicry," *Natural History*, April, 1962. Pp. 8–19.

CROW, J. F. "Ionizing Radiation and Evolution," *Scientific American*, September, 1959. Pp. 138–142.

DARWIN, C. *The Origin of Species.* New York: Mentor Books, 1958. (A paperback reprint. Darwin's style is heavy, but his reasoning is clear, and his abundant examples are entertaining. A "must" for every prospective biologist.)

DOBZHANSKY, T. *Evolution, Genetics, and Man.* New York: John Wiley & Sons, Inc., 1955. (This book skillfully weaves the materials of genetics, ecology, and taxonomy into an account of evolution that emphasizes the importance of the process to man. Very advanced.)

KETTLEWELL, H. B. D. "Darwin's Missing Evidence," *Scientific American*, March, 1959. Pp. 48–53.

MOORE, R., and EDITORS OF LIFE. *Evolution.* New York: Time, Inc., Book Division, 1962. (A book of many striking pictures and a text that stresses history rather than explanation. Fairly easy.)

PETERSON, R. T. "The Galapagos; Eerie Cradle of New Species," *National Geographic Magazine*, April, 1967. Pp. 540–585.

SHEPPARD, P. M. *Natural Selection and Heredity.* New York: Philosophical Library, Inc., 1959. (Clearly relates genetic principles to evolutionary processes. Advanced.)

SIMPSON, G. G., and W. S. BECK. *Life: An Introduction to Biology.* 2nd ed. New York: Harcourt, Brace & World, Inc., 1965. Chapters 15–17. (Probably the best account of the mechanism of evolution in any college biology textbook. Advanced.)

STEBBINS, G. L. *Processes of Organic Evolution.* Englewood Cliffs, N. J.: Prentice-Hall, Inc., 1966. (Excellent discussion, with many examples and good illustrations. Advanced.)

WALLACE, B. *Population Genetics.* (BSCS Pamphlet 12.) Boston: D. C. Heath & Co., 1964.

——, and A. M. SRB. *Adaptation.* Englewood Cliffs, N. J.: Prentice-Hall, Inc., 1961. (Focuses upon the roles of genetics and natural selection in the process of adaptation; little attention is devoted to speciation. Fairly easy to read, but the ideas are complex.)

# Section Six  MAN
# AND THE
# BIOSPHERE

In the preceding five sections we have developed some major themes that characterize modern biology. They may be expressed as follows:

1. Each organism continually interacts with its environment; environment affects the organism, and the organism affects environment.

2. Communities fluctuate, populations fluctuate, conditions within individuals fluctuate, but the tendency everywhere in the biosphere is always toward steady state.

3. The structure of an organism can be understood only in relation to function; conversely, the functioning of an organism is dependent on its structure.

4. Through the mechanisms of heredity, one generation is linked to the next; thus, all living things of the present have a continuity with the organisms of the past.

5. Living things have changed through time and are changing today.

6. What an organism does—its behavior—is a reflection of its heredity and its experience in its environment.

7. Biology, like any other science, is a process of seeking —an inquiry into the nature of the universe about us. Our present understanding of life is the result of a long history of observation, experimentation, and thought. Because old concepts and theories must be reconstructed as new knowledge is acquired, our understanding will always be in a state of change.

Perhaps you would word these somewhat differently. But if you can recognize that you have been exploring these large biological ideas through the year, your efforts in this course have not been in vain.

One important matter requires further exploration. In the preceding sections we have not neglected man, but neither have we greatly emphasized the biology of the human species. Yet—since we are human—we all have a particular interest in man. Therefore, a biology course ought to give special attention to the position of man as a species in the web of life. This is our final theme.

# The Human Animal

## THE UNIQUENESS OF MAN

Man is an animal. If you cut open a specimen, you find that the parts—heart, intestines, liver, lungs—differ little from the corresponding organs of dogs, cats, or monkeys. If you study man's nervous or endocrine coordination, his respiration, digestion, reproduction, or muscle contraction, you find the same general chemical and physical processes as in many other animals.

There is no difficulty in classifying man. Obviously he is a vertebrate. Among the vertebrates he is a mammal—he has hair, and his young are nursed with milk. To be sure, he has an unusually small amount of hair, but some mammals have even less—whales, for instance. He is also unusual among mammals in his bipedal locomotion, but this is also characteristic of kangaroos. Men, monkeys, and apes are very similar in the details of their anatomy, and they are therefore grouped together in the order Primates.

bipedal [bī′pə dəl; Latin: *bis,* twice, + *pedes,* feet]

Yet it is equally obvious that in a number of ways man is highly distinctive. Because in these ways he is so very different from every other living thing, you can argue that he is not really an animal at all, but a quite new sort of creature. But when the difference is investigated, it is found to be primarily based not on anatomy and physiology, but on behavior and accomplishment. The difference lies in man's way of life—his culture. The word "culture" is used by *anthropologists* to cover all human knowledge and all the human ways of doing things that are passed on from generation to generation by teaching and learning. Man's difference comes from the vast fund of information (and misinformation) that the species has accumulated and shared among its members.

anthropologists [ăn′thrə pŏl′ə- jĭstz; Greek: *anthropos,* man, + *logos*]: scientists who study man, his physical and mental characteristics, and his social institutions.

Man as an animal—physical man—is a proper subject of biological study. But it is far from easy to separate animal man from cultural man. In fact, the separation is impossible, because everything man does is affected by his culture. We eat, for example, because, as animals, we have to have food; but whether we eat oysters, rice, ham, grasshoppers, potatoes, spaghetti, or what have you, depends not so much on the nutritional value of these things as on our cultural attitude toward them. In the study of man, then, there is a broad overlap between the biological and the social sciences.

Every species has characteristics—structural, physiological, and behavioral—that set it off from other species. Sometimes such characteristics are conspicuous; sometimes it is difficult to see differences among closely related species. Although there is great variability among individuals, man, as a species, is clearly distinct in many biological characteristics from the other animals that are most like him—from other large primates.

## STRUCTURAL CHARACTERISTICS

Man's outstanding physical distinction is his ability to stand, walk, and run upright, on his hind legs. This ability, which leaves hands free for manipulating or carrying things, involves many anatomical modifications. The legs of man are longer than the arms—he differs in this from the great apes and other primates. Man's foot, which has a high

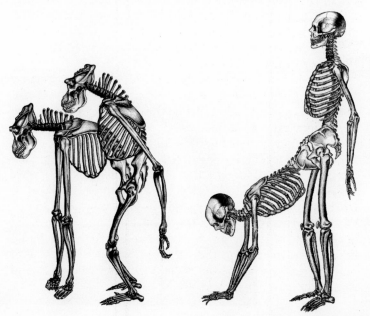

Figure 19 · 1
Skeletal proportions and postures of gorilla (*left*) and man (*right*).

See Figure 4·3

arch and the big toe in line with the others, is quite different from the foot of an ape. A human foot is good for walking or running, but not much good for grasping branches. The head is fixed to the spinal column in a way that enables man to look straight ahead when standing upright.

Man has a very large brain. In modern man the volume of the brain case is 1200 to 1500 cc, as compared with 350 to 450 cc in chimpanzees. There is no exact relation between brain size and intelligence—individuals with the largest brains are not necessarily the brightest—but the large human brain undoubtedly reflects great ability to learn. Other characteristics of the head are peculiarly human: the vertical face, the reduced projection of the jaws, the distinct chin, the prominent nose with its elongated tip, and the external mucous membrane of the lips.

Then there is the curious distribution of hair on the human body. This varies somewhat in different human populations. Most human individuals have long hair on the head; males of some populations have heavy beards. There are variable amounts of body hair and special patches of hair at the bases of all four appendages. We can only guess about the adaptive meaning of this hair distribution—and so far the guesses have not made much sense.

Man also differs from the apes in having canine teeth that are no more prominent than the other teeth. Since the time of Darwin, it has been argued that the small size of the

Figure 19 · 2

Comparison of facial features of man (*left*) and chimpanzee (*right*).

Charles Rogers

Nathan W. Cohen and Ziggi Brashears

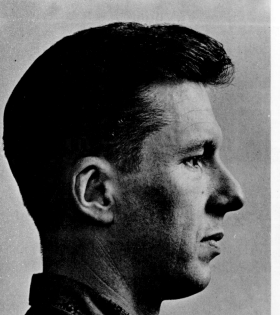
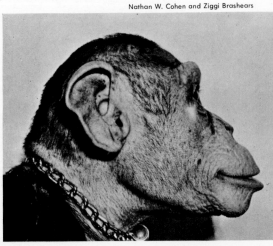

canine teeth is related to tool-using. For men with clubs, there is little advantage in having large canine teeth with which to bite enemy or prey.

Interpret this statement in both Lamarckian and Darwinian terms.

## PHYSICAL CAPABILITIES

What can the human body do? The records of athletic contests give us a good idea of the limits of its physical capabilities. Over short distances, such as the 100-m course, a man can run at a speed of 36 km per hour (about 22 mph). For longer distances, speed must be sacrificed in favor of endurance.

Many animals can run faster than man. Most of these have legs that are longer in proportion to their bodies than are human legs. In addition, the positions of the bony girdles in their shoulders and pelvises can be shifted advantageously at each step, as is most evident in the catlike cheetahs of Africa. These animals are able to chase antelopes at more than 100 km per hour (about 62 mph). The cheetah's shoulder girdle moves forward and back a long way (in relation to the hip girdle) during each stride, and both girdles swivel rather freely within the muscles.

pelvises [Latin: *pelvis*, a basin]: See Investigation 19.1.

X 1/18

Figure 19 · 3

Two stages in the running stride of a cheetah.

Man's size and build and the way he uses his body also determine his capabilities in other kinds of locomotion. From a standing position, a man can jump 1.6 m high or 3.5 m straight ahead. Human performance is much better from a running start: in the high jump, 2.2 m for a man and 1.9 m for a woman; in the broad jump, 8.3 m for a man and 6.7 m for a woman. An excited kangaroo can do better. He can jump to a height of 3 m and make a broad jump of 9 m. Normally, the human body has a lower density than water and can therefore float indefinitely in a calm sea. And man manages to swim fairly well. Over a 100-m course he can swim at an average speed of 6.8 km per hour. At the slower swimming pace needed to continue for 1.5 km, the speed drops to about 5.3 km per hour. Even with mechanical aids on hands and feet, man is too poorly streamlined to compete with a swordfish, which knifes through the water at 64 km per hour, or with a leatherback turtle, a finback whale, or a penguin, which can swim at 25 km per hour.

versatile    [vûr′sə til;    Latin: *vertere*, to turn]: here, to turn quickly from one ability or skill to many others

These comparisons leave man far behind one animal or another in any one physical ability. But he is more versatile than any of them. Indeed, versatility is man's specialty. It compensates for his rather poor sense of smell. It lets him make the fullest possible use of his rather limited hearing, which is inferior to that of cat, bat, or rat. It lets him make the most of his best-developed sense—that of vision. He interprets well the stimuli he detects, and he has an incredibly wide choice of ways to react to what he perceives.

### PHYSIOLOGICAL CHARACTERISTICS

Most of the structural distinctions of man are associated with behavioral rather than physiological peculiarities, though it is sometimes difficult to separate the two. Physiologically, man is not very different from other mammals, especially other primates. In many cases, therefore, biologists can apply knowledge gained from experimentation with other mammals to understanding human physiology. Though man's physiology shows no unique characteristics, some characteristics in the physiology of other mammals are developed to an extreme in man.

In man there is no breeding season; reproductive activity can occur at any time of the year. Therefore, in a human population individuals can be found with birthdays in all months of the year. Monkeys and apes have a tendency toward lack of seasonality in reproduction. It may be that this tendency is carried to an extreme in man partly because of his artificial shelters from seasonal effects. Most of man's domesticated animals, which also lead sheltered lives, tend to share this physiological peculiarity, even though the same (or closely related) species in the wild maintain their seasonal breeding periods. And animals that live with man—such as rats and mice—also show a tendency toward lack of seasonality in reproduction.

Few animals have as long a life-span as man. In the majority of organisms the weakening of the physiological processes at the onset of old age provides an opportunity for some predator or parasite to finish off the individual. This makes it difficult to determine the natural life-span of most organisms. But from records kept in zoos and aquariums, where animals lead protected lives, some data on possible length of life have been obtained for many species. Only the large tortoises are known to exceed the maximum ages attained by some humans. The *average* life-span of man is probably longer than that of any other animal, and it seems that this is only partly due to superior care and protection—in addition, his physiology is adjusted to a long existence.

Not only is man capable of long life; he also takes a long time to grow up. This is true no matter how we define "growing up." Many animals are independent from the time of hatching or birth. Mammals require at least a few weeks or months before they can fare for themselves, because they must be nourished by the mother's milk. The human child is completely dependent on adults for six to nine years—and partially so (even in primitive societies) for a time after that. The closest approach to this is among the great apes, where the young need perhaps two years to become independent. Man reaches reproductive age at about fourteen years; the apes, at about ten years; most other mammals—even those with life-spans approaching man's—much earlier, though the Indian elephant about equals man. Full skeletal development is reached in man at about twenty-two years; in the apes, at about twelve years.

These physiological characteristics—lack of a definite breeding season, long life-span, and slow development—probably have as much to do with the uniqueness of man as any of his structural characteristics. They make possible —and perhaps even necessary—the behavioral characteristics that distinguish him as a most remarkable animal.

Is there a physiological limit to the human life-span? If you think so, can you find any information about it?

## BEHAVIORAL CHARACTERISTICS

As a solitary individual, man is rather helpless—despite his big brain. Robinson Crusoe lived in a comparatively favorable environment, and he had the advantage of previous experience with other human beings. But imagine the plight of a solitary man in the forests of Europe during one of the ice ages. He would probably not have survived long. Normally, however, man is not solitary; he is a social animal. Of course, there are other social animals (pages 567–571). But insect societies are not really comparable to those of man; they are based on innate behavior, while man's behavior is mostly learned. And societies in other mammalian species, even in the apes, are not as highly organized as even the simplest human societies.

Much that is characteristic in human societies can be traced to the long period of growing up. Dependency on parents over many years insures that the young will be woven into the social group. During this period adults can teach and the young can learn. The experience of one generation can be passed to the next; the same discoveries need not be made anew by each individual. Thus knowledge accumulates within the group and culture becomes possible.

The transfer of knowledge depends on communication between individuals. Human beings may communicate by gestures, but it is obvious that these are usually just a substitute for language or are used for emphasis. Human language is not only more complicated than other communication methods—it is fundamentally different. It involves more than a system of cries and calls. It is dependent on the structural organization of the human brain. It is fundamental to being human, to the human achievement. Yet we have no knowledge of when man began to speak, no definite information concerning how language started. The languages of "primitive" peoples throw little light upon the early stages of language development; many such languages are in some respects more complex than our own. But there can be no doubt that talking is a fundamental human behavioral characteristic.

## INVESTIGATION 19.1

### THE SKELETAL BASIS OF UPRIGHT POSTURE

#### INTRODUCTION

It has been argued that man's big brain is an evolutionary result of the support offered by his upright posture. But whether his brain enlarged before or after his unique posture developed is the anthropological equivalent of the old question: "Which came first—the chicken or the egg?"

In a vertebrate, posture is a visible expression of skeletal structure. There-fore, a first understanding of the upright posture of man can be obtained from a study of the human skeleton. Comparison with the skeleton of a *quadruped* (four-footed) mammal should help to emphasize the characteristics of bipedal locomotion.

#### MATERIALS AND EQUIPMENT

Human skeleton, mounted
Cat skeleton, mounted
Rulers, 2

## PROCEDURE

Throughout this procedure observations are to be made on both cat and human skeletons. Thus, when you are directed to "Examine the skull," examine the skulls of *both* animals.

Vertebrate skeletons may be thought of as composed of two major divisions — the *axial* skeleton and the *appendicular* skeleton. The axial skeleton consists of the skull and the column of vertebrae (including the ribs that are attached to certain of the vertebrae), arranged along the longitudinal axis of the body. The appendicular skeleton consists of the shoulder girdle, the hip girdle, and the bones in the appendages, which are attached to the girdles.

Begin with the axial skeleton. Examine the general outline of the skull. • Which occupies the greater volume — the brain case or the bones of the face? In cat? In man? (1) • With respect to the rest of the skull, are the eye sockets directed forward, downward, backward, sideward, or upward? In cat? In man? (2) • What change in the facial bones of the cat would bring its eye sockets into the human position? (3)

Viewing the skeleton from the side, hold a ruler along the axis of the vertebrae in the upper part of the neck. • In which animal is the axis of the vertebrae closer to the vertical midline of the skull? (4) Holding the first ruler in position, place another ruler along the base of the teeth. • In which animal is the angle formed by the rulers closer to a right angle? (5) The *articulation* (jointing) of the skull with the first vertebra occurs around the *foramen magnum* ("big opening"). Through the foramen magnum the spinal cord connects with the brain. • In which animal is the foramen magnum closer to the posterior end of the skull? (6) If you look closely, you will notice roughened areas and ridges on the bones. These mark places where muscles were attached. Examine the back of the skull. • In which animal is there a greater area (in proportion to skull size) for muscle attachment? (7)

Examine the vertebral column. • Which animal has the greater number of vertebrae? (8) • Where are most of the "extra" vertebrae? (9) • In general, which animal (in proportion to its size) has the thicker vertebrae? (10) • How do the vertebrae in the region of the hip girdle differ in man and cat? (11) Observe the vertebral column from the side. • Ignoring the vertebrae of the neck and tail, in which animal does the vertebral column form a single arch? (12)

Now consider the appendicular skeleton. The hind legs are attached to the *pelvic* girdle — a set of bones fused together. • In proportion to its size, which animal has the heavier pelvis? (13) • Is the pelvis articulated with the vertebral column, or are the two structures fused together? In cat? In man? (14)

The forelegs (arms, in man) are attached to the *pectoral* girdle — which is made up of two broad, flat *scapulas,* two *clavicles* (collarbones), and a *sternum* (breastbone). • With respect to their attachment to each other, how do the bones of the pectoral girdle differ from the bones of the pelvic girdle? (15) • In which animal are the bones of the pectoral girdle more closely associated? (16) • How is the pectoral girdle attached to the vertebral column? In cat? In man? (17)

Compare the bones of the human hand with the bones of one of the cat's front feet. • In which animal are the bones of the *digits* (fingers or toes) longer in proportion to the total length of the appendage? (18) • In which animal is the inside digit (thumb, in man) articulated in such a way that it is opposable

(Investigation 4.1, page 109) to the outside digit? (19)

Compare the cat's posterior appendages with the legs of man. • In which animal is the knee joint closer to a 180° angle in normal standing position? (20) Consider each leg to be made up of upper leg, lower leg, and foot (including toes). • What fraction of the length of the upper leg does the length of the foot equal? In cat? In man? (21) • Which animal normally stands on its toes, with heel raised from the ground? (22)

## DISCUSSION

The following questions may help you to interpret your observations and to organize your thoughts. • What nonskeletal human characteristic is implied by your answer to Item 1? (23) Items 2 and 3 relate to a visual characteristic found in many primates. • What is the characteristic? (24) Observations reported in Items 4 to 7 are concerned with structural adaptations that make possible the support of a relatively heavy head in an upright position. Assume that the structure of man's distant ancestors was somewhat like that of the cat. • What mutations in the catlike structure would have brought about changes favorable to the development of both a large brain and an upright posture? (25)

• In a cat, where is most of the weight of the anterior part of the body supported? (26) • Where is the anterior weight supported in man? (27) • How do Items 10 to 13 relate to Items 26 and 27? (28)

• From the structure of its pectoral girdle, do you think a cat could easily support its weight on its forelegs? (29) • Can a man? (30) Of course, a man moving in an upright position does not need to support his weight on his arms. But he has the same kind of strong pectoral girdle that many primates use in moving about through trees. • How is this structural characteristic an advantage to man, who walks upright on the ground? (31)

• How is the position of the legs in a man who is poised to start a race similar to the normal position of the posterior appendages in a cat? (32) • What advantage does this position have for athlete and cat? (33) Try to stand for five minutes in this position. • What disadvantage does it have for man? (34)

## SUMMARY

• Summarize, in a paragraph, characteristics of the human skeletal system that are related to man's upright posture. (35)

## FOR FURTHER INVESTIGATION

Aristotle described man as a "featherless biped." The adjective was necessary because birds are also entirely bipedal. (Aristotle, of course, knew nothing of the dinosaurs, some of which were also bipeds, nor of kangaroos.) Using a mounted skeleton of a pigeon or chicken, make a comparison similar to the one you made with a cat.

## BECOMING HUMAN

We can only speculate about the origin of language; we have no direct evidence, because spoken words leave no fossils. But we have learned something about the evolution of human structure from fossil bones. The bones are no more than clues—but the scientist can learn a great deal from them.

## THE FOSSIL EVIDENCE

The great apes are more similar to men than are any other living animals. But if you look at the primate classification in Appendix II, you see that the great apes are put in one family, the Pongidae, and men in another, the Hominidae. When Charles Darwin published *The Descent of Man* in 1871, he based his discussion almost entirely on evidence from living species. Darwin thought that "missing links" between apes and men might never be found, since it is only by a rare accident that fossils are preserved; and animals of the tropical forest—where much of the evolution of the human line probably took place—are especially rare as fossils. Indeed, it is surprising that so many primate fossils *have* been found.

Pongidae [pŏn′jə dē′]
Hominidae [hŏ mĭn′ə dē′]

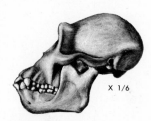
X 1/6

**Figure 19 · 4**
Skull of *Dryopithecus*, a Miocene primate that had characteristics common to both pongids and hominids.

Among primate fossils from Miocene times are those of the genus *Dryopithecus* (Figure 19 · 4), which has characteristics that might make it ancestral to either apes or men. Very few primate fossils have been found in the Pliocene, a period of about ten million years. When we come to the Pleistocene, all the fossils are clearly of either the hominid or the pongid type. From fossils it appears that the pongid and hominid lines have evolved separately for a long time.

*Dryopithecus*   [drĭ″ō pĭth′ə kəs]

To call the hominid fossils "ape-men" or "man-apes," then, is misleading, since they are not related to the apes we know today. Anthropologists avoid this problem by calling the fossils *protohominids*, but this is an awkward word. It might be better to call them "pre-men," which poses a nice question: When did the pre-men become men? The answer, of course, depends on how you define "man" —which can lead to many arguments. In any case, it was during the Pleistocene that the transition from pre-man to true man occurred. This epoch lasted for about two million years and ended only about ten thousand years ago. This was the epoch of the great ice ages, when continental glaciers of vast extent pushed down over the Northern Hemisphere. Four times the glaciers advanced, each advance separated from the next by a warm interglacial interval. There is good reason to believe that at present we are living in a fourth interglacial interval which began perhaps twenty thousand years ago.

proto- [Greek: *protos*, first]

**Pre-man.**   One day in the fall of 1924, Raymond Dart, a professor of anatomy at a university in South Africa, began studying a collection of fossil-bearing rocks from a

Ernest Shirley from *Time* Magazine

Figure 19 · 5
Raymond Dart: 1893———.
South African (Australian-
born) anatomist and pale-
ontologist.

*Australopithecus africanus* [ôs-
trä´lō pə thē´kəs ăf´ri kä´nəs]

Robert Broom: 1866–1951.
South African (Scottish-born)
paleontologist

quarry not far from his home in Johannesburg. Embedded in one piece of rock were parts of a skull unlike any he had ever seen before. When finally removed from the rock, a most remarkable skull was revealed. In some respects it resembled the skull of a five- or six-year-old child. In others, it was distinctly apelike. Dart named his find *Australopithecus africanus*—the "South African ape." He continued to study it and after four years of work succeeded in separating its jaws so that the teeth were fully revealed. They were remarkably like those of a human child. Moreover, because of the position of the foramen magnum, Dart felt certain that the skull had belonged to a creature that had held its head in a human position and had probably walked erect.

Another scientist, Robert Broom, who had been studying fossils of African mammals for many years, agreed with Dart. With their co-workers they began a search for more fossils that might provide evidence to confirm their conclusions. Over the next forty years enough fossil materials — skulls, leg bones, and pelvises — were collected to clearly indicate that groups of pre-men had indeed existed in South Africa during the early Pleistocene.

Far to the north and east of the sites in South Africa, in the Olduvai Gorge of Tanzania, Louis Leakey and his family have been finding and studying pre-human fossils for the past thirty years. The rock strata forming the walls of the gorge are relatively undisturbed, so that accurate dating of fossils included in them is possible by the potassium-argon method. From this site the Leakeys have recently obtained a group of australopithecine fossils basically similar to those from South Africa. The oldest of them are found between layers of rock believed to have been laid down about 1,759,000 years ago, at the beginning of the Pleistocene.

As more fossils were found, it became clear that there were not one but two species of *Australopithecus*. One included individuals weighing perhaps 70 kg and standing about 1.5 m high. This species, now named *Australopithecus robustus*, had very large teeth and powerful jaw muscles, both indicative of a herbivore. Dart's original species — *africanus* — was more slender, weighed about 50 kg, and stood about 1.2 m high. Although the fossil record is still far from complete, there is evidence that these two species of *Australopithecus* lived in Africa for about 750,000 years. During this time *A. africanus* became more and more manlike; *A. robustus*, on the other hand, remained remarkably unchanged.

**True man.**   The African fossils are hominid, but they are not *Homo;* this means that anthropologists believe they are more manlike than apelike but not enough like modern man to be placed in the same genus with him. For the next episode in the history of evolving man, the scene shifts from Africa to the Far East. Eugène Dubois, a young Dutch physician, had a strong conviction that fossil-bearing strata near Trinil, Java, would be a likely place to look for fossil

Olduvai [ōl'də wä']

Louis S. B. Leakey: 1903——. British (born in Kenya) paleontologist

See pages 343 – 345.

What does the fact that paleontologists continue to call all the varying fossils *Australopithecus africanus* indicate about the amount of change?

Eugène Dubois [dü'bwä']: 1858 – 1940. Dutch paleontologist

**Figure 19 · 6**

**Some hominid skulls. Can you see any characteristics that might distinguish the genus *Homo* from *Australopithecus*? That might distinguish *Homo sapiens* from *H. erectus*?**

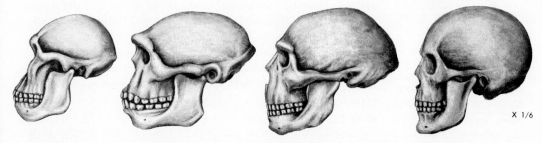

X 1/6

*Australopithecus*         *Homo erectus*          *Homo sapiens neanderthalensis*         *Homo sapiens sapiens*

Australopithecus          Homo erectus          Homo sapiens neanderthalensis          Homo sapiens sapiens

**Figure 19 · 7**

Artist's reconstruction of heads of some hominids. What characteristics do you think are directly based upon the skulls shown in Figure 19·6?

*Pithecanthropus erectus* [pĭth′ə-kǎn′thrə pəs ĭ rĕk′təs]

Davidson Black: 1884–1934. Canadian biologist

W. C. Pei [pā]: 1898———. Chinese paleontologist

X 1/2

**Figure 19 · 8**

A pebble tool. Such crude instruments have been found with the remains of *Homo erectus*. Is the use of tools a distinctively human characteristic?

evidence of man. In 1887 he resigned his position at a Dutch university and took a job as a surgeon in the Royal Dutch Army, assigned to a post near the Trinil site. The strata he wanted to examine had been laid down by volcanoes about five hundred thousand years ago. In two seasons of digging along the banks of the Solo River, Dubois unearthed a small piece of human jawbone, several teeth similar to those of apes, and part of a skull that suggested a brain too big for an ape and too small for any known man. In the next year he uncovered a fossil thighbone, and its straightness suggested that it came from an erect primate. Dubois gave this "Java man" the technical name *Pithecanthropus erectus*—the first fossil hominid to get wide public attention.

In 1929, after two years of excavation, Davidson Black and W. C. Pei discovered "Peking man." During the next twelve years parts of more than forty individuals were dug up from a cave floor at Choukoutien, near Peking. Whereas only a few crude flint tools had been found near the fossils of "Java man," many rough, stone tools chipped to an edge on one end (somewhat like modern chisels) were found among the split bones and punctured skulls of "Peking man" and the animals he ate. There is now general agreement that "Peking man" and "Java man" were closely related. Both have been renamed *Homo erectus*—in the same genus as modern man but recognized as a different species. Additional fossils of *Homo erectus* have been found in Tanzania, Algeria, South Africa, and Germany.

And now the scene of discovery shifts to Germany. There, in 1856, the first fossil similar to man was discovered in the Neanderthal Valley. At first this fossil was much misunderstood. Its age was disputed. But during the past hundred years a large amount of fossil material belonging to the same kind of hominid has been found throughout

Europe and in North Africa, Asia Minor, and western Siberia. It is now clear that *Homo sapiens neanderthalensis* was not a protohominid; he was a man—though perhaps not one you would like to meet on a dark forest path. The biological name indicates his placement in the same genus and species as ourselves—but he was enough different from us to be placed in a different subspecies. "Neanderthal man" was short, almost chinless, and had protruding ridges above his eyes. But he had a brain about as large as that of modern man, and the part of the brain that is known to be involved in speech was well developed. He lived in caves, used fire, buried his dead, and made good stone tools.

"Neanderthal man" flourished for about one hundred thousand years, during the third interglacial period and into the fourth ice age. At the beginning of this period, he was probably contemporary with *Homo erectus*. Near the end—about twenty-five thousand to fifty thousand years ago—he came into contact with a new group of hominids, "Cro-Magnon man."

**Modern man.** "Cro-Magnon man" is unhesitatingly placed in the same species and subspecies as ourselves (*Homo sapiens sapiens*) by anthropologists. He was tall and straight and had a brain as large as that of any modern member of the species. "Cro-Magnon men" were excellent toolmakers and fine artists. In addition to stone, they used bone, ivory, and the antlers of reindeer for tools. Some of these materials were engraved with designs or carved into the shapes of recognizable objects.

The relation of "Cro-Magnon man" to the *Homo sapiens* now existing in Europe is not clear. But the whole story of human paleontology is confused—more so than may appear from the account we have given here. The fossils of man are always fragmentary, and they are often difficult to date. Moreover, anthropologists have sometimes not been in close communication with other biologists, and vice versa. But the study of the whole Pleistocene epoch, in which most of the evolution of *Homo* occurred, is progressing rapidly. The immediate future is bound to bring forth much greater understanding of human origins.

### THE VARIETIES OF MAN

It is clear that all living hominids belong to the species that Linnaeus named *Homo sapiens*. We have ample evidence that the most diverse varieties can and do interbreed and produce fertile offspring. Yet populations of the human species differ considerably in appearance. There is a great range in size, from the tall peoples of northern Europe and the upper Nile River to the Pygmies of the Congo

*Homo sapiens neanderthalensis* [hō'mō' sāp'ē ənz nē-ănd'ər thəl ĕn'sĭs]

What do you think happened to "Neanderthal man" when modern man appeared? You might check your thinking with some of the references on pages 739–740.

Cro-Magnon [krō mǎg'nən]: after the Cro-Magnon cave, in France, where remains were discovered

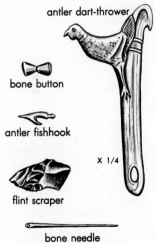

antler dart-thrower

bone button

antler fishhook

X 1/4

flint scraper

bone needle

flint blade

**Figure 19 · 9**
**Some tools of primitive man.**

forest. Skin color ranges from shiny black to very pale. There are also wide differences in the texture and distribution of hair on the body, in the shape of the skull, and in facial features, such as nose and lips.

On the basis of such differences, numerous attempts have been made to work out a classification of human populations, but there is no general agreement about such a classification. At one extreme, populations are designated as either "white," "black," or "yellow." At the other extreme, thirty or more different groups may be recognized. Human varieties show geographical patterns, just as do varieties of other organisms (pages 697–704). But no wild animal is as widely distributed as man, and few wander about as extensively. Gene flow among human populations has therefore been extensive. But before the mass migrations of populations in the last five hundred years, there was a rough correlation between geographical areas and certain human physical characteristics.

Europe and western Asia were inhabited by rather light-skinned peoples with thin lips; the males had heavy beards (unless they shaved) and relatively abundant body hair; head hair was either straight or wavy. In eastern Asia the human population had yellowish or yellow-brown skin, brown eyes, very little facial and body hair, straight, black head hair, and a fold in the upper eyelid (Figure 19 · 10). In Africa south of the Sahara, the common traits were dark skins, kinky head hair, relatively thick lips, and flattened noses. In Australia, curiously enough, the native peoples were somewhat similar to Europeans: head hair was curly, and the males had thick beards and abundant body hair; but the skin was generally quite dark. In America the population was similar in some ways to that of eastern Asia, but with the eye fold less developed.

From these sets of traits, some anthropologists have recognized Caucasoid, Mongoloid, Negroid, Australoid, and (sometimes) American Indian "races." But many subdivisions can be made within each of these groups, and wide transition zones link each (except the Australoid) to the others. There are also many oddities of distribution, such as similar-looking Pygmy peoples in the Congo and the Philippine Islands.

In recent years anthropologists have begun to use the gene frequencies of populations as a basis for classification. In this scheme they sometimes speak of "biological distance," which is simply a way of expressing the degree of similarity in the gene frequencies of two or more populations. In other words, the more similar the gene frequencies of populations, the less the biological distance between

Figure 19 · 10

*Above:* The Mongoloid eye fold. *Below:* An eye without the fold.

Caucasoid [kô′kə soid′; Caucasus, a mountain range in southeastern Europe, + Greek: eidos, a form, shape]

Mongoloid [mŏng′gə loid′; Mongolia, a region in central Asia, + eidos]

Negroid [nē′groid; Spanish and Portuguese: negro, black, + eidos]

Australoid [ô′strə loid′; Australia + eidos]

Figure 19 · 11
Examples of variation in
some physical characteristics among humans.

C. Bruce Hunter

American Indian (United
States).

Norman B. Tindale

Australoid (Australia).

Annan Photo Features

Caucasoid (Greece).

Annan Photo Features

Caucasoid (India).

Nathan W. Cohen

Mongoloid (China).

Howard G. Bergmann from Shostal

Negroid (United States).

them; conversely, the less similar the gene frequencies, the greater the biological distance. Of course, it is still a matter of anthropological judgment to decide just how biologically distant two populations must be before they can be considered different "races."

William C. Boyd: 1903——.
American physiologist

William C. Boyd has proposed a human classification based on the frequencies of the genes determining blood types. There are several advantages to using blood types as a basis for racial classification: First, the ways in which the blood-type genes are inherited are well known. Second, the blood type of an individual does not change with age or with changes in the environment. Third, natural selection does not seem to cause any rapid changes in the frequencies of blood-type genes; therefore, present frequencies indicate to some extent how human populations have mixed with one another in the past. Fourth, blood types are rather easy to determine from blood samples taken for various medical purposes; therefore, data for a large number of individuals representing many human populations are readily available for study.

Discussion of human races often gets involved with arguments about the superiority or inferiority of one race or another. There is no biological basis for such arguments. If we look at the matter from the physical point of view, we can argue that the most highly evolved are the Mongoloids, because they have the least hair; or the Negroids, because the peculiarly human lips are most highly developed among them; or the Caucasoids, because of the light-colored skin.

Usually, however, the argument turns out to be cultural rather than biological. But again each major race (except the Australoid) has developed a high civilization. The Caucasoids have become vain because the civilization of Europe has been the most powerful in the world for the last four or five hundred years—but this is no guarantee that it always will be. Three thousand years ago the Chinese had developed a great empire, while the barbaric inhabitants of the British Isles were painting their bodies blue and worshiping oak trees.

## INVESTIGATION 19.2

### BIOLOGICAL DISTANCE

#### PURPOSE

You will consider the following questions: To what extent are the Eskimos of Point Barrow, Alaska, the Indians of British Columbia, and the Navahos of New Mexico genetically related to each other? How do the migrations of human populations affect gene frequencies?

How can the mixing rate of two different populations be calculated?

## PROCEDURE

Recall that the four blood types, A, B, AB, and O, are determined by three allelic genes, $I^a$, $I^b$, and $i$ (page 655). Figure 19·12 shows the frequencies of these three genes in the Eskimo population of Point Barrow, Alaska; in the Indian population of British Columbia, Canada; and in the Navaho population of New Mexico. These gene frequencies have been calculated from the blood-type frequencies found in samples of the populations.

• On the basis of the $I^a$ gene frequencies, which two populations are most alike? (1)   • On the basis of the $I^b$ frequencies, which two populations are most alike? (2)   • On the basis of the $i$ frequencies, which two populations are most alike? (3)

For the next two questions there are no "correct" answers, only matters of opinion.   • Before beginning this investigation, would you have classified Eskimos, British Columbian Indians, and Navahos as members of one race? Explain your answer. (4)   • Now that you have proceeded this far, would you classify them as members of one race? Explain your answer. (5)

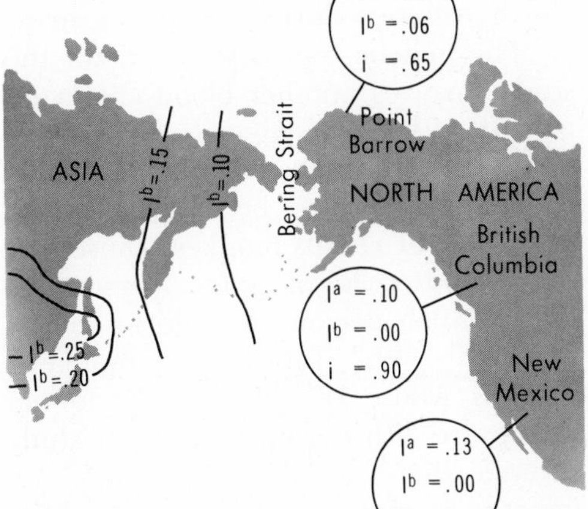

Now look again at Figure 19·12. Notice that it shows the frequency of gene $I^b$ in five regions of Asia.   • As you move westward and southward into Asia from the Bering Strait, what happens to the frequency of the $I^b$ gene? (6)   • As you move eastward and southward in North America from the Bering Strait, what happens to the frequency of the $I^b$ gene? (7)

Over much of central Asia the frequency of $I^b$ is .25–.30. Westward from central Asia into Europe, the frequency declines (Figure 18·18). There are several hypotheses to account for this situation, but we shall consider only one. Briefly, the hypothesis states that the primitive population of Asia had all three allelic genes, that Europe and America were populated from central Asia, and that the first emigrant populations from the Asian homeland either lacked the $I^b$ gene or lost it along the way.

How could an interbreeding population lose a gene? Loss by selection seems highly improbable, since the blood types apparently have neither selective advantage nor selective disadvantage. In *large* interbreeding populations where neither mutation nor selection is involved, the Hardy-Weinberg principle (pages 685–687) states that gene frequencies remain constant. But what about *small* populations—the kind very probably involved in all early human migrations? Consider the following situation.

Suppose that we had a human population with ABO blood-type genes distributed in the following frequencies: 25 percent $I^a$, 10 percent $I^b$, and 65 percent $i$. Suppose that it is a very small population, consisting of only fifty persons per generation. Of course, each individual has two genes for the ABO

$I^a$ = .29
$I^b$ = .06
$i$ = .65

Point Barrow

ASIA

Bering Strait

$I^b$ = .15
$I^b$ = .10

NORTH AMERICA

British Columbia

$I^b$ = .25
$I^b$ = .20

$I^a$ = .10
$I^b$ = .00
$i$ = .90

New Mexico

$I^a$ = .13
$I^b$ = .00
$i$ = .87

Figure 19 · 12

blood type. According to the Hardy-Weinberg principle, therefore, we should expect to find among the fifty children of one generation 25 $I^a$, 10 $I^b$, and 65 $i$ genes. Yet from experience in penny-flipping, card-dealing, and genetic experiments, you know that you don't always get *exactly* what is expected on the basis of probability. In penny-flipping, you *expect* to get "heads" as often as "tails"; but if you flip a penny only ten times, you might obtain 9 "heads" and 1 "tails" — or even all "heads" or all "tails."

Similarly, in the case of the small, hypothetical population of people, instead of getting expected results, we might find that purely by chance there were 26 $I^a$, 8 $I^b$, and 66 $i$ genes — or some other combination of frequencies. If this occurred, what should we expect in the next generation? Not 25 $I^a$, 10 $I^b$, and 65 $i$, but (according to the Hardy-Weinberg principle) a repetition of the *new* frequencies — that is, 26 $I^a$, 8 $I^b$, and 66 $i$. Of course, in the next (third) generation, the frequencies might again be the original ones (25:10:65), but they might result in a further reduction of the $I^b$ gene in the population. This might even happen a number of times, until the $I^b$ gene disappeared from the population. Then it could never return unless reintroduced by mutation or by immigration of $I^b$ genes in individuals from some other population.

Thus, as a result of *genetic drift*, as this process was named by the American geneticist Sewall Wright (1889———), the first populations of *Homo sapiens* to reach Europe and America may have had genes $I^a$ and $i$ only. • What blood types could they have had? (8) Later, according to the hypothesis, other emigrating populations carried the $I^b$ gene outward from central Asia and, by interbreeding, reintroduced the gene into American and European populations. • Considering the difficulties of primitive travel, where would you expect these later emigrant populations to be most numerous? Least numerous? (9) • On the basis of the frequencies of the $I^b$ gene, which of the North American populations shown in Figure 19·12 has probably had the more recent genetic contact with populations of Asia? (10) The frequency of the $I^b$ gene is .00 in the Basque population of southwestern France. • On the basis of the $I^b$ gene only, what can you say about the biological distance between the Basques, the natives of central Asia, and the Navahos? (11) • Does this mean that the Basques and the Navahos belong to one race? Why or why not? (12)

You have been proceeding on the assumption that genetic mixing between human populations does occur, but you have been given no data on *rate* of mixing. For a study of the rate of gene flow from one population to another, two populations with the following characteristics are needed: Both populations must be large; they must differ markedly in the frequencies of allelic genes at one or more loci; the traits determined by these genes must be easily and precisely identifiable; and, of course, the populations must be mixing. All of these characteristics are found in the Caucasoid and Negroid populations that have come into North America during recent centuries.

The genetic trait best suited for this study involves another blood characteristic. In 1940 Landsteiner (see page 654) discovered that material from the blood of rabbits that have been injected with the blood of rhesus monkeys causes the red blood cells of some persons to clump. Such persons are said to be "Rh positive" ("Rh" for rhesus monkey); persons whose red blood cells do not clump are "Rh negative." Further study showed that the Rh blood types are, genetically, more complex than the ABO types. Among the genes involved is one that has been symbolized **Rh°**. This gene can be rather easily identified, and its frequency differs markedly in the two populations you are considering.

In Negroid populations of Africa, the frequency of the **Rh°** gene is about .60; in Caucasoid populations of Europe, the frequency of the **Rh°** gene is about .03; in the American Negroid population, the frequency of the **Rh°** gene is about .44. From these figures the rate of mixing between African and European populations in North America can be computed.

• What is the difference between the frequencies of the **Rh°** gene in the African and European populations? (13) • What is the difference between the frequencies of the **Rh°** gene in the African and American Negroid populations? (14) The amount of mixing between the Caucasoid and Negroid populations in North America may be expressed as a percentage. • Divide your answer to Item 14 by your answer to Item 13 and multiply by 100. (15)

The year 1625 may be taken as the beginning of genetic mixing between Caucasoid and Negroid in America; the frequency of the **Rh°** gene in the American Negroid population was obtained from data gathered about 1950. • Assuming an average generation length of twenty-five years, how many generations of mixing could have occurred? (16) • On the basis of this number of generations, what was the average amount of mixing per generation? (17)

From calculations like this — crude though they may be — anthropologists can estimate the biological distance between populations, the routes of human migration, and the rates at which genetic differences among populations change. And from these studies some aspects of the biological history of man can be deduced.

## INVESTIGATION 19.3

### HUMAN BLOOD GROUPS

#### BACKGROUND INFORMATION

The major difficulty in blood transfusion comes from a clumping of the red blood cells. The clumps of red cells cannot pass through the capillaries, which therefore become clogged. If many capillaries are clogged, the circulatory system is blocked, and death may result.

Landsteiner demonstrated that the clumping of the red blood cells is brought about by a reaction between substances on the red-cell membranes and substances in the plasma. The reacting substances do not occur together in the blood of any one individual. But since different individuals have different sets of the substances, blood from one individual may contain the plasma substance that reacts with the red-cell substance of another individual.

In the ABO system of blood types, there are two red-cell substances, "A" and "B," and two plasma substances, "anti-A" and "anti-B." The following are the possible combinations: Individuals with A on their red cells have anti-B in their plasma. Individuals with B on their red cells have anti-A in their plasma. Individuals with both A and B on their red cells have neither anti-A nor anti-B in their plasma. Individuals with neither A nor B on their red cells have both anti-A and anti-B in their plasma.

## MATERIALS AND EQUIPMENT
### (for every four students)

Glass-marking crayon

Microscope slide, 1 per student

Sheet of white, unlined paper, 1 per student

Cotton balls, several per student

Alcohol, isopropyl, 70%

Forceps, 2

Sterile, disposable lancet, 1 per student

Anti-A serum

Anti-B serum

Toothpicks, 2 per student

Monocular microscope

## PROCEDURE

Using a glass-marking crayon, draw a line along the short axis of a microscope slide, dividing it into halves. In the up-per left-hand corner of the left half, write *A;* in the upper right-hand corner of the right half, write *B*. Place the slide on a sheet of white, unlined paper.

Wash your hands thoroughly. Using a ball of cotton dipped in alcohol and held in forceps, scrub the tip of a finger (on the left hand if you are right-handed, on the right hand if you are left-handed). Allow the alcohol to dry. Using a sterile, disposable lancet, make a small punc-ture in the tip of the finger. Wipe off the first drop of blood with a dry ball of cotton. Place a small drop of blood in the middle of each half of the slide. This may be done by touching the slide to the finger. Cover the puncture in the finger with a ball of cotton soaked in alcohol, and continue the procedure. (Hold the

Frank Manarchy (All Photos)

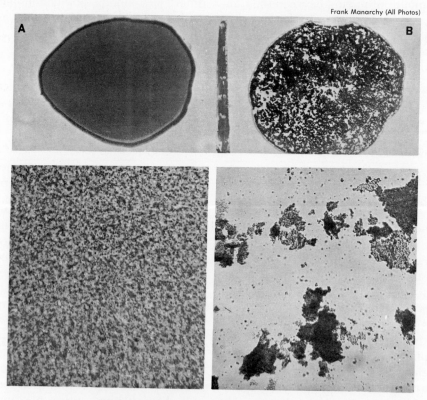

Figure 19 · 13

*Above:* Blood-typing slide. The blood is Type B.
*Below:* The same samples as seen with a micro-scope.    x 650

cotton in place with the thumb of the same hand for about five minutes.)

Immediately place a drop of anti-A *serum* on a drop of blood that lies on the A half of the slide. (Serum is plasma from which fibrinogen has been removed.) Use a toothpick to mix the blood and serum; be careful to mix them within as small an area as possible. Break the toothpick and discard it. Place a drop of anti-B serum on the drop of blood that lies on the B half of the slide. Use a second toothpick to mix the blood and serum. Break the toothpick and discard it.

Compare the material on each side of the slide with Figure 19·13, which shows both clumping and nonclumping reactions. You may check your naked-eye observations by examining the material under the low power of a microscope. Compare your slide with the slides of neighboring students.

## STUDYING THE DATA

If cells are clumped on Side A, your blood type is A.

If cells are clumped on Side B, your blood type is B.

If cells are clumped on both sides, your blood type is AB.

If cells are clumped on neither side, your blood type is O.

• What is your blood type? (1) (Caution: There are a number of factors that may produce errors in this test. *Your own determination of blood type must not be used for any medical purpose.* For this, only the results obtained by an experienced technician are satisfactory.)

Individual errors in determining blood type may occur, but such errors are not likely to greatly affect the percentages of blood types when data are reported by a large number of individuals. On the chalkboard tally the blood types of all individuals in your class. Other classes will do the same. Total the tallies and calculate the percentage of each type. • Which type occurs most frequently? (2) • Which type occurs least frequently? (3)

## SUMMARY

• Assuming that your determination is correct, name the red-cell and plasma substances in your blood — see "Background Information." (4) Large numbers of "foreign" red blood cells are introduced in blood transfusions; on the other hand, the introduced plasma is quickly diluted in the plasma of the recipient. • Keeping these facts in mind, describe what would happen to your circulation if you were given a transfusion of Type A. (5) • Of Type B. (6) • Of Type AB. (7) • Of Type O. (8) • Describe what would happen to the circulation of individuals of each type if you were the donor. (9)

• With respect to blood types, can the biology classes be considered a random sample of the population of your community? Explain. (10) Regardless of your answer to Item 10, assume that the percentages derived from the pooled class data represent the percentage in your community. Compare them with the percentages in the following samples:

|  | A | B | AB | O |
|---|---|---|---|---|
| London, England | 43 | 8 | 1 | 48 |
| Paris, France | 42 | 12 | 6 | 40 |
| Berlin, Germany | 43 | 14 | 6 | 37 |
| American Indian (Montana) | 76 | 0 | 0 | 24 |
| The Congo | 30 | 29 | 10 | 31 |
| Peking, China | 25 | 34 | 10 | 31 |
| Tokyo, Japan | 38 | 22 | 10 | 30 |

• Explain similarities and differences. (11)

Man is an animal and a part of the biosphere. But he differs greatly from all other animals. Biologically, human peculiarities are not so much matters of structure and physiology as of behavior and social organization. Anatomically, man differs from the other primates in his big brain and in skeletal and muscular characteristics associated with an upright posture. Physiologically, man is distinguished by a long period of dependency on parents and a lack of seasonality in breeding. Both of these physiological peculiarities were probably important in the development of human societies, language, and culture.

Fossil evidence of the family Hominidae is scanty, but it seems clear that the members of the family have been distinct from the Pongidae, the family of the apes, since Miocene times. Tool-using and even tool-making can be associated with hominid species as far back as the beginning of the Pleistocene. Throughout that epoch, hominids lived in many parts of the Old World. Since the middle of the most recent ice age, the species *Homo sapiens* has been the only living species of the family, though different subspecies can be recognized. Biologically, man has apparently remained substantially unchanged during the short geological time called the Recent—the last ten thousand years.

## GUIDE QUESTIONS

1. On what bases do all taxonomists classify man in the order Primates of the class Mammalia of the subphylum Vertebrata?
2. How can man be most clearly differentiated from all other animals?
3. What are the chief anatomical characteristics that distinguish man from apes?
4. How does man compare with other animals in his physical capabilities?
5. With what cultural characteristic of man can the lack of seasonality in human reproduction be linked?
6. How does the life-span of man compare with that of other animals?
7. How is the slow development of a human being related to culture?
8. What kind of communication is apparently dependent upon the organization of the human brain?
9. Why are primate fossils rare compared with those of, say, carnivores or hoofed mammals?
10. How does the primate genus *Dryopithecus* fit into the history of man?
11. What is the earliest hominid now known?
12. What are the relationships of "Java man" and "Peking man" to each other and to modern man?
13. When did the first man of our own species appear in the fossil record?
14. How is "Cro-Magnon man" related to existing men?
15. On what basis is the statement made that all existing men are a single species population?
16. What are some of the characteristics used in attempts to distinguish varieties of man?

## PROBLEMS

1. Why are tropical forests poor sources of fossil evidence? Consider both the conditions for fossilization and the conditions for finding fossils.

2. One of the difficulties with the anthropological concept of "race" may arise from a confusion of cultural and biological characteristics. Make a list of human characteristics that have been used by

anthropologists in their attempts to describe races of man. Now assume that the word "race" is equivalent to "subspecies" (Chapter 18). Which of the characteristics in your list are best suited for describing subspecies of man? Why are blood groupings particularly useful in attempts to define subspecies of man? Why are characteristics of skull shape less useful? Which of the two is easier to use in studying the subspecies of man in past geological time? (You might begin this investigation with William C. Boyd's *Genetics and the Races of Man*—Boston: Little, Brown & Co., 1950.)

3. A recent article in *Science*, the journal of the American Association for the Advancement of Science, refers to the Pleistocene as the *anthropogen* epoch. From the study of word roots in the marginal notes to this book, can you figure out the meaning of this word? Is it appropriate?

4. In this chapter you read: "Since the time of Darwin, it has been argued that the small size of the canine teeth is related to tool-using." Comment on this quotation in the light of the discussion of evolution in Chapter 18. Your comments may be improved by a rereading of the paragraph from which the quotation comes and the paragraph preceding it (pages 718–719).

5. What is *brachiation*? What anatomical evidence indicates that the ancestors of man were brachiating animals?

6. Review the fossil evidence for the early evolution of the hominids. Preferably your review should include more material than is contained in this book. Then attempt to write a definition of the genus *Homo* (one that would separate it from other hominid genera) and a definition of the species *Homo sapiens*.

7. Assume that the protohominids resembled *Homo sapiens* in lacking a breeding season. How would the social organization in a group of such animals differ from that in a wolf pack, in which there is a definite breeding season?

8. On September 23, 1789, nine Englishmen and seventeen Tahitians left Tahiti and sailed to Pitcairn, an isolated, uninhabited island in the South Pacific. For twenty-four years they and their descendants had no visitors, and since then their contacts with the rest of the world have been few. The effects of this isolation on both biological and social evolution are described in Harry L. Shapiro's *The Heritage of the Bounty*, rev. ed. (New York: Doubleday & Co., Inc., 1962). Can you find any evidence of random genetic drift in the Pitcairn Islanders?

## SUGGESTED READINGS

BRODRICK, A. H. *Man and His Ancestry*. New York: Fawcett Publications, Inc., 1964. (A recent account of the fossil history of man and how the fossils were discovered. Moderately difficult.)

EIMERL, S., I. DeVORE, and EDITORS of LIFE. *The Primates*. New York: Time, Inc., Book Division, 1965. (Attention is given to the ways in which the study of primate biology throws light on man. Many illustrations.)

HARRISON, R. J. *Man, the Peculiar Animal*. Baltimore: Penguin Books, Inc., 1958. (This is a biology of man that concentrates attention upon his anatomical and physiological peculiarities. Somewhat advanced.)

HOWELL, F. C., and EDITORS of LIFE. *Early Man*. New York: Time, Inc., Book Division, 1965. (Abundant colorful illustrations show both evidence and artists' interpretation of evidence. Fairly easy.)

LEAKEY, L. S. B. "Adventures in the Search for Man," *National Geographic Magazine*, January, 1963. Pp. 132–152.

MONTAGU, A. *Man: His First Million Years.* New York: New American Library of World Literature, Inc., 1958. (One of the leading anthropologists of the present day discusses both the biological and the cultural development of man.)

MÜLLER-BECK, H. "The Prehistoric Swiss Lake Dwellers," *Scientific American,* December, 1961. Pp. 138–144.

NAPIER, J. "The Antiquity of Human Walking," *Scientific American,* April, 1967. Pp. 56–66.

————. "The Evolution of the Hand," *Scientific American,* December, 1962. Pp. 56–62.

PAYNE, M. M. "The Leakeys of Africa: Family in Search of Prehistoric Man," *National Geographic Magazine,* February, 1965. Pp. 194–231.

SIMONS, E. L. "The Earliest Apes," *Scientific American,* December, 1967. Pp. 28–35.

# Man in the Web of Life

## MAN AND THE BIOLOGICAL COMMUNITY

Many chapters ago, your study of biology commenced with a rabbit hiding under a raspberry bush. Perhaps at first you thought that this was an uncomplicated introduction to the study of life. But it soon became apparent that cottontail and bush are but a small part of a very complex whole—a biological community of many kinds of organisms woven together with many kinds of relationships. And this community does not exist by itself; rather, it is controlled by factors of the abiotic environment, and, at the same time, it influences that environment. Then, when you looked into the structure and function of the individual organisms that make up biotic communities, you found that they are wholly dependent upon energy and materials that come from outside themselves—from other organisms and from the abiotic environment. Each organism, each organ, each cell, each chromosome—indeed each molecule of DNA—makes sense only in relation to the biosphere as a whole.

Is man an exception to all this? In Chapter 19 you looked at man as a biological species, singling out matters of structure and function and history that distinguish him from other organisms. But frequently in previous chapters you encountered man as just another example in discussions of various biological processes. Man fitted into the biological picture at every point—yet he always seemed to fit in a little differently than did other organisms. Perhaps this is only because we who write and read books are ourselves human beings. A historical comparison may give us some perspective.

**Figure 20 · 1**
A few food-gathering cultures still exist. This is a hunter in the Northern Territory of Australia.

Wide World

### STONE AGE MAN

If we look at man in the Stone Age, in a food-gathering stage of culture, it is not difficult to describe his probable relations with other organisms. As a hunter, man was a predator—a particularly efficient predator because of his use of tools, his intelligence, and his social organization. His niche was not unlike that of wolves. Human tribes, like wolf packs, traveled widely and were able to find food in a variety of biotic communities; but any particular pack or tribe, because of territorial behavior, was probably part of some particular community.

As a predator, man was a second- or third-order consumer. At times he was also to some extent a first-order consumer, eating berries, fruits, nuts—the plant products he could digest. And occasionally Stone Age man must have been food for other animals, such as the big cats, wolves, and crocodiles. But he was probably a minor food item for such animals; his tools, social organization, and intelligence, as well as his fire and shelters (once he had acquired these), protected him.

Always, however, man was a host for many kinds of parasites. In the Stone Age the human population was small, and it was widely scattered in small tribes. These conditions are not favorable for the spread of contagious diseases such as measles and smallpox. Pathogens of such diseases are maintained only in dense populations. Therefore, the important diseases of the Stone Age were probably those involving pathogens with alternate hosts. Yellow-fever virus can live in both men and monkeys, and it passes between them through forest mosquitoes. Thus, if monkeys are numerous, the virus can be maintained and occasionally infect people, no matter how scattered the human population.

See Figure 7 · 10.

We can look at Stone Age man, then, as a predator on other animals, as occasional prey for other predators, as a collector of various plant foods, and as a host for parasites. Man's ecological relationships changed only slowly through the nearly two million years of the Pleistocene period. But with the Agricultural Revolution—only fifteen thousand years ago—these relationships began to change rapidly.

Crops provided an increased food supply—and an increase in the human population resulted. The ceaseless search for food was replaced by periods of leisure, while crops grew and stored harvests were used. More rapid invention of tools and techniques resulted. Permanent villages and then towns arose. The use of metals was discovered, and animal power was harnessed. Man's relationship to the rest of the biosphere became very different from that of any other organism.

### INDUSTRIAL MAN

By comparing ancient and modern skeletons, anthropologists have concluded that man is physically the same today as he was fifteen thousand years ago. But he has learned a lot. And this learning, accumulated from one generation to the next through language and culture, has greatly altered his ecological position. He has continually increased his independence from the resources of any

Philip Gendreau

Figure 20 · 2

The primitive digging-stick agriculture of these Indonesian women can affect the biosphere only slightly.

**Figure 20 · 3**

Wheat harvesting in Nebraska. Industrial man converts complex plant communities to vast areas covered by a single species.

See pages 90–91.

particular biological community and has gradually shifted from being a *member* of a community to being a *maker* of communities.

This change has come about gradually since the Agricultural Revolution, but it was enormously accelerated by the Industrial Revolution. Within the past two hundred years man has replaced the power of animals with power sources that enable him to accomplish almost any task he can imagine—if he is willing to pay the price.

The efforts of industrialized, civilized man have resulted in simplification of ecosystems. In clearing land, he removes the diversified vegetation, usually replacing it with single crops—grains, vegetables, or trees. With the aid of fire and cooking, he has been able to move into the position of a first-order consumer; some human populations are almost entirely vegetarian. Where he remains a meat-eater, he tends to be a second-order consumer, raising grass and grains to feed cattle and poultry. Furthermore, man attempts to eliminate competitors. He does not like to share his apples with worms, his poultry with foxes, his sheep with wolves. He has tried (with increasing success) to make himself *terminal* in the food system by controlling the parasites that cause human diseases. He has even tried to defeat the saprovores with embalming and lead-lined caskets.

The complexity of natural communities tends to produce stability. But in simplified, man-made communities, natural checks and balances are reduced or eliminated. A field of wheat or corn or a cabbage patch offers a splendid opportunity for consumers that like wheat or corn or cabbage. The larvae of cabbage butterflies feed only on cabbage and a few closely related plants. Under natural conditions the butterfly must search out the appropriate plants on which to lay its eggs. In a cabbage field it need spend no time in searching; all the plants are suitable, and conditions are ideal for the multiplication of cabbage butterflies. The same principle applies to plant diseases. Under natural conditions spores of wheat rust might land on many plants unsuited to the growth of the wheat-rust fungus; but in a wheat field, a fungus on one infected plant can produce enough spores to infect most of the other wheat plants in the field.

X 1/2

Figure 20 · 4
Cabbage butterflies and their larva.

Industrial man not only has converted natural communities to his narrow desires but has created whole new artificial ecosystems—cities. Where once towns were isolated specks on the landscape, now the landscape tends to become submerged in concrete and steel. For many kilometers soil disappears under buildings, roadways, parking lots, and airports. A long strip of our country, from Maine nearly to North Carolina, has become a continuous urban area. Even within cities man tends to shut himself indoors, manufacturing weather year-round to suit his preference. The homeostatic mechanisms of the biosphere are continually being manipulated to make life in general, and urban life in particular, more immediately appealing to man. As a result, in only a few centuries industrial man has had a greater impact on the earth than his ancestors had in nearly two million years—indeed, greater than all other species of organisms which have ever occupied the earth.

## BIOLOGICAL PROBLEMS OF MODERN MAN

As the human population has gravitated toward city life, man has lost his sense of kinship with natural world ecosystems. In urban surroundings it becomes more and more difficult for people to realize that they are involved in the biosphere, in the web of life. Far from knowing the answers to the problems that assail them, they do not even know the origin of their difficulties.

gravitate [grăv′ə tāt′; Latin: gravis, heavy]: to move as though pulled by gravity

But you, as a student of biology, know what some of these problems are. A few were presented for your consideration at the beginning of this course. Now, with a year's study behind you, the problems may mean more to you than they did then. You may even think that you have some answers.

See page 33.

But before ending our biology course, let us consider a little further modern man and his biological dilemmas.

## DEATH AND DISEASE

There are still occasional victims of sharks, crocodiles, and snakes, but man long ago freed himself from most of the dangers of predation. And he has almost learned how to free himself from pathogens—even if this freedom is not enjoyed equally in all parts of the world.

The progress of medicine has been extraordinary since the time (less than a hundred years ago) when Pasteur, Koch, and others established the nature of infection. And the greatest progress has been in the control of the infectious diseases. This means especially that fewer individuals die in infancy or youth. In 1900 in the United States, 162 out of every 1000 infants died in the first year of life; by 1960 this figure had been lowered to 25 out of every 1000,

**Figure 20 · 5**

Causes of death in the United States (per 100,000 population).

| | CAUSES OF DEATH | 1900 | 1910 | 1920 | 1930 | 1940 | 1950 | 1960 | 1965 |
|---|---|---|---|---|---|---|---|---|---|
| INFECTIOUS DISEASES | influenzas and pneumonias | 203 | 162 | 208 | 103 | 70 | 31 | 37 | 32 |
| | tuberculosis (all forms) | 202 | 160 | 114 | 72 | 46 | 22 | 6 | 4 |
| | diarrheas and intestinal diseases | 133 | 117 | 54 | 26 | 10 | 5 | 4 | 4 |
| | diphtheria | 43 | 21 | 26 | 5 | 1 | 0.3 | 0.0 | 0.0 |
| | typhoid and paratyphoid fevers | 36 | 26 | 8 | 5 | 1 | 0.0 | 0.0 | 0.0 |
| | syphilis | 12 | 14 | 16 | 16 | 14 | 5 | 2 | 1 |
| | measles | 12 | 12 | 9 | 3 | 0.5 | 0.3 | 0.2 | 0.2 |
| | whooping cough | 12 | 11 | 12 | 5 | 2 | 0.7 | 0.1 | 0.0 |
| | scarlet fever | 10 | 12 | 5 | 2 | 0.5 | 0.0 | 0.0 | 0.0 |
| | malaria | 8 | 2 | 4 | 3 | 1 | 0.0 | 0.0 | 0.0 |
| | erysipelas | 5 | 4 | 3 | 2 | 0.0 | 0.0 | 0.0 | 0.0 |
| | smallpox | 2 | 0.4 | 0.6 | 0.1 | 0.0 | 0.0 | 0.0 | 0.0 |
| NONINFECTIOUS DISEASES | heart diseases | 132 | 159 | 159 | 206 | 293 | 300 | 366 | 366 |
| | cerebral hemorrhages and thrombosis | 72 | 76 | 82 | 81 | 91 | 100 | 107 | 104 |
| | cancer (all forms) | 63 | 76 | 83 | 97 | 120 | 140 | 151 | 153 |
| | bronchitis | 46 | 23 | 13 | 4 | 3 | 2 | 3 | 3 |
| | cirrhosis of liver | 13 | 14 | 7 | 7 | 9 | 7 | 11 | 13 |
| | appendicitis | 10 | 11 | 13 | 15 | 10 | 2 | 1 | 1 |
| | diabetes mellitus | 10 | 15 | 16 | 19 | 27 | 16 | 17 | 17 |
| | kidney diseases | 89 | 99 | 89 | 91 | 82 | 21 | 11 | 6 |
| | senility | — | 26 | 14 | 10 | 8 | 13 | 12 | 13 |
| | congenital malformations | 92 | 88 | 85 | 61 | 12 | 13 | 10 | 10 |
| OTHER | suicide and homicide | 14 | 22 | 17 | 25 | 21 | 18 | 15 | 17 |
| | accidents | 72 | 84 | 70 | 78 | 70 | 61 | 52 | 55 |
| | miscellaneous | 479 | 264 | 202 | 196 | 186 | 205 | 139 | 143 |
| | all causes | 1770 | 1498 | 1310 | 1132 | 1078 | 962 | 944 | 942 |

chiefly because we have learned to control the infections that are particularly dangerous to infants.

We still die, but we die later and from different causes. Figure 20·5 shows how the pattern of death has changed in the United States. In 1900 the three diseases that caused the most deaths were influenzas and pneumonias (grouped together), tuberculosis, and diarrheas—all infections. In 1965 they were heart disease, cancer, and cerebral hemorrhage—none infections and all chiefly diseases of old age. Diseases such as typhoid, diphtheria, scarlet fever, and smallpox have almost disappeared.

pneumonias [nū mō′nyəz, nōō-mō′nyəz; Greek: *pneumon*, a lung]

diarrheas [dī′ə rē′əz; Greek: *dia*, through, + *rheein*, to flow]

Much of this decrease in fatal infectious disease has come through the discovery of drugs and antibiotics—a long series of chemical agents effective against bacteria and other protists. As yet little progress has been made in finding chemicals effective in curing virus diseases. But smallpox, yellow fever, poliomyelitis, and (most recently) measles can be prevented by artificial immunization—and, from the viewpoint of both individuals and populations, *prevention* of disease is more important than cure.

Equally important in reducing infectious disease have been sanitation and public-health practices that prevent the spread of infections. Epidemiologists and medical ecologists have learned the importance of pure drinking water, of proper sewage disposal, of food inspection, of insect control. As more is learned about the life histories of pathogens, including the ways in which they are transmitted from host to host, physicians can deal with the problems of prevention more intelligently.

But not all disease problems have been solved. In many species of pathogens, populations resistant to chemicals have evolved. Drugs and antibiotics were new factors in the environment of the pathogens. Natural selection started to operate. The individual pathogenic organisms most susceptible to the drugs were rapidly eliminated; but more resistant individuals were able to survive and multiply. Similar hazards exist in the control of vector-borne diseases. For example, the present control of malaria is based upon reducing the numbers of mosquitoes by spraying with DDT. But again natural selection has started to operate, and in many parts of the world mosquitoes are developing resistance to this chemical.

susceptible to [sə sĕp′ tə bəl; Latin: *sub*, under, + *capere*, to take]: easily affected by

When we turn from infectious diseases to other kinds, the outlook is less bright. A great deal has been learned about the deficiency diseases, and these can be controlled where people have the money for an adequate diet. Some knowledge has been gained of human hereditary diseases—and there is a genetic factor in many disease

See pages 220–221.

situations. But we still have much to learn about human genetics before we can artificially improve genotypes. And mental illness has become an increasing problem as civilization has become more complex.

Then there are the degenerative diseases that appear chiefly in old age—more and more important as more people live longer. The degenerative diseases present us some fascinating questions: How far can we hope to postpone death? And if we succeed in reducing deaths from degenerative diseases, how will this influence the distribution of age-groups in our population? What will be the economic impact of an increasingly larger proportion of people in the older age-groups?

As usual, discussion of a problem has tended to raise new questions. But one point is clear: man's increased ability to cope with disease has resulted in a decrease in death rates. This decrease in mortality has been greatest in the technologically advanced countries where science developed and where there is a good supply of scientific man power—Europe, the United States, Japan. But increasing international medical cooperation is slowly reducing mortality everywhere.

See pages 41–42.

Mortality is one of the four population determiners. A decrease in the human death rate must affect human population size. And this brings us to the major biological problem facing man today.

## HUMAN POPULATION

Because in many regions it is difficult to take accurate censuses, no one knows exactly how many people there are in the world. United Nations *demographers* (students of human population) estimated the world population in 1960 at 2.9 billion; and they calculated that this population was increasing at a rate of 1.7 percent every year.

demographers   [dĭ mŏg′rə-fûrz; Greek: *demos*, the people, + *graphein*, to write]

Using this rate of increase, calculate the world population for the present year according to the 1960 prediction. Can you find more recent estimates for comparison with the prediction?

In the world as a whole, approximately 187 babies are born every minute, or about 270,000 every day. Something like 142,000 people die every day. Since, at present, there is neither world immigration nor world emigration, the daily world population increase is about 128,000. Thus, every two weeks the human population increases enough to populate a new city the size of Detroit. During a year the increase adds up to more than 47,000,000.

Increase of population is not something happening only in *other* countries. In 1967 the population of the United States was 200,000,000. This was an increase of 20,000,000 since 1960. And, though birth rate is declining, the increase continues—partly because of longer survival of the elderly, but mostly because the many children that resulted from

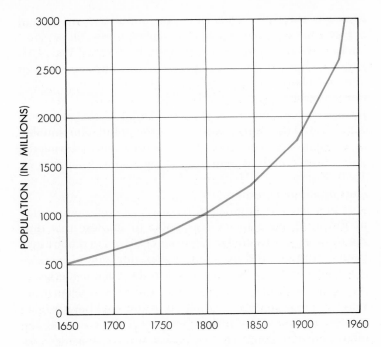

Figure 20 · 6
Estimated world population of *Homo sapiens* during the past three centuries. Compare this graph with the one you drew in Investigation 2 · 1.

post–World War II marriages are now reaching reproductive age. Thus our population is growing at about the same rate as that of the world as a whole.

Information on the numbers of *Homo sapiens* in past centuries is even less precise than information on present-day numbers, but demographers have made some ingenious calculations. It has been estimated that about 5 km² of good hunting territory is required to support a human individual in a food-gathering culture. Since there are only about 50,000,000 km² of such territory on Earth, ten million individuals would be the maximum possible Stone Age population. With the development of agriculture, many more people could be supported on the same amount of land, and this probably started the first spurt of human population. The Romans and the ancient Chinese carried out censuses, but their fragmentary records are difficult to interpret. The Roman Empire at the time of Augustus is thought to have had about 55,000,000 inhabitants. The population declined with the breakup of the Empire, probably reaching a low by 500 A.D.

Augustus Caesar (Gaius Octavianus): 63 B.C. – 14 A.D.

For the population of England, we have some fairly definite figures. In 1086 William the Conqueror commanded that an inventory be made of his new possession. This inventory, the *Domesday Book*, was most thorough. It survives as two huge manuscript volumes in the English Public Record Office. An American historian studied the *Domesday*

*Book* very carefully to determine the population of England at that time and came out with a total of 1,099,766 persons. In 1377, to raise money for the Hundred Years' War, Parliament imposed a tax on every person fourteen years of age and above in the kingdom. Apparently the tax collection was carried out efficiently. From a study of the records, historians concluded that the population at that time was 2,232,373. Therefore, it seems that the population doubled in less than three centuries; and it doubled again during the next three hundred years, reaching about 4,000,000 by 1650. But between 1650 and 1950, the population of England multiplied *ten* times!

Elsewhere the population records are even poorer than in England, but it seems reasonable to suppose that during these centuries similar increases occurred in other European countries. And now this accelerating rate of increase is worldwide. What has happened to the human species?

There seems to be no simple and clear explanation. When we consider the population of the world as a whole, we can, of course, immediately rule out the effects of immigration and emigration. Because we are aware of the tremendous influence of modern medicine on death rates, our first thought might be that the great population increase is simply due to the reduction of mortality. But in 1650 or even 1750 medicine was hardly more effective than it had been in the centuries before. The effects of sanitary and medical improvement were not evident until after 1800 — yet the population increase started well before then.

The rapid acceleration in the growth of human population during the seventeenth and eighteenth centuries was contemporaneous with the beginning of the Industrial Revolution, which provided more jobs and, by improving methods of cultivation, more food. It looks as if the beginning of the great "population explosion" was due to increased natality — probably acting through earlier marriage — rather than to decreased mortality.

In modern heavily industrialized regions, however, natality has tended to decline. The birth rate in the United States in 1900 was 38 per thousand of population per year. It reached a low of 16.6 in the depression year of 1933 and remained around 17 until 1940, when an increase began that accelerated in the years following World War II. Birth rates in the 1950's varied between 23 and 25 but by 1965 had declined to 19.4.

Using the 1965 birth and death rates of the United States, calculate the rate of population increase at that time. Can you find more recent data for comparison?

Death rates, on the other hand, have shown a steady decline in the United States — from 17.2 per thousand of population per year in 1900 to 9.4 in 1965. The same steady downward trend in death rates has occurred in all industrialized countries. And now, with international developments in public health and medicine, the death rate everywhere is declining. In Ceylon in 1947, an intensive campaign to control malaria by spraying with DDT caused the death rate to drop abruptly from 20 to 13 — and during the same period there was a slight increase in the birth rate, from 38.4 in 1946 to 40.2 in 1948. In 1962 the introduction of a measles vaccine reduced the infant death rate in Upper Volta (Africa) by half; the birth rate there is 48.

On a worldwide scale natality exceeds mortality: that is the simple basis for the present growth of the human population. And a brief review of your graphs from Investigation 2.1 indicates the future. Demographers, using methods similar to yours and projecting the present rates of mortality and natality, have calculated that by 2560 A.D. there would be one person for every 5 $m^2$ of land surface — forest, desert, tundra, everything. Obviously, this is intolerable; but what is to prevent it?

We can consider the possibilities. There is no immigration into the world, so this cannot be reduced. Emigration

Wide World

Figure 20 · 7

The population "meter" of the U.S. Bureau of the Census presents a moment-by-moment estimate of population size (*upper left*). Each of the lower dials shows one of the four population determiners. The large upper dial shows the algebraic sum of these four rates, and this sets the speed at which the numerals turn in the population estimate. The picture was taken late in 1967.

from the world is an approaching possibility, but not even the most imaginative scientist can foresee emigration on a scale that would affect the human population problem. Mortality can rise: disease, starvation, and war are still with us and can increase. Some human societies have deliberately used mortality to control their numbers: in ancient Greece and in Tahiti unwanted infants were left to die in the fields; Eskimos left old people behind when they moved their villages. Few people today would be willing to approve of these or similar practices; indeed, almost everyone is willing to generously support all efforts to reduce mortality still more.

The only population determiner remaining is natality. Everywhere today increasing numbers of thoughtful people realize that a reduction of human natality must be achieved. Biologists have developed a number of methods. For many years devices that prevent sperm cells from reaching egg cells during copulation have been used. Recently, increasing knowledge of the function of hormones in the menstrual cycle has led to synthetic hormones that prevent ovulation—and therefore prevent the formation of zygotes. And a device that is inserted in the uterus by a physician may prevent a zygote from implanting in the uterine wall —and therefore prevent the development of an embryo. Other methods of lowering natality exist or are being planned. But there are non-biological objections to all the methods. All are unacceptable to some people, and most are unacceptable to many.

Meanwhile the human population continues to increase —and at an increasing rate. The control of human births remains the primary human problem.

### RESOURCES

Every organism requires energy and substances from its environment. Therefore the size of any species population has meaning only in relation to the environment in which the species exists. For the human species we refer to all the material things that man requires for his existence as the *resources* of his environment.

It is customary to classify resources as either *renewable* or *nonrenewable*. Renewable resources are those that can maintain themselves or be continuously replaced if managed wisely. Living things—crops, animals, forests—belong to this class. Soil is a renewable resource, but soil is renewed very slowly; forming an entirely new soil requires far more time than does growing a new crop of timber. Water also can be considered a renewable resource.

We might think of all substances as renewable, since

See Figure 1 · 20.

matter is not ordinarily lost from the surface of our planet. But for all practical purposes the gas, coal, and oil that we burn cannot be used again, even though the carbon remains in the atmosphere or is picked up again by plants; and the iron of cans rusting on a dump is lost to us, even though it remains in the soil. The cycles of these substances are too long for any possible management, so such substances are classed as nonrenewable resources.

**Food.**   Malthus considered food supply to be the limiting factor for human population. Through most of history it has certainly been a very important factor. Famines and starvation have struck many human populations repeatedly.

Malthus: See pages 38–39.

We who live in industrial nations—particularly we who live in the United States—are likely to forget this. In our part of the world, the application of science to agriculture and the use of machinery to replace the labor of man and animals have so enormously increased the production of food that starvation is practically unknown. In 1910, when the population of the United States was about 92,000,000, 13,500,000 persons were employed in agriculture. Among a population of more than 179,000,000 in 1960, only about 7,000,000 were so employed—half as many people working to produce food for twice the population. Yet, in that fifty

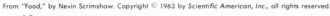
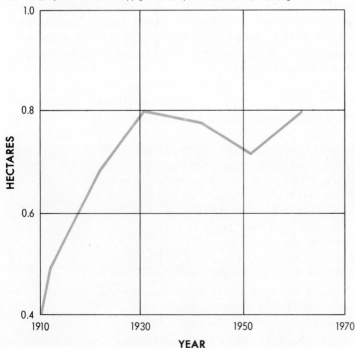

**Figure 20 · 8**
Changes in the amount of agricultural land required to feed one person in the United States.

years, production, whether calculated per man working or per hectare of crop, increased even faster than population.

The situation in agriculture, like the situation in medicine, looks rosy as long as we limit our view. But when we look beyond the borders of our own and of a relatively few other countries, the picture is different. In January, 1966, the government of India estimated that unless additional food became available 21,000,000 of its citizens faced starvation and at least 100,000,000 would suffer hunger. At best the average Indian receives 1800 to 2000 Calories per day, while daily intake of an average American is over 3000 Calories.

But the number of Calories is not the only factor in judging the adequacy of human nutrition. Even 3000 Calories, if obtained entirely from corn bread or rice, will not nourish a person. Food is the source not only of energy but of chemical substances. And man requires some specific kinds of such substances—vitamins and, particularly, certain amino acids that are rare in plant proteins. But animal protein is expensive. To give an American consumer 3000 Calories of food that supplies the required vitamins and amino acids, the American farmer must raise 11,000 Calories in plant substance, most of which goes to feed animals.

Why do not people in other parts of the world imitate us? All they need to do is buy tractors and gasoline, use better fertilizers, plant crops that have been improved through genetics, and control insects and pathogens. Perhaps first they should send their children to school to learn about these things. No schools? Build them. But where do they get the money? And where do they get the teachers?

Obviously the answers to such questions are not easy — though they are very important for all the world, including the United States. Often, however, we can be of little help,

adequacy: here, that which is sufficient

Figure 20 · 9

Geneticists have contributed greatly to the increased food production of technologically advanced nations. In two strains of corn (*left*) that have been inbred for several generations, many undesirable recessive traits are homozygous. By crossing these strains, the traits are made heterozygous and the hybrid (*right*) is of greatly improved quality.

Dekalb Hybrid Corn

Dekalb Hybrid Corn

whatever our intentions. We know quite a bit about *our* soils, *our* climates, *our* crops. But soils, climates, and crops may be quite different in other parts of the world. Even when agricultural scientists develop crops that provide food having the proper nutritional quality, people may reject the food because they do not like it! This is a matter of tradition and culture. Food is a biological resource, but its production and distribution involve many problems that are not strictly biological. And while these problems await solution, the populations demanding to be fed are increasing.

**Power.**   Food is the source of biotic energy for consumers. Man as a consumer requires food. But in shaping his environment, man directs other energies besides those in his own muscles. For ages he directed the biological energy of other animals to his own ends. And very early man used the energy in wind and later in falling water. Now all of industrial civilization depends upon non-biotic energy — and upon industrialization depend the new food-production methods that *might* catch up with the population if population increase can be slowed down. Human demands for energy will probably triple by the year 2000. It seems quite likely that these demands can be met, but some shifts in the sources of energy will be required.

Such shifts have already occurred in the United States. Figure 20 · 10 shows the drastic reduction in use of wood for fuel and the simultaneous increase in the use of coal, oil, and gas up to about 1900. If the use of coal continues to decline as it has during the past half century, remaining supplies will probably satisfy the demand well into the

**Figure 20 · 10**

The history and probable future of power sources in the United States.

H. H. Landsberg, *Resources in America's Future.* Baltimore: The Johns Hopkins Press.

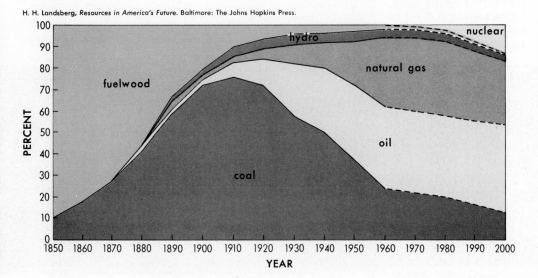

twenty-first century. But near the end of the twentieth century, the supply of readily available oil and natural gas will be low and the cost to remove new supplies from the earth will be so high that it will be necessary to utilize other sources of energy. Nuclear energy seems likely to become important by the end of the century, and direct conversion of solar radiation into electricity may increase.

**Soils and forests.** Although the waters of the earth are a source for some of man's food—almost all, in a few human cultures—agriculture is by far the principal source. And the basis of agriculture is soil. But soil provides man with much more than food. Through agriculture soil produces fibers of many kinds, and through forestry soil produces a variety of useful items, including paper and lumber.

For the first settlers in America, the great forest was an enemy to be destroyed and replaced with cultivated fields. Yet, at the same time, the British government recognized the value of the forest as a timber resource, especially for shipbuilding. In 1681 William Penn decreed that in Pennsylvania one acre of forest must be left for every five acres cleared. But there was no way to enforce this decree, and only small fragments of the original forest have survived. It was not until 1891, under President Harrison, that the first national forests were established in the United States. These forests have been expanded greatly in the present century and have been managed so as to achieve a

**Figure 20 · 11**

Block harvesting of timber in the Douglas-fir region of Oregon. The bare areas are quickly reseeded by the surrounding forest.

American Forest Products Industries

**Figure 20 · 12**
Another method of harvesting timber: selective logging in Michigan. Though 40 percent of the timber volume was removed, the forest community is only slightly disturbed.

**Figure 20 · 13**
Tree-planting machines have replaced hand labor in reforesting burned and cleared lands.

balance between harvest and growth. And great lumber corporations have recognized that their continued existence depends upon management policies designed to maintain the forests they own. Because the life-span of most trees is long in comparison with the human life-span, forest management is almost necessarily a concern of governments and corporations rather than of individuals.

Forests not only provide lumber and pulpwood; they also serve to reduce erosion and control floods. When vegetation is removed from land, water sweeps over the surface of the ground instead of sinking in. Especially in hilly country, soil may be completely washed away. In forest biomes, trees cannot be established again, and resources that should be renewable are lost. Soil conservation and forest conservation are thus closely related, and both are certainly important for the survival of industrial civilization. Sometimes it takes a disaster to make us realize this. One good effect of the great dust storms of the 1930's was to increase the attention given to soil conservation in the United States.

See page 293.

**Figure 20 · 14**

Squandering a resource that is difficult to renew: (*above*) on an Indiana hillside; (*below*) on a nearly level field in New Jersey.

J. C. Allen and Son

Soil Conservation Service, USDA

**Land.** Forests represent another kind of resource, a less tangible resource than any of those previously mentioned—"open space." This has been a characteristic, indeed a molding force, of the United States throughout its history. Even today as you travel across some parts of our country, it is hard to believe that the time is approaching when space—land area—will be in short supply. Every day, however, there is less open countryside—and more cities and suburbs, industries, highways, and airports. This will continue; it is an inevitable consequence of increasing population density.

tangible   [tăn′jə bəl;   Latin: *tangere*, to touch]: real, in the sense of being touchable

Every organism requires some living space. We have seen effects of crowding on populations of mice and ponderosa pines, and have examined the concept of territoriality. No one knows what the minimum space for a human being may be or the length of time the minimum may be tolerated. Certainly some people have existed under very crowded conditions for long periods. But there is evidence that, at least in industrial environments, accidents, mental illness, and other undesirable effects result from inability to get away from crowds occasionally.

See pages 48–49, 559–561.

That a great many people feel a need for open space, even though they may not be able to explain it, is shown by the number of businesses catering to the desire for outdoor recreation. Each year more than twenty-five million people go to the forests or other open lands for hunting and fishing. But millions more go for other purposes—to camp, to picnic, to swim, to photograph, or just to look and to breathe fresh air. To do all this, it was estimated in 1960 that they spent eleven billion dollars!

**Figure 20 · 15**

Often the search for open recreational space is in vain. On Assateague Island, Maryland, campers are as crowded as at their city or suburban homes.

Sunpapers Photo by Cook

**Figure 20 · 16**

Multiple use of space: forest products, water-flow control, water for electric power, and boating and fishing recreation are all provided at Norris Lake, Tennessee.

Each year increasing population increases the demand for land, and amount of land per person decreases. Therefore careful thought must be given to how each area can be used to best advantage, so you will be hearing about the land-management policy called "multiple use"— which really means "getting the most out of your ecosystem."

**Figure 20 · 17**

Elk are "shot" by photographers as well as by hunters—and many other persons find pleasure in merely watching them.

With careful planning, the same piece of countryside can be used for a variety of purposes: hunting, fishing, timber production, agriculture, mining, recreation, grazing, watershed protection and water storage, human habitation, and so on. Such planning requires not only thought but also knowledge of the nation's various ecosystems. The time may come when governments will have not only defense, engineering, diplomatic, and political advisers but ecological advisers as well.

**Wildlife.** Forests and other "open" lands provide habitats for the many species that have not been domesticated by man or that have not learned to live in man's structures. All the value of such lands for hunters and fishermen depends upon the wildlife resource. And much of their value for other people who flock to state and national parks, forests, and seashores also depends upon wildlife. The bare face of Death Valley has a certain grandeur, but most people find even a desert more interesting when it is dotted with living things.

The problem of wildlife resources is basically the same as the problem of land, because wildlife first of all requires a habitat—space in which to live and space of a particular kind. When a marsh is turned into a wheat field, the land supports more people, but it no longer supports ducks. This is a clear-cut case and illustrates another of the consequences of increasing human population. But, fortunately, it is an oversimplification. Reduction of marsh and increase of wheat fields can also result in a rise of pheasant population. In the management of wildlife, as in the management of other resources, choices must be made, and these choices usually involve the study of many interacting ecological factors.

One objective of wildlife management is to prevent the extinction of species. Extinction, of course, is nothing new. But with civilized man altering whole ecosystems, it has been going on at a very rapid rate. On the average, since 1900 one species of mammal has disappeared somewhere in the world every year. Zoologists have compiled a list of six hundred mammals that now seem to be in danger of extinction. At the present rate, these ought to last another six hundred years; but since the human population is increasing ever more rapidly, the rate at which other animals disappear will probably also increase.

What difference does it make that passenger pigeons and dodoes have disappeared from the earth? Or that whooping cranes may disappear tomorrow? Europeans are probably perfectly happy that lions disappeared from their continent about 300 B.C., and there is certainly no room for

Why do speculations concerning life on Mars or Venus arouse more interest than descriptions of the chemical composition of the planets?

X 1/14

**Figure 20 · 18**
Whooping cranes are the tallest of North American birds. Efforts to save the remaining population have received wide publicity.

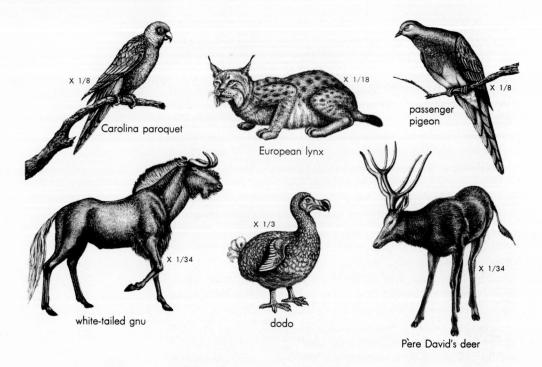

X 1/8
Carolina paroquet

X 1/18
European lynx

passenger
pigeon
X 1/8

X 1/34
white-tailed gnu

X 1/3
dodo

P`ere David's deer
X 1/34

**Figure 20 · 19**

Some animals that have been exterminated or nearly so through the activities of man.

St. Francis of Assisi (Giovanni Francesco Bernardone): 1182–1226. Italian churchman

Albert Schweitzer [shvīt′sər]: 1875–1965. German musician, missionary, physician

Aldo Leopold: 1886–1948. American forester

packs of wolves in the vicinity of New York City. It may be difficult to argue a case for each threatened species, but the *total* effect of man's activities does become frightening. Is there no room on our planet for anything except man, the animals he uses, and those that get along with him whether he likes them or not—rats, cockroaches, and starlings?

In this question, as in all the problems we are discussing in this chapter, much more than a matter of science faces us: Have we the *right* to kill off the organisms we don't like or don't want? When men were battling with bears for a sheltering cave, such a question did not arise. But for many years some men—particularly in Asia—have answered No. And in our Western civilization St. Francis joined them. In modern times people as different as the medical missionary Albert Schweitzer and the American forester Aldo Leopold have argued that we have a responsibility toward other organisms. It is dangerous to argue that "might makes right," that our own interests come first. Man learned in World War II how easily the idea of exterminating inconvenient kinds of living things can be applied to kinds of people.

### THE QUALITY OF THE ENVIRONMENT

Man has always been faced with the problem of getting rid of his wastes. At one time this was simply solved by

Figure 20 · 20

On the Beach

moving to a new cave. But as our numbers increased, we spread over more and more of the land; as our technology developed, we had more and different types of wastes to get rid of. The size of the total environment remained constant, but the amount of undesirable material which man throws off into his atmosphere, spreads over or buries on his land, or dumps into his rivers and oceans has increased to the point where his actual existence is seriously threatened by his contamination of the very environment which has so long sustained him.

Our environmental pollution has now reached the point that drastic measures must be undertaken. There is no new cave to move to and, if we continue our present course, we will be trapped.

Harris B. Stewart, Jr., in *Science 154: 1966;* November 25, 1966. Copyright 1966 by the American Association for the Advancement of Science.

With these words the American Association for the Advancement of Science announced the theme of its 1966

Figure 20 · 21

In March, 1967, the oil tanker *Torrey Canyon* broke up in the English Channel. Oil ruined miles of beaches and killed thousands of seabirds such as these. Even without wrecks, oil pollution is a continuing problem in marine waters.

Wide World

See pages 321–322.

detergents [dĭ tûr′ jənts; Latin: *de*, from, + *tergere*, to wipe]: chemical cleaning agents

Figure 20 · 22

Today even the air is a resource that man must conserve. Under certain conditions, smoke and the wastes from gasoline engines produce a smog that is poisonous to all living things—including man, who creates it.

convention. The writer was from the Environmental Science Services Administration, a new branch of the federal government that Congress had organized in 1965, partly in response to the pollution problem.

Pollutants are of many kinds—sewage, household detergents, plastic and glass containers, chemicals from in-

Grant Heilman

Robert H. Daines

Figure 20 · 23
Effects of sulfur dioxide, an air pollutant derived from fuels, on parts of a violet plant. Plants are sensitive detectors of such pollution.

dustrial plants, radioactive substances, chemicals used in the control of man's competitors for crops, automobile exhaust gases, silt, smoke, even hot water. All have one basic effect: they worsen the environment. Each, however, acts in its own way. Each, therefore, must be studied separately. But some interact with others, and some become involved in complicated ways with the web of life. So the study of environmental pollution, like all ecological studies, is complex.

Consider the effects of pollutants in the atmosphere. They are often irritating to human eyes and lungs. But effects of atmospheric pollution on the biosphere may be less direct. The burning of "fossil fuels"—coal and oil—by industrial man has enormously increased the rate at which $CO_2$ is added to the atmosphere. Photosynthetic organisms have not kept pace in removing this $CO_2$. As a result, atmospheric $CO_2$ has increased about 20 percent in the twentieth century. $CO_2$ is known to trap infrared radiation and prevent its escape from the earth; on the other hand, it interferes little with radiant energy arriving from the sun. Because of those facts, some ecologists and physicists believe the increase of atmospheric $CO_2$ may explain the .1.6°C increase in mean world temperature since 1900.

But effects of atmospheric pollution are not this simple. In the years since 1940 a *decline* of 0.3°C in world temperature has been measured, and pollution can explain this, also. Fuels produce wastes other than $CO_2$. Besides visible smoke, many substances are in the form of invisible particles in the

**Figure 20 · 24**

Radiation damage to a forest ecosystem. Organisms in an experimental forest at Brookhaven, New York, are exposed to radioactive cesium-137 for twenty hours each day. A nearby unir-radiated forest is used as a control.

See Figure 1 · 16.

pesticide [pĕs' tə sīd'; Latin: *pestis*, any destructive thing, + *caedere*, to kill]

atmosphere. These particles reflect solar radiation, preventing part of it from reaching the surface of the earth. The water vapor trails left by jet aircraft do the same. But whether $CO_2$ increases world temperature or waste particles in the atmosphere decrease it is less important than the fact that man's wastes do have such widespread effects on the biosphere.

Now consider a radioactive pollutant. Strontium-90, like other radioactive isotopes of elements, has probably always existed in the biosphere in small amounts. But recent activities of man, particularly the testing of atomic weapons, have increased the quantity. Chemically strontium is very much like calcium and is used by organisms in a similar way. But if strontium-90 gets into an animal in place of calcium, it releases radiations that harm or kill living tissues. The strontium cycle, like the calcium cycle, can run from green plants to cows and from cow's milk to man. But not all the strontium-90 that might be in a cow's food goes into her milk; much of it stays in her own skeleton or passes out as wastes. In fact, the metabolism of a cow discriminates against strontium in synthesizing muscle and milk. The contaminated plants a cow eats contain twice as much strontium as the cow's muscles and seven times as much as her milk. If strontium-90 pollutes the atmosphere, it is obviously safer to drink milk than to eat green vegetables.

Perhaps more dangerous at present than radioactive substances are "pesticides." These are poisons that are used to kill pests—that is, organisms that are harmful to man, his

Seller's Aviation

**Figure 20 · 25**
Aerial spraying of an orchard with insect poisons. Small planes are used because of their ability to turn easily.

Wide World

**Figure 20 · 26**
Rachel Carson (1907–1966), biologist and author who directed public attention to problems created by the increasingly widespread use of chemical "pesticides."

domestic animals, or his crops. Because of the basic similarity in metabolism of all living things, it is difficult to find a substance that is poisonous to one organism and not to another, particularly another closely related one. For example, a substance poisonous to wasps (which might be considered pests) is very likely to be poisonous also to honeybees (which seldom are considered pests).

In the struggle to produce enough food for the growing human population, poisons against fungi, nematodes, mites, many insects, and other organisms are necessary.

**Figure 20 · 27**
**Western grebe.**

But their ever-increasing use endangers the biosphere. Some (DDT, for example) are very resistant to chemical change. Therefore, even small amounts of DDT, when used repeatedly, build up to large amounts in soil and water. Further, some poisons are concentrated in the bodies of organisms; DDT accumulates especially in fats. In Clear Lake, California, DDT was applied at the rate of 14, 20, and 20 parts per billion of lake water in 1949, 1954, and 1957 respectively. In 1957 all lake organisms that were tested contained DDT. Grebes that had died from poisoning were found to contain concentrations of DDT 80,000 times greater than that in the lake water. Fat in some fishes showed a concentration of DDT 140,000 times greater than that in the lake water.

Chemists are now attempting to develop poisons that disintegrate in soils and waters and that do not accumulate in food chains. They are also synthesizing hormone-like substances that interfere with the metabolism of some species but do not harm others. Meanwhile biologists are extending methods of controlling pests by nonchemical means.

Many scientists are exploring ways to deal with other pollutants. But daily their task becomes more difficult. As human population increases, and especially as a larger portion of the population becomes industrialized, human wastes increase and pollution of the environment mounts.

## A COMPARISON

The late Alan Gregg, medical director of the Rocke-
feller Foundation, compared present human population
growth within the biosphere with the growth of a cancerous
tissue within an organism. This tissue somehow escapes the
ordinary growth controls and multiplies at the expense of
all the other tissues, as man is multiplying at the expense of
the rest of the biosphere. If you could ask the cancer cells,
they would surely think they were doing fine—but when at
last the organism is killed, they die, too. There is a frightening possibility that man, with his apparently limitless increase in numbers and his increasing power to destroy the
rest of the biosphere, may multiply his way to destruction.

Alan    Gregg:    1890–1957.
American physician

## VALUES

Alexander Pope, in an often quoted line, said that "the
proper study of mankind is man." Man is an interesting
creature, to be sure. And we are not going to gain complete
understanding of him by studying mice—or rabbits and
raspberry bushes either, for that matter. We have the paradox of man as *apart* from nature and of man as a *part* of
nature. He is capable of unique achievements—of poems,
symphonies, religious exaltation, and compassion. But at
the same time he eats, sleeps, breathes, matures, reproduces, and dies, as do other animals. He is a part of the
ecosystem, and we cannot understand him by studying only
man and ignoring the rest of the biosphere.

Alexander  Pope: 1688–1744.
British poet

Biology is not merely a subject, a thing-in-itself; it is a
part of the web of knowledge, and its important meanings
are in relation to this web as a whole. The web is spun in
the mind of each individual. The value of biology, then, is
the value you have found in the course of the year: the
knowledge, understanding, and appreciation you have
derived from the study. Each individual will find somewhat
different relationships between biology and history, literature, art, social studies, other sciences, and the events of the
workaday world.

Biology has recreational values. And this is of tremendous importance at a time when more and more people
have more and more leisure. Biological collecting—of insects, plants, or shells, for example—has a long and honor-
able history, not to mention being fun. Many amateurs
have made important contributions to science while at the
same time finding personal satisfaction in their hobbies.
But one does not have to collect objects; collecting observations can be equally fascinating. The microscope or even

**Figure 20 · 28**

Man's powers to shape his environment may lead toward
depletion and ruin or toward continuing usefulness.

**Choices in a grassland ecosystem.**

Soil Conservation Service, USDA

Nebraska Game, Forestation and Parks Commission

Soil Conservation Service, USDA

**Choices in a forest ecosystem.**

Haven Kolb

Miller Photography

**Choices in an urban ecosystem.**

Miller Photography

the hand lens can be a window into a world that is all about us—but one that we never otherwise see. It can be fun to look at this subvisible world; it can also be fun to look at the visible world with appreciative eyes and binoculars.

Biology has practical values. It underlies agriculture and medicine, and is involved to a greater or lesser extent with many other human activities.

Biology is a science, and through the study of any single science we can gain a greater appreciation of the scientific enterprise as a whole. Science is one of the great human creative activities. We may think of it as something that has given us automobiles, television, antibiotics, frozen foods. But behind these things are great ideas, the products of human minds. In biology we can think of Linnaeus, who invented the system of classifying organisms that has served us so well for more than two hundred years; of Darwin, who developed a theory of evolution through natural selection and thus made understandable the patterns of classification, paleontology, biogeography, and development; of Pasteur, with the theory of infection as a cause of disease; or of Mendel, with the discovery that heredity operates through units rather than through blending.

Even the way we think has been greatly influenced by science. We no longer live in a flat world under an arched firmament. We no longer scare demons to cure disease. We may avoid walking under a ladder or throw some spilled salt over a shoulder or be slightly worried by black cats. But these are play worries rather than real terrors. Because every citizen is influenced by science, he should have some understanding of what science is—and in this course we have tried to provide opportunities for such an understanding.

Now, somewhere between the triviality of hobbies and the grandeur of science, you should have developed an appreciation of the living world around you. You should have learned something about how your body works and something about the workings of an oak tree or a squirrel. You should be able to look at landscapes with more understanding eyes. And from knowing these things, you should be able to find more pleasure in them.

"It is interesting to contemplate a tangled bank, clothed with many plants of many kinds, with birds singing on the bushes, with various insects flitting about, and with worms crawling through the damp earth, and to reflect that these elaborately constructed forms, so different from each other, and dependent upon each other in so complex a manner, have all been produced by laws acting around us. These laws, taken in the largest sense, being Growth with Reproduction; Inheritance which is almost implied by reproduction; Variability from the indirect and direct action of the conditions of life, and from use and disuse; a ratio of increase so high as to lead to a Struggle for Life, and as a consequence to Natural Selection, entailing Divergence of Character and the Extinction of less-improved forms. Thus, from the war of nature, from famine and death, the most exalted object which we are capable of conceiving, namely, the production of the higher animals, directly follows. There is grandeur in this view of life . . . that, whilst this planet has gone cycling on according to the fixed laws of gravity, from so simple a beginning endless forms most beautiful and most wonderful have been, and are being, evolved."

DARWIN, *The Origin of Species*

## GUIDE QUESTIONS

1. What was the ecological niche of Stone Age man?
2. What change in man's method of obtaining his biological energy first greatly changed his ecological niche?
3. How has man's position in food webs changed since the Stone Age?
4. Why does complexity in a community tend to decrease the extent of the fluctuations in populations?
5. By what means have infectious diseases been brought under control in many parts of the world?
6. How does natural selection act as a factor in the control of infectious disease today?
7. What changes have occurred in the principal causes of death in the United States during the twentieth century? How do these changes affect problems of maintaining health?
8. What is happening at present to the human population density in the world as a whole?
9. Of what value are demographic studies on the human population of past centuries?
10. How is the problem of human population related to medical problems?
11. What are the possible ways in which the growth of human population may be controlled?
12. How are problems of resource conservation related to the problem of human population?
13. Trout for sports fishing and trees for timber are both classed as renewable resources. Does "renewable" have the same meaning for both?
14. What factors have been involved in the increase of the human food supply?
15. Why cannot the food problem be considered only in terms of Calories?

16. Why is modern biological knowledge —applied so successfully in the United States—insufficient to solve the world's agricultural problems?

17. Why would the problem of providing power for machinery continue to exist even if human population increase were controlled?

18. Why is the forest resource difficult for individuals to manage?

19. What relations exist between the forest and soil resources of an ecosystem?

20. Why are problems of land usage basically ecological problems?

21. How are wildlife problems related to problems of land usage and of human population density?

22. Why has the problem of environment pollution become so great in our industrial civilization?

23. Why is the term "pesticide" misleading?

24. In what way is the organism man acting in the biosphere as cancer cells act in the tissues of an individual?

## PROBLEMS

1. No attempt has been made in this book to define "life." Having studied biology for a year, you may wish to try. Compare your definition with those of other students in your class.

2. Poisoning is not the only method used to control organisms that destroy man's agricultural crops. Find out what is meant by "biological control." Discuss methods of biological control from the viewpoint of ecological principles. What kinds of information are needed in applying biological controls? How do the effects of biological controls on ecosystems differ from those of chemical controls?

3. American foreign-aid policies have political, ethical, and economic aspects that are important and often stressed. They also have biological aspects, which are not often stressed but which underlie the other three. Your year as a biology student should enable you to pick out some of the biological aspects of the foreign-aid program and discuss them—particularly their economic implications.

4. This book has included enough history to show something of the international character of biological science. Construct a chart or table to demonstrate this feature of biology, beginning with biologists named in the text. What nationalities can you add through your own efforts?

5. An anthropologist who has studied the Pygmies of the Congo recently reported this statement by a Pygmy: "When the forest dies, we die." Comment on the ecological understanding of this "savage."

6. Diagram a Stone Age food web centered on man. Be sure to include the protists!

7. Demographers are concerned with more than changes in the total numbers of persons; they are also interested in the *structure* of populations—the relative numbers of individuals of various kinds. For example, two populations of the same size may have different proportions of males and females. Or two populations of the same size may have different proportions of children and adults. Such data often provide much information about a population.

   a. The total populations of the United States and Ceylon are quite different, but more important is the fact that the population of the United States has a smaller proportion of children than that of Ceylon. What hypotheses can you suggest on the basis of this information?

   b. We may divide the population of the United States into three groups: (1) persons under twenty, most of whom are not self-supporting; (2) persons twenty to sixty-five, most of whom are working; (3) persons over sixty-five, most of whom are retired. In recent years the first and third groups have been increasing more rapidly than the second group. What hypotheses can you suggest to explain this? Can you see a future economic problem in this situation?

   c. In human females reproduction occurs mostly between the ages of fifteen and forty-five. Suppose this age-group increases more slowly than the age-group over forty-five but the number of children per female remains the same.

What will happen to the birth rate in the population when expressed as births per thousand of population?

d. The average age at which a female has her first child is higher in Nation A than in Nation B, but the average age of death is about the same in both nations. From this information, make a guess about the rate of population growth in the two countries. What additional information would make your guess more reliable?

8. For hundreds of years Chinese peasants maintained the fertility of their fields with the aid of human feces. Carbon dioxide wastes returned to the atmosphere provide a raw material for photosynthesis. These two facts indicate that the terms "waste" and "pollutant" are not synonymous. Under what circumstances does a waste become a pollutant?

9. The Agricultural Revolution is not as well known as the Industrial. Find out what archaeologists have been able to learn of this important turning point in man's history. You might begin with Sauer, C. O., *Agricultural Origins and Dispersals*, New York: American Geographical Society, 1952.

## SUGGESTED READINGS

BATES, M. *Man in Nature*. 2nd ed. Englewood Cliffs, N.J.: Prentice-Hall, Inc., 1964. (Parallels our Chapters 19 and 20 rather closely, but provides a much more detailed account. Fairly easy.)

BECKER, H. F. *Resources for Tomorrow*. New York: Holt, Rinehart & Winston, Inc., 1964. (A small book that surveys present United States resources and emphasizes the need for intelligent planning for future use.)

CARSON, R. *Silent Spring*. Boston: Houghton Mifflin Co., 1962. (Describes the effects of man's attempts at chemical control of undesired organisms. Some biologists disagree with a number of Miss Carson's interpretations, but the data are accurate.)

DAVIS, K. "Population," *Scientific American*, September, 1963. Pp. 62–71.

DOBZHANSKY, T. *Mankind Evolving: The Evolution of the Human Species*. New Haven, Conn.: Yale University Press, 1962. (A geneticist considers man's past evolution and the future possibilities for both biological and cultural evolution of man. Advanced.)

GORDON, M. *Sick Cities*. Baltimore: Penguin Books, Inc., 1952. (Already somewhat out-of-date account of problems man faces in an urban environment.)

HAAGEN-SMIT, A. J. "The Control of Air Pollution," *Scientific American*, January, 1964. Pp. 24–31.

KELLY, C. F. "Mechanical Harvesting," *Scientific American*, August, 1967. Pp. 50–59.

LYNCH, K. "The City as Environment," *Scientific American*, September, 1965. Pp. 209–214.

MALTHUS, T., J. HUXLEY, and F. OSBORN. *On Population: Three Essays*. New York: New American Library of World Literature, Inc., 1960. (The eighteenth-century work by Malthus is accompanied by twentieth-century essays on the same problem by two eminent biologists.)

PADDOCK, W., and P. PADDOCK. *Famine—1975!* Boston: Little, Brown & Co., 1967. (Prediction is always risky, but the reasoning and statistics in this book are difficult to contradict.)

SCRIMSHAW, N. S. "Food," *Scientific American,* September, 1963. Pp. 72–80.

SEARS, P. B. *Where There Is Life.* New York: Dell Publishing Co., Inc., 1962. (The science of ecology developed in the perspective of human problems. Fairly easy.)

SINGER, C. *A History of Biology.* Rev. ed. New York: Henry Schuman, Inc., 1950. (Traces the development of the science from the time of Aristotle.)

TURNBULL, C. M. "The Lesson of the Pygmies," *Scientific American,* January, 1963. Pp. 28–37.

UDALL, S. L. "The Ecology of Man and the Land Ethic," *Natural History,* June, 1965. Pp. 32–41.

WILLIAMS, C. M. "Third-Generation Pesticides," *Scientific American,* July, 1967. Pp. 13–17.

WOODWELL, G. M. "The Ecological Effects of Radiation," *Scientific American,* June, 1963. Pp. 40–49.

# Appendix I

## SOME GENERAL PROCEDURES

On the whole, biologists are perhaps no more orderly or cleanly than other people. But the nature of their work demands that an unusual amount of orderliness and cleanliness be maintained during scientific work. First, observations and experiments must be verifiable. Therefore, the biologist must know what he has done and how he has done it. Good order helps ensure this. Second, the biologist frequently works with dangerous, disease-producing microscopic organisms. The biologist who is not cleanly is not likely to survive very long.

In the classroom laboratory there is additional need for orderliness and cleanliness, because space and apparatus must be shared with other classes. How to achieve these conditions depends upon each classroom situation.

### USE OF MATERIALS

#### Apparatus

It is still possible to do some kinds of biological work with very few and very simple tools. But as biologists have probed deeper, they have often found it necessary to use many kinds of apparatus for handling and observing their materials. There are right ways and wrong ways to use each piece of apparatus. "Right" refers to ways that will aid in obtaining scientific information, and "wrong" refers to ways that will hinder or even mislead. Therefore, it is necessary to learn how to use such equipment—from beakers and flasks to balances and microscopes.

#### Living Materials

All biologists deal with living things; this is what marks them as biologists. Though some biologists have no need to handle living things directly in their daily work, no general biology laboratory, no biology classroom, can get along without living materials. This poses some special problems in caring for such materials.

*Plants.* Most plants must be provided with light, soil, and water. Requirements for these differ a great deal among different kinds of plants. Therefore the care of classroom plants should be the responsibility of individual students, who will learn how to deal with the plants in their charge. All students, however, need to realize that plants—being living things—can be injured or killed, so it is necessary to handle plants carefully and gently.

*Animals.* Most animals require more care and more frequent attention than do plants. General rules are:

1. Provide an escape-proof container suitable for the animal.
2. Keep the container clean. This is necessary for the health of the animal. Cages of small birds and mammals should be cleaned daily.
3. Provide water at all times.
4. Feed regularly. The frequency of feeding depends upon the kind of animal being fed. Small birds and mammals may be provided with a continuous food supply.
5. Treat laboratory animals with humanity and kindness at all times. Cruelty has no place in biology.
6. When animals must be disposed of or released, the teacher will provide a suitable method.

*Microorganisms.* Very special methods are needed for the handling of most microorganisms. Special instructions are given when needed.

## RECORD-KEEPING

Science deals with verifiable observations. No one—not even the original observer—can check an observation that is hazy, indefinite, or half-remembered. All scientists must, therefore, keep clear and accurate records of what they have observed, made *at the time of observation.*

### The Data Book

The best method of keeping such records is to jot them down in a data book. This should be a stiff-cover book, permanently bound (not loose-leaf), preferably with unlined pages.

Records should usually be kept in diary form, the date being the first item recorded. If observations on two or more investigations are made on the same day, the numbers or abbreviations of the titles can be used as subheadings.

Data are usually recorded in one of three forms. First, they may be recorded in words. In the laboratory, time is short, so you should make these notes brief but to the point. It is not necessary to write complete sentences, but single words are seldom satisfactory, either. Phrases are usually most useful.

Second, observations may be recorded in the form of sketches. A drawing often records an observation more easily, completely, and accurately than words. Remember, however, that sketches of this kind are not intended to be works of art. Their success depends upon your ability to observe, not upon your artistic talent. They should be simple, usually without shading, and drawn with a hard pencil.

Third, data may be recorded numerically—as measurements. It is important to give the units in which measurements are made. Often, numerical data are most easily recorded in the form of a table.

*Under no circumstances* should data be jotted down on other papers to be copied into the data book later. This practice might increase neatness, but it will *decrease* accuracy. Both are virtues in a scientist, but neatness is of value *only* when it increases accuracy. The data book is *your* record. Your teacher may want to look at your data book to help you with your work, but he is interested in the accuracy of your data, not in the blots and stains that are a normal hazard of field and laboratory work.

Remember to:

1. Record accurately.
2. Record completely.
3. Record immediately.

More and more, science is becoming a cooperative enterprise—a team activity. Much of your own laboratory work will be done as a member of a team. Therefore your data book will sometimes contain data contributed by other members of your team. It is important that you know what you have observed yourself and what other members of your team have observed. You can know this if you encircle (or record in a different color) the observations made by others. You should be able to say: "This I know because I saw it; that I believe because I have confidence in my teammates."

The data book should *not* be used to record notes from reading or from class discussion. Such information may be useful, but it is not from firsthand observation.

### Laboratory Reports

Communication is a most important part of science. Discoveries become a part of science only when they are made known to others—when they are published. In publishing scientific work, the writer must express himself so clearly that another person can repeat his procedures exactly. The reader must know what material was used (in biology, this includes the kind of organism) and be able to comprehend every detail of the work. Scientists must be free to communicate, but they can use this freedom only if they know *how* to communicate. Scientific reports are usually written in a rather standard form, somewhat as follows:

1. Title

2. Introduction: Usually states how the problem arose, and often gives a summary of past work

3. Materials and equipment

4. Procedure (or Method): Complete and exact account of what was done in gathering the data

5. Results: Data obtained from the procedure, often in the form of tables and graphs

6. Discussion: Relates the data to the purpose of the work

7. Conclusion: Summary of the meaning of the results; often suggests further work that might be done

8. References: Published scientific reports that have been specifically mentioned

If you undertake work on an independent problem, your report should follow this form. But for the usual work in this course, you do not have to be so elaborate. You are communicating with your fellow students and the teacher, who already know a great deal about the work. Occasionally the teacher may wish you to do a rather complete job of reporting—for the sake of practice. Usually, however, he will want a much shorter report—perhaps merely the answers to the questions in the investigation.

Use material from your data book as the basis for your reports. In any report, however—even one written for the teacher or your classmates—you are not writing for yourself; you are trying to communicate ideas to others. Therefore you need to be especially careful about neatness, spelling, and sentence structure—all of which contribute to clearness of expression. Often you will need to construct graphs to make your data easier to understand. In short, the task of writing a report is very different from recording data. But both are a part of the scientist's work.

## CONCERNING MEASUREMENTS

In 1790 the French government adopted a new system of measurement to replace the many systems that were being used in France. This system, called the *metric* system, had a decimal basis—that is, it was based on multiples of ten—just as did the money system that had recently been adopted by the young government of the United States. As years went by, almost all nations followed the United States in adopting a decimal monetary system, and almost all adopted the French decimal system of measurement. Today among the nations of the world, only Britain, Canada, Australia, and the United States legally use other systems of measurement. And even in those countries the metric system is used by scientists.

The basic unit in the metric system is the *meter*. From this unit all others are derived. The meter is the distance between two scratches on a platinum-iridium bar that is kept in the vaults of the International Bureau of Measures near Paris. The United States Bureau of Standards has copies of this bar. Fractions and multiples of the meter are designated by prefixes: *milli-* ($\times$ 0.001), *centi-* ($\times$ 0.01), *deci-* ($\times$ 0.1), *deka-* ($\times$ 10), *hecto-* ($\times$ 100), and *kilo-* ($\times$ 1000).

The metric unit of volume is the *liter,* which is defined as the volume of a cube having an edge 10 centimeters long. The metric unit of weight is the *gram,* which is defined as the weight of a milliliter of pure water at 4 degrees Celsius (4°C). The metric unit of surface is the *are,* which is defined as an area of 100 square meters. Areas and volumes may also be indicated by the squares and cubes of linear units.

Familiarity with units of the metric system is best acquired through repeated use of them. Memorizing many equivalents in the British system is a waste of time. At the start, however, a few equivalents may be helpful for reference:

| | | |
|---|---|---|
| 1 centimeter = .3937 inches | 1 inch = 2.54 cm |
| 1 meter = 39.37 inches | 1 yard = .914 m |
| 1 kilometer = .62 miles | 1 mile = 1.6 km |
| 1 liter = 1.057 liquid quarts | 1 quart = .95 l |
| 1 gram = .035 ounces | 1 ounce = 28.34 g |
| 1 kilogram = 2.2 pounds | 1 pound = .453 kg |
| 1 hectare = 2.47 acres | 1 acre = .405 ha |

| SCALE | LENGTH | VOLUME | WEIGHT | SURFACE |
|---|---|---|---|---|
| 0.001 | millimeter (mm) | milliliter (ml) | milligram (mg) | |
| 0.01 | centimeter (cm) | | | |
| 0.1 | decimeter (dm) | | | |
| 1 | meter (m) | liter (l) | gram (g) | are |
| 10 | dekameter (dkm) | | | |
| 100 | hectometer (hm) | | | hectare (ha) |
| 1000 | kilometer (km) | | kilogram (kg) | |

Figure A · 1

Units of linear measure and some other common units of the metric system. Abbreviations are given in parentheses.

Following are some useful additional units:

micron ($\mu$):   a unit of length equal to one millionth of a meter; $1000\mu = 1$ mm

calorie:   the quantity of heat needed to raise the temperature of 1 g of water 1°C

Calorie:   equal to a kilocalorie

curie:   the amount of any radioactive substance that emits the same number of alpha rays per unit of time as does 1 g of radium

In countries using British units of measure, temperature is usually expressed on a scale devised by Gabriel Daniel Fahrenheit (1686 – 1736). In countries using the metric system, temperature is expressed on a scale devised by Anders Celsius (1701 – 1744). The Celsius scale is sometimes called *centigrade*. Figure A · 2 shows why this term is used and compares the two scales.

There is only one system of units for measuring time, though in many parts of the world (and in the armed forces of the United States) hours are designated from midnight to midnight with one set of twenty-four numbers — thus making "A.M." and "P.M." unnecessary.

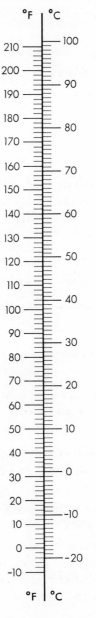

**Figure A · 2**

Comparison of Fahrenheit and Celsius (centigrade) temperature scales.

# Appendix II

## A CATALOGUE OF LIVING THINGS

This appendix shows one way in which taxonomists arrange the major groups of living organisms. It does not take into account the many extinct groups known to us only from fossils.

In general, the classification is not carried below the level of class. In some cases, however, it has been thought advisable to give examples at the family level. In two groups—insects and mammals—a more detailed classification at the order level is given. Finally, to show how complicated classification can become at the lower levels, a complete classification of the primate order of mammals is carried to the family level.

In examples, common names are used wherever appropriate. Where scientific names are necessary, names of genera rather than of individual species are usually given. References to figures in the text are provided only where the Appendix illustrations do not include a representative diversity of examples.

## KINGDOM PROTISTA

### PHYLUM SCHIZOMYCETES

[Greek: *schizein*, to cut, split,+*myketes*, mushrooms]

Bacteria, Actinomycetes, and Rickettsias

Extremely minute (usually 1 to 5$\mu$). Usually unicellular, without distinct nucleus. Most lack chlorophyll. Occur singly, as colonies, or as chains of individuals. Unlike the "true" bacteria, the actinomycetes produce slender, branched filaments. The relationships of the ultramicroscopic rickettsias are uncertain, but they may be thought of as highly modified Schizomycetes. About 1600 species.

Figures 6 · 5,   6 · 22 (*A*)

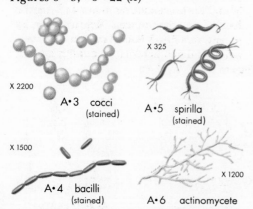

X 2200

A·3  cocci
(stained)

X 325

A·5  spirilla
(stained)

X 1500

A·4  bacilli
(stained)

X 1200

A·6  actinomycete

### PHYLUM CYANOPHYTA

[Greek: *kyaneos*, dark blue, + *phyton*, a plant]
Blue-Green Algae

Single cells or colonies in filaments, sheets, or irregular masses. Reproduction by fission. No organized nuclei or plastids. Chlorophyll often masked by other pigments. Mostly aquatic, but some occur on soil or other plants. About 1500 species.

Figure 5 · 30 (*Oscillatoria*)

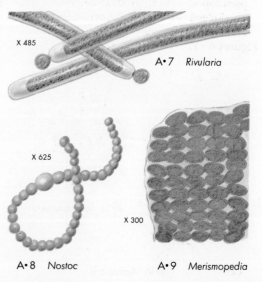

X 485

A·7  *Rivularia*

X 625

X 300

A·8  *Nostoc*

A·9  *Merismopedia*

# PHYLUM MASTIGOPHORA

[Greek: *mastigo*, whip, + *-phoros*, bearing, carrying]

Flagellates

Microscopic or almost so. Locomotion by whiplike flagella. Occur singly or as colonies. Some contain chlorophyll. Colonial forms sometimes considered to be intermediate between protists and multicellular plants or between protists and sponges. About 2000 species.

Figures 6 · 14, 6 · 15

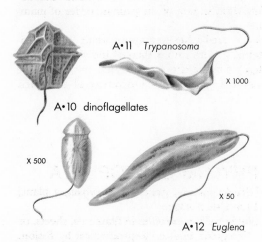

A·11   Trypanosoma

X 1000

A·10   dinoflagellates

X 500

X 50

A·12   Euglena

# PHYLUM SARCODINA

[Greek: *sarx*, flesh, + *-eidos*, form]

Sarcodinans

Microscopic or almost so. Locomotion by pseudopods. Many produce intricate shells or skeletal structures. Others are naked. About 8000 species.

Figures 6 · 17, 6 · 18

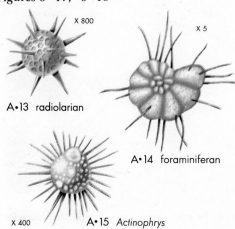

X 800

X 5

A·13   radiolarian

A·14   foraminiferan

X 400

A·15   Actinophrys

# PHYLUM SPOROZOA

[Greek: *spora*, a seed, + *zoion*, an animal]

Sporozoans

Microscopic. Usually no locomotion, but pseudopods or flagella may occur in certain stages of some species. Parasites with complicated life histories. About 2000 species.

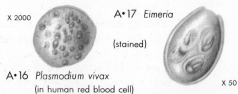

X 2000

A·17   Eimeria

(stained)

A·16   Plasmodium vivax
(in human red blood cell)

X 50

# PHYLUM CILIOPHORA

[Latin: *cilium*, eyelash, + Greek: *-phoros*, bearing, carrying]

Ciliates

Microscopic or almost so. Locomotion by cilia. About 5000 species.

Figure 6 · 20

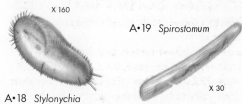

X 160

A·19   Spirostomum

A·18   Stylonychia

X 30

# PHYLUM MYXOMYCETES

[Greek: *myxa*, mucus, slime, + *myketes*, mushrooms]

Slime Molds

Macroscopic masses of living substance with hundreds of nuclei inside one membrane. Each mass moves about and engulfs food like a giant ameba. Reproduction by spores, as in fungi. Found on decaying vegetation in damp habitats. About 450 species.

Figure 6 · 22 (*B, C, D*)

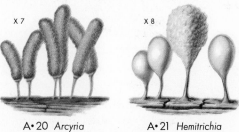

X 7

X 8

A·20   Arcyria

A·21   Hemitrichia

# KINGDOM PLANTAE

## PHYLUM CHLOROPHYTA

[Greek: *chloros*, green, + *phyton*, a plant]
Green Algae
Single cells, filaments, ribbons, sheets, tubes, or irregular masses. Chlorophyll seldom masked by other pigments. Food usually stored as starch. About 6000 species.
Figure 5 · 30 (*Ulva, Enteromorpha*)

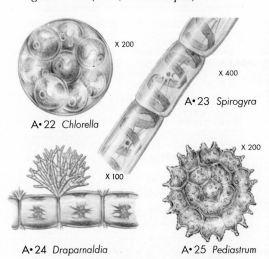

X 200
A· 22 *Chlorella*

X 400
A· 23 *Spirogyra*

X 100
A· 24 *Draparnaldia*

X 200
A· 25 *Pediastrum*

## PHYLUM CHRYSOPHYTA

[Greek: *chrysos*, gold, + *phyton*, a plant]
Golden Algae
Mostly microscopic. Many with shells of silica. Chlorophyll usually masked by yellow pigments. Food often stored as oil. About 5700 species.

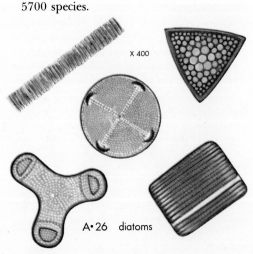

X 400
A· 26 diatoms

## PHYLUM PHAEOPHYTA

[Greek: *phaios*, brown, + *phyton*, a plant]
Brown Algae
Almost all macroscopic and marine. Chlorophyll usually masked by brownish pigments. Food stored as carbohydrates, but not as starch. About 1000 species.
Figure 5 · 30 (*Laminaria, Fucus, Ascophyllum*)

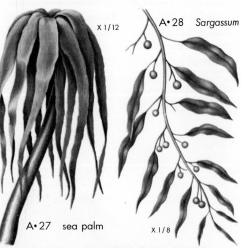

X 1/12
A· 28 *Sargassum*
A· 27 sea palm
X 1/8

## PHYLUM RHODOPHYTA

[Greek: *rhodon*, a rose, + *phyton*, a plant]
Red Algae
Almost all macroscopic and marine. Chlorophyll usually masked by red pigments. Complex life histories. Reproductive cells not capable of locomotion. Food stored as carbohydrates, but not as starch. About 2500 species.
Figure 5 · 30 (*Polysiphonia, Chondrus*)

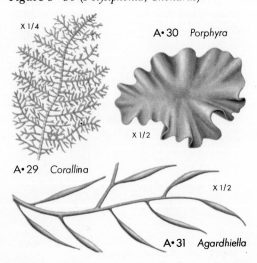

X 1/4
A· 30 *Porphyra*
A· 29 *Corallina*
X 1/2
X 1/2
A· 31 *Agardhiella*

# PHYLUM MYCOPHYTA

[Greek: *mykes*, mushroom, + *phyton*, a plant]
Fungi
No chlorophyll. No vascular tissues. Structure primarily a system of threadlike cell groups — hyphae. Mostly saprovores, but many are parasitic on plants or animals. About 75,000 species.

## CLASS PHYCOMYCETES

[Greek: *phykos*, seaweed, + *myketes*, mushrooms]
"Algal" Fungi
Hyphae usually not divided by cross walls. About 1500 species.
Figure 5 · 31

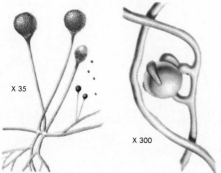

X 35

X 300

A· 32    *Rhizopus*          A· 33    *Saprolegnia*

## CLASS ASCOMYCETES

[Greek: *askos*, bag, bladder, + *myketes*, mushrooms]
Sac Fungi
Hyphae divided by cross walls. A few unicellular species. Spores of a definite number (usually 8), produced in a sac-like structure, the ascus. Often form lichen partnerships with green or blue-green algae. About 25,000 species.
Figures 5 · 27,   5 · 28

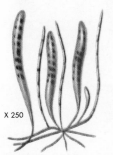

X 250

X 70

A· 34    *Neurospora*

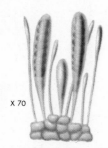

A· 35    apple scab

## CLASS BASIDIOMYCETES

[Greek: *basis*, base, + *myketes*, mushrooms]
Club Fungi
Hyphae divided by cross walls. Spores produced on the surface of a clublike structure, the basidium. About 23,000 species.
Figure 5 · 26

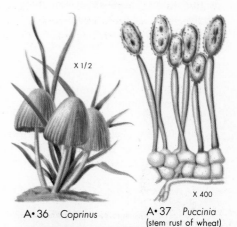

X 1/2

X 400

A· 36    *Coprinus*          A· 37    *Puccinia*
(stem rust of wheat)

## CLASS DEUTEROMYCETES

[Greek: *deuteros*, second, secondary, + *myketes*, mushrooms]
Fungi Imperfecti
Fungi whose life histories are so little known that they cannot be placed in any of the other classes. This is, therefore, a taxonomic grouping of convenience, not of relationship. About 24,000 species.
Figures 3 · 10,  7 · 2,  7 · 7

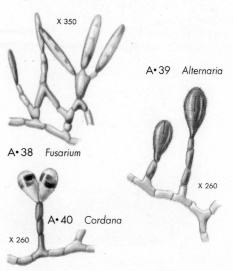

X 350

A· 39    *Alternaria*

A· 38    *Fusarium*

A· 40    *Cordana*

X 260

X 260

# PHYLUM BRYOPHYTA

[Greek: *bryon*, moss, + *phyton*, a plant]
Bryophytes

Small (less than 40 cm tall). Mostly terrestrial. Often bear structures resembling stems and leaves, but lack vascular (conducting) tissue. Well-developed alternation of generations; the gametophyte generation is the more conspicuous, with the sporophyte more or less dependent upon it. About 24,000 species.

## CLASS HEPATICAE

[Greek: *hepatikos*, liver-like (from the shape of the leaves)]
Liverworts

Gametophytes flat, often simple, branching masses of green tissue, sometimes with leaflike structures. About 8500 species.

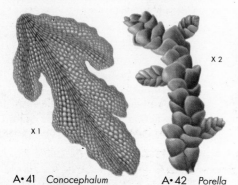

X 2

X 1

A•41    *Conocephalum*          A•42    *Porella*

## CLASS ANTHOCEROTAE

[Greek: *anthos*, flower, + *keras*, horn]
Hornworts

Gametophytes similar to those of liverworts; sporophytes live longer and are capable of continuous growth. About 50 species.

X 1

A•43    *Anthoceros*

## CLASS MUSCI

[Latin: *muscus*, moss]
Mosses

Gametophytes developed from alga-like masses of green threads; usually erect (not flat), with leaflike structures arranged in radial symmetry around a stalk. About 15,000 species.

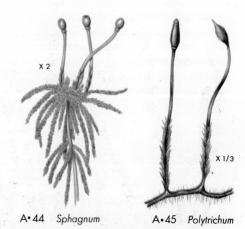

X 2

X 1/3

A•44    *Sphagnum*          A•45    *Polytrichum*

# PHYLUM TRACHEOPHYTA

[Greek: *tracheia*, windpipe, + *phyton*, a plant]
Vascular Plants

Vascular (conducting) tissue always present. Alternation of generations; sporophytes conspicuous; gametophytes much reduced (often microscopic) and in many cases dependent upon sporophytes. About 211,900 species.

## SUBPHYLUM PSILOPSIDA

[Greek: *psilos*, bare, + *opsis*, appearance]
No roots. Forking stems, with spore cases at the tips of short branches. 4 species.

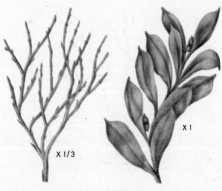

X 1/3

X 1

A•46    *Psilotum*          A•47    *Tmesipteris*

## SUBPHYLUM SPHENOPSIDA

[Greek: *sphen*, a wedge, + *opsis*, appearance (from the shape of the leaves)]

Horsetails

Roots and jointed stems. Small leaves (mere traces in living species) arranged in a circle around each stem joint. Spore cases borne on stem structures resembling cones. 32 species.

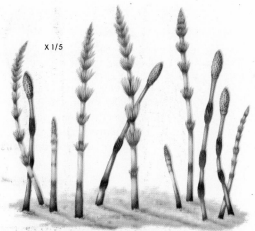

X 1/5

A• 48   *Equisetum*

## SUBPHYLUM LYCOPSIDA

[Greek: *lycos*, wolf, + *opsis*, appearance (so named because the roots of a lycopod were thought to resemble a wolf's claw)]

Club Mosses

Roots, stems, and small leaves. Spore cases borne in various ways, usually on modified leaves grouped to form structures something like cones. About 1100 species.

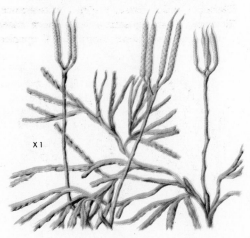

X 1

A• 49   *Lycopodium*

## SUBPHYLUM PTEROPSIDA

[Greek: *pteron*, feather, + *opsis*, appearance]

Ferns, Gymnosperms, and Angiosperms

Most have roots, stems, and leaves. The positions of the leaves are marked in the vascular tissue of the stem by a gap. About 210,700 species.

### CLASS FILICINEAE

[Latin: *filix*, ferns]

Ferns

Gametophytes independent of sporophytes. Free-swimming sperm cells. About 10,000 species.

Figures 5 · 16,   5· 17

X 1/10

X 1/4

A• 50   climbing fern          A• 51   cinnamon fern

### CLASS GYMNOSPERMAE

[Greek: *gymnos*, naked, + *sperma*, seed]

Gametophytes microscopic, within tissues of sporophytes. Seeds "naked" (not enclosed in a fruit), attached to the surface of a modified leaf. About 700 species.

Figures 5 · 12,   5 · 13

X 1/4

A• 52   hemlock          A• 53   ginkgo

## CLASS ANGIOSPERMAE

[Greek: *angeion*, a small container, capsule, + *sperma*, seed]

Flowering Plants

Gametophytes microscopic, within tissues of sporophytes. Seeds enclosed in a fruit. Sperm cells in pollen tubes. About 200,000 species. (There are more than 300 families in the class Angiospermae. A few of the common families are given in the following subclasses. Orders are omitted.)

### Subclass Dicotyledoneae

[Greek: *dis-*, two, double, + cotyledon]

"Dicots"

Flowering plants. Two cotyledons in the seed. Leaves usually have veins that form a network. Flower parts usually in fours or fives or multiples of these numbers.

**Family Fagaceae** (Oak Family). Trees and shrubs. Pistils and stamens in separate flowers. Flowers radially symmetrical, with 4 to 7 sepals, no petals, few to many stamens, 1 pistil, and inferior ovary.

X 1/3

A•54   oak

**Family Ranunculaceae** (Buttercup Family). Herbaceous. Flowers radially symmetrical, with few to many sepals and petals, many stamens and pistils, and superior ovary.

X 1/6

A•55   larkspur

**Family Cruciferae** (Mustard Family). Herbaceous. Flowers radially symmetrical, with 4 sepals, 4 petals, 2 sets of stamens (4 long and 2 short), 1 pistil, and superior ovary. Often have a turnip-like or cabbage-like odor.

X 1/6

A•56   field mustard

**Family Rosaceae** (Rose Family). Flowers radially symmetrical, with 5 sepals, 5 petals, numerous stamens, 1 to many pistils, and superior or more or less inferior ovary.

A•57   wild rose

**Family Leguminosae** (Bean Family). Flowers bilaterally symmetrical, with 5 sepals, 5 petals, 10 stamens, 1 pistil, and superior ovary.

X 1/2

A•58   sweet pea

**Family Umbelliferae** (Parsley Family). Herbaceous. Flowers radially symmetrical, with 5 small sepals, 5 petals, 5 stamens, 1 pistil, and inferior ovary.

X 1/2

A•59   Queen Anne's lace

**Family Polemoniaceae (Phlox Family).** Flowers radially symmetrical, with 5 sepals (united), 5 petals (united), 5 stamens, 1 pistil, and superior ovary.

A·60 phlox      A·61 Jacob's ladder

**Family Labiatae (Mint Family).** Flowers bilaterally symmetrical, with 5 sepals (united), 5 petals (united), 2 or 4 stamens, 1 pistil, and superior ovary. Stems usually square in cross section.

A·62 scarlet sage      A·63 coleus

**Family Scrophulariaceae (Snapdragon Family).** Flowers bilaterally symmetrical, with 5 sepals, 5 petals (2 forming an upper lip and 3 forming a lower lip), 4 stamens (in 2 unlike pairs), 1 pistil, and superior ovary.

A·64 snapdragon      A·65 butter and eggs

**Family Caprifoliaceae (Honeysuckle Family).** Flowers radially or bilaterally symmetrical; 4 or 5 sepals, 4 or 5 petals (united), 4 or 5 stamens, 1 pistil; ovary inferior.

A·66 honeysuckle      A·67 snowberry

**Family Compositae (Composite Family).** Small flowers in dense groups, each group appearing to be a single, large flower; individual flowers radially or bilaterally symmetrical, with sepals reduced to bristles or scales, 5 petals (united), 5 stamens, 1 pistil, and inferior ovary.

A·68 *Gaillardia*      A·69 dandelion

### Subclass Monocotyledoneae

[Greek: *monos*, one, single, + cotyledon]

"Monocots"

Flowering plants. One cotyledon in the seed. Leaves usually have parallel veins. Flower parts usually in threes or multiples of three.

**Family Alismataceae (Water Plantain Family).** Herbaceous. Aquatic or marsh plants. Flowers radially symmetrical, with 3 sepals, 3 petals, 6 to many stamens, 6 to many pistils, and superior ovary.

A·70 arrowhead

Family Gramineae (Grass Family). Stems usually hollow. Flowers radially symmetrical, with no sepals or petals (but scalelike structures present), 1 to 6 stamens, 1 pistil, and superior ovary. Leaves sheathing stem.

A·71  wheat              A·72  bamboo

Family Cyperaceae (Sedge Family). Herbaceous. Stems usually solid. Flowers radially symmetrical, with no sepals or petals (but scalelike structures present), 1 to 3 stamens, 1 pistil, and superior ovary. Leaves sheathing stem.

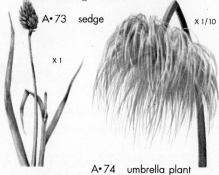

A·73  sedge

A·74  umbrella plant

Family Commelinaceae (Spiderwort Family). Herbaceous. Flowers radially or somewhat bilaterally symmetrical, with 3 sepals, 3 petals, 3 or 6 stamens, 1 pistil, and superior ovary.

A·75  dayflower       A·76  spiderwort

Family Liliaceae (Lily Family). Flowers radially symmetrical, with 3 sepals, 3 petals (sepals and petals often colored alike, thus appearing to be 6 petals), 3 or 6 stamens, 1 pistil, and superior ovary.

A·77  tulip          A·78  tiger lily

Family Amaryllidaceae (Amaryllis Family). Herbaceous. Flowers radially symmetrical, with 3 sepals, 3 petals, 6 stamens, 1 pistil, and inferior ovary.

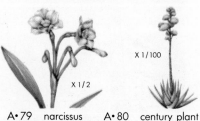

A·79  narcissus      A·80  century plant

Family Iridaceae (Iris Family). Herbaceous. Flowers radially or somewhat bilaterally symmetrical, with 3 sepals, 3 petals, 3 stamens, 1 pistil, and inferior ovary.

A·81  gladiolus        A·82  iris

Family Orchidaceae (Orchid Family). Herbaceous. Flowers bilaterally symmetrical, with 3 sepals, 3 petals (united), 1 or 2 stamens, 1 pistil, and inferior ovary.

A·83  orchid

# KINGDOM ANIMALIA

## PHYLUM PORIFERA

[Latin: *porus*, pore, + *ferre*, to bear]
Sponges
Mostly marine. Adults always attached to
some solid object. Body wall consists of two
cell layers. Pores in body wall connected
to an internal canal system. About 4200
species.
Figure 4 · 40

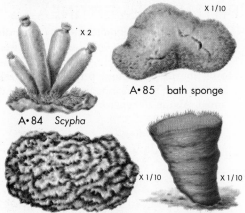

A·84  *Scypha*

A·85  bath sponge

A·86  sheep's-wool sponge   A·87  fringed basket

## PHYLUM COELENTERATA

[Greek: *koilos*, hollow, + *enteron*, intestine]
Coelenterates
Mostly marine. Body wall consists of 2 cell
layers and jelly-like material between. Sac-
like digestive cavity with a single opening
("mouth"). Radially symmetrical. Tentacles
with stinging cells. About 9200 species.

### CLASS HYDROZOA

[Greek: *hydor*, water, + *zoion*, animal]
Single individuals or colonies. Digestive
cavity undivided. Simple sense organs.
About 3000 species.

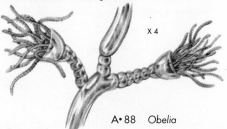

A·88  *Obelia*

### CLASS SCYPHOZOA

[Greek: *skyphos*, a cup, can, + *zoion*,
animal]
Single individuals that float or swim; a
few species have attached stages in the
life history. Digestive cavity divided.
Rather complex sense organs. About
200 species.
Figure 4 · 39

A·89  *Aurelia*

### CLASS ANTHOZOA

[Greek: *anthos*, flower, + *zoion*, animal]
Single individuals or massive colonies.
Often produce limy skeletons. No float-
ing or swimming stages. Digestive
cavity divided. About 6000 species.
Figure 2 · 1

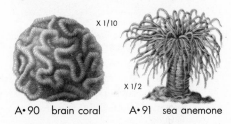

A·90  brain coral      A·91  sea anemone

## PHYLUM CTENOPHORA

[Greek: *ktenos*, comb, + *-phoros*, carrying or
bearing]
Comb Jellies
Marine. Somewhat resembling jellyfish, but
without stinging cells. Free-swimming, by
means of 8 rows of cilia. About 100 species.

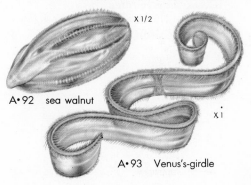

A·92  sea walnut

A·93  Venus's-girdle

# PHYLUM PLATYHELMINTHES

[Greek: *platys*, flat, + *helmins*, worm]

Flatworms

Free-living or parasitic. Usually flat and bilaterally symmetrical. Branched or unbranched digestive cavity with a single opening, or no digestive cavity. Bodies consist of 3 cell layers. About 6000 species.

## CLASS TURBELLARIA

[Latin: *turba*, disturbance (so named because the cilia cause tiny currents in the water)]

Mostly marine, but some freshwater or terrestrial species. Free-living. Usually have cilia on the outside. About 1500 species.

Figure 4 · 38

A·94    planarian    X 3

## CLASS TREMATODA

[Greek: *trematodes*, having holes]

Parasitic. No external cilia. Usually possess suckers. Digestive system present. About 3000 species.

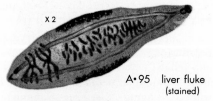

A·95    liver fluke
(stained)    X 2

## CLASS CESTODA

[Greek: *kestos*, girdle]

Parasitic. No external cilia. No digestive system. About 1500 species.

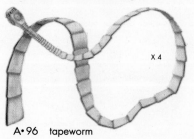

A·96    tapeworm    X 4

# PHYLUM MESOZOA

[Greek: *mesos*, middle, + *zoion*, animal]

Parasitic in flatworms, mollusks, and annelids. Minute; worm-shaped. Simple structure; no digestive system. About 45 species.

A·97    Pseudicyema    X 20

# PHYLUM NEMERTINEA

[Greek: *Nemertes* (the name of a water nymph in mythology)]

Ribbon Worms

Mostly marine. Flat and unsegmented. Digestive tube with 2 openings (mouth and anus). About 500 species.

A·98    Cerebratulus    X 1/4

# PHYLUM ASCHELMINTHES

[Greek: *ascos*, bag, bladder, + *helmins*, worm]

Freshwater, marine, or terrestrial. Freeliving or parasitic. Bilaterally symmetrical. Internal organs lie in a body cavity developed between endodermal and mesodermal cell layers. About 12,500 species.

## CLASS ROTIFERA

[Latin: *rota*, wheel, + *ferre*, to bear]

Rotifers or Wheel Worms

Microscopic. Freshwater or marine. Bilaterally symmetrical. Numerous cilia around mouth. About 2000 species.

Figure 4 · 35

A·99    Asplanchna    X 28

## CLASS GASTROTRICHA

[Greek: *gaster*, belly, + *thrix*, hair]

Freshwater and marine. Free-living. Microscopic. Cilia on ventral surface. Surface of body covered with cuticular scales. 140 species.

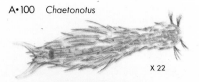

A·100    *Chaetonotus*

X 22

## CLASS KINORHYNCHA

[Greek: *kinein*, to set in motion, + *rhynchos*, snout or beak]

Marine. Minute. Protrusible spiny snout. Outer surface of body covered with cuticular plates arranged in rings. 100 species.

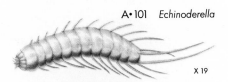

A·101    *Echinoderella*

X 19

## CLASS PRIAPULIDA

[Greek: *Priapos*, a god of gardens and vineyards]

Marine. Free-living. Mouth region with spines. Body covered with rings of cuticle. 5 species.

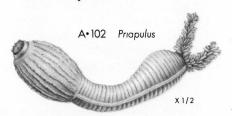

A·102    *Priapulus*

X 1/2

## CLASS NEMATOMORPHA

[Greek: *nema*, thread, + *morphe*, form]

Horsehair Worms

Young are parasitic in arthropods; adults are free-living and have much reduced digestive tubes. About 200 species.

X 1/2

A·103    *Gordius*

## CLASS NEMATODA

[Greek: *nema*, thread]

Roundworms

Parasitic or free-living. Cylindrical bodies, bilaterally symmetrical. Digestive tube with mouth and anus. About 10,000 species.

Figures 4·36, 4·37

A·104    *Ascaris*

X 1/3

# PHYLUM ACANTHOCEPHALA

[Greek: *akantha*, spine, + *kephale*, head]

Spiny-headed Worms

Young parasitic in arthropods; adults parasitic in intestines of vertebrates. No digestive system. About 100 species.

A·105    *Oncicola*

X 1

# PHYLUM BRYOZOA

[Greek: *bryon*, moss, + *zoion*, animal]

Moss Animals

Mostly marine, living in attached colonies. U-shaped digestive tube. Mouth encircled in a crown of tentacles. About 3000 species.

A·106    *Electra*

X 10

# PHYLUM BRACHIOPODA

[Greek: *brachion*, arm, + *pous*, foot]

Lamp Shells

Marine. Symmetrical, 2-piece shells, enclosing a pair of "arms" bearing tentacles. About 120 species.

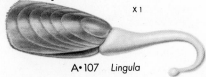

X 1

A·107    *Lingula*

# PHYLUM PHORONIDEA

[Greek: *Phoronis* (name of a mythological character)]

Marine. Living in tubes in mud. A pair of "arms" bearing tentacles. U-shaped digestive tube. About 15 species.

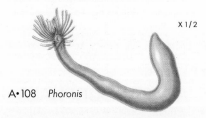

A·108    *Phoronis*

# PHYLUM CHAETOGNATHA

[Greek: *chaite*, hair, + *gnathos*, jaw]

Arrowworms

Marine. Free-swimming or floating. Bilaterally symmetrical. Straight digestive tube. About 30 species.

A·109    *Sogitta*

# PHYLUM MOLLUSCA

[Latin: *mollis*, soft]

Mollusks

Marine, freshwater, or terrestrial. Bilaterally symmetrical or unsymmetrical. The mantle is a fold of tissue over the body; it usually secretes a limy shell. No segmentation. Well-developed digestive, circulatory, and nervous systems. About 70,000 species.

## CLASS AMPHINEURA

[Greek: *amphis*, double, both sides of, + *neuron*, nerve]

Marine. Shell composed of 8 overlapping plates (exposed or hidden). No distinct head. About 630 species.

A·110    chitons

## CLASS MONOPLACOPHORA

[Greek: *monos*, solitary, + *plax*, tablet, flat plate, + *-phoros*, bearing, carrying]

Marine. Single shell with a curved apex. Broad, flattened foot. Found in deep ocean trenches. 3 species.

A·111    *Neopilina*

## CLASS GASTROPODA

[Greek: *gastros*, stomach, + *pous*, foot]

Marine, freshwater, or terrestrial. Shell (if present) coiled. Head usually distinct. About 55,000 species.

Figures 4·29,  4·41 (sea slug)

A·112    snail

## CLASS SCAPHOPODA

[Greek: *skaphe*, boat, + *pous*, foot]

Marine. Shells form a tapering tube. Food-catching tentacles on head. About 200 species.

A·113    tooth shell

## CLASS PELECYPODA

[Greek: *pelekys*, a hatchet, + *pous*, foot]

Marine or freshwater. Some attached; others burrow in mud or sand. Shells in 2 parts, hinged. About 15,000 species.

Figure 4·41 (scallop)

A·114    clam

## CLASS CEPHALOPODA

[Greek: *kephale*, head, + *pous*, foot]

Marine. Small, internal shell; in a few cases shell is external, coiled, and internally divided. Several tentacles on head. Locomotion by jet of water. About 400 species.

Figures 4·30,  9·22

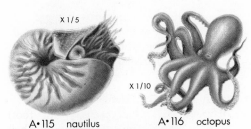

X 1/5

X 1/10

A·115   nautilus        A·116   octopus

# PHYLUM ANNELIDA

[Latin: *anulus*, a ring]

Segmented Worms

Marine, freshwater, or terrestrial. Bilaterally symmetrical. Body internally and externally segmented. Appendages either not jointed or lacking. Main nerve cord ventral. About 6500 species.

## CLASS POLYCHAETA

[Greek: *polys*, many, + *chaite*, hair]

Mostly marine. Burrowers or tube-builders. Usually with paddle-like appendages on each body segment. About 3500 species.

Figure 4·41 (feather worm)

X 1/2

A·117 clam worm

## CLASS OLIGOCHAETA

[Greek: *oligos*, few, + *chaite*, hair]

Mostly freshwater or terrestrial. Appendages small or lacking. About 2500 species.

Figure 9·7

A·118   earthworm

X 1

## CLASS HIRUDINEA

[Latin: *hirudo*, leech]

Rather flat. Appendages lacking. Suction disks at each end. About 250 species.

A·119   leech        X 1/2

# PHYLUM ARTHROPODA

[Greek: *arthron*, joint, + *pous*, foot]

Arthropods

Marine, freshwater, or terrestrial. Bilaterally symmetrical. Body segmented, but segments often fused. Jointed appendages. Body and appendages covered with a jointed exoskeleton. Main nerve cord ventral. About 750,000 species.

## CLASS ONYCHOPHORA

[Greek: *onyx*, nail, claw, + *-phoros*, carrying or bearing]

Terrestrial. Tropical. Wormlike. Paired legs. Poorly developed segmentation. Combine many annelid and arthropod characteristics. About 80 species.

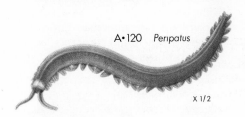

A·120   *Peripatus*

X 1/2

## CLASS CRUSTACEA

[Latin: *crusta*, rind]

2 pairs of antennae. Respiration by gills. About 25,000 species.

Figure 4·27

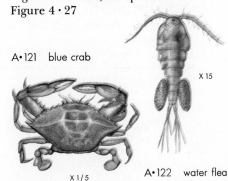

A·121   blue crab

X 15

X 1/5

A·122   water flea

## CLASS ARACHNIDA

[Greek: *arachne*, spider]

No antennae. Segmentation reduced. 4 pairs of legs. No jaws (feeding appendages may resemble claw-bearing legs). About 15,000 species.

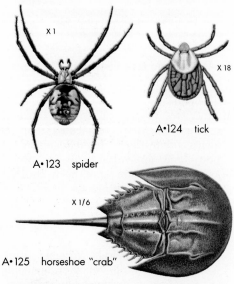

X 1

X 18

A•124 tick

A•123 spider

X 1/6

A•125 horseshoe "crab"

## CLASS DIPLOPODA

[Greek: *diploos*, two, double, + *pous*, foot]

Millepedes

1 pair of short antennae. Entire body segmented; round in cross section. 2 pairs of legs on each segment. About 6000 species.

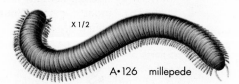

X 1/2

A•126 millepede

## CLASS CHILOPODA

[Greek: *cheilos*, lip, + *pous*, foot]

Centipedes

1 pair of long antennae. Entire body segmented; flat. 1 pair of legs on each segment. About 800 species.

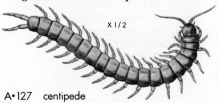

X 1/2

A•127 centipede

## CLASS INSECTA

[Latin: *in*, into, + *secare*, to cut, divide (from the segmented bodies)]

1 pair of antennae. Body divided into head, thorax, and abdomen. 3 pairs of legs on thorax. About 700,000 species. (The following are the more common orders in the class Insecta.)

ORDER THYSANURA [Greek: *thysanos*, tassle, + *oura*, tail]. Small. Wingless. Soft scales on the body. 3 long bristles at posterior end.

A•128 silverfish

X 5

ORDER EPHEMEROPTERA [Greek: *ephemeros*, temporary (literally, existing but one day), + *pteron*, feather, wing]. 2 pairs of transparent wings; hind wings smaller. 2 or 3 long "tails." Immature forms are aquatic.

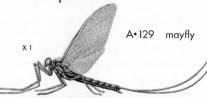

A•129 mayfly

X 1

ORDER ODONATA [Greek: *odous*, tooth]. 2 similar pairs of long wings. Antennae short. Abdomen long and slender. Immature forms aquatic.

X 1/2

A•130 damselfly

ORDER ORTHOPTERA [Greek: *orthos*, straight, + *pteron*, wing]. Terrestrial. Front wings leathery; hind wings folded, fanlike. Chewing mouth parts.

X 1

A•131 grasshopper

**ORDER ISOPTERA** [Greek: *isos,* equal, + *pteron,* wing]. 4 wings alike in size, with many fine veins, or wings lacking. Chewing mouth parts. Social.

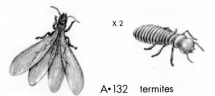

X 2

A·132 termites

**ORDER ANOPLURA** [Greek: *anoplos,* unarmed, + *oura,* tail]. Wingless. Flat. Sucking or piercing mouth parts. Parasitic on mammals.

X 20

A·133 louse

**ORDER HOMOPTERA** [Greek: *homos,* alike, + *pteron,* wing]. 2 pairs of wings, arched above the body, or wings lacking. Jointed sucking beak at base of head.

A·134 leafhopper

X 6

**ORDER HEMIPTERA** [Greek: *hemi-,* half, + *pteron,* wing]. Front wings thick at the base, thin at the tips; hind wings thin. Jointed beak on front of head.

X 1

A·135 water strider

**ORDER LEPIDOPTERA** [Greek: *lepidos,* scale, + *pteron,* wing]. 2 pairs of wings covered with soft scales. Coiled, sucking mouth parts in adults. Young are wormlike (caterpillars).

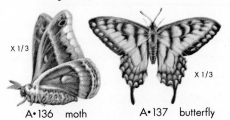

X 1/3

X 1/3

A·136 moth      A·137 butterfly

**ORDER DIPTERA** [Greek: *dis,* twice, + *pteron,* wing]. 1 pair of wings (hind wings reduced to small rods). Antennae short. Sucking mouth parts. Young are wormlike and either terrestrial (maggots) or aquatic.

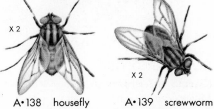

X 2

X 2

A·138 housefly      A·139 screwworm

**ORDER COLEOPTERA** [Greek: *koleos,* a sheath, + *pteron,* wing]. Front wings form a hard sheath; hind wings folded beneath them. Chewing mouth parts. Young usually wormlike (grubs).

X 2

X 2

A·140 hister beetle   A·141 cucumber beetle

**ORDER HYMENOPTERA** [Greek: *hymen,* membrane, + *pteron,* wing]. Front wings much larger than hind wings, with the 2 pairs hooked together, or wings lacking. Chewing or sucking mouth parts. Young are wormlike. Many social species.

X 2

A·142 wasp

# PHYLUM ECHINODERMATA

[Greek: *echinos*, hedgehog, + *derma*, skin]
Echinoderms

All marine. Adults radially symmetrical; radiating sections (when present) are called "arms." Larvae bilaterally symmetrical. Internal, limy skeleton, usually with many projecting spines. A system of water-filled tubes, acting on the suction principle, catches food and assists in locomotion. About 5000 species.

## CLASS CRINOIDEA

[Greek: *krinon*, lily, + *-eidos*, appearance]
Attached (at least when young). Many highly branched "arms." About 635 species.

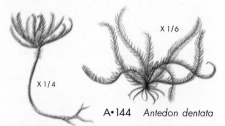

A•143   sea lily

A•144   *Antedon dentata*

## CLASS ASTEROIDEA

[Greek: *aster*, star, + *-eidos*, appearance]
Usually 5 "arms," joined to the body at broad bases. About 1500 species.

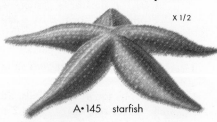

A•145   starfish

## CLASS OPHIUROIDEA

[Greek: *ophis*, serpent, + *oura*, tail, + *-eidos*, appearance]
Usually 5 long, slim "arms" (sometimes branched), clearly distinguished from the body. About 1500 species.

A•146   brittle star

## CLASS ECHINOIDEA

[Greek: *echinos*, hedgehog, + *-eidos*, appearance]
Spherical or disk-shaped. No "arms." Long spines or short, hairlike projections from body. Skeleton of interlocking plates. About 770 species.

A•147   sand dollar

A•148   sea urchin

## CLASS HOLOTHURIOIDEA

[Greek: *holothourion*, a kind of water animal, + *-eidos*, appearance]
Somewhat cylindrical. No "arms." Tentacles around mouth. No spines. Skeleton consists of particles embedded in the leathery skin. About 600 species.
Figure 4 • 32

A•149   sea cucumber

# PHYLUM CHORDATA

[Greek: *chorde*, string of a musical instrument]
Chordates

Marine, freshwater, or terrestrial. Bilaterally symmetrical. Hollow dorsal nerve tube and a stiff notochord beneath it (may be lost or replaced during development). Several pairs of pharyngeal pouches in the "throat" region (these may become perforated during development, forming slits). Some segmentation, especially in arrangement of muscles and nerves. About 46,000 species.

## SUBPHYLUM HEMICHORDATA

[Greek: *hemi*, half, + *chorde*, string of a musical instrument]
Marine, wormlike. Conspicuous proboscis used for burrowing in mud and sand. Dorsal nerve cord and pharyngeal slits. Notochord doubtfully present. About 100 species.

A•150   acorn worm

## SUBPHYLUM UROCHORDATA

[Greek: *oura*, tail, + *chorde*, string of a musical instrument]

Marine. Larvae free-swimming; adults usually attached. Notochord and part of nervous system usually disappear during development. About 700 species.

Figure 4 · 20

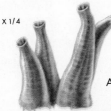

X 1/4

A·151    sea squirt

## SUBPHYLUM CEPHALOCHORDATA

[Greek: *kephale*, head, + *chorde*, string of a musical instrument]

Marine. Free-swimming. Translucent. Well-developed, hollow dorsal nerve cord, notochord, and pharyngeal slits in adults. About 28 species.

X 1

A·152    lancelet

## SUBPHYLUM VERTEBRATA

[Latin: *vertebra*, joint]

Notochord replaced by a "backbone" of vertebrae during development. Enlarged anterior end of the nerve cord (brain) protected by cartilage or bone. Most species have appendages in pairs. About 45,000 species.

### CLASS AGNATHA

[Greek: *a-*, without, + *gnathos*, jaw]

No jaws. No paired fins. Skeleton of cartilage. Heart with one ventricle. 10 species.

Figure 4 · 18 (lamprey)

X 1/10

X 1/10

A·153    hagfish        A·154    lamprey

## CLASS CHONDRICHTHYES

[Greek: *chondros*, cartilage, + *ichthyes*, fish]
Cartilaginous Fishes

Skeleton of cartilage. 5 or more pharyngeal slits externally visible. Ventral mouth and nostrils. Heart with one ventricle. About 600 species.

Figure 4 · 18 (sawfish)

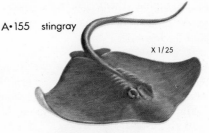

A·155    stingray

X 1/25

## CLASS OSTEICHTHYES

[Greek: *osteon*, bone, + *ichthyes*, fish]
Bony Fishes

Skeleton of bone (at least in part). Pharyngeal slits covered (not externally visible). Heart with one ventricle. About 20,000 species.

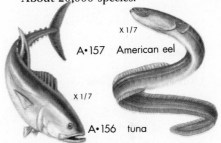

X 1/7

A·157    American eel

X 1/7

A·156    tuna

## CLASS AMPHIBIA

[Greek: *amphis*, double, on both sides of, + *bios*, life]

Larvae usually aquatic, with gills; adults usually terrestrial, with lungs. 2 pairs of appendages (small or lacking in some species). No claws. Heart with one ventricle. About 2800 species.

Figure 4 · 16 (salamander)

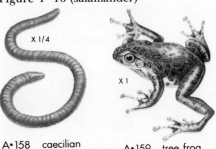

X 1/4

X 1

A·158    caecilian        A·159    tree frog

## CLASS REPTILIA

[Latin: *repere,* to creep]

Both young and adults breathe by lungs. Eggs with shells; membrane in egg encloses water. 2 pairs of appendages (small or lacking in some species) with claws. Scales on skin. Heart with two ventricles but with an opening in wall separating them (in most species). About 7000 species.

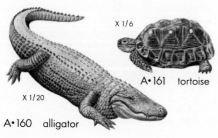

X 1/6

A•161  tortoise

X 1/20

A•160  alligator

## CLASS AVES

[Latin: *avis,* bird]

Birds

Scales modified as feathers. Eggs as in reptiles, but shell always hard. Front appendages usually modified as wings. Heart with two ventricles. About 8600 species.

X 1/20

A•162  albatross

## CLASS MAMMALIA

[Latin: *mamma,* breast]

Scales modified as hairs. Mammary glands of females secrete milk. Fewer bones than in reptiles. Teeth usually of 4 well-defined types (incisors, canines, premolars, molars). Heart with two ventricles. About 5000 species.

### ORDER MONOTREMATA [Greek: *monos,* one, + *trema,* hole]. Egg-laying. Mammary glands without nipples.

X 1/8

A•163  platypus

### ORDER MARSUPIALIA [Greek: *marsypos,* pouch, bag]. Young born in very undeveloped state and transferred to a pouch, where they remain tightly attached to the nipples.

X 1/20

A•164  koala

X 1/20

A•165  wallaby

### ORDER INSECTIVORA [Latin: *insectum,* insect, + *vorare,* to eat]. Numerous teeth of all four mammalian kinds; none highly specialized.

A•166  mole

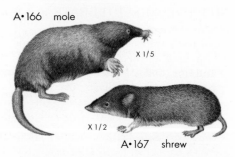

X 1/5

X 1/2

A•167  shrew

### ORDER CHIROPTERA [Greek: *cheir,* hand, + *pteron,* wing]. Web of skin between fingers and between front limbs and hind limbs, allowing flight.

X 1/4

A•168  bat

**ORDER PRIMATES** [Latin: *primus*, first]. Eyes usually directed forward. Nails usually present instead of claws. Teeth much like those of insectivores.

The complexity of classification is shown in the following example, a complete classification of the order Primates.

Suborder Prosimii

    Infraorder Lemuriformes

        Superfamily Tupaioidea

            Family Tupaiidae (tree shrews)

        Superfamily Lemuroidea

            Family Lemuridae (lemurs)

            Family Indriidae (lemurs, indris)

        Superfamily Daubentonioidea

            Family Daubentoniidae (aye-ayes)

    Infraorder Lorisiformes

            Family Lorisidae (lorises, pottos, galagos)

    Infraorder Tarsiiformes

            Family Tarsiidae (tarsiers)

Suborder Anthropoidea

        Superfamily Ceboidea

            Family Cebidae (New World monkeys)

            Family Callithricidae (marmosets)

        Superfamily Cercopithecoidea

            Family Cercopithecidae (Old World monkeys, baboons)

        Superfamily Hominoidea

            Family Pongidae (apes)

            Family Hominidae (man)

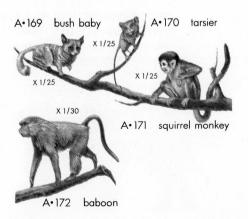

A•169   bush baby

X 1/25

X 1/25

X 1/30

A•170   tarsier

X 1/25

A•171   squirrel monkey

A•172   baboon

X 1/30

A•173   chimpanzee

X 1/30

A•174   gorilla

**ORDER EDENTATA** [Latin: *edentare*, to make toothless]. No front teeth; molars in some species.
Figure 8 · 22

X 1/15

A·175   sloth

**ORDER PHOLIDOTA** [Greek: *pholis*, scale]. No teeth. Body encased in scales formed from modified hairs.
Figure 4 · 11 (pangolin)

A·176   pangolin

**ORDER TUBULIDENTATA** [Latin: *tubulus*, small tube, + *dens*, tooth]. Teeth few in adults but numerous in the embryos. Toes ending in "nails" that are intermediate between claws and hoofs.
Figure 4 · 11 (aardvark)

X 1/30

A·177   aardvark

**ORDER RODENTIA** [Latin: *rodere*, to gnaw]. Chisel-like incisors, growing continually from the roots; no canines; broad molars.
Figures 8 · 15 (beaver), 8 · 32

X 1/12

X 1/30

A·178   porcupine          A·179   squirrel

**ORDER LAGOMORPHA** [Greek: *lagos*, hare, + *morphe*, form]. Teeth similar to those of rodents, but with 4 upper incisors instead of 2. Tail very short.
Figure 18 · 11

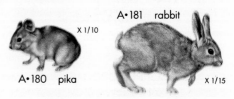

A·181   rabbit

X 1/10

A·180   pika          X 1/15

**ORDER CETACEA** [Greek: *ketos*, whale]. Marine. Front limbs modified as flippers; hind limbs absent. No hair on adults. Eyes small. Head very large.

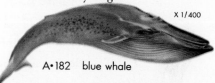

X 1/400

A·182   blue whale

**ORDER CARNIVORA** [Latin: *carnis*, flesh, + *vorare*, to eat]. Incisors small; canines large; premolars adapted for shearing. Claws usually sharp.
Figure 2 · 30

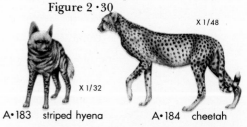

X 1/48

X 1/32

A·183   striped hyena          A·184   cheetah

**ORDER PROBOSCIDEA** [Greek: *pro-*, before, in front of, + *boskein*, to feed, graze]. Herbivorous. Upper incisors modified as tusks; molars produced 2 to 4 at a time as older ones wear out. Nose and upper lip modified as a trunk.

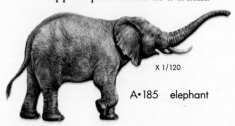

X 1/120

A·185   elephant

**ORDER SIRENIA** [Latin: *siren,* a kind of mermaid]. Aquatic. Herbivorous. No hind limbs. Broad, flat tail, expanded as a fin. Few hairs.

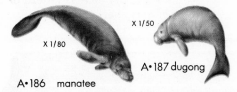

X 1/50

X 1/80

A•187 dugong

A•186    manatee

**ORDER PERISSODACTYLA** [Greek: *perissos,* uneven, + *daktylos,* finger or toe]. Herbivorous. Well-developed molars. 1, 3, or 5 toes, modified as hoofs.

Figures 8 · 35 (zebra), 8 · 39 (tapir)

X 1/40

A•188    rhinoceros

**ORDER ARTIODACTYLA** [Greek: *artios,* even, + *daktylos,* finger or toe]. Herbivorous. Most have complex stomachs. 2 or 4 toes, modified as hoofs. Often have horns or antlers.

Figure 8 · 24 (bison)

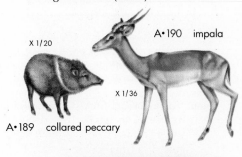

A•190    impala

X 1/20

X 1/36

A•189    collared peccary

X 1/60

A•191    hippopotamus

# Index

An asterisk (*) indicates an illustration (chart, diagram, graph, map, or picture).
Boldface numbers indicate pages carrying explanations of terms.

Aardvark, 116*, 802*
Abiotic environment: comparative study of, 98–99; effects of organisms on, 94, 96; as part of ecosystem, 94. See also Environment
Absorption of materials, 486, 489
Acacia tree, 3*
Acadian flycatcher, 68*, 267
Acanthocephala, 793*
Acanthometra elastica, 203*
Acetic acid, 416, 423
Acetyl coenzyme A, 416
Acetylsalicylic acid, 219
Acidity of soils, 238
Acidity of soil water, 236
Acorn worm, 329*, 798*
Actinomycetes, 194, 237, 782*
Actinophrys, 783*
Actinosphaerium eichorni, 203*
Active transport: in cells, 392; in kidney tubules, 509; of mineral nutrients from soil to roots of plants, 455; through phloem cells, 463; through villi, 489
Adaptive convergence, 369–370
Adaptive radiation, 368–369
Adenosine diphosphate (ADP), 414–415, 426*, 436
Adenosine monophosphate, 425
Adenosine triphosphate (ATP), 414–415, 417, 419, 424, 426*, 433, 434, 435, 436
ADP, See Adenosine diphosphate
Adrenal glands, 514
Adrenalin, 514–515
"Advancement Score" for plants, 180–181*
Aedes aegypti, 231
Agardhiella, 784*
Agnatha, 799*

Agnathan, 123*, 124
Agricultural employment (U.S.), 753
Agricultural land, amount required to feed one person, 753*
Agricultural Revolution, 743, 744
Agrobacterium tumefaciens, 232, 233
Ailanthus, 295*
Air pollution, 764*, 765–766
Akepa, 697*
Alaska brown bear, 67*
Alaska tundra, 261*. See also Tundra
Albatross, 800*
Alders, 245
Algae, 792*; diversity among, 176*, 177–178; as food for snails, 75; lack of vascular systems, 473; mutualism in lichens, 88; in ponds, 308; in soils, 237. See also Blue-green algae; Brown algae; Golden algae; Green algae; Red algae
"Algal" fungi, 785*
Alimentary canal: of bird, 485*; of roundworm, 484*
Alismataceae, 789*
Alkalinity: of soils, 238–239; of soil water, 236
Alleles, 632, 635, 649–650. See also Genes
Allergies, 220–221
Alligators, 74, 519*, 800*
Allosaur: role in food web, 30*
Alternaria, 240*, 785*
Alternation of generations, 591, 599*, 600, 627
Alternation of hosts, 225, 231, 742
Altitude, effects of, 281–282
Alveoli, 494
Amaryllidaceae, 790*

Amaryllis family, 790*
Amebas, 202–203, 241, 393* 482
American eel, 799*
American Indian, 730, 731*
American tapir, 286*
Amino acids, 424*, 507–508
Ammonia, 506, 508
Amnion, 363, 607
Amoeba proteus, 203*
AMP. See Adenosine monophosphate
Amphibia, 799*
Amphibians: in coal age, 353; diversity among, 120, 121*; territorial behavior in, 561
Amphineura, 794*
Androgens, 617
Anemia, 500
Angiospermae, 788–790, 788*, 790*
Angiosperms: absence in coal age, 352; diversity among, 160–161, 164–165; fertilization and reproduction of, 595–599; the flower, 159–160, 166*; monocots and dicots, 161–164
Animal behavior: communication, 564–566; perceptual worlds, 571–572; periodicity in, 557–559; social behavior, 567–570; territoriality, 559–564
Animal characteristics, observation of, 7–8
Animalia, 791–803, 791*, 803*
Animal kingdom, 107; annelids, 131–132; arthropods, 124–131; chordates, 113–124; coelenterates, 137; comparison of structure and function of animals 147–149; diversity of structure in, 139–142; echinoderms, 133–134; mollusks, 132–133; sponges, 138; "worms," 134–136